THE HOLT SCIENCE PROGRAM

SCIENCE 1 *Observation and Experiment* by Davis, Burnett, and Gross

SCIENCE 2 *Experiment and Discovery* by Davis, Burnett, and Gross

SCIENCE 3 *Discovery and Progress* by Davis, Burnett, and Gross

MODERN BIOLOGY by Moon, Otto, and Towle

MODERN CHEMISTRY by Dull, Metcalfe, and Williams

MODERN PHYSICS by Dull, Metcalfe, and Williams

LIVING THINGS by Fitzpatrick and Bain

MODERN PHYSICAL SCIENCE by Brooks and Tracy

MODERN HEALTH by Otto, Julian, and Tether

HUMAN PHYSIOLOGY by Morrison, Cornett, and Tether

The electron interference
pattern from a crystal
diffraction experiment
(opposite) offers convincing
evidence that electrons
have wave properties.
*(Radio Corporation
of America)*

These patterns formed by
silicon carbide crystals,
magnified 1000 times, help
scientists to learn more
about how crystals grow.
(General Electric)

NEW YORK

Charles E. Dull

H. Clark Metcalfe

John E. Williams

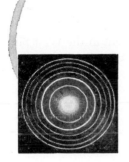

MODERN PHYSICS

HOLT, RINEHART AND WINSTON, INC.

The Authors of MODERN PHYSICS

H. Clark Metcalfe is Head of the Science Department in the Wilkinsburg Senior High School, Wilkinsburg, Pennsylvania.

John E. Williams is a member of the Science Department in the Newport Harbor High School, Newport Beach, California.

Charles E. Dull was Head of the Science Department in the West Side High School, and Supervisor of Science for the Junior and Senior High Schools, Newark, New Jersey.

The Artists of MODERN PHYSICS

Design, Format, and Drawings . . . Felix Cooper
Cover and Title Page . . . Peter Berkeley

Unit opening photographs: Unit 1, American Steel and Wire; Unit 2, Wide World Photos; Unit 3, General Motors Corporation; Unit 5, National Aeronautics and Space Administration; Unit 6, Perkin-Elmer Corporation; Unit 7, The Anaconda Company; Unit 8, Westinghouse; Unit 9, Wide World Photos.

60P11

Copyright © 1960 by
HOLT, RINEHART AND WINSTON, INCORPORATED
Library of Congress Catalog Card Number: 60-5032

Printed in the United States of America
11950-0710

PREFACE

During the past several years scientists and educators have proposed various changes in the physics curriculum of the American secondary school. As an outcome of these suggestions, some of them conflicting, much experimental work is currently being done on both an organized and an informal basis by science teachers in adapting their curricula to the recent changes which have occurred in physics itself. In preparing this revision of MODERN PHYSICS, outstanding and experienced physics teachers in many different types of schools in all parts of the United States were consulted, and the manuscript was developed in response to their recommendations. Consequently, this book incorporates the proved subject matter of previous editions with the most useful and recent concepts of physics.

The objective in MODERN PHYSICS has always been to present physics with a directness and a simplicity that will enable every student to achieve maximum comprehension. A real understanding of science is always its own best motivation.

In preparing this revision of the text, certain comprehensive changes were necessarily made. Because more content in the physical science area is now being taught in the elementary and junior high school, much of the introductory material qualitatively developed in previous editions has been eliminated; the quantitative development of this material has, however, been retained. Thus it has been possible to introduce much of the new in physics, using the *concept* of energy to tie together all the traditional branches of the science. New chapters have been added on measurement, atomic structure, alternating current circuits, resonance, vacuum tube characteristics, vacuum tube circuits, and circuit applications. Changes in the content of the other chapters are too numerous to mention specifically, but the over-all result is to present physics by means of a logical organization and in thoroughly understandable prose, which will meet the needs of today's secondary school students.

The successful use of this text is based on the supposition that the student has completed one science course at the junior high school level and has received adequate preparation in algebra and geometry. The elementary trigonometry required for the problem work is presented in the text proper. A *Mathematics Refresher* presents a brief review of the mathematical skills required of the average physics student.

MODERN PHYSICS abounds in instructional aids which are helpful to both the teacher and the student. Each unit is introduced by means of a *preview photograph* to point up the subject matter content. Each chapter contains a *Vocabulary* which defines the essential scientific terms used in that chapter, and pronounces phonetically those which teachers have indicated prove difficult. This is a practical aid for the student in mastering the *language of physics*. As an additional aid to his understanding, whenever a new scientific word or term occurs in the text it is again defined the first time it appears. Following the presentation of a topic involving a mathematical relationship, one or two *Sample Problems* and solutions are given in detail. These are appropriately set off from the text and give the method for solving that particular problem. A uniform procedure has been followed in problem solving. The applicable formula is stated, and the unknown is isolated. Then the problem values and units are substituted and the problem is solved.

At the end of each chapter there is a *Summary* and a list of *Terms to Define*. Included also as a part of the activity program of each chapter (and in some necessary cases scattered through the text of the chapter) are two sets of *Questions* and two sets of *Problems*, graded and differentiated as *Group A* and *Group B*. The materials in the *A* sets are planned as basic material for *all* students. The *A* problem sets contain problems based on both the English and metric systems of units, given alternately as far as practicable. Vector analysis problems in these sets are right triangle problems requiring both graphical and mathematical solutions. The *B* sets of questions and problems are more difficult, so as to provide for individual or group differentiation. Very difficult, or honor, problems are marked with a bullet (●). The *Group B* problems emphasize MKS system unit computations almost exclusively. The vector analysis problems in these sets are non-right triangle problems which require both graphical and mathematical solutions. This edition includes an enlarged table of trigonometric functions to whole degree values and a four-place table of logarithms.

Great care has been taken to use color in the diagrams wherever it will aid understanding and have meaning, to label each part clearly, and to employ three-dimensional effects where pertinent. Four-color printing of both photographs and line drawings has been used in certain sections of the text where it is most useful, especially in Chapter 17.

The following persons have been very helpful in offering many suggestions which we have been pleased to incorporate in this revision: Jack Saroff, Wilbur H. Lynch Senior High School, Amsterdam, New York; Earl Cleaves, Bethlehem Central Senior High School, Delmar, New York; R. E. Davis, Arcadia High School, Arcadia, Ohio; Lyle Watson, Science Consultant, Seattle Public Schools, Seattle, Washington; Harry E. Tropp, H. B. Plant High School, Tampa, Florida; Jesse D. Ridgeway, Jr., Woodrow Wilson Memorial High School, Fisherville, Virginia; Morris Hoffman, Chairman, Department of Physics, East High School, Denver, Colorado; David B. Scott, Head of the Science Department, Roosevelt High School, Seattle, Washington; Joseph D. Reding, Treadwell High School, Memphis, Tennessee; R. W. Youngblood, Woodlawn High School, Birmingham, Alabama; Earl Sundeen, Eastman Kodak Company, Rochester, New York; Willard Allphin, Sylvania Electric Products, Inc., Salem, Massachusetts; and Alfred Naish, Supervisor of Science, Buffalo, N.Y. To them we extend our sincere thanks.

The entire manuscript has been critically read and evaluated by: Harry E. Tropp, H. B. Plant High School, Tampa, Florida; Homer Knoss, Senior High School, Fairmont, Minnesota; Father Richard D. Spohn, S. J., St. Ignatius High School, San Francisco, California; Walter E. Hauswald, Sycamore Community High School, Sycamore, Illinois; and Albert Thorndike, Milton Academy, Milton, Massachusetts. Their comments and suggestions have been most helpful, and we wish to express our sincere thanks to them.

Most of the material in *Research on Your Own* was written by Wayne L. French, Shaker Heights High School, Shaker Heights, Ohio. We are grateful for his help.

CONTENTS

Read this page before you read your textbook.

1. Keep your eyes and your mind continually open. In science we base each conclusion on known facts and nothing can be taken for granted. Your eyes must be trained to observe carefully and your mind must be equally trained to reason from observations, both printed and otherwise, so as to draw logical conclusions from the observed data. With open eyes and inquiring mind you will go far in your work.

2. Get your bearings by examining the Table of Contents on pages vii and viii. What is the scope of this book? Are certain words in the chapter titles unfamiliar? Possibly they are now but by the time your work is completed at the end of the course, you will be familiar with all of them. This over-all glance at the subject matter content will give you a perspective necessary to understand what you will be reading.

3. After your teacher has made the assignment for which you will be responsible at the next class meeting, it's up to you to know what to do about preparing it. But first, be sure you understand exactly what is expected of you—what pages to read, what words to know, what questions, problems, projects or other activities to do, and whether the assignment is to be written or oral or both. If you are not sure, don't hesitate to ask. Write down all parts of the assignment in your notebook.

4. Skim over the assigned text material hastily to get a general idea what it is about, paying special attention to the paragraph headings in **boldface type.** These are key items in your textbook and form the basis for its organization.

5. Having obtained a general idea as to the subject matter of your assignment, go over the material carefully and give it your thorough concentration. Ask yourself repeatedly, Do I understand this? and if you cannot honestly answer yes, then read it again. As you read, study the drawings, tables, and photographs and read the captions which explain them. In the drawings, examine each label and learn the part of the drawing to which the label relates. Trace with a blunt object (not a pencil) the drawing of any process (such as flow of liquids and gases or movement of electrons) and understand what takes place, in which direction, and why.

6. In your reading, pay special attention to the scientific words and terms printed in *boldface italic type.* These are key words and are important to a clear understanding of the text. Many of them will be unfamiliar but you must know them and be able to define each one. Science is not a difficult subject if you learn its language, but you will never succeed unless you master this essential aspect of it. Each new word or term is printed in *boldface italics* the first time it appears, but it may and probably will be used again later. If you find that you do not understand the pronunciation and meaning of a new word, look it up immediately in the *Glossary.* Similarly, if you have forgotten such a word or term and can't remember on what page you originally met it, turn to the *Glossary* at the back of the book and look up its definition.

7. Having read the material assigned and learned the new scientific words and terms, turn to the questions at the end of the chapter which cover the text material you have completed. Answer each one fully and, if you are unable to do so, return to that part of the text which is still unclear. Reread it with the question in mind until you have the answer. Use the same procedure with the problems.

UNIT **1**

Matter and energy

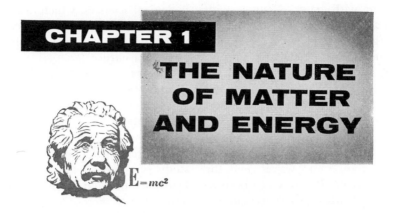

CHAPTER 1

THE NATURE OF MATTER AND ENERGY

$E = mc^2$

1. Physics combines knowledge that is both old and new. Physics is as old as Ancient Greece and yet as new as tomorrow's newspaper. Some of the discoveries and principles you will study in physics were the work of such ancient scholars as Archimedes (ark-ih-*mee*-deez), Democritus (deh-*mock*-rih-tus), and Thales (*thay*-leez). You may recall from your previous study of science that Archimedes told us how a solid behaves when placed in a liquid. Democritus first described materials as being composed of ultimate particles. Thales discovered some effects of static electricity.

During the seventeenth, eighteenth, and nineteenth centuries, physics made tremendous strides because of experimental

VOCABULARY

Energy. The ability to do work.

Force. A push or a pull.

Gas. The state of matter which has no definite shape or volume.

Impenetrability. The property of matter by virtue of which two objects cannot occupy the same space at the same time.

Inertia. The property of matter which requires that a force be exerted on it in order to change its position or motion.

Law. A statement of scientific fact concerning natural phenomena.

Liquid. The state of matter which has a definite volume, but no definite shape.

Mass. The measure of the quantity of matter.

Mass density. Mass per unit volume.

Matter. Anything which occupies space and has weight.

Physics. The physical science which deals with matter and energy and with the transformations of energy.

Porosity. The property of having small openings or spaces between the particles.

Solid. The state of matter which has a definite shape and a definite volume.

Volume. The measure of the amount of space which matter occupies.

Weight. The measure of the attractive force of the earth for a body.

Weight density. Weight per unit volume.

Work. That which is done when a force acts on matter and moves it.

work such as that of Galileo with falling bodies, Boyle with gases, Newton with gravitation and light, and Volta with electricity. So great was this progress that, near the end of the nineteenth century, one famous scientist declared that all the important discoveries had been made and that the work of future physicists would be only to refine the work of the past.

Then in quick succession came the discovery of X rays, radioactivity, the structure of the atom, radio waves, and the theory of relativity. Progress has been so rapid, some scientists feel that man has learned as much physics in the past 60 years as he did in all previous recorded time.

Today we profit by the results of these discoveries. We travel faster and higher than ever before in jet airplanes. We enjoy the entertainment provided by color television. We use electricity produced by nuclear reactions. We solve complex problems at amazing speed with electronic computers. We send into orbit artificial satellites whose instruments report on conditions in outer space. We fire missiles which land on targets thousands of miles away. Between the time of this writing and of your reading, even more remarkable scientific achievements will undoubtedly take place.

In a strict sense, these results of the discoveries of physics are not physics itself. They are the products of the use of physics by engineers and craftsmen. In your study of physics you will learn some basic truths of nature which man has discovered. You will also learn how some of these discoveries were made. There are still many areas where man's knowledge is incomplete. We shall inquire into these areas. Finally, you will learn enough practical applications of physics to appreciate the many useful purposes to which this knowledge is being put.

2. Physics is a fundamental science. For our purpose, the sciences can be divided into two main branches: (*1*) the biological sciences, which deal with living things; and (*2*) the physical sciences, which deal primarily with the nonliving aspects of nature.

Physics is the physical science which deals with matter and energy and with the transformations of energy. In this chapter we shall explain the terms "matter" and "energy" well enough to allow you to understand this statement. However, during your study of physics you will be continually learning more and more about matter and energy.

Chemistry is another of the physical sciences. Perhaps you have already studied high school chemistry. If so, you know that it is the science which deals with the composition of matter and changes in the composition of matter.

Mathematics is the science of our number system. It gives us a means of expressing relationships we observe in nature and of performing useful and necessary computations. Mathematics serves as a "language of science."

3. The concept of matter. We have said that physics is a science which deals with matter. What do we mean by matter? The best way to explain this is to give some examples. Wood, iron, copper, gold, and salt are typical examples of matter. Liquids such as water, alcohol, gasoline, and turpentine are matter. Gases like oxygen and nitrogen in the atmosphere are matter, too. All of these materials take up space. They all have weight. Tentatively we may say that *matter is anything which occupies space and has weight.* This is a partial description of matter, but it does not give us a complete definition. Scientists, despite all their knowledge of the nature and properties of matter, have never been able to define it satisfactorily.

4. The general properties of matter. In order to gain a wider knowledge of the properties of matter as we start our study of physics, we shall first discuss several

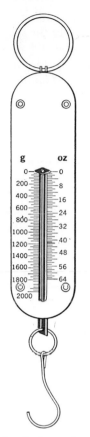

Fig. 1-1. A spring balance is used for measuring weight.

length, width, and thickness. In the laboratory we can use an *indirect* method to find the volume of any solid, no matter how irregular it may be. For determining the volumes of liquids and gases we can use special graduated containers.

6. The meaning of weight. Suppose you have a baseball in your hand. The ball is attracted toward the earth by gravity. You know this is true because you can feel the pull of the earth on it. Furthermore, if you release it, the ball will fall to the ground.

The attraction of the earth for a body acts as a *pull* on the body. We may say that the earth exerts an *attractive force* on the body. The term **force,** as used in physics, *may be tentatively defined as a push or a pull. The measure of the attractive force of the earth for a body is called the* **weight** *of the body.*

In the laboratory we find the weight of a body by suspending it from a spring balance, a device used for measuring forces. Since the measurement of weight is the measurement of force, a spring balance is a suitable instrument to use. See Fig. 1-1. The balance reading tells us the amount, or magnitude, of the force of gravitational attraction on the body. In other words, it tells us the weight of the body.

The weight of a body depends on two things: (*1*) the quantity of matter that it contains, and (*2*) the strength of the gravitational attraction where the weighing is being made. The quantity of matter in a body does not vary with location. However, the strength of the gravitational attraction on a fixed quantity of matter may vary with location. The attraction of the earth for a particular object will be less on a mountain than in a valley. The object will weigh less 100 miles above the surface of the earth than it will at the surface. But if the object is taken down into a deep shaft mine, it will also weigh less than it does at the surface. We will

properties which all kinds of matter have in common. These are called the *general properties of matter.* From our preliminary description of matter we know that two of these properties are volume and weight. From our examples of matter, we know it exists as *solids, liquids,* and *gases.* Matter has several other general properties, too, such as *mass, inertia, density, impenetrability,* and *porosity.* These will be defined and discussed later in this chapter.

5. The meaning of volume. If matter occupies space, it has the property of volume. *Volume is the measure of the amount of space which matter occupies.* When you studied arithmetic, you learned how to find the volume of rectangular objects *directly* by obtaining the product of their

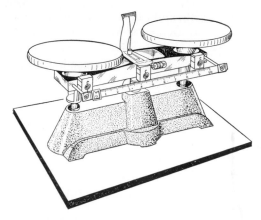

Fig. 1-2. A platform balance is used to compare an unknown mass with known masses.

study the relationship between weight and gravitation in detail in Chapter 4.

7. The three states of matter. You will recall from your earlier study of science that matter exists in three physical states: *solid*, *liquid*, and *gaseous*. A block of ice has a definite shape and a definite volume. It does not need lateral (side) support to maintain its shape. Neither its shape nor its volume can be easily changed by external pressure. *Solids* have a definite shape and a definite volume.

Now if we raise the temperature sufficiently, the solid ice melts and becomes liquid water. The water produced still occupies a definite volume, although its volume is different from that of the ice. But the water requires lateral support. Without this support it spreads out over the surface on which the block of ice rested. If we wish to confine the water we must use a container providing lateral support; then the water takes the shape of this container. But because the water occupies a definite volume, it has one free (unrestrained) surface. *Liquids have a definite volume, but take the shape of their containers.*

If we raise the temperature of the water sufficiently, we can cause it to boil and produce steam. Steam is an example of matter in the gaseous state. In order to confine the steam we shall need a closed container. The steam will completely fill it, no matter what its size, because the steam has no definite volume. Since the steam must be held in a completely closed container, it has no free surface and takes the shape of its container. *Gases have neither a definite shape nor a definite volume*, but they expand to fill a container of any volume.

We observe that water can exist as a solid, a liquid, or a gas, depending primarily on its temperature. This is true of many kinds of matter. We usually think of iron as a solid, but it can exist as a liquid or a gas if we raise its temperature sufficiently. Likewise oxygen exists as a gas in the air, but it can be cooled and converted to a liquid, or cooled still further and converted to a solid.

Both liquids and gases are called *fluids* because they flow freely. They require containers to hold them. Fluids which cannot exist as liquids having a free surface at ordinary conditions of temperature and pressure are correctly called *gases*. The gaseous state of a fluid which exists as a

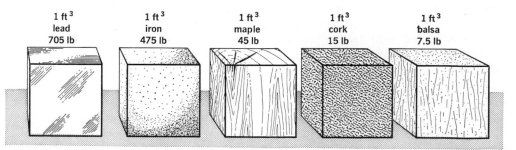

1 ft³	1 ft³	1 ft³	1 ft³	1 ft³
lead	iron	maple	cork	balsa
705 lb	475 lb	45 lb	15 lb	7.5 lb

Fig. 1-3. These blocks show that materials have different weight densities.

Fig. 1-4. The speed and comfort of a flight in a jet airplane is the result of many discoveries of physics. (Boeing Airplane Co.)

liquid under normal conditions is called a *vapor*. Thus we should speak of water vapor and oxygen *gas*.

8. Mass and inertia. Suppose we have a solid rubber ball which has a diameter of 3 inches. The rubber ball contains a definite quantity of matter. We might compress it and thereby reduce its volume, but the quantity of matter remains the same. We might take the ball up on a high mountain, or even to the moon. The quantity of matter in the ball would remain the same, although its weight would vary. *The measure of the quantity of matter which a body contains is called its* **mass**. The mass of a body does not vary with location.

In the laboratory, we usually determine the mass of an object by comparing its mass with that of known masses using an equal-arm platform balance. See Fig. 1-2. Unfortunately, this procedure is called "weighing," even though it is mass and not weight which is being measured.

Because matter has mass, it also possesses inertia. In order to move matter, change its direction of motion, or stop it, we must exert a force on it. *This property of matter which requires that a force be exerted on it in order to change its position or motion is called* **inertia**. *The mass of a body is the measure of its inertia.*

9. The meaning of density. People say that lead is heavy or that cork is light. These statements are not very meaningful. A *cubic foot* of cork is heavier than a *cubic inch* of lead. However, one cubic inch of lead is heavier than one cubic inch of cork. In order to compare the two materials, we must use equal volumes. Then the proper way to state the comparison would be, "Lead is *more dense* than cork."

Suppose we have blocks of lead, iron, maple, cork, and balsa, each with a volume of exactly one cubic foot. If we determine their weights, we find they are decidedly different, as shown in Fig. 1-3. *The weight of a unit volume of a substance is called its* **weight density.**

Using experimental or comparison methods, we may determine the mass of each block. When we compare these masses of equal volumes, we can calculate the mass density of each substance. *The mass of a unit volume of a substance is called its* **mass density.**

10. The impenetrability of matter. When two drivers attempt to get their automobiles into the same space at the same time, the result may be dented fenders or perhaps a terrible accident. We cannot pour water into a bottle through a narrow opening unless we allow air inside the bottle to escape. When we drive a nail into a piece of wood, the nail must push the wood fibers aside. From examples such as these we conclude that *two objects cannot occupy the same space at the same time.* This property of matter is called *impenetrability.*

We can use this property to find the volume of an irregularly shaped solid, such as a lump of coal. This is the indirect method for determining volume referred to in Section 5. We first put enough water into a graduated cylinder to cover the coal. Then we read the volume of water from the graduations marked on the

Fig. 1-5. As these roller-coaster cars move downgrade, their potential energy is transformed into kinetic energy. (H. Armstrong Roberts)

Fig. 1-6. The displacement method for finding the volume of an irregular solid depends on the general property of impenetrability.

cylinder. Next we lower the coal into the water, as shown in Fig. 1-6. The water level rises because the coal takes the place of some of the water in the cylinder. The difference between this new water level and the original level equals the volume of the lump of coal. This method enables us to find the volume of any insoluble, impervious solid.

11. The porosity of matter. We have little trouble seeing the *minute openings*, or *pores*, of a bath sponge. However, the porous nature of a cement block is less obvious. Water nevertheless will seep through a cement block foundation unless the exterior of the cement is waterproofed. Iron and silver have still smaller pores, but water under tremendous pressure can be forced through them. When one quart of water is mixed with one quart of alcohol, we get slightly less than two quarts of the resulting mixture. This happens because both liquids are slightly porous. Some of the alcohol particles occupy spaces between the particles of water, and vice versa.

The odor of a perfume or of naphthalene (moth balls) spreads throughout a room because the air in the room is porous, and can permit vapors from the perfume or naphthalene to penetrate it.

12. The concept of energy. We did not include heat, light, and electricity in our examples of matter. They do not fit our description of matter because they do not take up space. We cannot weigh them either. These are forms of energy. *Energy may be described as the ability to do work.* In the physical sense, **work** *is done when a force acts on matter and moves it.* We use *heat energy* to turn a steam turbine. *Electric energy* drives refrigerators, clocks, and washing machines. A photographer uses *light energy* when he exposes a photographic plate. You hear a person speaking because he is communicating with you by means of *sound energy.* The *mechanical energy* of the moving pistons in an automobile engine is transmitted to the wheels by the crankshaft, transmission, drive shaft, differential gears, and rear axles. *Nuclear energy* is used to generate electric power and to drive naval vessels.

You have probably already learned that there are two kinds of energy: *potential* energy, or energy due to position; and *kinetic* energy, or energy due to motion. The cars of a roller coaster acquire potential energy as they are drawn to the top of the first incline. But as the cars roll downgrade, this potential energy is transformed into kinetic energy, which is sufficient to carry the car up the next grade. On the upgrade, however, some of the kinetic energy is turned into potential energy again.

One form of energy can be converted into another form of energy. A familiar example is that of falling water (mechanical energy) turning a water turbine which drives an electric generator (electric energy). The electric energy produced may be used in an electric stove (heat energy), fluorescent lamp (light energy),

Fig. 1-7. Albert Einstein (1879–1955) was an outstanding theoretical physicist. This photograph was taken at about the time he predicted the relationship between matter and energy. (Bettmann Archive)

in charging a storage battery (chemical energy), or in operating a loudspeaker (sound energy).

13. The relation of matter and energy. By studying nuclear experiments, scientists have discovered that matter and energy are related. Albert Einstein (1879–1955) predicted this relationship early in this century. According to Einstein's theory, matter and energy are related by the equation $E = mc^2$; E represents the amount of energy, m is the amount of matter, and c is the velocity of light. In the last 25 years a variety of experiments have proved this relationship to be true.

Even in the most violent *chemical* reactions the amount of matter changed into energy is unbelievably small. Suppose we burn 6 tons of carbon with 16 tons of oxygen. All the energy released as heat and light during this burning will make the products of combustion only 0.00007 ounce

For many years scientists believed that matter could neither be created nor destroyed. This belief was called the *law of conservation of matter.* (*A law in science is a statement of how phenomena in nature are related, as demonstrated by laboratory experiments.*) During that time, no loss of material could be detected in any chemical changes, even with the most sensitive measuring devices. From our example of burning carbon, we can see why this was so. The instruments used in earlier times were just not sensitive enough. It was also believed that energy could neither be created nor destroyed. This belief was called the *law of conservation of energy.* The most sensitive devices for detecting energy showed no loss of energy when one form was changed to another. Thus, at that time, matter and energy were considered to be unrelated.

We know now that matter and energy are related—that they are not separate and distinct. Consequently we must combine the law of conservation of matter and the law of conservation of energy into one new law. This one states that *matter and energy are interchangeable;* and that *the total amount of energy and matter in the universe is constant.* If energy appears, some matter must have disappeared. If energy disappears, matter must always appear in its place. This is demonstrated in dramatic fashion by the explosions of atomic bombs and hydrogen bombs.

Fig. 1-8. The largest nuclear power plant in the United States is located at Dresden, Illinois. Its atomic reactor, housed in the dome-shaped structure at the right, produces 180,000 kilowatts of electric power. (General Electric)

lighter than the 22 tons of material with which we started. Only in nuclear reactions, like the explosion of a hydrogen bomb, does the amount of matter which is transformed into energy become significant.

Summary

The science of physics had its origin in ancient times. It developed slowly after the Renaissance, but has expanded very rapidly during this century. Physics deals with matter and energy and with energy transformations. Matter is anything which occupies space and has weight. It has several general properties; among these are volume, weight, physical state, mass, inertia, density, impenetrability, and porosity. Energy is the ability to do work and appears as heat, electricity, light, sound, mechanical energy, and nuclear energy. Energy may be potential or kinetic. Matter and energy are interchangeable; the total amount of energy and matter in the universe is constant.

TERMS TO DEFINE

biological science	kinetic energy	porosity
$E = mc^2$	law	potential energy
energy	liquid	solid
fluid	mass	spring balance
force	mass density	states of matter
forms of energy	matter	vapor
gas	physical science	volume
impenetrability	physics	weight
inertia	platform balance	weight density

QUESTIONS

A   1. What recent achievements are the result of discoveries in physics?

2. Give five examples each of (a) solids; (b) liquids; and (c) gases.

3. What enables us to distinguish (a) a solid from a liquid; (b) a liquid from a gas?

4. What condition primarily determines the physical state of a substance?

5. How does the mass of an object on the earth compare with the mass of the same object if it were on the moon?

6. Upon what factors does the weight of a body depend?

7. (a) Will the mass density of a material vary with location? (b) Will its weight density vary?

8. Describe an experiment which shows that a liquid is porous.

9. What property of matter do we determine by using (a) a spring balance; (b) a platform balance?

10. In what forms does energy occur in (a) operating an electric refrigerator; (b) taking a photograph using a flash bulb; (c) carrying on a conversation by telephone; (d) using a flashlight; (e) exploding an atomic bomb?

B   11. (a) Distinguish between physical sciences and biological sciences. (b) Name various sciences and tell to which of these classes they belong.

12. What is the function of mathematics in science?

13. How can you find the volume of (a) a rectangular block of brass; (b) an irregularly shaped rock; (c) a large piece of rock salt?

14. How will the weight of a body at San Francisco compare with its weight at Denver?

15. Why does a liquid have one free surface?

16. Distinguish between a liquid and a fluid.

17. Distinguish between a vapor and a gas.

18. What term other than "weighing" would you suggest to describe the process of comparing the mass of an object with that of known masses, using a platform balance?

19. If we know the weight of an object and its volume, what mathematical process must we perform in order to determine its weight density?

20. Why has it been only recently that scientists have found that matter and energy are interchangeable?

RESEARCH ON YOUR OWN

1. Devise experiments to determine the length of time needed for an odor to reach you. For example, what is the time interval between the moment food starts to cook and the moment you smell it, or between the moment you empty perfume into an open dish and the moment you smell it? Compare results with different substances under similar and varying conditions.

2. Pour an exactly measured quantity of alcohol into an identical quantity of water. Can you detect a loss of volume? What do you think has happened to the weight per unit volume of the mixture as compared with the weight per unit volume of the alcohol?

3. Consult current science magazines. Find several topics which, while not new, are new in the forefront of physical science study. For example, has the Peltier effect received recent attention?

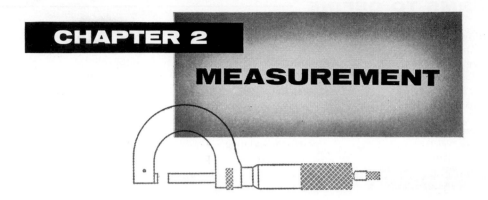

CHAPTER 2

MEASUREMENT

1. The development of measurement in physics. We learned in Chapter 1 that physics helps us explain the behavior of matter and energy. In the great civilizations of Ancient Egypt, Greece, and Rome, philosophers pondered over natural events. The great Greek teacher Aristotle enlisted the aid of many students throughout the ancient world in his work of observing and comparing natural phenomena. By speculating on the facts then known to him, he tried to fit his observations into a logical scheme. In later times, his followers relied on his observations and

VOCABULARY

Abscissa. The horizontal distance of a point from the Y axis.

Component. One of the several vectors combined algebraically or geometrically to yield a resultant vector.

Direct proportion. The relation between two quantities if their ratio is a constant.

Displacement. A change of position.

Inverse proportion. The relation between two quantities if their product is a constant.

Order of magnitude. An approximation to the nearest power of ten.

Ordinate. The vertical distance of a point from the X axis.

Resolution. The process of separating a single vector into two vectors acting in given directions.

Resultant. A vector representing the algebraic or geometric sum of several component vectors.

Scalar quantity. A quantity which can be expressed completely by a magnitude in appropriate units.

Scientific notation. Mathematical notation in which a number has the form $M \times 10^n$.

Significant figures. The digits which indicate the number of units we are reasonably sure of in making a measurement.

Vector. An arrow whose length indicates the magnitude of a vector quantity and whose direction indicates the direction of the vector quantity.

Vector quantity. A quantity which requires both a magnitude and a direction for its complete description.

speculation instead of experimenting for themselves. Although some of Aristotle's conclusions were wrong, they were accepted as truth for many centuries.

One of the reasons for the lack of scientific advancement by the Romans was their cumbersome system of writing numbers. You are already familiar with Roman numerals such as V for 5, X for 10, and MCMLX for 1960, but what about trying to add, subtract, multiply, or divide using Roman numerals? Very difficult, isn't it? Furthermore, the Romans had no way of expressing zero in their system. These handicaps prevented the development of satisfactory systems of measurement and computation until the Roman system was replaced by the present Arabic system about the thirteenth century.

It was not until the sixteenth century, however, that experimentation using measurements became accepted as a means of learning the truths of nature. The experimentation which Leonardo da Vinci and Galileo developed was both qualitative and quantitative. When observing a particular phenomenon, they asked "*Why* does it happen?" and "*To what extent* does it happen?" They began to use measurement as an important part of each experiment. It was this introduction of measurement in experimentation which brought about the rapid growth of physics as a science.

1   SYSTEMS OF MEASUREMENT

2. The systems of measurement used in physics. Physics would not be the precise study it is today if it did not make use of systems of measurement. In almost every physics experiment it is important to be able to measure accurately the quantities of materials, the magnitudes of forces, the amounts of energy, or the passage of time. *All the units of measurement in physics can be expressed in terms of length, mass, time, temperature, and electric charge.* In this chapter we shall consider the units of length, mass, and time. Units of temperature are described in Chapter 9, and the unit of electric charge is explained in Chapter 18.

Measurement in science poses problems that are more complicated than those we meet in the use of everyday units of measure. Everyday units like inches, gallons, and tons are used for the direct measurement of single quantities. Very infrequently are we called upon to change gallons of gasoline to cubic inches of gasoline or to convert tons of liquid ammonia to gallons of liquid ammonia. Consequently, in the everyday system, units of convenient size for particular purposes were developed independently. Smaller units were commonly derived from larger ones by dividing by 2, 4, 8, 12, 16, etc. Larger units were derived from smaller ones by multiplying by 2, 3, $5\frac{1}{3}$, 2000, 5280, etc. No thought was given to the interrelationship between different kinds of measures like measures of length and measures of volume, or measures of volume of substances and measures of their corresponding weights. The lack of simple relationships between units, and the practice of division into halves, quarters, and eighths, although we use a decimal (by tens) number system, make it very difficult to carry out computations with the everyday units of measure.

A scientific system, on the other hand, is made up of units of convenient size which can be easily reproduced anywhere with great precision. These units are interrelated so that computations involving several types of units simultaneously can be performed easily. The decimal number system we use makes it convenient for a scientific system of measurement to be based also on units related to one another by powers of ten.

Unfortunately, in the United States both the everyday system, called the English system, and a scientific system, called the metric system, are used. For many years there have been scientists and engineers who have urged us to do away with the cumbersome English system. Some progress is being made—certain industries and some branches of the United States armed forces have gone over to metric measures. Yet, even with the easily recognized advantages of the metric system, we still make most commercial measurements in the English system. Consequently, the systems of measurement used by physicists include both everyday measures and scientific measures. In line with the trend away from the use of the English system of measurement, most of the work in this book involves the metric system.

Three systems of measurement are now commonly used by physicists in the United States. Two of these are variations of the *metric absolute system:* (1) the *meter-kilogram-second* or *MKS system,* and (2) the *centimeter-gram-second* or *CGS system.* The MKS system is widely used in mechanics and electricity. The CGS system is used somewhat in mechanics, but more generally in heat. The third system of measurement is an adaptation of the English system, called the *English gravitational system.* It is also known as the *foot-pound-second* or *FPS system.* Note that each of these systems is designated by an abbreviation representing three of the *basic units* in the system.

3. The metric absolute system. The metric system of measurement was developed in France near the end of the eighteenth century; it is a *decimal system* similar to that used for United States money. Today the metric system is used almost exclusively in all civilized countries except Great Britain and the United States, while in scientific work it is used throughout the world.

In a decimal system of measurement, units differ in size by multiples of 10. Thus in U.S. money, 10 mills equals 1 cent; 100 mills or 10 cents equals 1 dime; 1000 mills, 100 cents, or 10 dimes equals 1 dollar. When we perform computations with multiples of 10, it is very convenient to use an exponential method of expression. You should recall the following equivalents from your study of algebra.

Positive and Negative Powers of 10
$10^0 = 1$

$10^1 = 10$	$10^{-1} = 0.1$
$10^2 = 100$	$10^{-2} = 0.01$
$10^3 = 1000$	$10^{-3} = 0.001$
$10^4 = 10{,}000$	$10^{-4} = 0.0001$
$10^5 = 100{,}000$	$10^{-5} = 0.00001$
$10^6 = 1{,}000{,}000$	$10^{-6} = 0.000001$
etc.	etc.

Using these expressions, we may say that there are 10^2 cents in 1 dollar, or that 1 mill is 10^{-3} dollar.

There are three important metric units you must learn right at the start. The *meter* is a unit of *length;* the *liter* (lee-ter) is a unit of *volume;* and the *gram* is a unit of *mass.* The common subdivisions of each of these, as well as of other metric units, are formed by the use of the prefixes *centi–*, 10^{-2}; and *milli–*, 10^{-3}. The most common multiple for many units of the metric system is formed by using the prefix *kilo–*, 10^3. The complete set of metric system prefixes follows:

Metric System Prefixes			
deka–	10^1	deci–	10^{-1}
hecto–	10^2	centi–	10^{-2}
kilo–	10^3	milli–	10^{-3}
mega–	10^6	micro–	10^{-6}

Thus a centimeter is 10^{-2} meter; a milliliter is 10^{-3} liter; and a kilogram is 10^3 grams.

4. Units of length in the metric system. The devisers of the metric system intended to base the units on natural standards. The meter was to be exactly 10^{-7} of the

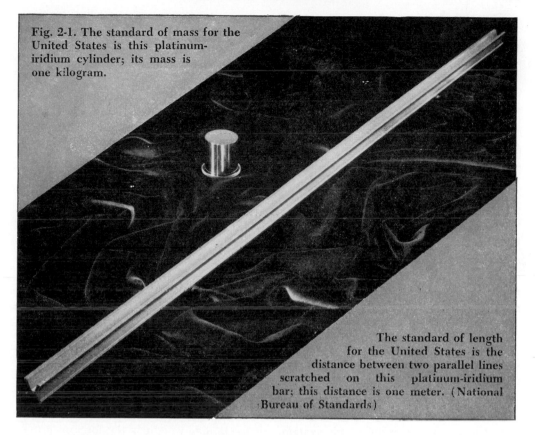

Fig. 2-1. The standard of mass for the United States is this platinum-iridium cylinder; its mass is one kilogram.

The standard of length for the United States is the distance between two parallel lines scratched on this platinum-iridium bar; this distance is one meter. (National Bureau of Standards)

distance from the earth's equator to either pole. However, because of a slight error, the meter only approximates this distance.

By definition, the *standard meter* is the distance, measured at 0° C, between two parallel lines scratched on a platinum-iridium bar kept at the International Bureau of Weights and Measures at Sèvres, near Paris, France. From this standard many copies have been made. The United States standard meter bar is kept at the National Bureau of Standards in Washington, D.C. See Fig. 2-1.

You will find the table below, which gives the relationships between common metric units of length, very useful in your study of physics.

In order to give you an idea of the magnitude of these units, here are some approximate equivalents. A centimeter is approximately 0.4 inch. A meter is slightly longer than a yard. A kilometer is slightly more than 0.6 mile. More precise equivalents for metric and English units of length are given in Section 9.

5. Metric units for area and volume. For measuring areas of surfaces, the *square meter* (m²) or the *square centimeter* (cm²) is

Relationships Between Metric Units of Length
10^1 *millimeters* (mm) = 1 *centimeter* (cm)
10^2 *centimeters* = 1 *meter* (m)
10^3 *meters* = 1 *kilometer* (km)

generally used. A floor 3 meters long and 2 meters wide has an area of 6 square meters. Using abbreviations and arithmetic notation,

$$3 \text{ m} \times 2 \text{ m} = 6 \text{ m}^2$$

One type of volume unit in the metric system is the *cubic meter* (m^3) or the *cubic centimeter* (cm^3). A box 2 meters long, 1 meter wide, and 1.5 meters deep has a volume of 3 cubic meters.

$$2 \text{ m} \times 1 \text{ m} \times 1.5 \text{ m} = 3 \text{ m}^3$$

The other type of volume unit is derived from the length units as follows. If we construct a cubic box with inside dimensions of 10 cm on each side, it will hold 1000 cm^3. This volume was intended by the originators of the metric system to equal 1 *liter* (l). There is a slight difference, but for practical purposes the two are equivalent. (Actually 1 liter = 1000.027 cm^3.) Thus we say that *1 liter is equivalent to 1000* cm^3, and 10^{-3} liter, or a *milliliter* (ml), equals 1 cm^3. A liter is slightly larger than a U.S. liquid quart.

6. Units of mass in the metric system. In the United States, the standard of mass is the platinum-iridium cylinder shown in Fig. 2-1. It is about 1.5 inches high and about 1.5 inches in diameter. The mass of this very precisely made cylinder is one kilogram. The United States

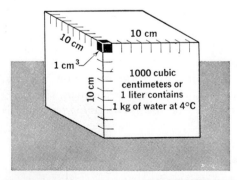

Fig. 2-2. The relationship between the units of length, volume, and mass in the metric system.

cylinder is a copy of the *standard kilogram* kept at the International Bureau of Weights and Measures. The standard kilogram weighs slightly more than 2.2 pounds.

The originators of the metric system planned to relate the units of length, volume, and mass directly to one another. The *kilogram* (kg) was intended to be the mass of 1000 cm^3, or of one liter, of distilled water at its temperature of maximum density, 4° C. Today, *the liter is defined as the volume occupied by one kilogram of water at 4° C.* We have learned that this volume is not exactly 1000 cm^3. However, for practical purposes we may say that one kilogram of water, one liter of water, and 1000 cm^3 of water have the same mass. See Fig. 2-2. Then, *one milliliter of water or one cubic centimeter of water has a mass of one gram* (g). The gram is a very small unit: a new five-cent piece has a mass of almost exactly 5 grams. A large mass unit, the metric ton, equals 10^3 kilograms.

7. Force and weight units in the metric system. In Chapter 1, Section 6, we learned that weight is the force of gravitational attraction on a body. While the strength of gravitational attraction does vary with location, for a particular location it is constant. Thus, at a given place, the weights of objects are directly proportional to their masses. Consequently, in the metric system, force and weight units are *derived units* which are directly proportional to the basic mass units. The factor relating these two types of units is a constant which depends on the strength of gravitational attraction.

The *units of force (weight)* in the metric system are the *newton* (nt) and the *dyne*. For locations having the latitude and altitude of New York City, the equivalents shown in the box on the opposite page may be used. They are approximately true for most of the rest of the United States. Thus we must exert a force of 9.80 newtons to lift a mass of 1 kilogram, or a force of

Relationship Between Metric Force and Mass Units		
Force (weight) in newtons = mass in kilograms $\times \dfrac{9.80 \text{ newtons}}{\text{kilogram}}$		
Force (weight) in dynes = mass in grams $\times \dfrac{980 \text{ dynes}}{\text{gram}}$		

980 dynes to lift a mass of 1 gram. We may also say that a mass of 1 kilogram weighs 9.80 newtons, and a mass of 1 gram weighs 980 dynes. A more detailed explanation of these force units will be given in Chapter 4.

8. Problem solving in physics. In physics you will frequently be called upon to solve many types of problems. The first problems utilize the facts about the metric system which we have just learned. An orderly procedure in problem solving, followed right from the start, will make this part of your work in physics easier. Most problems can be worked out by observing these five steps:

Step 1. Read the problem carefully to determine what quantities are given and what quantity is required.

Step 2. Select and write down the formula relating these quantities, which you can use to solve the problem.

Step 3. Solve the formula algebraically, if necessary, for the term which represents the required quantity.

Step 4. Substitute the problem values *and units* in the formula.

Step 5. Solve. *First*, perform the computation with the units alone. *Second*, perform the numerical computation.

The Sample Problem on pages 16–17 illustrates this orderly procedure in prob-

lem solving. Study it carefully before going on.

9. The English gravitational system. This is essentially the system which we use in our daily life. For units of *length* we use inches (in.), feet (ft), yards (yd), or miles (mi). In the English system *the basic unit of length is the foot.* In the United States, the yard is defined in terms of the standard meter. *One yard is 0.9144 meter,* giving us the following important equivalents:

1 meter = 39.37 inches	
1 inch = 2.5400 centimeters	

The English system units of *area* used in physics are square inches (in.²) or square feet (ft²). A comparison between a square centimeter and a square inch is shown in Fig. 2-3.

Our common *volume* units are cubic inches (in.³), cubic feet (ft³), quarts (qt), and gallons (gal). A cubic inch and a cubic centimeter are compared in Fig. 2-4. A comparison of the liquid quart and the liter is shown in Fig. 2-5.

In our discussion of the metric system, we listed mass units as basic units, and force (weight) units as derived units. *In the English gravitational system, the opposite is true: force (weight) units are basic units, while mass units are derived units.* **The pound** (lb) is the *basic unit of force (weight).* In the

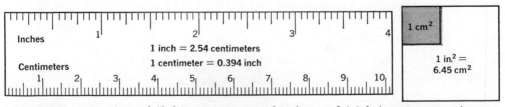

1 inch = 2.54 centimeters
1 centimeter = 0.394 inch

1 cm²

1 in.² = 6.45 cm²

Fig. 2-3. A comparison of (left) centimeters and inches, and (right) a square centimeter and a square inch.

Sample Problem

A box is 25.0 cm long, 15.0 cm wide, and 10.0 cm deep. (*a*) What is the area of the bottom of the box? (*b*) What is the volume of the box in liters? (*c*) What mass of water, in grams, will the box hold? (*d*) What force, in newtons, is required to lift the box filled with water if the box has a mass of 500 g?

Solution

(*a*) *Step 1*. A reading of the problem indicates that the length and width of the box are given. We are asked to calculate the area of the bottom of the box.

Step 2. The applicable formula is Area = length × width.

Step 3. Since this formula already has Area isolated at the left of the equals sign, we do not need to rearrange it.

Step 4. We substitute the problem values and units in the formula. Area = 25.0 cm × 15.0 cm.

Step 5. The *first step* in solving should always be to perform the computation with the units alone to determine whether the unit in which the answer will be expressed is the correct one. This step acts as a check on the correctness of both the formula and your substitution: cm × cm = cm². The square centimeter (cm²) is a suitable unit for area. The *second step* is to perform the numerical part of the computation: 25.0 × 15.0 = 375. Combining this with the unit part of the answer, Area = 375 cm².

Summarizing these five steps, the work may be shown as:

Area = length × width

Area = 25.0 cm × 15.0 cm

Area = 375 cm²

Observe how the five steps are followed and the work recorded in solving the remaining parts of this problem.

(*b*) Volume = length × width × depth

Volume = 25.0 cm × 15.0 cm × 10.0 cm

But cm × cm × cm = cm³, and the problem asks for the volume in liters. Consequently we must multiply by a conversion factor which relates cm³ to liters. The conversion factor to use is $\dfrac{1 \text{ liter}}{1000 \text{ cm}^3}$.

$$\text{Volume} = 25.0 \text{ cm} \times 15.0 \text{ cm} \times 10.0 \text{ cm} \times \frac{1 \text{ liter}}{1000 \text{ cm}^3}$$

[Note that $\text{cm} \times \text{cm} \times \text{cm} \times \dfrac{\text{liter}}{\text{cm}^3} = \text{liter (liters)}$]

Volume = 3.75 liters

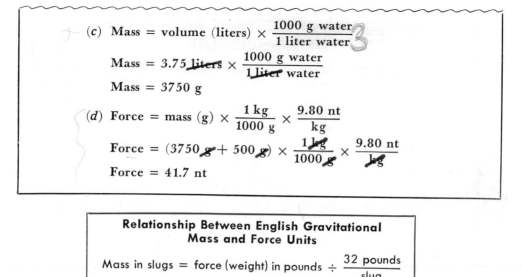

(c) Mass = volume (liters) × $\dfrac{1000 \text{ g water}}{1 \text{ liter water}}$

Mass = 3.75 liters × $\dfrac{1000 \text{ g water}}{1 \text{ liter water}}$

Mass = 3750 g

(d) Force = mass (g) × $\dfrac{1 \text{ kg}}{1000 \text{ g}}$ × $\dfrac{9.80 \text{ nt}}{\text{kg}}$

Force = (3750 g + 500 g) × $\dfrac{1 \text{ kg}}{1000 \text{ g}}$ × $\dfrac{9.80 \text{ nt}}{\text{kg}}$

Force = 41.7 nt

Relationship Between English Gravitational Mass and Force Units

Mass in slugs = force (weight) in pounds ÷ $\dfrac{32 \text{ pounds}}{\text{slug}}$

United States, the pound is defined in terms of the weight of the standard kilogram. The standard kilogram weighs 2.2046 lb. One pound, then, is the weight of a mass of 453.6 g. Other force (weight) units in the English gravitational system are the ounce (oz) and the ton (tn). The English system is not a scientific system of measurement with units which are readily convertible from one to another. Table 1, Appendix B, gives the relationship between the various units in the English system. Table 2, Appendix B, gives useful metric-English equivalents.

The English gravitational system unit of *mass*, the *slug*, is a derived unit which is directly proportional to the force

(weight) unit, the pound. At the latitude and altitude of New York City, the relationship shown above is correct. It is approximately true for most of the rest of the United States. Thus we must exert a force of 32 lb to lift a mass of 1 slug; we may say that a mass of 1 slug weighs 32 lb.

10. Units of time. Both the English gravitational system and the metric absolute system use the same units of time. The *basic unit of time* is the *second* (sec). There are 60 seconds in a *minute* (min), 60 minutes in an *hour* (hr), and 24 hours in a *day* (da). The second we use as a unit of time is actually the *mean solar second*, which is $\frac{1}{86,400}$ of a mean solar day (60 sec/min × 60 min/hr × 24 hr/da =

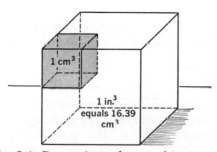

Fig. 2-4. Comparison of one cubic centimeter and one cubic inch.

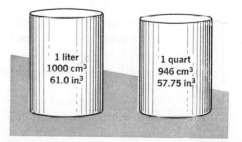

Fig. 2-5. The liter is slightly larger than the U.S. liquid quart.

COMPARISON OF THE THREE BASIC SYSTEMS OF MEASUREMENT

	Length (l)	Area (A)	Volume (V)	Mass (m)	Force (Weight) (F)	Time (t)
MKS	meter (m)	square meter (m²)	cubic meter (m³) or liter (l)	kilogram (kg)	newton (nt)	second (sec)
CGS	centi- meter (cm)	square centi- meter (cm²)	cubic centi- meter (cm³) or milliliter (ml)	gram (g)	dyne	second (sec)
FPS	foot (ft)	square foot (ft²)	cubic foot (ft³) or quart (qt)	slug	pound (lb)	second (sec)

Sample Problem

How many inches are there in 2.50 meters?

Solution

Length (in.) = length (m) × conversion factor
From Table 2, Appendix B, we find that 1 m = 39.37 in., or that there are 39.37 in./m. This is our *conversion factor.*
Length = 2.50 m × 39.37 in./m
Length = 98.4 in.
If the table in Appendix B had given 1 in. = 0.0254 m, we could have used this for a conversion factor also. The factor would have been 1 in./0.0254 m.
Length = 2.50 m × 1 in./0.0254 m
Length = 98.4 in.
Note that the unit of the numerator of the conversion factor must be the unit of the measurement you are seeking; the unit of the denominator of the conversion factor must be the unit of the measurement you already know.

Fig. 2-6. The weight of a kilogram mass is more than twice that of the avoirdupois pound.

86,400 sec/da). The *mean solar day* is the average interval between the instants the sun is at its highest point on successive days throughout an entire year.

Instruments commonly used for measuring short intervals of time in the laboratory are a spring-driven stopwatch or an electric stopclock. Other working standards for measuring time are pendulums of suitable lengths or oscillating quartz crystals.

11. Comparison of units in the MKS, CGS, and FPS systems of measurement. So far we have described units of length, area, volume, mass, force (weight), and time in the metric absolute and the English gravitational systems. The table opposite will help you group these units into the three systems used in physics. In each system the basic units are shown in red. The units shown in black are derived units. The symbols used for designating these quantities are also shown.

The Sample Problem at the bottom of the opposite page illustrates the method of converting a measurement made in one system to its equivalent in another system.

2 MAKING MEASUREMENTS

12. The method of making measurements. Suppose we wish to measure the length of a laboratory table. We must first select a suitable unit of length in which to express the measurement. Do we wish to use the English or the metric system? If the English system, do we wish to express the length in inches, feet, or yards? Or if we choose the metric system, shall we express the length in millimeters, centimeters, or meters?

Suppose we decide to make our measurement in the metric system, using centimeter units. Now we must count the number of centimeter units which can be placed along the edge of the laboratory table. To facilitate this counting we use a meter stick which has 100 centimeter units marked off on it. When we place the meter stick along the table, we find that the table is one meter stick long (100 cm) plus between 52 and 53 centimeters of a second length of the meter stick. See Fig. 2-7. Thus the length of the table is between 152 cm and 153 cm. Meter sticks usually have the numbered centi-

meter divisions subdivided into millimeters. Now, looking carefully at the meter stick, we see that the end of the table lies between the 52 cm, 3 mm and the 52 cm, 4 mm marks. Using the meter stick to the limit of its accuracy, we estimate that the table ends 0.7 of the way between the 52 cm, 3 mm mark and the 52 cm, 4 mm mark. Expressing the length of the table in centimeter units, the measurement is 152.37 cm. One of the advantages of the metric system is that even though we have measured the length of the table in centimeters, we can readily convert this measurement to millimeters or to meters, or to any other metric unit

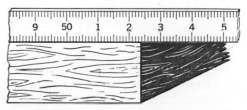

Fig. 2-7. Using a meter stick, we may measure length to the nearest hundredth of a centimeter.

of length: 152.37 cm = 1523.7 mm = 1.5237 m, etc. Could we have converted the measurement of the table in inches to feet or yards so easily?

Accurate measurements are of extreme importance to a physicist. The system of measurement or the unit chosen has no bearing on the accuracy of the measurement. The measuring instrument used and the technique with which it is used determine the accuracy of a measurement. Sometimes the techniques of making measurements are quite complicated. However, the principle of making any direct measurement is still the same: *select a suitable unit, and count how many times that unit is taken.* What is the reading on the slide scale shown in Fig. 2-8?

13. Significant figures. In Section 12 we expressed the length of the laboratory table as 152.37 cm. We read the 152.3 cm directly from the meter stick, and estimated the 0.07 cm. Using a meter stick as our measuring device, this was the greatest precision we could obtain. We feel reasonably certain that the length is 152.37 cm, and not 152.36 cm or 152.38 cm. But we have no idea of the digit which should be in the third decimal place. *The digits which tell us the number of units we are reasonably sure of having counted in making a measurement are called* **significant figures.** Our measurement was expressed to five significant figures—four certain, one estimated. It is usual in making a measurement to have one estimated significant figure; the other significant figures are certain. The slide scale reading in Fig. 2-8 is 2.63 g. This measurement is expressed to three significant figures—two certain, one estimated.

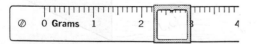

Fig. 2-8. The slide scale on a platform balance enables us to measure mass to the nearest hundredth of a gram.

The greater the number of significant figures obtained when making a measurement, the more accurate is the measurement. Conversely, a measurement made to only a few significant figures is not a very accurate one, although it may be the best man is capable of making, and quite useful for its intended purpose.

In the examples we have given so far, we could easily determine the number of significant figures, because each digit used to express the magnitude of the measurement was significant. However, when we use the ordinary system of notation, this is not always the case. A few examples will illustrate this. The average distance from the earth to the moon is 239,000 miles. Does this number have six significant figures? No, this measurement is given to an accuracy of only three significant figures. The 2, the 3, and the 9 are significant. The three zeros which follow only serve to locate the decimal point (understood). Likewise 0.000584 cm contains only three significant figures. The zeros are used in order to locate the decimal point. In an attempt to overcome these difficulties, the following rules for determining the number of significant figures have been set up:

1. All nonzero digits are significant: 159.75 g contains five significant figures.

2. All zeros between two nonzero digits are significant: 108.005 m contains six significant figures.

3. Unless otherwise indicated, *all zeros to the left of an* **understood** *decimal point but to the right of a nonzero digit are* **not** *significant:* 202,000 mi contains three significant figures.

4. All zeros to the left of an **expressed** *decimal point and to the right of a nonzero digit are significant:* 202,000. mi contains six significant figures.

5. All zeros to the right of a decimal point but to the left of a nonzero digit are **not** *significant:* 0.000647 kg contains three significant figures. (The single zero conventionally placed to the left of the decimal point in such an expression is never significant.)

6. *All zeros to the right of a decimal point and to the right of a nonzero digit are significant:* 0.07080 cm and 20.00 cm each contain four significant figures.

14. Scientific notation. Physicists are frequently concerned with very large and very small numbers, as well as with those of conventional magnitude. For example, the speed of light in a vacuum is 29,979,-280,000 cm/sec, and the mass of an electron is 0.000,000,000,000,000,000,000,-000,000,910,83 g. Numbers such as these are difficult to understand and inconvenient to use when expressed in ordinary notation.

For convenience in writing numbers of any magnitude so as to express their degree of accuracy by using only figures which are significant, scientific notation was devised. *In this notation a number has the form*

$$M \times 10^n$$

where M is a number between 1 and 10 and n is a positive or negative integer.

To change a number into scientific notation:

1. *Determine M by moving the decimal point so that you leave only one nonzero digit to the left of it.*

2. *Determine n by counting the number of places you have moved the decimal point; if moved to the left, n is positive; if to the right, n is negative.*

The speed of light expressed in scientific notation is 2.997928×10^{10} cm/sec, while the mass of an electron is 9.1083×10^{-28} g. In scientific notation only significant figures are included in the M part of the number. Thus, at a glance, you can tell the number of significant figures and the accuracy of the measurement. All zeros included in the M part of the number are significant. Thus the distance from the earth to the sun, 93,005,000 miles, which

cannot be expressed in ordinary notation to three-significant-figure accuracy without confusion, can be expressed in scientific notation as 9.30×10^7 mi, with no uncertainty as to which digits are significant.

15. Arithmetic operations with significant figures. The results of mathematical operations performed with measurements can be no more accurate than the original measurements themselves. Accordingly, we must observe certain precautions when performing such calculations so that we do not imply a greater accuracy in our result than was originally obtained in our measurements.

1. *Addition and subtraction.* Suppose we are required to find the sum of the following measurements of length: 2.6 m, 12.57 m, and 0.395 m. Since the first measurement is uncertain in the "tenths" place, the sum should not be expressed to more than tenths of a meter. Accordingly, we first round all measurements to the number of decimal places in the number with fewest decimal places; here, to tenths. Thus 12.57 m rounds to 12.6 m and 0.395 m rounds to 0.4 m. Then we add: 2.6 m + 12.6 m + 0.4 m = 15.6 m.

In subtraction, a similar procedure is followed. Round off to the number of decimal places in the measurement with fewest decimal places; then subtract.

When working with numbers expressed in scientific notation, convert all terms to the same power of ten before adding or subtracting. See the Sample Problems on page 22 for examples of each type of computation.

2. *Multiplication and division.* Suppose we wish to find the volume of a metal block 15.42 cm long, 5.53 cm wide, and 2.70 cm high. If we multiply 15.42 cm by 5.53 cm to find the area of one surface, the product is 85.2726 cm². But remember (a) the last significant figure in a measurement is uncertain; (b) the product of any number by an uncertain digit is also uncertain;

Sample Problem

Add 17.35 g, 25.6 g, and 8.498 g.

Solution

The measurement known to fewest decimal places is 25.6 g, known only to tenths. Rounding the other measurements to tenths, 17.35 g becomes 17.4 g and 8.498 g becomes 8.5 g; 17.4 g + 25.6 g + 8.5 g = 51.5 g.

Sample Problem

Add 6.75×10^3 cm and 4.52×10^2 cm.

Solution

Numbers in scientific notation must first be converted to the same power of 10: 4.52×10^2 cm = 0.452×10^3 cm. Rounding to hundredths, this becomes 0.45×10^3 cm, and 6.75×10^3 cm + 0.45×10^3 cm = 7.20×10^3 cm.

Sample Problem

Subtract 36.8 km from 97 km.

Solution

Rounding 36.8 km to whole kilometers, it becomes 37 km, and 97 km − 37 km = 60. km. Note that a decimal point is used to show that there are two significant figures in this result.

Sample Problem

Subtract 6.43×10^{-2} m from 1.38×10^2 m.

Solution

Converting, 6.43×10^{-2} m = 0.000643×10^2 m, which is negligible when compared to 1.38×10^2 m. The difference is thus 1.38×10^2 m.

and (c) only one uncertain digit is retained in any computation. In the product 85.2726 cm², the digits .2726 are uncertain. Retaining only one uncertain digit, the product becomes 85.3 cm².

Following the same procedure, 85.3 cm² × 2.70 cm = 230.310 cm³. But the digits 0.310 are uncertain, so the volume expressed to the proper number of significant figures is 230. cm³.

In general, *the proper number of significant figures will* **usually** *be retained in a product, if the product is rounded to the same number of significant figures as the factor having the fewer significant figures. This is not a rigid rule; there are many examples which do not conform exactly.* However, it can serve you as a guide, and will prevent you from carrying unnecessary digits from step to step in a series of computations.

A similar procedure is followed for division. In general, *the quotient should* **usually** *be expressed to the same number of significant figures as the term with fewer significant figures,* whether it be the dividend or the divisor. As before, *this rule is only a guide; there are exceptions.*

The *M* portions of numbers expressed in scientific notation are multiplied or divided in the manner already described. The laws of exponents govern the multiplication or division of the 10^n terms. See the Sample Problems on page 24 for additional examples of both types of computations.

Sometimes in physics we make justifiable approximations to simplify our computations without reducing the number of significant figures. For example, the speed of light is 2.997928×10^{10} cm/sec. This value is so close to 3×10^{10} cm/sec that this rounded-off value is commonly used for the speed of light in all but the most precise computations. However, when we use 3×10^{10} cm/sec we do not attribute to this value an accuracy of only one significant figure. From the actual value for the speed of light you will see

that 3×10^{10} cm/sec has an accuracy equivalent to expressing the speed of light to three significant figures (2.997928×10^{10} cm/sec expressed in three significant figures is 3.00×10^{10} cm/sec). Consequently in computations involving this or other such approximated values, the number of significant figures in the other measurements will usually govern the number of significant figures we retain in the answer.

16. Orders of magnitude. Frequently in physics a very approximate value for a measurement or for the result of a computation is sufficient or is all that can be obtained because of experimental difficulties. Usually this approximate value is the closest power of ten to the best determination of the actual value. Such *an approximation to the nearest power of ten is called the* **order of magnitude.** The distance from the earth to the sun is 93,000,-000 miles. The order of magnitude of the distance from the earth to the sun is 10^8 miles, since 93,000,000 miles is closer to 10^8 miles than it is to 10^7 miles. The mass of an electron is 9.1083×10^{-28} g. The order of magnitude of the mass of an electron is 10^{-27} g. The three tables which you will find on pages 25 to 27 show orders of magnitude of distance, mass, and time. These tables are included to give you an idea of the broad range covered by man's measurements of these quantities.

Study of the tables reveals interesting relationships. Under Orders of Magnitude of Time, note that the expected total life of the sun as a normal star is 10^9 times the human life span. Under Orders of Magnitude of Distance, note that the distance to the farthest photographed galaxy is 10^{17} times the mean distance from the earth to the moon. The table of Masses of Some Common Objects does not cover such a wide range of magnitudes as the others, but observe that 10^{12} check marks written in pencil would have a mass of a metric ton.

Sample Problem

Multiply 10.7 ft by 9.5 ft.

Solution

10.7 ft × 9.5 ft = 101.65 ft², with the digits 1.65 uncertain. Rounding, and retaining one uncertain digit, the product is 102 ft². (Note that this example is an exception to the general rule.)

Sample Problem

Multiply 2.75×10^6 by 4.8×10^{-2}.

Solution

2.75 × 4.8 = 13.200, with the digits 3.200 uncertain. Retaining one uncertain digit, this product is 13.
$10^6 \times 10^{-2} = 10^4$
$13 \times 10^4 = 1.3 \times 10^5$ in proper scientific notation.

Sample Problem

Divide 68.73 by 22.9.

Solution

Only three significant figures are required for the quotient, so find the first four digits of the quotient and round to three. 68.73 ÷ 22.9 = 3.001, which, when rounded, gives a quotient of 3.00.

Sample Problem

Divide 8.92×10^4 by 1.35×10^{-3}.

Solution

8.92 ÷ 1.35 = 6.61, rounded to three significant figures; $10^4 \div 10^{-3} = 10^7$. The quotient is 6.61×10^7.

ORDERS OF MAGNITUDE OF TIME

Time Interval (sec)	Associated Event	Time Interval (sec)	Associated Event
10^{18}	Expected total life of the Sun as a normal star	10^0	Time between heartbeats (1 second)
10^{17}	Time elapsed since first land life	10^{-1}	Time for .30 caliber bullet to cover 100 meters
10^{16}	Time for Sun to revolve around galaxy	10^{-2}	Time for electric fan to complete one revolution
10^{15}	Time elapsed since dinosaurs	10^{-3}	Time for fly to beat its wings once
10^{14}	Remaining life of Niagara Falls	10^{-4}	
10^{13}	Time elapsed since earliest men	10^{-5}	Time during which firecracker is exploding
10^{12}		10^{-6}	Time for high-speed bullet to cross a letter of type
10^{11}	Time elapsed since beginning of Christian Era	10^{-7}	Time for electron beam to go from source to screen in TV tube
10^{10}			
10^{9}	Human life span	10^{-8}	Time for light to cross a room
10^{8}	Time elapsed since you began school	10^{-9}	Atom emits visible light
10^{7}	Time for Earth to revolve around the Sun (year)	10^{-10}	
		10^{-11}	Time for light to penetrate window pane
10^{6}			
10^{5}	Time for Earth to rotate once on its axis (day)	10^{-12}	Time for oxygen molecule to spin once
10^{4}	Duration of average baseball game	10^{-13}	
		10^{-14}	
10^{3}	Time for light from the Sun to reach the Earth	10^{-15}	Time for electron to revolve around proton in hydrogen atom
10^{2}	One minute		
10^{1}		10^{-16}	
10^{0}	Time between heartbeats (1 second)	10^{-17}	
		10^{-18}	
		10^{-19}	
		10^{-20}	Time for innermost electron to revolve about nucleus in heaviest atom
		10^{-21}	
		10^{-22}	Time for proton to revolve once in nucleus

The table above and those on pages 26 and 27 are adapted from *Physics*, Volume 1, prepared by the Physical Science Study Committee, Massachusetts Institute of Technology.

ORDERS OF MAGNITUDE OF DISTANCE

Distance (m)	Associated Distance	Distance (m)	Associated Distance
10^{25}	Distance to farthest photographed object (a galaxy)	10^{0}	One yard
		10^{-1}	Width of your hand
10^{24}	Domain of the galaxies	10^{-2}	Diameter of a pencil
10^{23}	Domain of the galaxies	10^{-3}	Thickness of a window pane
10^{22}	Distance to the Great Nebula in Andromeda (nearest galaxy)	10^{-4}	Thickness of a piece of paper
10^{21}	Distance to the smaller Magellanic Cloud	10^{-5}	Diameter of a red blood corpuscle
10^{20}	Distance of the Sun from the center of our galaxy	10^{-6}	Average distance between successive collisions of molecules in air
10^{19}	Distance to the North Star	10^{-7}	Thickness of an oil film on water
10^{18}	Greatest distance measurable by parallax	10^{-8}	Average distance between molecules of air gases in a room
10^{17}	Distance to the nearest star		
10^{16}		10^{-9}	Size of a molecule of oil
10^{15}		10^{-10}	Average distance between particles of a crystalline solid
10^{14}			
10^{13}	Distance of Neptune from the Sun	10^{-11}	
10^{12}	Distance of Saturn from the Sun	10^{-12}	Average distance between atoms in center of densest stars
10^{11}	Distance of the Earth from the Sun	10^{-13}	
10^{10}	Distance of Mercury from the Sun	10^{-14}	Size of the largest atomic nucleus
10^{9}	Radius of the Sun	10^{-15}	Diameter of a proton
10^{8}	Mean distance from the Earth to the Moon		
10^{7}	Radius of the Earth		
10^{6}	Radius of the Moon		
10^{5}	Length of Lake Erie		
10^{4}	Average width of the Grand Canyon		
10^{3}	One mile		
10^{2}	Length of a football field		
10^{1}	Height of a shade tree		
10^{0}	One yard		

Too Large to Measure by Geometric Means

Too Small to Measure by Geometric Means

MASSES OF SOME COMMON OBJECTS		
Object	**Mass**	**Order of Magnitude of Mass (g)**
A check mark written in pencil	about a microgram	10^{-6}
A fly wing	50 micrograms	10^{-4}
A postage stamp	20 milligrams	10^{-2}
A dime	2.5 grams	10^{0}
A nickel	5.0 grams	10^{1}
A silver dollar	25 grams	10^{1}
A paperback book	200 grams	10^{2}
A pound	453.5924277 grams (legal definition)	10^{2}
A pint of water	473 grams	10^{2}
A quart of water	about 950 grams	10^{3}
One liter of water	1000 grams	10^{3}
A metric ton	1000 kilograms	10^{6}

3 MATHEMATICS IN PHYSICS

17. Physics uses mathematics as a tool. For many years in school you have studied arithmetic, algebra, and geometry as different branches of mathematics. You have found considerable use for arithmetic in your daily life, but perhaps not very much use as yet for algebra and geometry. However, as you continue with your study of physics, you will be using mathematics extensively. Here you will be using mathematics in its function as a tool for learning.

The Mathematics Refresher, page 618, contains a summary of knowledge and skills from arithmetic, elementary algebra, and plane geometry, which you will find useful in physics. You should review the information and sample problems *immediately*, and study carefully any topic with which you are not familiar. The rest of this chapter is devoted to topics which you may not as yet have taken up in your regular mathematics courses but which you will need for your further study of physics.

18. Proportion. In Chapter 1, Section 9, we defined the weight density of a substance as its weight per unit volume. Using D_w for weight density, w for weight, and V for volume, this definition can be expressed by the formula

$$D_w = \frac{w}{V}$$

If we use equal-volume samples of various substances, we observe that *the density of a substance is proportional to the weight of the sample.* The heavier the sample, the greater the density of the substance, and the lighter the sample, the less the density of the substance. Therefore we may say, the density of a sample and its weight are *in direct proportion*, provided the volume of all samples is the same. *Two quantities are in **direct proportion** if their ratio is a constant.*

Graphs are frequently helpful in interpreting physical relationships. Let us plot a graph to show direct proportion. We shall use the following data:

Material	Weight of 0.1 ft³ (lb)	Density (lb/ft³)
Balsa	0.75	7.5
Cork	1.5	15
Maple	4.5	45
Ice	5.7	57
Sulfur	12.5	125

☞ We shall use the point O, Fig. 2-9, as the origin of the graph. The horizontal line through O, xx', is called the X axis. On it we measure off distances from the origin, or *abscissas*, equivalent to the various weights. For convenience we shall use one small space to represent 1.0 lb. The vertical line through O, yy', is called the Y axis. On it we measure off distances from the origin, or *ordinates*, equivalent to the various densities. We shall use one small space to represent 10 lb/ft³. Point a on the graph represents the data for balsa, a sample weight of 0.75 lb and a density of 7.5 lb/ft³. Similarly, point b represents the data for cork, c for maple, d for ice, and e for sulfur. Finally we draw a line through these points. We find that this graph is a straight line, OS. We conclude that *when two quantities are in direct proportion, their graph is a straight line.*

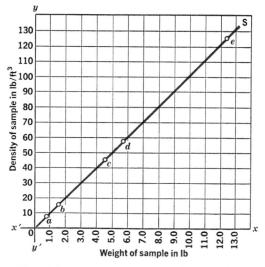

Fig. 2-9. When two quantities are in direct proportion, their graph is a straight line.

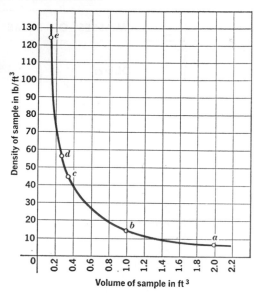

Fig. 2-10. When two quantities are in inverse proportion, their graph is a hyperbola.

Two quantities are in **inverse proportion** *if their product is a constant.* Again, let us use the formula for weight density, $D_w = w/V$. If V is varied without any change in w, that is, if we use samples of the same weight but of varying volume, the greater V is, the smaller D_w becomes and the smaller V is, the greater D_w becomes. The densities of materials are *inversely proportional* to their volumes, provided the weights of the samples are the same. Let us use the following data for 15-lb samples of various materials to illustrate this.

Material	Volume of 15 lb (ft³)	Density (lb/ft³)
Balsa	2.0	7.5
Cork	1.0	15
Maple	0.33	45
Ice	0.26	57
Sulfur	0.12	125

In Fig. 2-10 the volumes have been plotted as abscissas and the densities as ordinates. Point a represents the data for balsa, b for cork, c for maple, d for ice,

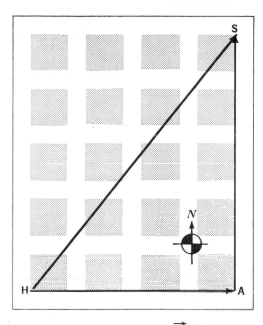

Fig. 2-11. The displacement $\overrightarrow{HS}$ is the sum of the displacements $\overrightarrow{HA}$ and $\overrightarrow{AS}$.

e for sulfur. *The shape of the graph, a hyperbola, is typical of an inverse proportion.*

19. Scalar and vector quantities. So far we have discussed quantities of length, area, volume, mass, weight, density, and time. All of these quantities except (weight) may be expressed by a single number with suitable units. For instance, the length of a table can be completely described by saying it is 1.5 m long. Or the mass of a steel block is completely described when it is given as 50. kg. *Quantities,* such as these, *which can be expressed completely by a single number with appropriate units are called* **scalar quantities,** *or simply,* **scalars.** The single number required is the magnitude.

We have already explained that weights are forces. Forces have magnitude but they cannot be completely described by magnitude alone. To describe a force completely, we must also indicate the direction in which it acts. Weights are forces which act toward the center of the earth. *Quantities,* such as forces, *which require both*

a magnitude and a direction for their complete description are called **vector quantities.** We will take up forces as vector quantities in detail in Chapter 3. However, before we can do that, we must learn how to perform computations with vector quantities generally.

20. Displacement: a vector quantity. When you travel from home to school you undergo what the physicist calls *a change of position,* or a **displacement.** You change your position on the earth's surface. Suppose you are asked, "How do you go from home to school?" and you answer, "I walk nine blocks." Obviously you have not completely described how you make the trip so anyone else could make it without error. You have told how far you walk. But you have left out the second necessary piece of information—the direction in which you go. Thus, you see, a displacement is a vector quantity. Both a magnitude and a direction are required for its complete description.

Let us assume that Fig. 2-11 shows the location of your home, *H,* and your school, *S.* When you travel from home to school, you undergo a displacement from *H* to *S.* The line *HS,* with its arrowhead, shows the direction and magnitude of this displacement by the most direct route. Such an arrow may be used to represent any vector quantity. The arrow itself is called a **vector.** *The length of a vector indicates the magnitude of the vector quantity. The direction in which the vector is drawn indicates the direction of the vector quantity.*

Obviously you cannot go directly from *H* to *S* by the most direct route unless you cut through other people's property; in a built-up city area, houses and stores would probably prevent this, also. From the map shown in Fig. 2-11, you might get to school by going from *H* to *A* and then to *S.* The portion of your trip from *H* to *A* may be represented by the vector *HA* and the portion from *A* to *S* by the vector *AS.* But the net result of your travels is

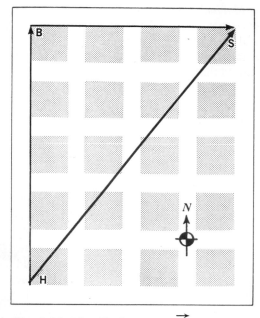

Fig. 2-12. The displacement $\overrightarrow{HS}$ is also the sum of the displacements $\overrightarrow{HB}$ and $\overrightarrow{BS}$.

still shown by the vector HS. Using $\overrightarrow{HA}$, $\overrightarrow{AS}$, and $\overrightarrow{HS}$ to represent these three vector quantities, we may write

$$\overrightarrow{HA} + \overrightarrow{AS} = \overrightarrow{HS}$$

Possibly on another day you go from home to school by the route shown in Fig. 2-12. In this case

$$\overrightarrow{HB} + \overrightarrow{BS} = \overrightarrow{HS}$$

But $\overrightarrow{HB} = \overrightarrow{AS}$ and $\overrightarrow{BS} = \overrightarrow{HA}$. Thus we see that vectors may be added in either order and produce the same sum.

You need not go to school by even a reasonably direct route. Suppose you travel the route shown in Fig. 2-13. Then we may write

$$\overrightarrow{HC} + \overrightarrow{CD} + \overrightarrow{DE} + \overrightarrow{EF} + \overrightarrow{FG} + \overrightarrow{GS} = \overrightarrow{HS}$$

In each of the three cases we have described, $\overrightarrow{HS}$, *which represents the net displacement*, is the **resultant vector,** or simply the **resultant.** The other vectors are called **component vectors,** or **components.**

Vectors may also be subtracted. A careful look at Fig. 2-11 and some thought should convince you that

$$\overrightarrow{HS} - \overrightarrow{AS} = \overrightarrow{HA}$$

Similarly from Fig. 2-12,

$$\overrightarrow{HS} - \overrightarrow{HB} = \overrightarrow{BS}$$

Addition or subtraction of the magnitudes of vectors alone is not so simple a task. For instance, the magnitude of $\overrightarrow{HA}$ plus the magnitude of $\overrightarrow{AS}$ does not give the magnitude of $\overrightarrow{HS}$. The problem of computing the magnitude and direction of a resultant vector if the magnitudes and directions of the component vectors are known is explained in the following sections.

21. Displacements acting in a straight line. Suppose you walk from your home eastward along a straight street three blocks to the drugstore and then one block further eastward to the hardware store. The resultant displacement is obviously four blocks eastward. See Fig. 2-14.

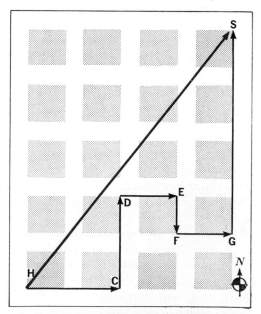

Fig. 2-13. Even though a very indirect route is taken, the resultant displacement is still the sum of the component displacements.

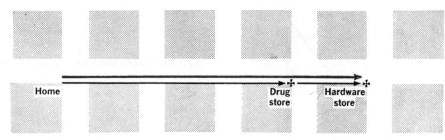

Fig. 2-14. The resultant of two component vectors acting in the same direction has a magnitude equal to the arithmetic sum of the magnitudes of the component vectors and acts in the same direction.

However, suppose you walked eastward the four blocks to the hardware store, and then westward the one block back to the drugstore. What is the resultant displacement now? In this case the resultant displacement is three blocks eastward. See Fig. 2-15. *The resultant of two component vectors acting in the same or opposite directions has a magnitude equal to the algebraic sum of the magnitudes of the component vectors. It acts in the same direction as the component having the greater magnitude.*

22. Displacements acting at right angles. Let us use as an example the route from home to school shown in Fig. 2-11. Suppose $\overrightarrow{HA}$ is 1.00 km eastward, and $\overrightarrow{AS}$ is 1.25 km northward. We are to find the magnitude and direction of the resultant $\overrightarrow{HS}$. First we must construct a diagram to scale. See Fig. 2-16. Since the component displacements $\overrightarrow{HA}$ and $\overrightarrow{AS}$ occur sequentially, we draw their vectors

head to tail with a right angle between. Then we draw the resultant $\overrightarrow{HS}$ from the tail of the first vector to the head of the second.

From the scale of our drawing we can determine graphically that the magnitude of $\overrightarrow{HS}$ is 1.6 km and its bearing is N 39° E or 039°. Bearing is the direction of one point from another on the earth's surface. See Fig. 2-17.

Using the formula for any right triangle,

$$c = \sqrt{a^2 + b^2}$$

where c is the length of the hypotenuse and a and b are the lengths of the sides,

$$c = \sqrt{(1.00 \text{ km})^2 + (1.25 \text{ km})^2}$$

$$c = \sqrt{2.56 \text{ km}^2}$$

$$c = 1.60 \text{ km}$$

In a *right triangle* the *tangent* of the angle between the hypotenuse and a side is the ratio of the length of the side opposite the

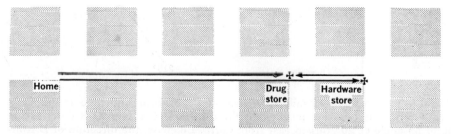

Fig. 2-15. The resultant of two component vectors acting in opposite directions has a magnitude equal to the arithmetic difference between the magnitudes of the component vectors. It acts in the same direction as the component having the greater magnitude.

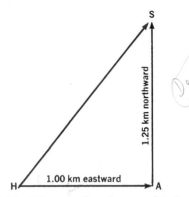

Fig. 2-16. Diagram for the graphical and trigonometric determination of the resultant of two component vectors acting at right angles.

angle to the length of the side adjacent to the angle. In Fig. 2-16,

$$\tan \angle SHA = \frac{AS}{HA} = \frac{1.25 \text{ km}}{1.00 \text{ km}} = 1.25$$

From Table 3 in Appendix B, we find that the angle which has a tangent of 1.25 is 51.3°. So the bearing of $\overrightarrow{HS}$ is N 38.7° E, or 038.7°.

For suggestions for short-cut solutions of 45°–45°–90° and 30°–60°–90° right triangles, see the Mathematics Refresher.

23. Displacements acting at any angle. Suppose you hike 5.00 km east, then turn and hike 7.00 km N 15.0° W. How far are you from your starting point, and what is your present bearing from your starting point?

First construct a diagram to a convenient scale as shown in Fig. 2-18. Graphically, we determine that displacement $\overrightarrow{XZ}$ has a magnitude of 7.5 km and its bearing is N 25° E.

For a trigonometric solution we first use the cosine law to determine the magnitude of $\overrightarrow{XZ}$. The general form of the cosine law is

$$c = \sqrt{a^2 + b^2 - 2ab \cos C}$$

in which a, b, and c are the sides of any triangle and C is the angle opposite side c.

Let $a = 5.00$ km, $b = 7.00$ km, and $C = 75.0°$. The value $\cos 75.0° = 0.259$ is obtained from Table 3 in Appendix B.

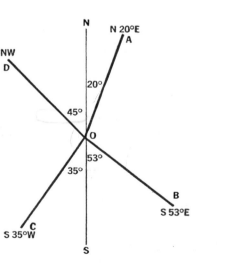

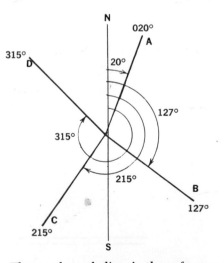

Fig. 2-17. Two methods of indicating bearing. The north-south line is the reference. Left: The bearing N 20° E means that the direction of A from O is described by the side of an angle of 20° turned east from north. Likewise, the direction of B from O is described by the side of an angle of 53° turned east from south. Right: A bearing of 020° means that the direction of A from O is described by the side of an angle of 20° turned clockwise from north. The direction of B from O is described by the side of an angle of 127° turned clockwise from north.

Substituting,

$$c = \sqrt{(5.00 \text{ km})^2 + (7.00 \text{ km})^2 - 2(5.00 \text{ km} \times 7.00 \text{ km} \times 0.259)}$$
$$c = 7.48 \text{ km}$$

To determine the bearing of $\overrightarrow{XZ}$ we now use the sine law. In its general form,

$$\frac{a}{\sin A} = \frac{b}{\sin B} = \frac{c}{\sin C}$$

For our purpose we need only

$$\frac{b}{\sin B} = \frac{c}{\sin C}$$

which on being solved for $\sin B$ yields

$$\sin B = \frac{b \sin C}{c}$$

From Table 3 in Appendix B, the value $\sin 75.0° = 0.966$. Substituting,

$$\sin B = \frac{7.00 \text{ km} \times 0.966}{7.48 \text{ km}}$$
$$\sin B = 0.904$$
$$B = 64.7°$$

So the bearing of Z from X is N 25.3° E.

In the vector diagram for the problem above, all the angles were acute angles. In all cases this may not be so. If $\angle C$, the angle between the component vectors, is

an obtuse angle, its cosine cannot be read directly from Table 3 in Appendix B. In order to utilize the table values, we use the following relationship: *The cosine of an obtuse angle equals the cosine of its supplement but is opposite in sign.* For example, $\cos 120.0° = -\cos (180.0° - 120.0°) = -\cos 60.0° = -0.500$.

In applying the sine law to determine the magnitude of an obtuse angle, you must remember that *the sine of an obtuse angle equals the sine of its supplement.* For example, $\sin 120.0° = \sin (180.0° - 120.0°) = \sin 60.0° = 0.866$. See the Sample Problem on page 34.

The resultant of two vectors acting at an angle of between 0° and 180° is the geometric sum of the component vectors.

24. Resolution of a displacement. Suppose you fly on a bearing of 160.0° for 1000. miles. How far south and how far east are you from your starting point? This is a problem in *resolving* the given displacement into two displacements, one

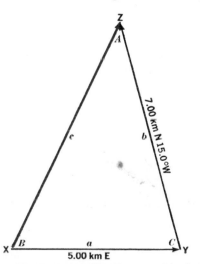

Fig. 2-18. Diagram for the graphical and trigonometric determination of the resultant of two component vectors acting at an acute angle.

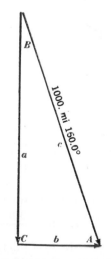

Fig. 2-19. Diagram for resolution of a displacement. A single vector may be resolved into two vectors which act in given directions.

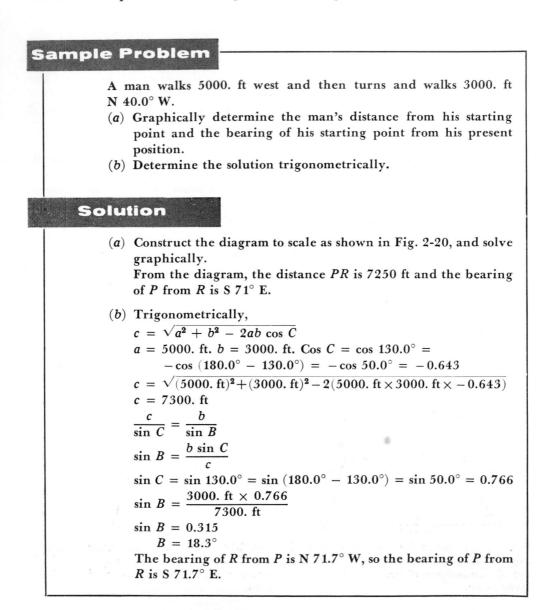

Fig. 2-20. Diagram for the graphical and trigonometric determination of the resultant of two component vectors acting at an obtuse angle.

Sample Problem

A man walks 5000. ft west and then turns and walks 3000. ft
N 40.0° W.

(*a*) Graphically determine the man's distance from his starting
point and the bearing of his starting point from his present
position.

(*b*) Determine the solution trigonometrically.

Solution

(*a*) Construct the diagram to scale as shown in Fig. 2-20, and solve
graphically.

From the diagram, the distance PR is 7250 ft and the bearing
of P from R is S 71° E.

(*b*) Trigonometrically,

$$c = \sqrt{a^2 + b^2 - 2ab \cos C}$$

$a = 5000.$ ft. $b = 3000.$ ft. Cos $C = \cos 130.0° =$
$-\cos (180.0° - 130.0°) = -\cos 50.0° = -0.643$

$$c = \sqrt{(5000. \text{ ft})^2 + (3000. \text{ ft})^2 - 2(5000. \text{ ft} \times 3000. \text{ ft} \times -0.643)}$$

$c = 7300.$ ft

$$\frac{c}{\sin C} = \frac{b}{\sin B}$$

$$\sin B = \frac{b \sin C}{c}$$

$\sin C = \sin 130.0° = \sin (180.0° - 130.0°) = \sin 50.0° = 0.766$

$$\sin B = \frac{3000. \text{ ft} \times 0.766}{7300. \text{ ft}}$$

$\sin B = 0.315$

$B = 18.3°$

The bearing of R from P is N 71.7° W, so the bearing of P from
R is S 71.7° E.

being southward and the other eastward.

First draw the given displacement, and construct the separate southward and eastward displacements as shown in Fig. 2-19.

Since $\angle B$ is 20.0° and $\angle C$ is 90.0°, $\angle A$ will be 70.0°.

Graphically, a is estimated at 950 miles while b is about 350 miles.

Using the sine law,

$$\frac{a}{\sin A} = \frac{b}{\sin B} = \frac{c}{\sin C}$$

and substituting,

$$\frac{a}{\sin 70.0°} = \frac{b}{\sin 20.0°} = \frac{1000. \text{ miles}}{\sin 90.0°}$$

Solving, $a = 940.$ miles and $b = 342$ miles. Thus you are 940. miles south and 342 miles east of your starting point.

Summary

Physics did not develop into an exact science until Roman numerals were replaced by Arabic numerals and speculation was replaced by experimentation. Measurement is fundamental to experimentation in physics.

All measurements in physics can be expressed in terms of length, mass, time, temperature, and electric charge. Three systems of measurement are now commonly used by physicists in the United States: the meter-kilogram-second system, the centimeter-gram-second system, and the foot-pound-second system. Each of these consists of various basic and derived units.

The measurement of any quantity consists of selecting a suitable unit and counting the number of times the unit is taken. The accuracy to which a measurement is made is indicated by the number of significant figures in which it is expressed. Scientific notation overcomes the difficulties in the use of significant figures in ordinary notation. Various rules have been established for performing calculations with significant figures, to insure the accuracy of the results. Frequently a measurement may be expressed in an approximate fashion by giving the order of magnitude.

Mathematical skills needed for physics include an understanding of proportion, scalar and vector quantities, and displacements. Vectors acting in the same or opposite directions are added algebraically, while vectors acting at an angle are added geometrically.

TERMS TO DEFINE

abscissa	FPS system	ordinate
basic unit	gram	resultant
centi-	inverse proportion	scalar quantity
CGS system	kilo-	scientific notation
component	liter	significant figures
conversion factor	mean solar second	sine law
cosine law	meter	slug
derived unit	milli-	standard kilogram
direct proportion	MKS system	standard meter
displacement	newton	vector
dyne	order of magnitude	vector quantity

QUESTIONS

A 1. In what five types of units can all physical measurements be expressed?

2. (*a*) Name the three systems of measurement commonly used by physicists. (*b*) Give the basic units in each system.

3. (*a*) What part of a centimeter is a millimeter? (*b*) What part of a liter is a milliliter? (*c*) What part of a kilogram is a centigram?

4. (*a*) What force, in newtons, must be used to lift a mass of 1 kg? (*b*) What force, in dynes, must be used to lift a mass of 1 g? (*c*) What is the mass of an object which weighs 32 lb?

5. List in order the steps to be followed in solving physics problems.

6. What principle is observed in making any measurement?

7. What are the rules for adding, subtracting, multiplying, and dividing with significant figures?

8. What is the order of magnitude?

B 9. Name two factors which prevented scientific advancement among the Romans.

10. Give the value of each of the eight metric system prefixes as a power of ten.

11. (*a*) What is the difference in definition between a cubic decimeter and a liter? (*b*) For practical purposes, what is their relationship?

12. (*a*) What is a conversion factor? (*b*) To what must all conversion factors be equal?

13. What advantages does scientific notation have over ordinary notation in expressing the results of measurements?

14. (*a*) What is the shape of the graph of two quantities which are in direct proportion? (*b*) What is the shape of the graph of two quantities which are in inverse proportion?

15. Why is mass a scalar quantity, while weight is a vector quantity?

16. What is the difference between arithmetic addition and geometric addition?

PROBLEMS

A 1. How many significant figures are there in each of the following expressions? (*a*) 173.2 m;   (*b*) 205 cm;   (*c*) 4000 km; (*d*) 0.025 g; (*e*) 700. 1; (*f*) 0.09050 ml.

2. Convert each of the expressions in Problem 1 to scientific notation.

3. Convert each of the following to scientific notation:
(*a*) 175,000,000
(*b*) 602,300,000,000,000,000,000,000
(*c*) 0.000047
(*d*) 0.000,000,000,000,000,000,000,001,672,39

4. What is the order of magnitude of each of the expressions in Problem 3?

5. (*a*) Add 16.24, 3.8, and 27.965. (*b*) Add 16.24 m, 3.8 cm, and 27.965 km, expressing the sum in meters.

6. (*a*) Subtract 98.757 from 163.2. (*b*) Subtract 98.757 g from 163.2 kg, expressing the difference in kilograms.

7. (*a*) Multiply 6.5, 28.3, and 49.7. (*b*) Multiply 6.5 cm, 28.3 mm, and 49.7 cm, expressing the product in cm³.

8. (*a*) Divide 345 by 70.1. (*b*) Divide 345 g by 70.1 cm³.

9. The Empire State Building is 1248 ft high. What is its height in meters?

10. What is the length of a 100.-m track in inches?

11. The free baggage allowance for international tourist-class airplane passengers is 44.0 lb. What is this weight allowance in newtons?

12. A tank is 25.00 m long, 10.00 m wide, and filled with water to a depth of 2.00 m. (*a*) What is the mass of the water in the tank in kilograms? (*b*) What is the weight of the water in newtons?

13. A man making deliveries to stores in a neighborhood travels from the warehouse 5 blocks west, 3 blocks north, 7 blocks east, 2 blocks south, 4 blocks south, 3 blocks west, 1 block north, 3 blocks west, and 2 blocks north. How far, and in what direction, must he go to return to the warehouse? Draw a diagram as part of your solution.

14. An automobile is driven 30.0 mi N and then 25.0 mi W. (*a*) Determine graphically the distance and bearing of the automobile from its starting point. (*b*) Determine the distance and bearing by calculation.

15. An airplane flies 200. km on a bearing of 090.° and then turns and flies 100. km on a bearing of 000.°. (*a*) Determine graphically the distance and bearing of the airplane from its starting point. (*b*) Determine the distance and bearing by calculation.

B **16.** Plot a graph to show the relationship between miles and kilometers. Use 0 mi, 10 mi, 20 mi, etc., to 100 mi as abscissas and the corresponding number of kilometers as ordinates. (*a*) What is the shape of the graph? (*b*) Why does it have this shape? (*c*) From the graph read off the number of kilometers equal to 25 miles. (*d*) How many kilometers in 57 miles? (*e*) How many miles in 82 kilometers?

17. The length of a vibrating string is related to the frequency of the tone it emits. Plot a graph of the following data for a typical vibrating string, using lengths as abscissas and frequencies as ordinates.

Length (cm)	Frequency (cycles/sec)
7.50	1024
15.0	512
20.0	384
30.0	256
40.0	192
60.0	128
80.0	96
120	64
240	32

(*a*) What is the shape of the graph? (*b*) What relationship exists between the length of a vibrating string and the frequency of the tone it emits? (*c*) From the graph, read off the frequency the string would have if it were 75.0 cm long. (*d*) How long must the string be to vibrate at the rate of 400. cycles/sec?

18. A party of hikers walks 6.00 km from camp on a bearing of S 20.0° E, then turns and walks 8.00 km on a bearing of N 30.0° E. (*a*) Determine graphically the direct distance and bearing back to camp. (*b*) Determine this distance and bearing by calculation.

19. A farmer plowing on the contour of his land plows 150.0 m N 45.0° W, then turns and plows 50.0 m S 20.0° W. (*a*) Determine graphically the distance and bearing of the farmer's present position from his starting point. (*b*) Determine this distance and bearing trigonometrically.

20. A helicopter takes off on a straight path which makes an angle of 65.0° with the horizontal, and reaches an altitude of 350. m above the airport. (*a*) Determine graphically its horizontal distance from the take-off point and the distance actually traveled by the helicopter. (*b*) Determine these distances by calculation.

RESEARCH ON YOUR OWN

1. Find the area of the top of the demonstration table in square inches, using a yardstick for measurement. Do the same, using a meter stick. Obtain the answer in square centimeters. Convert each answer into the larger units, square yards and square meters. Assuming your answers to be correct, how many square yards are there in a square meter? How many square meters in a square yard?

2. Make a number of estimations of lengths, such as the height of the ceiling, width of the room, length of the room, height of a laboratory table, length of the hallway, width of the hallway, etc. Then make accurate measurements in feet and inches. Are your estimates closer to the truth on horizontal measurements or vertical measurements? Try a similar experiment using metric units of length.

3. Hold in your outstretched hand a known mass such as 0.5 kg. Have a friend replace this mass with a book or other object. How accurately can you estimate the mass of the object by comparison with the previously known mass? Repeat the experiment, supporting your elbow so that your forearm instead of your outstretched arm holds the weight.

4. Obtain a piece of peg board. Assume the distance between holes to be unity and make arrows of any stiff material in multiples of this distance. You can also make arrows representing multiples of the square root of two, square root of three, etc. Glue short lengths of ⅛-in. dowel rods to the back of the arrows. Use your board and arrows to demonstrate the addition and subtraction of vectors.

5. Using library research sources, prepare a report on the historical development of the metric system. What circumstances were favorable to its adoption?

6. Investigate the history of the adoption of a system of weights and measures in the United States.

7. Report on how a stroboscope can be used to measure short intervals of time. Build a simple stroboscope and demonstrate its use.

UNIT **2**

Force and motion

CHAPTER 3

FORCE

1 FORCE VECTORS

1. The concept of force. In Chapters 1 and 2 we learned some of the fundamental quantities of physics and how they are measured and represented graphically. We are now ready to begin an extensive study of one of the most important concepts of physics—force. Force is an essential factor in the construction of a bridge or the motion of an artificial satellite. We need a knowledge of force to understand the structure of matter. Force is directly related to work and energy; and

VOCABULARY

Center of gravity. That point at which all of the weight of an object may be considered to be concentrated.

Center of moments. The point from which the lengths of all the moment arms are measured.

Coefficient of friction. The ratio of the force needed to overcome friction to the normal force pressing the surfaces together.

Couple. Two forces of equal magnitude which act in opposite directions, but not in the same line.

Equilibrant force. The force which produces equilibrium.

Equilibrium. The state of a body in which there is no change in its motion.

Force. That which produces or prevents motion, or has a tendency to do so.

Friction. A force which opposes motion.

Linear motion. Motion along a line.

Parallel forces. Forces acting in the same or opposite directions.

Resolution of forces. The separation of a single force into two component forces acting in definite directions on the same point.

Resultant force. The single force which has the same effect as two or more forces acting together.

Rotary motion. Motion about a point which acts as a pivot.

Torque. The product of a force and the length of the moment arm on which it acts.

energy includes heat, sound, and light. We must know what force is in order to describe gravitation, magnetism, and static electricity. The concept of force pervades the entire subject of physics. It is natural, therefore, that we begin with this topic.

In Chapter 1, Section 6, we tentatively defined force as a push or a pull. That definition was sufficient to introduce you to the concept of force, but for a detailed study, we shall need a more comprehensive definition. Forces do not always push or pull an object. Some combinations of forces just balance each other, and the object on which they act remains stationary. In other cases, balanced forces

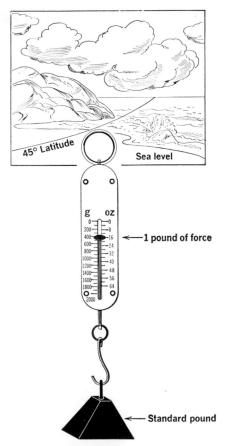

Fig. 3-1. At 45° latitude and at sea level, one pound of force is needed to overcome the earth's attraction for the standard pound.

may keep an object moving at a constant speed in a straight line. A force acting on an object may also increase or decrease its speed or change its direction. A force may move the particles of which an object is composed and thus change the shape of the object.

We exert a force if we push against a truck, whether we move the truck, or only try to move it. We also exert a force if we pull on a heavy piano, whether we move the piano, or only try to move it. *Forces produce or prevent motion, or they have a tendency to do so.*

2. Forces acting on a body. Most of the forces which act on an object are caused by other objects in contact with it. When you exert a force to close a door, your hand is in contact with the door. A liquid within a container exerts a force against the inside walls of its container, and is in contact with it. Other forces, such as magnetic or electric forces, may act on a body without being in actual physical contact with it. For the present we shall be concerned with only one force of this type: the force of gravitation exerted by the earth. This force causes bodies to fall toward the earth. We measure it when we find the weight of an object.

3. Units of force. In Chapter 2 we learned that there are certain standards of measurement in both the metric and English systems. The standard mass in the metric system is the platinum-iridium cylinder called the *standard kilogram.* By action of the Congress of the United States a similar cylinder, having 0.4535924277 the mass of the standard kilogram, is called the *standard pound.* The **pound,** the basic unit of force in the English gravitational system, *is defined as the weight of the standard pound at sea level and 45° latitude.* The conditions of sea level and 45° latitude are necessary because the strength of gravitational attraction varies with changes in altitude and latitude. See Fig. 3-1. The units of force in the metric system, the *newton* and the *dyne,* are derived units. Their relation to the corresponding mass units is explained in Chapter 2, Section 7.

4. The measurement of force. A spring balance is commonly used to measure force. The pull of the earth on a standard pound suspended from the hook of a balance will stretch the spring a certain distance. Any other suspended object that stretches the spring this same distance also weighs a pound. Two such objects will stretch the spring farther than one object. Three of them will stretch the spring still farther. Graduations corresponding to these distances are marked on the face of the balance, and a pointer attached to the spring indicates the reading. In Fig. 3-2 we see a typical spring balance being used to measure a force.

The spring balances used in physics laboratories are usually calibrated in ounces and grams. In the systems of measurement we are using, force may be measured in ounces but not in grams. The values read on the gram-scale should be converted to newtons or dynes of force by means of the relationships given in Chapter 2, Section 7.

5. Force vectors. We cannot completely describe a force by giving its magnitude alone. The expression "A force of 5 pounds" is incomplete. We must also know the direction in which the force acts. Thus, you see, forces are like displacements—they require both a magnitude and a direction for their complete description. Forces can therefore be represented by vectors; *force is a vector quantity.*

The vector used to represent a force is called a *force vector.* Suppose we wish to draw a vector to represent a force of 10. nt acting eastward upon point *O.* We select a suitable scale, and draw a line ten units long eastward from point *O,* as shown in Fig. 3-3. A force vector is always represented as a *pull* upon the point where the force acts. The arrowhead indicates the direction in which the force acts.

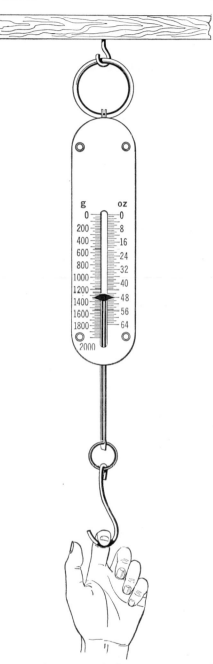

Fig. 3-2. This spring balance measures the force exerted by the hand pulling down on the hook of the balance.

Fig. 3-3. This vector represents a force of 10 nt acting eastward.

2 COMPOSITION OF FORCES

6. The resultant force. In Chapter 2 we learned that two or more component displacements can be combined to give a single resultant displacement. In the same way it is possible to combine the effects of two or more forces to give the single resultant force which produces the same effect. *When two or more forces act concurrently (simultaneously) at a point, the resultant force is that single force applied at the same point which would produce the same effect.*

The resultant of two or more concurrent forces is really a substitute for those forces. When we use the resultant we assume that it takes the place of the separate forces and we need not consider them further. Unlike the football substitute, who does not always produce the same effect as the man he replaces, a resultant force must produce exactly the same effect as all the forces for which it is substituted.

Displacements are vector quantities which usually occur in sequence, that is, one after another; forces, on the other hand, usually act simultaneously. In the following sections we shall learn the methods for determining resultants of concurrent force vectors.

7. Forces acting in a straight line. Suppose one boy pulls eastward on a rope with a force of 40. lb and another boy joins him and pulls on the rope in the same direction with a force of 60. lb. The resultant force is 100. lb acting eastward on the rope. One man, taking the place of the boys, could produce the same effect by pulling eastward on the rope with a force of 100. lb. See Fig. 3-4.

Now suppose one boy pulls eastward with a force of 40. lb and another boy pulls westward on the same point with a force of 60. lb. The resultant force is 20. lb pulling westward on the point. See Fig. 3-5. *The resultant of two forces acting in the same or in opposite directions upon the same point has a magnitude equal to the algebraic sum of the forces and acts in the direction of the greater force.*

8. Forces acting at right angles. Suppose one force of 10 0 nt acts eastward upon an object at point O. Another force of 15.0 nt acts southward upon the same point. Since these forces act *simultaneously* upon point O, the vector diagram is constructed with the tails of both vectors at O. See Fig. 3-6. From our drawing we see that the first force tends to move the object along OE toward E. The second force tends to move the object along OS toward S. When the forces act simultaneously, the object tends to move along the diagonal of the parallelogram of which the two forces are sides, or along OR toward R. *The resultant of two forces acting at an angle of between 0° and 180° upon a given point is equal to the diagonal of a parallelogram of which the two force vectors are sides. (This is a method of geometric addition.)*

You can readily make a graphic determination of the magnitude and bearing of the resultant force from the diagram constructed to scale. The trigonometric solution makes use of the facts that the opposite sides of a parallelogram are equal, and the diagonal of a parallelogram divides it into two congruent triangles. Thus, in Fig. 3-6, $OE = SR$, and in the triangle OSR, $\angle OSR = 90.0°$, $OS = 15.0$ nt, and $SR = 10.0$ nt. The magnitude and bearing

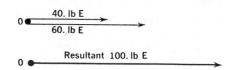

Fig. 3-4. The resultant of two forces acting in the same direction on the same point has a magnitude equal to the sum of the forces and acts in the same direction.

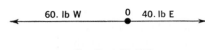

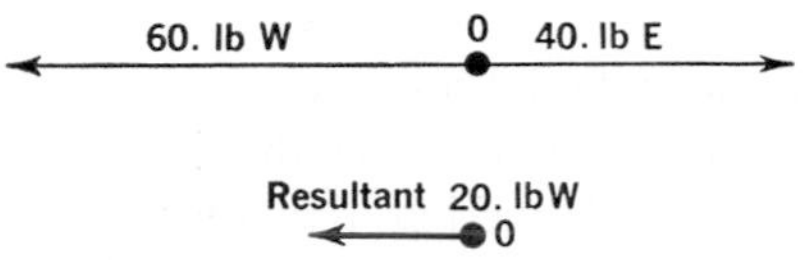

Resultant 20. lbW

Fig. 3-5. The resultant of two forces acting in opposite directions on the same point has a magnitude equal to the difference between the forces and acts in the direction of the greater force.

of the resultant *OR* can now be determined by the method described in Chapter 2, Section 22. See the Sample Problem below.

9. Forces acting at an acute angle. The angle between two forces acting on the same point is generally not a right angle. Figure 3-7 represents the vectors for two forces, 10.0 nt E and 15.0 nt S 40.0° E, acting on point *O*. The angle between the two forces is thus 50.0°. The parallelogram is completed as shown. Observe that the diagonal vector representing the resultant *is drawn from the point*

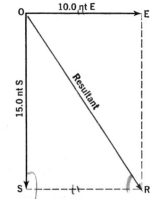

Fig. 3-6. Diagram for the graphic and trigonometric determination of the resultant of two component force vectors acting at right angles.

on which the two original forces are acting, since the resultant must also act on this point. (The other diagonal of the parallelogram, *EA*, is *not* the resultant of the two forces.) A graphic solution may be easily made from the diagram constructed to scale. The trigonometric solution, using one of the two triangles into which the resultant

Sample Problem

Calculate the magnitude and bearing of the resultant of the two forces acting on point *O* as shown in Fig. 3-6.

Solution

Triangle *OSR* is a right triangle.

$OR = \sqrt{OS^2 + SR^2}$

$OR = \sqrt{(15.0 \text{ nt})^2 + (10.0 \text{ nt})^2}$

$OR = 18.0 \text{ nt}$

$\tan \angle ROS = \dfrac{SR}{OS}$

$\tan \angle ROS = \dfrac{10.0 \text{ nt}}{15.0 \text{ nt}} = 0.667$

$\angle ROS = 33.7°$

Bearing of $OR = S\ 33.7°\ E$

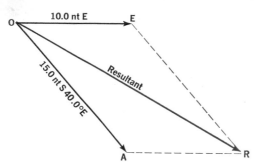

Fig. 3-7. Diagram for the graphic and trigonometric determination of the resultant of two component force vectors acting at an acute angle.

divides the parallelogram, may be made by the method described in Chapter 2, Section 23. See the Sample Problem below.

10. Forces acting at an obtuse angle. The resultant is very different if the angle

between the same two forces is 140.0°. The parallelogram is constructed to scale in the same manner, using the force vectors as sides, and making the angle between them 140.0°. This parallelogram is shown in Fig. 3-8. The diagonal must be drawn from O, the point on which the two forces are acting. The graphic solution may be made from the diagram. The trigonometric solution is made by the method described in Chapter 2, Section 23. See the Sample Problem on the opposite page.

11. Three or more forces acting on the same point. Sometimes three or more forces act at different angles upon the same point. We may find their resultant by first finding the resultant of two of them. We use the vectors of these first two forces as sides of a parallelogram, and find the diagonal. Then we construct a

Sample Problem

Determine the magnitude and bearing of the resultant of the two forces shown in Fig. 3-7.

Solution

$\angle EOA = 50.0°$

$\angle OAR = 130.0°$ (Why?)

By the cosine law, $OR = \sqrt{OA^2 + AR^2 - 2(OA)(AR)(\cos \angle OAR)}$

$\cos \angle OAR = \cos 130.0° = -\cos(180.0° - 130.0°) = -\cos 50.0° = -0.643$

$OR = \sqrt{(15.0 \text{ nt})^2 + (10.0 \text{ nt})^2 - 2 \times 15.0 \text{ nt} \times 10.0 \text{ nt} \times (-0.643)}$

$OR = 22.8 \text{ nt}$

By the sine law, $\dfrac{OA}{\sin \angle ORA} = \dfrac{OR}{\sin \angle OAR}$

$\sin \angle ORA = \dfrac{OA \times \sin \angle OAR}{OR}$

$\sin \angle OAR = \sin 130.0° = \sin(180.0° - 130.0°) = \sin 50.0° = 0.766$

$\sin \angle ORA = \dfrac{15.0 \text{ nt} \times 0.766}{22.8 \text{ nt}} = 0.504$

$\angle ORA = 30.3°$

The bearing of OR from O is S 59.7° E

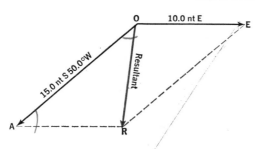

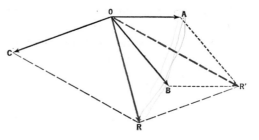

Fig. 3-8. Diagram for the graphic and trigonometric determination of the resultant of two component force vectors acting at an obtuse angle.

Fig. 3-9. Three forces, $\overrightarrow{OA}$, $\overrightarrow{OB}$, and $\overrightarrow{OC}$, act at different angles upon point O. To find their resultant, we first construct the parallelogram $OAR'B$, and find the resultant of $\overrightarrow{OA}$ and $\overrightarrow{OB}$. This is $\overrightarrow{OR'}$. Then we construct a second parallelogram, $OR'RC$, using the third force, $\overrightarrow{OC}$, and the resultant of the first two forces, $\overrightarrow{OR'}$, as sides. The diagonal of this parallelogram, $\overrightarrow{OR}$, is the resultant of the three forces.

second parallelogram using this diagonal and the third force vector as sides. The diagonal of the second parallelogram is the resultant of the three concurrent forces. This method may be used for both graphic and trigonometric solutions. See Fig. 3-9.

Sample Problem

Determine the magnitude and bearing of the resultant of the two forces shown in Fig. 3-8.

Solution

$\angle EOA = 140.0°$

$\angle OAR = 40.0°$

By the cosine law, $OR = \sqrt{OA^2 + AR^2 - 2(OA)(AR)(\cos \angle OAR)}$

$\cos \angle OAR = \cos 40.0° = 0.766$

$OR = \sqrt{(15.0 \text{ nt})^2 + (10.0 \text{ nt})^2 - 2 \times 15.0 \text{ nt} \times 10.0 \text{ nt} \times 0.766}$

$OR = 9.7 \text{ nt}$

By the sine law, $\dfrac{OA}{\sin \angle ORA} = \dfrac{OR}{\sin \angle OAR}$

$\sin \angle ORA = \dfrac{OA \times \sin \angle OAR}{OR}$

$\sin \angle OAR = \sin 40.0° = 0.643$

$\sin \angle ORA = \dfrac{15.0 \text{ nt} \times 0.643}{9.7 \text{ nt}} = 0.99$

$\angle ORA = 98°$ ($\angle ORA$ is an obtuse angle)

The bearing of OR from O is S 8° W. The data of the problem do not permit a more accurate answer.

12. The equilibrant force. *Equilibrium is the state of a body in which there is no change in its motion.* A body in equilibrium is either at rest or moving at constant speed in a straight line. In our present work with forces, we shall be content with the conditions for equilibrium of bodies at rest; conditions for equilibrium of bodies in motion will be discussed in Chapter 4.

Two conditions are required for a body at rest to be in equilibrium. It must have neither linear (straight line) motion nor rotary (twisting) motion. However, we need consider only one of these when we deal with forces acting at a point. *The first condition for equilibrium, no linear motion, is met when no unbalanced forces act on the body.* We shall take up the second condition for equilibrium in Section 17.

If there are to be no unbalanced forces acting on a body, the vector sum of all the forces acting on a body must be zero. Suppose one boy pulls on a wagon with a force of 40. lb and another boy pulls on the wagon with a force of 40. lb in exactly the opposite direction. The second force just balances the first and produces equilibrium. The second force is said to be the *equilibrant* of the first force.

It is easy to find the equilibrant of two or more forces acting upon the same point. First we find their resultant. Then, since the equilibrant must balance the effect of this resultant, the equilibrant must have the same magnitude but act in the opposite direction. In Fig. 3-6, we found that a single force, $\overrightarrow{OR}$, could be substituted for the two forces $\overrightarrow{OE}$ and $\overrightarrow{OS}$. In order to counteract the resultant force, $\overrightarrow{OR}$, an

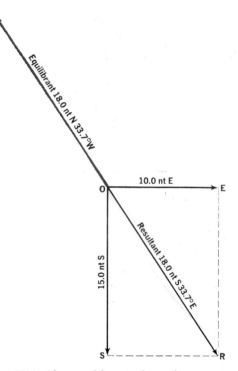

Fig. 3-10. The equilibrant of two forces acting at a point is applied at the same point. It equals the magnitude of their resultant, but acts in the opposite direction.

equilibrant force $\overrightarrow{OQ}$ must be applied at the same point, O, as shown in Fig. 3-10. Its direction must be exactly opposite to that of the resultant, and its magnitude must be equal to that of the resultant. *When two or more forces act together at a point, the* **equilibrant force** *is that single force applied at the same point which produces equilibrium. The equilibrant force has a magnitude equal to that of the resultant of the separate forces, but it acts in the opposite direction.*

QUESTIONS

A **1.** What more extensive definition of force has been presented in this chapter?
2. What do we measure when we weigh an object?

3. (*a*) What are the basic units of force in the MKS, CGS, and FPS systems? (*b*) How are they related to the corresponding basic units of mass?

4. What instrument is normally used for measuring forces?
5. What three facts about a force are represented by a force vector?
6. What is a resultant force?
7. How do we calculate the magnitude and direction of the resultant of two forces which act in the same direction in the same straight line on a single point?
8. How do we calculate the magnitude and direction of the resultant of two forces which act on the same point, but in opposite directions?
9. How may we determine mathematically the magnitude and direction of the resultant of two forces which act at right angles to each other on the same point?
10. (a) What is equilibrium? (b) What condition must be met for forces acting on a point to be in equilibrium?

11. (a) What is an equilibrant force? (b) At what point must it be applied? (c) How does it compare with its corresponding resultant force?

B 12. (a) Give some examples of forces which act on an object because other objects are in contact with it. (b) Give some examples of forces which act on an object without being in actual physical contact with it. (c) What is the most common force of this type?
13. How may we determine mathematically the magnitude and direction of the resultant of two forces which act at any angle to each other on the same point?
14. What method may be followed to find the magnitude of the resultant of three or more forces which act simultaneously on the same point?

PROBLEMS

Note: In solving Problems 3 through 14 (a) construct a diagram using a suitable scale; (b) determine the solution graphically; (c) determine the solution mathematically.

A 1. (a) What force in newtons is needed to lift a mass of 25 kg? (b) What force in dynes will be required?
2. A body has a mass of 75 slugs. What is its weight in pounds?
3. Two forces act simultaneously on point A. One force is 5.0 nt N; the other is 15.0 nt N. Determine the magnitude and bearing of the resultant force.
4. A force of 11.0 lb E and a force of 17.0 lb W act on point B. Determine the magnitude and bearing of the resultant force.
5. Two forces, one of 3.00×10^8 dynes S and one of 4.00×10^8 dynes W, act on point C. What is the magnitude and bearing of the resultant?
6. A force of 5.00 lb acts westward on point D. A force of 30.0 lb acts northward on point D. Determine the magnitude and bearing of the resultant.
7. Two forces act on point E. One is 20.0 nt N while the other is 20.0 nt S 60.0° E. (a) Determine the magnitude and bearing of the resultant force. (b) Determine the magnitude and bearing of the equilibrant force.
8. A force of 25.0 lb acts southward on point F. A second force of 20.0 lb acts westward on this same point. (a) Determine the magnitude

and bearing of the resultant force. (b) Determine the magnitude and bearing of the equilibrant force.
9. A boy weighs 600. nt. If he sits in the middle of a hammock which is 3.0 m long and sags 1.0 m, what force is exerted by the hammock ropes?
10. A boy weighing 100. lb sits on a swing. If the swing is pulled to one side with a horizontal force of 75.0 lb, what is the force exerted by the swing ropes?

B 11. One force of 10.0 nt E acts on point G. A second force of 30.0 nt acts S 60.0° W on the same point. (a) Determine the magnitude and bearing of the resultant. (b) Determine the magnitude and bearing of the equilibrant.
12. A force of 20.0 lb N 25.0° W and a force of 10.0 lb N 35.0° E act on point H. (a) Determine the magnitude and bearing of the resultant. (b) Determine the magnitude and bearing of the equilibrant.
13. Three forces act simultaneously on point J. One force is 10.0 nt N; the second is 15.0 nt W; the third is 15.0 nt N 30.0° E. Determine the magnitude and bearing of the resultant.
14. A force of 25.0 lb S 60.0° E acts on point K. A second force of 15.0 lb N 15.0° W and a third force of 30.0 lb S 70.0° W also act on point K. What is the magnitude and bearing of the equilibrant force?

3 RESOLUTION OF FORCES

13. Resolving a force into two components. We have just learned how to find the single force which can produce the same effect as two component forces acting upon the same point. We next must learn how to find the value of the components if we are given the magnitude and direction of a single force and the directions in which its components act.

This problem in *resolution of forces* is the converse of a problem in composition of forces. We are given the diagonal of a parallelogram, and the angle between the diagonal and each side. We must construct the parallelogram and find the length of the sides. *Resolution of forces is the separation of a single force into two component forces acting in definite directions on*

the same point. Usually, the two components into which a single force is to be resolved act at right angles to each other. Problems involving the resolution of forces may be solved graphically from a diagram constructed to scale or trigonometrically by the method described in Chapter 2, Section 24. See the Sample Problem.

14. Resolving the force of gravity. A force may act on an object in a direction in which the object cannot move. However, it may be possible to resolve this force into two components. The object may then move in the direction of one of the components, just as though that were the only force acting upon the object.

An object placed on an inclined plane

Sample Problem

A force of 10.0 nt S 37.0° E acts on point *O*. Find the magnitude of the eastward and southward components of this force.

Solution

Draw southward and eastward lines from point *O*, and construct the given force vector, $\overrightarrow{OR}$. Complete the parallelogram *OSRE*, Fig. 3-11, using $\overrightarrow{OR}$ as its diagonal. Placing arrowheads at *S* and *E* completes the two component vectors $\overrightarrow{OS}$ and $\overrightarrow{OE}$. The graphic solution may be made from the diagram. The trigonometric solution is

$$\frac{OS}{\sin \angle ORS} = \frac{SR}{\angle ROS} = \frac{OR}{\angle OSR}$$

$$\sin \angle ROS = \sin 37.0° = 0.602$$
$$\sin \angle ORS = \sin 53.0° = 0.799$$
$$\sin \angle OSR = \sin 90.0° = 1.00$$
$$\frac{OS}{0.799} = \frac{SR}{0.602} = \frac{10.0 \text{ nt}}{1.00}$$

$OS = 7.99$ nt, southward component
$SR = 6.02$ nt, eastward component

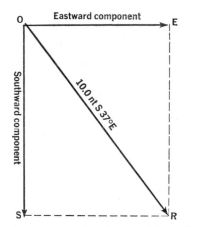

Fig. 3-11. Diagram for the graphic and trigonometric determination of the eastward and southward components of a 10.0-nt force acting S 37° E.

is attracted by the earth. The force of attraction is the weight of the object. See Fig. 3-12. The plane prevents the motion of the object along $\overrightarrow{OW}$, the direction in which the earth's attraction acts. The force of attraction may, however, be resolved into two components. One component, $\overrightarrow{OD}$, acts perpendicular to the surface of the plane and tends to break the plane. The other force, $\overrightarrow{OF}$, acts parallel to the plane and tends to pull the object down the plane.

Using $\overrightarrow{OW}$ as the diagonal, we can construct the parallelogram $ODWF$ and find the relative values of the sides $\overrightarrow{OF}$ and $\overrightarrow{OD}$

by plotting to scale. In this special case, we also can calculate these values if the height and length of the inclined plane are known. The triangles ABC and OWF are similar. (The sides are mutually parallel or perpendicular.) Therefore, $\overrightarrow{OW} : \overrightarrow{OF} = AB : BC$. But $\overrightarrow{OW}$ represents the weight of the object, W; $\overrightarrow{OF}$, the force W_p tending to pull the object down the plane; AB, the length of the plane, l; BC, the height of the plane, h. The weight of the object is related to the force tending to pull it down the plane in the same way that the length of the plane is related to its height, or,

$$W : W_p = l : h.$$

In a similar fashion it may be shown that the force tending to break the plane is related to the weight of the object in exactly the same way that the base of the plane is related to its length.

Making the plane steeper increases the force $\overrightarrow{OF}$ and decreases the force $\overrightarrow{OD}$. This steeper inclined plane is shown in Fig. 3-13. The vector $\overrightarrow{OE}$, which is equal and opposite to $\overrightarrow{OF}$, represents the force needed to keep the object from sliding down the plane. The steeper the plane, the greater this force becomes.

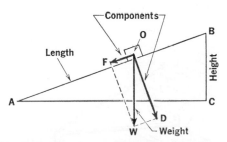

Fig. 3-12. The force of gravity may be resolved into two component forces. One component acts down the plane; the other acts against the plane.

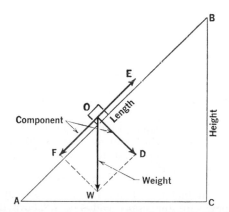

Fig. 3-13. When the inclined plane is made steeper, the component acting down the plane is increased, while the component acting against the plane is decreased.

QUESTIONS

A   **1.** What is meant by (*a*) composition of forces; (*b*) resolution of forces?

2. (*a*) What is a component force? (*b*) What is the usual angle between the component forces into which a single force is resolved?

3. How does a problem in resolution of forces differ from a problem in composition of forces?

4. When we push on the handle of a lawn roller, into what two components may the force we exert be resolved?

5. A boy pulls a wagon along a level road by means of a handle which makes a 30.° angle with the horizontal. Into what two components may the force he exerts on the handle be resolved?

B   **6.** The transmitting tower of a TV station is supported by guy wires which extend from the top of the tower to the ground. The wires make a 30.° angle with the tower. Into what two components may the force which the tower exerts on each guy wire be resolved?

7. A large crate rests on an inclined plane. (*a*) Into what two forces may the weight of the crate be resolved? (*b*) Which force may cause the crate to move?

8. A man parks his automobile on a hill. (*a*) Into what two components may the weight of the automobile be resolved? (*b*) Which force is counteracted by the brakes of the automobile?

PROBLEMS

Note: In solving each of the following problems (*a*) construct a diagram using a suitable scale; (*b*) determine the solution graphically; (*c*) determine the solution mathematically.

A   **1.** A force of 2.00×10^6 dynes N 45.0° E acts on point *A*. Determine the magnitudes of the northward and eastward components of this force.

2. A force of 15.0 lb acts S 30.0° W on point *B*. What are the magnitudes of its westward and southward components?

3. A man pushes with 150.0 nt of force on the handle of a lawn roller. The angle between the handle and the ground is 45.0°. Determine the magnitudes of the horizontal and vertical components of this force.

4. A boy pulls a loaded wagon with a force of 25.0 lb. The handle of the wagon makes an angle of 30.0° with the ground. What are the magnitudes of the horizontal and vertical components?

5. A truck weighing 1.00×10^5 nt is parked on a hill which rises 3.00 m in each 100. m of road. What force tends to make the truck roll down the hill?

6. A safe which weighs 500. lb is being rolled up an inclined plane. The plane is 10.0 ft long with the upper end 4.00 ft above the lower end. (*a*) What force tends to make the safe roll back down the plane? (*b*) What is the force that the safe is exerting perpendicular to the inclined plane?

B   **7.** A force of 25.0 nt acts N 55.0° W on point *C*. What are the magnitudes of the northward and westward components of this force?

8. A force of 35.0 lb acts N 80.0° W on point *D*. Determine the magnitudes of the northward and westward components.

9. The rafters of a roof meet at an angle of 120.0°. What force is exerted along the rafters by an object weighing 6.00×10^3 nt suspended from the peak?

10. A boy pulls a sled along level ground. If the rope on which he is pulling makes an angle of 20.0° with the ground and the boy pulls with the force of 15.0 lb, determine the horizontal and vertical components of this force.

11. A sign weighing 500. nt is supported as shown in the diagram below. Determine the magnitudes and directions of the forces exerted by *AB* and *CB*.

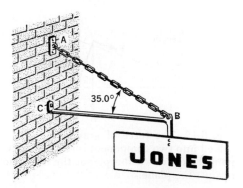

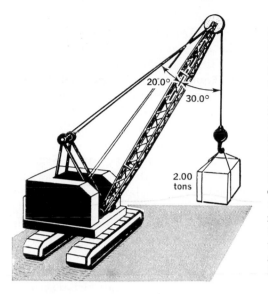

12. A block of stone weighing 2.00 tons is to be raised by a crane. The angle between the load cable and the crane boom is 30.0°. The boom is held in place by a tie cable which forms an angle of 20.0° with the boom. See the diagram, left. Determine the magnitude of the thrust force of the boom and of the tie force of the cable.

13. A crate having a mass of 100. kg rests on an inclined plane which makes an angle of 5.00° with the horizontal. (*a*) What force does the crate exert perpendicular to the plane? (*b*) What force tends to make the crate slide down the plane?

14. What force is required to move an automobile weighing 3500. lb up a 10.0° ramp?

15. What force must be exerted to prevent a truck weighing 15.0 tons from rolling down an inclined plane which makes an angle of 3.00° with the horizontal?

4 PARALLEL FORCES

15. The nature of parallel forces. Suppose two boys carry a heavy load on a stick between them. The boys exert an upward force on each end of the stick, while the load exerts a downward force. These obviously are three parallel forces; they act in the same or opposite directions. Also, while they act on the same body, *they act on the body at different places.* The upward forces act at the ends of the stick while the downward force acts somewhere between them. *Parallel forces act in the same or opposite directions. The resultant of parallel forces has a magnitude equal to the algebraic sum of all the forces and acts in the direction of this net force.*

16. The moment of a force—torque. To understand how a load is distributed between two parallel forces, we must learn about the moment of a force, or the *torque* produced by a force. Suppose we have a rigid bar, *AB*, as in Fig. 3-14. At end *A*, force *F'*, 40. lb, acts downward. At end *B*, force *F*, 20. lb, acts downward. The bar can pivot about the fixed point *C*. The force *F* tends to turn the bar *AB*

clockwise about *C* while the force *F'* tends to turn it counterclockwise. How effective is each force in producing rotation? Experiments show that the effectiveness of any force in producing rotation depends on the magnitude of the force and the length of the arm on which it acts. The effectiveness of a force in producing rotation is called *the moment of a force, or*

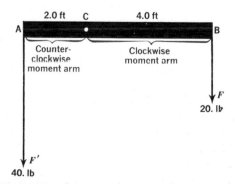

Fig. 3-14. **The torque produced by a force equals the product of the force times the length of the moment arm on which it acts. If the forces act perpendicular to the bar, the lengths of the moment arms are measured along it.**

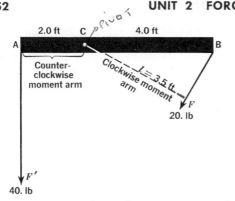

Fig. 3-15. If the force does not act at right angles to the bar, the length of the moment arm upon which the force acts is the perpendicular length from the center of moments to the line of direction of the force.

the torque produced by the force. The moment of a force, or its **torque,** *equals the product of the force and the length of the moment arm on which it acts. The length of the moment arm is measured perpendicularly from the pivot point to the line of action of the force.* The pivot point serves as a center of moments. *The* **center of moments** *is the point from which the lengths of all the moment arms are measured.* It may be a real pivot point or only an imaginary one. For example, in Fig. 3-14, the force F, 20. lb, acting upon the moment arm BC, 4.0 ft long, has a clockwise torque of 80. lb-ft. The force F', 40. lb, acting upon the moment arm AC, 2.0 ft long, has a counterclockwise torque of 80. lb-ft also. In this case the forces act at right angles to the bar AB, so the lengths of the moment arms are measured along AB, from the real pivot point, C.

If the force F is not applied perpendicularly to the bar AB but is applied as shown in Fig. 3-15, the length of the arm upon which this force acts is no longer BC. The length of the moment arm upon which force F acts is measured perpendicularly from the center of moments to the line of direction of the force. The torque in this case equals the product of the force F and the length *l*.

Note that the units of torque are derived

units. In the FPS system a unit of torque is the *pound-foot.* In the CGS system it can be the *centimeter-dyne,* while in the MKS system it can be the *meter-newton.*

17. Equilibrium with parallel forces. Again, two boys carry a load on a stick between them, as in Fig. 3-16. The stick is 8.00 ft long. The load, which weighs 160. lb, is placed 3.00 ft from the boy at A and 5.00 ft from the boy at B. Neglecting the weight of the stick, what part of the load does each boy carry? When the boys are holding the stick with the load, the stick is in equilibrium. From Section 12, we know that when the stick is in equilibrium there are no unbalanced forces acting upon it. Since the load of 160. lb attached to the stick exerts a downward force, the boys must exert a *combined* upward force of 160. lb. *This counterbalancing of forces in opposite directions prevents* linear motion.

When parallel forces act on an object, a second condition must be met to bring about equilibrium. The torques produced by the forces must balance, since the forces do not all act on the body at the same point or in the same direction. *The second condition for equilibrium is that the sum of all the clockwise torques equals the sum of all the counterclockwise torques. This counterbalancing of torques in opposite directions prevents* rotary motion.

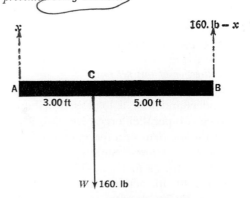

Fig. 3-16. We calculate the load which each boy carries by applying the two conditions necessary for equilibrium.

5 CENTER OF GRAVITY

19. The center of gravity. Figure 3-21 represents a stone lying on the ground. Since every part of the stone has weight, every part must be attracted by the earth. All the downward forces exerted on the stone because of its weight are parallel. The actual weight of the stone is the resultant of all these separate parallel forces, and the point of application of this resultant force is called the *center of gravity*. *The center of gravity of any object is that point at which all of its weight may be considered to be concentrated.*

If we attach a string to this stone at a point directly above the center of gravity and pull upward, the stone can be lifted without any rotation. An object can be balanced on the point of a knife placed directly beneath its center of gravity. A force acting on the center of gravity of an object produces only linear motion. Suppose we try to overturn the stone shown in Fig. 3-21. If we exert our lifting force at A, B becomes the pivot point. Force A acts clockwise upon the moment arm AB. The weight of the stone, concentrated at C, acts counterclockwise. Its moment arm is less than CB. Since the force at A is applied on a longer moment arm than is the

weight of the stone, the force needed to overturn the stone will be less than that required to lift it completely off the ground.

Since the weight of an object is a force acting downward from its center of gravity, the weight of an object can be considered along with upward and downward forces in problems dealing with parallel forces. See the Sample Problem opposite.

20. Finding the center of gravity. Suppose we tie a plumb bob at one end of a piece of twine, and hold the twine by its other end so that the bob is free to swing. The bob finally comes to rest in such a position that if the line of the cord is extended downward, it will pass through the center of gravity of the earth. This bob and cord form a *plumb line* which we can use to find the center of gravity of a flat object of irregular shape, such as that shown in Fig. 3-22. First we suspend the object from one point, such as P in the diagram, so that it is free to turn about the point of suspension. The object may

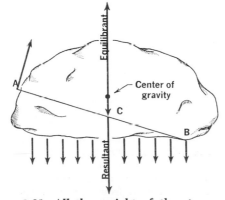

Fig. 3-21. All the weight of the stone appears to be concentrated at its center of gravity.

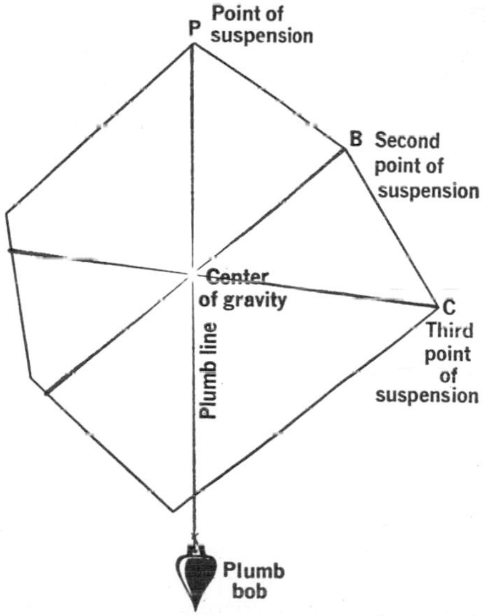

Fig. 3-22. An experimental method for finding the center of gravity.

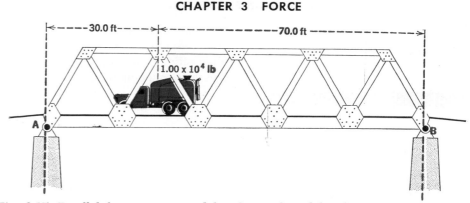

Fig. 3-17. Parallel forces are exerted by the truck and by the piers supporting the bridge.

We have seen above that the combined upward force exerted by the boys must be 160. lb. But how much force does each exert? If we use C as a center of moments, for equilibrium the clockwise torque exerted by the boy at A must equal the counterclockwise torque exerted by the boy at B. Let x = the force exerted by the boy at A. Then 160. lb − x = the force exerted by the boy at B. The clockwise torque is $x \times 3.00$ ft, and the counter-clockwise torque is $(160. \text{ lb} - x) \times 5.00$ ft. At equilibrium, these torques are equal. Thus, $x \times 3.00$ ft $= (160. \text{ lb} - x) \times 5.00$ ft. Solving, $x = 100.$ lb, the force exerted by the boy at A. Then the force exerted by the boy at B is 60. lb. The Sample Problem below gives a similar example worked by a slightly different method. Both problems can be solved by either method.

In solving problems in which parallel forces are exerted on a pivoted beam or

Sample Problem

The bridge AB shown in Fig. 3-17 is 100.0 ft long. A truck weighing 1.00×10^4 lb is 30.0 ft from one end of the bridge. Calculate the upward force which must be exerted by each pier to support this weight. Neglect the weight of the bridge.

Solution

Let x equal the upward force exerted by pier A, and use B as a center of moments.

clockwise torque = counterclockwise torque

$x \times 100.$ ft $= 1.00 \times 10^4$ lb $\times 70.0$ ft

$x = 7.00 \times 10^3$ lb, the upward force exerted by pier A

Let y equal the upward force exerted by pier B, and use A as a center of moments.

clockwise torque = counterclockwise torque

1.00×10^4 lb $\times 30.0$ ft $= y \times 100.$ ft

$y = 3.00 \times 10^3$ lb, the upward force exerted by pier B

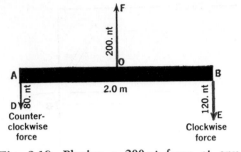

Fig. 3-18. Placing a 200-nt force at any point O prevents linear motion.

pole, first try using the pivot point as the center of moments about which to calculate the torques. If the beam or pole is not pivoted, any point may be used as the center of moments, but it is usually easier to select one end as the center of moments.

Now, let us take another problem of equilibrium in parallel forces. Suppose we have two parallel forces, D and E, of 80. nt and 120. nt respectively. These two forces act upon a bar at points A and B, Fig. 3-18. A force of 200. nt applied in the opposite direction at any point O will prevent linear motion since this force equals the sum of the two forces, 80. nt + 120. nt. In order to prevent rotary motion, this 200.-nt force must be located at such a point on the bar that the clockwise and counterclockwise torques are equal. In order to calculate this position, let us use B as a center of moments. The counterclockwise torque will be that of the 80.-nt force acting on the 2.0-m

moment arm, or 1.6×10^2 m-nt. The clockwise torque will be that of the 200.-nt force acting on a moment arm of unknown length from point B. Let us call this unknown length x. The clockwise torque will be 200. nt $\times x$. At equilibrium, the torques are equal. Thus, 200. nt $\times x = 1.6 \times 10^2$ m-nt. Solving, $x = 0.80$ m, the distance from B at which the 200.-nt force must be applied to prevent rotary motion. See Fig. 3-19.

To summarize: *Any number of parallel forces are in equilibrium if the sums of the opposite forces are equal, and the sum of all the clockwise torques equals the sum of all the counterclockwise torques.*

18. The nature of a couple. From our study of equilibrium in parallel forces, we see that linear motion can be prevented by means of resultant forces of equal magnitude which act in opposite directions. In order to prevent rotary motion, these resultant forces must also act in the same line. Let us consider, however, the situation in which *two forces of equal magnitude act in opposite directions, but not in the same line.* Such a pair of forces is called a **couple.** See Fig. 3-20. You apply a couple to the steering column of an automobile when you turn the steering wheel using both hands. The effect of such a pair of forces is, of course, to produce rotation. The torque of a couple does not depend upon the point about which rotation takes place. It is equal to the product of one

of the forces times the perpendicular distance between them. A couple cannot be balanced by a single force, since this force would produce linear motion no matter in

what direction or where it was applied. A couple can be balanced only by another couple which is equal in magnitude but opposite in direction.

QUESTIONS

A   **1.** (*a*) What are parallel forces? (*b*) How can we calculate the resultant of two parallel forces which act in the same direction? (*c*) How can we calculate the resultant of parallel forces which act in opposite directions?
2. (*a*) How do we calculate the torque produced by a force which acts at right angles to a pivoted bar? (*b*) Name a unit of torque for the MKS system, for the CGS system, and for the FPS system.
3. If a bar on which parallel forces act is to be in equilibrium, what conditions must be met?
4. What is usually the most convenient point about which to calculate the torques in a parallel force problem?

B   **5.** How do we calculate the torque produced by a force which does not act at right angles to a pivoted bar?
6. (*a*) What is a couple? (*b*) How is the torque of a couple calculated?

PROBLEMS

Note: For each problem, draw a force diagram using a suitable scale, and then perform the necessary calculations.

A   **1.** Paul and Henry are carrying a sack weighing 6.0×10^2 nt on a pole between them. If the pole is 2.00 m long and the load is 0.50 m from Paul, what force does each boy exert? Neglect the weight of the pole.
2. A bridge is 80.0 ft long. What force must the pier at each end of the bridge exert to support an automobile weighing 2.00 tons which is 30.0 ft from one end of the bridge? Neglect the weight of the bridge.
3. A painter stands on a plank 3.00 m long, which is supported at each end by a stepladder. The painter weighs 900. nt. If he stands 1.00 m from one end of the plank, what force is exerted by each stepladder? Neglect the weight of the plank.
4. Two boys weigh 100. lb and 125 lb respectively. They wish to balance on a seesaw. If the 100.-lb boy sits 5.00 ft from the center, how far from the center must the 125-lb boy sit? Neglect the weight of the seesaw.
5. A bar 5.00 m long has a weight of 50.0 nt attached to one end and a weight of 80.0 nt attached to the other end. Neglecting the weight of the bar, determine the magnitude, direction of action, and point of application of the equilibrant force.

B   **6.** A boy is chinning himself on a bar 4.00 ft long. His left hand is placed 1.00 ft from the left end of the bar while his right hand is 2.00 ft from the right end of the bar. The boy weighs 150. lb and his weight is supported equally by his hands. What force must be exerted by the poles which support the ends of the chinning bar? Neglect the weight of the bar.
7. A bricklayer weighing 8.00×10^2 nt stands 1.00 m from one end of a scaffold 3.00 m long. A pile of bricks weighing 3.20×10^2 nt is 1.50 m from the other end of the scaffold. What force must be exerted on each end of the scaffold in order to support it? Neglect the weight of the scaffold.
8. A wooden bar 10.0 ft long is pivoted 3.0 ft from end A. A weight of 250. lb is attached at end A. At the other end of the bar a weight of 75 lb is attached. Where must a weight of 100. lb be attached to the bar in order to produce equilibrium? Neglect the weight of the bar.
9. A beam 4.00 m long is supported at both ends. A weight of 5.00 nt is attached 1.00 m from end A; a weight of 800. nt is attached 1.50 m from end A; and a weight of 300. nt is attached 1.25 m from end B. Neglecting the weight of the beam, calculate the force exerted by the supports at each end of the beam.

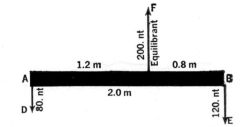

Fig. 3-19. Placing the 200-nt force 0.8 m from B prevents both linear and rotary motion and produces equilibrium.

Fig. 3-20. A pair of forces of equal magnitude acting in opposite directions but not in the same line is called a couple.

swing about this point, but it finally comes to rest with its center of gravity directly below the point of suspension. If we drop the plumb line from point P, the center of gravity of the object will lie somewhere on this line; then a line drawn on the object along the plumb line must pass through the center of gravity. Let us next suspend the object from point B and again draw a line along the plumb line. In order to check our results, we may suspend the object from a third point, C, and again draw a line along the plumb line. Since each of these lines passes through the center of gravity, the center of gravity is the point at which the lines intersect.

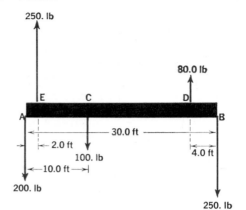

Fig. 3-23. In order to produce equilibrium, we must apply a force which prevents both linear and rotary motion.

Sample Problem

A bar, AB, is 30.0 ft long. It weighs 100. lb and its center of gravity, C, is 10.0 ft from A. At A a force of 200. lb acts downward. At B a force of 250. lb acts downward. At D, 4.0 ft from B, a force of 80.0 lb acts upward. At E, 2.0 ft from A, a force of 250. lb acts upward. (*a*) What is the magnitude and direction of the force which must be used to produce equilibrium? (*b*) Where must it be placed?

Solution

Construct the diagram to scale as shown in Fig. 3-23.

(*a*) Let the known upward forces be positive and the known downward forces be negative. The algebraic sum will give the resultant force which must be counterbalanced to prevent linear motion.

250. lb + 80.0 lb − 200. lb − 100. lb − 250. lb = −220. lb

Thus 220. lb additional upward force is needed to prevent linear motion.

(*b*) Use A as the center of moments and let x be the distance from A to the point where the 220.-lb force must be applied. To prevent rotary motion,

clockwise torque = counterclockwise torque

100. lb × 10.0 ft + 250. lb × 30.0 ft =
            250. lb × 2.0 ft + 80.0 lb × 26.0 ft + 220. lb × x

x = 26.9 ft, the distance from A to the point where the 220.-lb force must be applied.

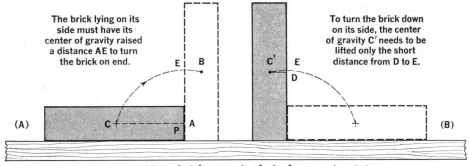

The brick lying on its side must have its center of gravity raised a distance AE to turn the brick on end.

To turn the brick down on its side, the center of gravity C' needs to be lifted only the short distance from D to E.

(A)   (B)

Fig. 3-24. These bricks vary in their degree of stability.

21. Stable equilibrium. If the position of an object in stable equilibrium is slightly altered, the object will tend to return to its original position. An object in stable equilibrium cannot be overturned unless its center of gravity is first raised. Both bricks shown in Fig. 3-24 are in stable equilibrium, but their degree of stability differs. To turn brick (A) on its edge, P, the center of gravity, C, must be raised to the point E. When the center of gravity passes beyond the vertical line EP, it is no longer over the area *originally* included within the base. The brick now falls into the position shown by the dashed lines. In falling, its center of gravity is lowered from E to B. The brick is once again in a state of stable equilibrium. Let

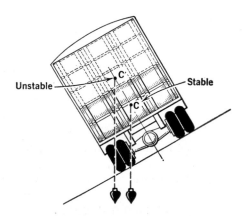

Fig. 3-25. The truck is stable when a plumb line dropped from the center of gravity falls within the area described by the wheels.

us now look at brick (B). This represents the same brick, but its original position this time is standing on end. In order to overturn this brick, we must raise its center of gravity from C' to E. Beyond this point, the center of gravity is no longer over the area of the original base (the end of the brick). The brick falls to the position shown by the dashed lines, because in this position its center of gravity is lowest.

With the brick originally on its side, the center of gravity must be raised the distance from A to E, Fig. 3-24 (A), before the brick may be turned on end. When the brick is originally on end, the center of gravity must be raised the distance from D to E, Fig. 3-24 (B), before the brick falls on its side. The distance EA is much greater than ED, so the brick has much greater stability when it is on its side. *The stability of an object may be increased by enlarging the base, and by lowering the center of gravity as far as possible.*

A truck loaded with steel sheets is less likely to upset than one loaded with barrels made from the same weight of steel. The center of gravity of the load of steel sheets is much lower. In Fig. 3-25, the loaded truck on the sloping road will upset if the load is high enough to raise the center of gravity to C'. A plumb line dropped from C' falls outside the area described by the wheels. If the top of the load is removed, the center of gravity is lowered, perhaps to *C*. A plumb line dropped from *C* falls within the area described by the wheels, showing that the load is then stable.

22. Unstable equilibrium. An egg standing on its end and a person walking a tightrope are both examples of unstable equilibrium. In either case, as soon as the slightest movement occurs, the center of gravity may fall outside a plumb line dropped to the point of support. The center of gravity is lowered at once and the object falls. In unstable equilibrium, the center of gravity is above a single point of support.

23. Neutral equilibrium. A ball lying on a table is in neutral equilibrium. A cylinder or a cone lying on its side and a bal-

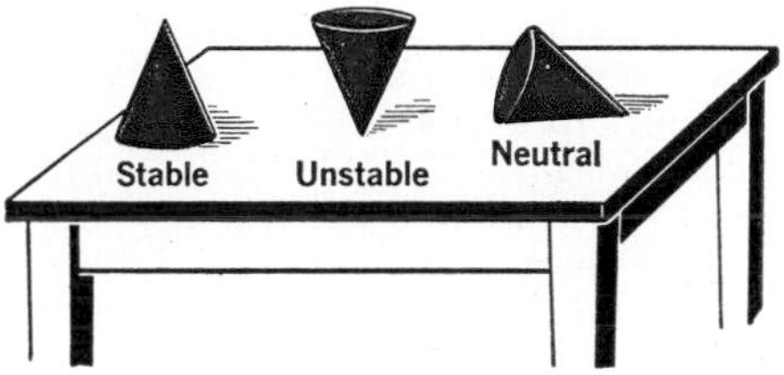

Fig. 3-26. Types of equilibrium.

Stable   Unstable   Neutral

anced wheel free to turn on its axle are other examples of neutral equilibrium. These objects come to rest in any position since the center of gravity is neither raised nor lowered when the object is turned. Figure 3-26 illustrates the differences between stable, unstable, and neutral equilibrium.

QUESTIONS

A 1. What is the center of gravity of an object?
2. (*a*) What is meant by stable equilibrium? (*b*) How may the stability of an object be increased?
3. When is an object in (*a*) unstable equilibrium; (*b*) neutral equilibrium?
4. Explain two possible adjustments that can be made so two young boys of unequal weight may balance on a seesaw.
5. Why is it possible to round a curve safely at higher speed in a low-slung sports car than in a regular model automobile?
6. Ocean freighters add ballast if they are carrying a light cargo. What is the purpose of ballast and where should it be placed?

B 7. Describe how you can find experimentally the center of gravity of an irregularly shaped plane object.
8. Why may all of the weight of an object be considered to act at its center of gravity?

PROBLEMS

Note: For each problem, draw a force diagram using a suitable scale, and then perform the necessary calculations.

A 1. A steel beam of uniform cross section weighs 2.5×10^8 dynes. If it is 500. cm long, what force is needed to lift one end of it?
2. A wooden telegraph pole 15.0 ft long is tapered so that the center of gravity is 6.0 ft from one end. It weighs 400. lb. What force is required to lift each end?
3. A bar 4.0 m long weighs 400. nt. Its center of gravity is 1.5 m from one end. If a weight of 300. nt is attached at the heavy end and a weight of 500. nt is attached at the light end, what are the magnitude, direction of action, and point of application of the equilibrant force?
4. A bridge 60.0 ft long is supported by a pier at each end. The bridge weighs 50.0 tons. If a load of 7.5 tons is located 15.0 ft from one end, what load does each pier support?

B 5. A bar 5.0 m long has its center of gravity 1.5 m from the heavy end. If it is placed on the edge of a block 1.5 m from the light end and a weight of 750. nt added to the light end, it will be balanced. What is the weight of the bar?
6. A painter's scaffold 10.0 ft long is supported by ropes attached at each end. The scaffold weighs 100. lb. One painter weighing 150. lb stands on the scaffold 4.0 ft from one end while a second painter weighing 175 lb stands on the scaffold 2.0 ft from the other end. What is the tension on the ropes supporting the scaffold?

7. A uniform bar 25.0 m long weighs 1.000×10^4 nt. From end *A* a weight of 2.50×10^3 nt is hung. At *B*, the other end of the pole, there is a weight of 3.50×10^3 nt. An upward force of 3.00×10^3 nt is exerted 4.0 m from *B*, while an upward force of 4.00×10^3 nt is exerted 8.0 m from *A*. Determine the magnitude, direction of action, and point of application of the equilibrant force.

8. A paperhanger weighing 150. lb stands in the center of a plank 8.0 ft long. The plank weighs 50. lb. It is supported at each end by stepladders which have an angle of 45.0° between each pair of legs. Calculate the compressional force in each of the four legs of each stepladder as they support the plank and paperhanger.

9. If the truck that is shown in Fig. 3-25 is 2.50 m wide, and is parked on a curve which slopes at a 15.0° angle, what is the maximum height of the center of gravity for stable equilibrium?

6 FRICTION

24. The nature of friction. When we attempt to roll or slide one object over another we find that *there is a force which opposes the motion. This force is called* **friction.** Several ideas have been presented to explain friction. Some physicists believe that friction is caused by irregularities in the surfaces of the objects. As the uneven surfaces are rubbed together, they tend to interlock and offer resistance to motion. If surfaces are polished, we should expect friction between them to be lessened. Experiments have shown, however, that there is a limit to the amount by which friction may be reduced by polishing the surfaces. If they are made too smooth, the friction between them actually increases.

Other physicists believe that electrical forces similar to those which hold atoms and molecules together are partly the cause of friction. Friction may also be caused by the adhesion of molecules of one surface to those of the other surface. By using radioactive materials, scientists have learned that when two surfaces slide over each other, minute quantities of one surface are rubbed off on the other surface.

25. Friction as a help. Have you ever watched a poor driver trying to get his automobile under way on an icy pavement? The rear wheels may spin but the car does not go forward. There must be friction between the tires and the pavement before the automobile can move. We would be unable to walk if there were no friction between the soles of our shoes and the sidewalk.

When we apply the brakes on an automobile, the friction of the brake lining on the brake drum slows down the wheels. The friction between the tires and the roadway enables us to bring the car to a stop.

Friction helps in less obvious ways. Friction holds a screw in wood and enables us to use nails to fasten boards together. If friction were eliminated, dishes would slide off the table unless the table was perfectly level.

26. Friction as a hindrance. When moving an object, we find friction is a disadvantage. We mount heavy pieces of furniture on wheels. We polish and lubricate bearings to reduce friction. The proper maintenance of automobiles, bicycles, motors, and other machines depends upon regular lubrication.

27. Sliding friction. Friction experiments are difficult to perform, and the results are not always easy to express simply. The following statements about sliding friction hold true in many cases. There are, however, outstanding exceptions to some of them.

1. If you slide this book over a desk top, you will readily observe that friction acts parallel to the table top. It also acts in the direction opposite to that in which you move the book. *Friction acts parallel to the surfaces which are sliding over one another, and in the direction opposite to that of the motion.*

2. The degree of friction differs not only among different materials, but also among different surfaces composed of the same material. *Friction depends upon the materials and their surfaces.*

3. Suppose we hook a spring balance to an object and pull horizontally. We find that more force is needed to start the object sliding than to keep it sliding. *Sliding friction is less than starting friction.*

4. We do not notice much difference in the friction of sled runners on snow when we change the speed at which we pull a sled. However, if a person attempts to stop his automobile with a steady pressure on the brake pedal, the car comes to a jolting halt. In this case, friction apparently increases with a decrease in speed. With objects moving at high velocities, a bullet moving through a gun barrel for example, friction decreases with an increase in velocity. Ultimately, here, a speed is reached beyond which there is little decrease in friction. At this speed the friction between the surfaces of the bullet and the gun barrel produces enough heat to melt the bullet, which is then surrounded by a thin film of molten metal as it moves through the barrel. Within the range of medium speeds, *sliding friction is nearly independent of the speed of sliding.*

5. Surprisingly, the force needed to slide a brick along a table is almost the same whether the brick lies on a side, on edge, or on end. *Friction is practically independent of the area of contact between the surfaces.*

6. It does not require as much force to slide an empty chair across the floor as it does to slide the same chair when a 200-lb man is sitting on it. *Friction is directly proportional to the force pressing the two surfaces together.*

Experiments under very special condi-

Fig. 3-27. The treads on this bulldozer increase the friction between it and the earth. Thus the bulldozer can exert a greater action force against the earth beneath it and push greater loads of earth before it. (Photo by Caterpillar)

tions have shown that the force of friction is in fact directly proportional to the area of contact and is independent of the force holding the surfaces together. Under ordinary conditions, however, the force holding the surfaces together deforms the surfaces and determines the actual area in contact. Consequently the statements given in paragraphs 5 and 6 concerning friction usually hold true.

28. The coefficient of friction. We see that, for practical purposes, sliding friction depends upon the nature of the surfaces and upon the force pressing them together.

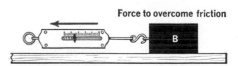

Force to overcome friction

Fig. 3-28. Measuring the force needed to overcome sliding friction.

We may compare the friction between different surfaces by using the coefficient of friction. *The **coefficient of friction** is the ratio of the force needed to overcome friction to the normal force pressing the surfaces together.* The coefficient of friction is represented by the Greek letter μ (mu). If the force needed to overcome friction is represented by F and the normal force by N, then

$$\mu = \frac{F}{N}$$

The coefficient of friction varies with the nature of the surfaces in contact and the degree of polish of the surface. See the Sample Problem below.

29. Increasing friction. A train engineer sands the rails so that the drive wheels of the Diesel locomotive will not slip. Some buses and trucks are also equipped with sanders. These devices enable the driver to drop sand or fine gravel in front of the rear wheels so that they will not spin on icy pavements. We use chains or snow tires on the rear wheels of automobiles when roads are covered with snow and ice, and we throw cinders on slippery hills and curves during the winter to increase friction.

30. Reducing friction. We use several methods to reduce friction. Machines which must operate with very little friction may be designed with one or more of the following:

1. Polished bearings. If a wheel is to turn easily on an axle, both contact surfaces may be polished. The materials may be hard so that they will not wear away rapidly or easily become grooved.

2. Anti-friction metals. When steel slides

Sample Problem

A block weighs 100. lb. A force of 30. lb is required to keep it in uniform motion on a horizontal surface. What is the coefficient of friction?

Solution

Since the block is moving on a horizontal surface, its weight is the normal force pressing the surfaces together.

$$\mu = \frac{F}{N}$$

$$\mu = \frac{30. \text{ lb}}{100. \text{ lb}}$$

$\mu = 0.30$, the coefficient of friction.

(Note: If the block is not moving on a horizontal surface, the weight of the block must first be resolved into the components tending to move the block along the surface and pushing the block against the surface. See Section 14 of this chapter. The component of the weight tending to move the block along the surface will either aid or hinder the force overcoming friction depending on the direction of motion of the block. The force pushing the block against the surface is the normal force needed in the formula.)

over an alloy of lead and antimony, the coefficient of friction is less than when steel slides on steel. Bearings are sometimes lined with such an alloy to reduce friction.

3. Ball bearings or roller bearings. The coefficient of friction of steel balls rolling on steel may be as low as 0.002. This is only about $\frac{1}{100}$ as much as that of steel sliding on steel. Roller bearings are made in various designs to reduce friction in different kinds of machines.

4. Lubricants. If oil is used as a lubricant, an oil film flows between the bearing surfaces. This separates them so that fluid friction is substituted for solid friction. Fluid friction is generally much less than solid friction. This topic is discussed further in Chapter 8.

Fig. 3-29. Roller bearings are used to reduce friction on modern railroad cars. They are tapered to resist sidewise movement of the axle. (Timken Roller Bearing Co.)

QUESTIONS

A 1. (*a*) What is friction? (*b*) What ideas have physicists presented to explain friction?
2. Give several examples of the way in which friction may be helpful.
3. What methods do we use to reduce friction?
4. Why is it possible for bulldozers to clear land rapidly in almost any sort of terrain?
5. If there were no friction, would it be possible (*a*) to tie a knot in a piece of string; (*b*) to make the string itself?
6. How does sliding friction compare with starting friction?
7. (*a*) What does the amount of sliding friction usually depend on? (*b*) Of what is it independent?
8. What is the *coefficient of friction?*

B 9. What is the orientation of the force of friction to two surfaces which are moving over one another?

10. Suppose you are driving an automobile down a long hill. The hill is not steep enough to require shifting into a lower gear, but the car will go too fast if the brakes are not applied. How should the brakes be applied— with a light but constant pressure, or more heavily and intermittently?
11. In what ways do we increase the friction between the soles of our shoes and the surface with which they come in contact?
12. Name as many devices as you can which are used to increase the friction between the tires of an automobile and the pavement.
13. Why does the use of a lubricant reduce the friction in a bearing?
14. (*a*) Under what conditions is the weight of an object the normal force pressing it to the surface over which it is moving? (*b*) How is the normal force determined from the weight of the object under other conditions?

PROBLEMS

Note: For each problem, draw a force diagram using a suitable scale, and then perform the necessary calculations.

A 1. A wooden block weighs 2.00×10^5 dynes. If a force of 1.00×10^4 dynes is required to keep it in motion on a horizontal surface, what is the coefficient of sliding friction?

2. The coefficient of sliding friction between two metal surfaces is 0.15. What force will be required to slide a block of metal weighing 5.0 lb over the metal top of a table?
3. In a coefficient of friction experiment, a force of 45 nt was needed to slide an object weighing 125 nt over a horizontal surface. Calculate the coefficient of friction.

4. A force of 10. lb is required to move a loaded sled weighing 60. lb over the snow on a level road. What is the coefficient of friction of the sled against the snow?

5. A crate weighing 1.25×10^3 nt slides down an inclined plane at uniform speed. The plane is 6.0 m long. Its height is 3.0 m. What is the coefficient of friction of the crate against the inclined plane?

6. A block of wood just slides down a 3.0-ft long inclined plane when one end of the plane is raised 1.0 ft. The block of wood weighs 0.2 lb. Calculate the coefficient of friction.

B   **7.** A box having a mass of 50.0 kg is dragged across a horizontal floor by means of a rope tied on the front of it. The coefficient of friction between the box and the floor is 0.300. If the angle between the rope and the floor is 30.0°, what force must be exerted on the rope to move the box at uniform speed?

8. A carton weighing 90.0 lb is to be moved up an inclined plane 12.0 ft long and 4.0 ft high. The coefficient of friction is 0.30. What force is necessary in order to move the carton at uniform speed up the plane?

9. The coefficient of friction between a metal block and the inclined surface over which it will slide is 0.200. If the surface makes an angle of 20.0° with the horizontal and the block has a mass of 80.0 kg, what force is required to slide the block at uniform speed up the plane?

10. A safe weighing 500. lb is to be lowered at uniform speed down an incline 10.0 ft long from the bed of a truck 4.00 ft high. The coefficient of friction is 0.500. (*a*) Is the component of the weight tending to move the safe down the plane greater or less than the force needed to overcome friction? (*b*) Will the safe have to be held back or pushed down to make it move with uniform speed? (*c*) What force must be exerted parallel to the plane to accomplish this?

ummary

Forces produce or prevent motion, or they have a tendency to do so. Forces are vector quantities. The resultant of two or more forces applied simultaneously at a point is that single force applied at the same point which would produce the same effect.

Equilibrium is the state of a body in which there is no change in its motion. When two or more forces act together at a point, the equilibrant force is that single force applied at the same point which produces equilibrium. A single force may be resolved into two or more components, usually acting at right angles to each other.

Parallel forces act in the same or opposite directions. The torque produced by a force equals the product of the force and the length of the moment arm on which it acts. For equilibrium in parallel forces the sums of the forces in opposite directions must be equal and the sum of all the clockwise torques must equal the sum of all the counterclockwise torques. Two forces of equal magnitude which act in opposite directions but not in the same line constitute a couple.

The center of gravity of any object is that point at which all of the weight of the object may be considered to be concentrated. Equilibrium may be stable, unstable, or neutral. The stability of an object may be increased by enlarging the base, and by lowering the center of gravity as far as possible.

Friction is a force which opposes motion. The coefficient of friction is the ratio of the force needed to overcome friction to the normal force pressing the surfaces together.

TERMS TO DEFINE

center of gravity
center of moments
centimeter-dyne
coefficient of friction
composition of forces
couple
dyne
equilibrant force
equilibrium

force
force vector
friction
linear motion
meter-newton
neutral equilibrium
newton
parallel forces
parallelogram of forces

pound
pound-foot
resolution of forces
resultant force
rotary motion
spring balance
stable equilibrium
torque
unstable equilibrium

RESEARCH ON YOUR OWN

1. Obtain a brick, a board 3 or 4 ft long, several sheets of paper 8½ by 11 in., and some cellulose tape. Tape the paper on one face of the brick to provide a smooth surface. Fasten a pulley to the edge of a table and attach a string to the brick to run over the pulley. Using weights, apply just enough force to the string to draw the brick along the surface with uniform motion. Test all three faces of the brick in this way, and measure the coefficient of friction. What differences do you find? Using the same equipment, test a face of the brick on which you have glued three penny-size circles of thick paper. The circles should be spaced so that the surface of the brick does not touch the board. Measure the coefficient of friction and compare the results with those of the earlier experiment.
2. Support a meter stick horizontally by putting your left forefinger under the 10-cm mark and your right under the 70-cm mark. Estimate what centimeter mark would be above your fingers if you brought your hands toward each other with a uniform motion. Try it, moving your hands slowly. Repeat the experiment with your fingers equally spaced from the 50-cm mark. Does each hand slide at the same rate on the stick? What happens when you repeat the experiment supporting one end of the stick with a gum eraser instead of your finger? Try the experiments again, moving your hands rapidly. How can the principle demonstrated by your findings be applied to the starting and braking of an automobile?
3. Compare the force necessary to tip over an empty aluminum tumbler with that needed to tip over the tumbler full of water.
4. Look up the subject of friction in several reference books and advanced texts. Do you find agreement on the effect of speed on the amount of friction? Is there agreement on the cause of friction? Write a brief summary of your findings.
5. Roll four pieces of paper 2 by 6 in. into cylinders of about 1½ in. diameter, using rubber bands to keep the paper rolled. Use the cylinders to support a flat object, forming a kind of table. Estimate the weight the cylinders will support, and test your estimate by experiment.

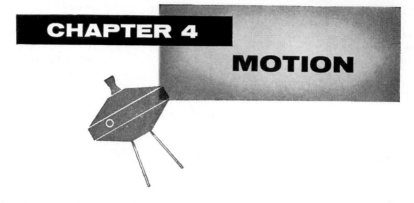

CHAPTER 4

MOTION

VOCABULARY

Acceleration. Rate of change of velocity.

Angular velocity. The rate of rotary motion.

Centrifugal reaction. The reaction force which is equal in magnitude to the centripetal force but acts in the opposite direction.

Centripetal force. The force that deflects a body from its linear path and compels it to move along a curve.

Circular motion. Motion of a body along a curved path of constant radius.

Force of gravitational attraction. The mutual force of attraction between bodies.

Gyroscope. A wheel and axle mounted so that it is free to turn in any direction.

Impulse. The product of a force and the length of time it acts.

Inertia. The property of matter which requires a force to be exerted on it in order to accelerate it.

Mass. The measure of the inertia of a body.

Momentum. The product of the mass of an object and its velocity.

Motion. A continuing change of place or position.

Pendulum. A body suspended so that it can swing to-and-fro about a horizontal axis.

Periodic motion. The motion of an object when it continually moves back and forth over a definite path in equal intervals of time.

Precession. The motion about a third axis resulting from the geometric addition of angular velocities about two different axes.

Rotary motion. The motion of a body turning about an axis.

Simple harmonic motion. Periodic motion in which (1) the object goes equal distances in opposite directions from the equilibrium position; (2) the object completes each cycle in the same amount of time; (3) the force exerted on the object and the resulting acceleration are directly proportional to the displacement of the object from the equilibrium position; and (4) the force and acceleration are directed toward the equilibrium position.

Speed. Rate of motion.

Velocity. Rate of displacement.

1 VELOCITY

1. Motion. If you drive across Texas from Dallas to El Paso, you are moving from one location to another. You may fly from Cheyenne, Wyoming, to Seattle, Washington, or you may go from physics class in one room to English class in another room. In each instance you are changing your location. During the time you are making these changes, your body is in motion. *Motion may be defined as a continuing change of place or position.*

In Chapter 2 we defined a displacement as a change of position. *Motion is the process by which an object undergoes a displacement. A displacement is the result of motion.* In our study of forces in Chapter 3 we found there are two kinds of motion which must be prevented in order to produce equilibrium in a body at rest; these are linear motion and rotary motion. *Linear motion is motion in a straight line. Rotary motion is motion about an axis.*

2. Speed. An automobile normally has a speedometer which tells you its **speed,** or *rate of motion,* at each particular instant as you drive along. When you go on a long automobile trip, you are interested in the *average speed* you have maintained during each day. Suppose you traveled from Dallas to El Paso, a distance of 637 mi, in 13.5 hr. Your average speed would be 637 mi ÷ 13.5 hr = 47.2 mi/hr.

$$\text{Average speed} = \frac{\text{distance traveled}}{\text{elapsed time}}$$

We generally measure speed in mi/hr. However, we may also use such units as ft/sec, cm/sec, and m/sec.

3. Velocity. *Speed* and *velocity* are commonly given the same meaning. In physics, speed and velocity have definite, separate meanings. The speed of an object indicates how fast it is moving, that is, the distance the object will travel in a given time. It tells us nothing, however, about

the direction in which the object is moving. Suppose you start from Chicago and travel for 10. hr at an average *speed* of about *45 mi/hr.* At the end of this time, you may be in Minneapolis, Nashville, or Pittsburgh. If you drive in a circular path, you may even be back in Chicago.

The quantity in physics which combines the speed of an object with the direction in which it moves is called velocity. *Velocity may be defined as the rate of displacement,* that is, *the rate of motion in a particular direction.* In the example given above, if you travel from Chicago for 10. hr with a velocity of about *45 mi/hr northwestward,* you arrive in Minneapolis. If your velocity is *45 mi/hr southward,* you reach Nashville. If your velocity is *45 mi/hr southeastward,* you reach Pittsburgh.

Average velocity is defined by the formula

$$v_{av} = \frac{s}{t}$$

where v_{av} is average velocity, s is displacement, and t is elapsed time. If the route is direct, so that the distance traveled and the displacement are the same, average velocity and average speed are numerically the same. However, if the distance traveled is greater than the displacement, the average speed will be numerically greater than the average velocity.

Motion is said to be *uniform* when the velocity is constant; that is, when an object undergoes equal displacements in each succeeding unit of time. An automobile maintaining a velocity of 50. mi/hr along a perfectly straight, level road is an example of uniform motion. If either the speed of the car or the direction in which it is going is changed, its motion is *variable.* When the motion is variable, the displacements a car undergoes in equal periods of time are unequal.

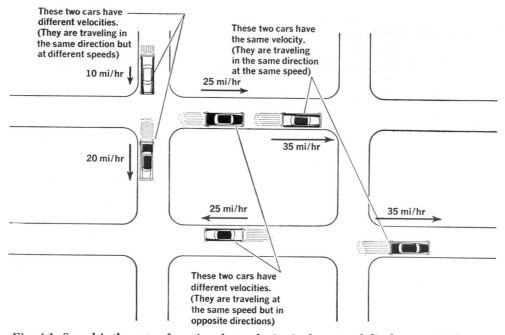

Fig. 4-1. Speed is the rate of motion, but velocity is the rate of displacement. The vectors represent the displacements of the cars in equal units of time.

4. Velocity vectors. Since displacement is a vector quantity, and velocity is the rate of displacement (a vector quantity divided by a scalar quantity), *velocity is also a vector quantity.* We may apply the same principles of vectors, discussed in Chapters 2 and 3, to the solution of problems involving velocities.

Suppose an airplane flies through still air with a velocity of 300. mi/hr eastward. Suddenly a tail wind with a velocity of 15 mi/hr eastward springs up. What is the resultant velocity of the airplane? The magnitude of the resultant velocity is the algebraic sum of the magnitudes of the component velocities. It has the same direction as the component velocities. Therefore, 300. mi/hr eastward + 15 mi/hr eastward = 315 mi/hr eastward, the resultant velocity of the airplane. This is shown graphically in Fig. 4-2.

Now let us take the opposite case. The

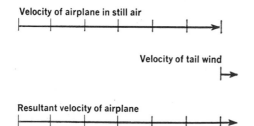

Fig. 4-2. The magnitude of the resultant of two velocities in the same direction is the algebraic sum of the magnitudes of the component velocities. The resultant has the same direction as the component velocities.

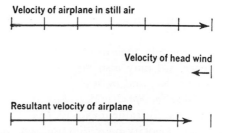

Fig. 4-3. The magnitude of the resultant of two velocities in opposite directions is the algebraic sum of the magnitudes of the components. It has the same direction as the greater velocity.

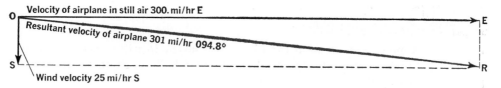

O Velocity of airplane in still air 300. mi/hr E → **E**

Resultant velocity of airplane 301 mi/hr 094.8°

S

Wind velocity 25 mi/hr S → **R**

Fig. 4-4. The resultant of two velocities acting at an angle to each other is the diagonal of the parallelogram constructed by using the component velocity vectors as sides. The resultant velocity vector is the geometric sum of the component velocity vectors.

airplane flies eastward, but the wind is a head wind. Its velocity is 15 mi/hr westward. What is the resultant velocity of the airplane? Again, the magnitude of the resultant will be the algebraic sum of the magnitudes of the components, and so, in this case, the resultant will have the direction of the greater velocity. Therefore, 300. mi/hr eastward + 15 mi/hr westward = 285 mi/hr eastward. The vectors for this problem are shown in Fig. 4-3.

In a third case, the airplane still flies eastward with a velocity of 300. mi/hr, but now the wind has a velocity of 25 mi/hr southward. What is the resultant velocity of the airplane? In Fig. 4-4, $\overrightarrow{OE}$ represents the velocity of the airplane, 300. mi/hr eastward. The vector representing the velocity of the wind, 25 mi/hr southward is $\overrightarrow{OS}$. To find the resultant velocity, we construct the parallelogram of velocities, OERS. The diagonal of this parallelogram $\overrightarrow{OR}$ is the resultant velocity. When we compute its magnitude we find it to be 301 mi/hr. Its bearing is 094.8°.

However, the pilot of the airplane does not want to get 25 miles south of his course for each hour of flight. What change must he make in the velocity of his airplane so that he stays on course despite the wind blowing from the north? Our problem is now one in the resolution of velocities. The *resultant velocity* we wish to obtain is 300. mi/hr eastward. This is represented by $\overrightarrow{OR}$ in Fig. 4-5. It will be the diagonal of our velocity parallelogram. We know one component of this velocity, that of the wind, 25 mi/hr southward. This is represented by $\overrightarrow{OS}$. To complete our parallelogram, we first draw *SR*. Then from *O*, we draw $\overrightarrow{OV}$ parallel and equal to *SR*. Connecting *V* with *R* completes the parallelogram. $\overrightarrow{OV}$ represents the velocity the airplane must maintain. This velocity is computed to be 301 mi/hr with a bearing of 085.2°. By heading his airplane on a bearing of 085.2° and increasing his speed to 301 mi/hr, the pilot will actually travel with a velocity of 300. mi/hr eastward. See the Sample Problems on pages 70 and 71.

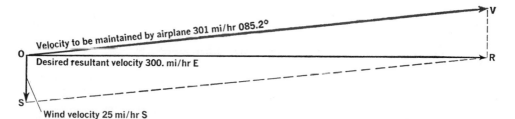

→ **V**

Velocity to be maintained by airplane 301 mi/hr 085.2°

O

Desired resultant velocity 300. mi/hr E → **R**

S

Wind velocity 25 mi/hr S

Fig. 4-5. The vector representing the velocity which the airplane must maintain is the geometric difference between the desired resultant velocity vector and the wind velocity vector.

Sample Problem

A man rows a boat at the rate of 4.0 mi/hr in still water. He heads the boat directly across a stream which flows at the rate of 3.0 mi/hr. What is his resultant velocity?

Solution

In Fig. 4-6 $\overrightarrow{OB}$ represents the velocity at which the man rows the boat and $\overrightarrow{OC}$ represents the velocity of the current of the stream. When we construct the parallelogram of velocities, OBRC, the resultant velocity is represented by $\overrightarrow{OR}$. Its magnitude and angle with respect to $\overrightarrow{OB}$ may be found graphically, or trigonometrically according to the method of Chapter 2, Section 22.

$OR = \sqrt{\overline{OB}^2 + \overline{OC}^2}$ Why?

$OR = \sqrt{(4.0 \text{ mi/hr})^2 + (3.0 \text{ mi/hr})^2}$

$OR = 5.0 \text{ mi/hr}$

$\tan \angle BOR = \dfrac{OC}{OB}$ Why?

$\tan \angle BOR = \dfrac{3.0 \text{ mi/hr}}{4.0 \text{ mi/hr}} = 0.75$

$\angle BOR = 37°$

QUESTIONS

A   **1.** (*a*) What is motion? (*b*) Distinguish between linear motion and rotary motion.
2. (*a*) What is speed? (*b*) In what units may speed be measured? (*c*) To which system of measurement does each unit which you named belong?
3. (*a*) What is velocity? (*b*) Distinguish between speed and velocity.
4. (*a*) Describe the motion of an object which has uniform speed. (*b*) Describe the motion of an object which has uniform velocity.
5. Why is speed a scalar quantity but velocity a vector quantity?
6. How can we determine the magnitude and bearing of the resultant of two velocities which act in the same or in opposite directions?

B   **7.** (*a*) Does a change in the speed of an object always produce a change in its velocity? (*b*) Does a change in the velocity of an object always indicate a change in its speed? Explain.

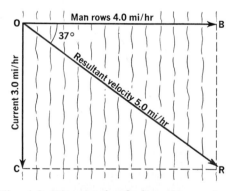

Fig. 4-6. Diagram for finding the resultant of two velocities acting at right angles to each other.

8. How can we determine the magnitude and bearing of the resultant of two velocities which act at any angle to each other?
9. Describe the method of determining the magnitudes of the two component velocities acting at right angles to each other into which a single velocity can be resolved.

Sample Problem

What must be the velocity of a boat to cross a river 1.5 mi wide in 15 min? The river flows at the rate of 2.0 mi/hr.

Solution

The resultant velocity of the boat must be 1.5 mi directly across the river in 15 min. This is a velocity of 6.0 mi/hr at an angle of 90.° with the current of the river. In Fig. 4-7, $\overrightarrow{OR}$ represents the resultant velocity, 6.0 mi/hr; $\overrightarrow{OC}$ represents the velocity of the river, 2.0 mi/hr. The velocity parallelogram is OVRC. $\overrightarrow{OV}$ represents the velocity which the boat must maintain in order to follow a path directly across the river. The magnitude and direction of $\overrightarrow{OV}$ may be determined graphically, or trigonometrically by the method of Chapter 2, Section 22.

$OV = \sqrt{\overline{OC}^2 + \overline{OR}^2}$ Why?

$OV = \sqrt{(2.0 \text{ mi/hr})^2 + (6.0 \text{ mi/hr})^2}$

$OV = 6.3 \text{ mi/hr}$

$\tan \angle VOR = \dfrac{OC}{OR}$ Why?

$\tan \angle VOR = \dfrac{2.0 \text{ mi/hr}}{6.0 \text{ mi/hr}} = 0.33$

$\angle VOR = 18°$

PROBLEMS

Note: In solving each of the following problems (a) construct a diagram using a suitable scale; (b) determine the solution graphically; (c) determine the solution mathematically.

A 1. The highway distance from Indianapolis to Denver is 1712 km. (a) If the driving time is 29.25 hr, what is the average speed for the trip? (b) What is the direction of this displacement?

2. Minneapolis and Des Moines are 259 mi apart. (a) If a man makes the trip to Des Moines in 7 hr 5 min, what is his average speed? (b) What is the direction of his displacement?

3. A motor boat travels 20. km/hr in still water. What will be the magnitude and direction of the velocity of the boat if it is directed upstream on a river which flows at the rate of 4 km/hr?

4. An airplane flying toward St. Louis has

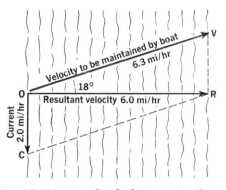

Fig. 4-7. Diagram for finding a second component velocity when one component velocity and the resultant velocity are known.

a velocity with respect to the air of 325 mi/hr northward. What is the velocity of the airplane with respect to the ground if the wind is blowing with a velocity of 15 mi/hr southward?

5. A man can row a boat at the rate of 5.0 km/hr in still water. He heads directly across a river which flows at the rate of 5.0 km/hr. Determine the magnitude and direction of his resultant velocity.

6. An airplane flies on a bearing of 270.0° at 220. mi/hr. If the wind has a velocity of 20.0 mi/hr from 180.0°, determine the magnitude and bearing of the resultant velocity.

7. An airplane is to maintain a velocity of 500. km/hr on a bearing of 045.0°. If the wind is blowing at 50.0 km/hr from 315.0°, what should be the magnitude and bearing of the velocity of the airplane to offset the effect of the wind?

8. What must be the magnitude and direction of the velocity maintained by a speedboat if it is to go with a resultant velocity of 30.0 mi/hr directly across a river which flows at 5.00 mi/hr?

B **9.** Determine the magnitude and bearing of the resultant velocity of 75.0 m/sec N 25.0° E and 100.0 m/sec S 25.0° E.

10. What are the magnitudes of the component southward and eastward velocities of a velocity of 100. ft/sec S 75.0° E?

11. Resolve a velocity of 65.0 km/hr N 25.0° W into its component northward and westward velocities.

12. A boat is to cross a river on a course directed 20.0° upstream to a dock 2500. ft distant in 10.0 min. If the river flows at the rate of 1.5 mi/hr, at what angle upstream must the boat be headed and what must be its speed in mi/hr through the water?

13. An airplane must fly at a ground speed of 450. km/hr on a bearing of 170.0° to be on course and on schedule. If the wind is from 220.0° at 25.0 km/hr, on what bearing and at what air speed must the pilot fly?

2 UNIFORMLY ACCELERATED MOTION

5. Acceleration. Only under very unusual circumstances can an automobile be driven at constant velocity. When we drive through a large city we must continually stop for red traffic lights. When they change to green we start on our way again. In addition to stopping, starting, turning, and going up and down grades, we may drive at various speeds.

When we change the velocity of an automobile, we accelerate it. If the velocity goes from 25 mi/hr to 35 mi/hr, we have changed the velocity 10 mi/hr. If this change takes place in 5 sec, the rate of change is 10 mi/hr in 5 sec, or $\frac{2 \text{ mi/hr}}{\text{sec}}$. In physics, *the rate of change of velocity is called* **acceleration.** In equation form,

$$a = \frac{v_f - v_i}{t}$$

where a is acceleration, v_f is final velocity, v_i is initial velocity, and t is elapsed time. In the example given,

$$a = \frac{35 \text{ mi/hr} - 25 \text{ mi/hr}}{5 \text{ sec}}$$

$$a = \frac{2 \text{ mi/hr}}{\text{sec}}$$

Since acceleration is the ratio of a vector quantity (velocity) to a scalar quantity (time), acceleration is also a vector quantity.

An object that has a velocity of 2 ft/sec at the end of the first second, 4 ft/sec at the end of the next second, 6 ft/sec at the end of the third second, and so on, has accelerated motion. In each second the difference between the final and initial velocity is 2 ft/sec. Thus the acceleration is $\frac{2 \text{ ft/sec}}{\text{sec}}$. If an automobile accelerates to 2 mi/hr in the first second, 4 mi/hr in the next second, and 6 mi/hr in the third second, the change in velocity during each second is 2 mi/hr. The acceleration is $\frac{2 \text{ mi/hr}}{\text{sec}}$. In both of these examples the acceleration is constant. Such motion is *uniformly accelerated motion.* An object that has a velocity of 2 ft/sec at the end of the first second, 5 ft/sec at the end of the next second, and 10 ft/sec at the end of the third second also has accelerated motion. In this case, however, the acceleration is not uniform, it is *variable.*

Since acceleration is the rate of change of a rate of motion, time enters into the

Fig. 4-8. Galileo Galilei (1564–1642), a great Italian scientist, formulated the laws of accelerated motion and falling bodies. (Bettmann Archive)

unit twice. In the equation defining acceleration, the unit for the numerator is a length unit divided by a time unit, while the unit for the denominator is a time unit. Thus typical units for acceleration which we have already used are $\frac{ft/sec}{sec}$ or $\frac{mi/hr}{sec}$. Where the two units of time are the same, as in $\frac{ft/sec}{sec}$, we carry out the indicated mathematical operation, ft/sec ÷ sec, and obtain ft/sec". Note: ft/sec ÷ sec = ft/sec × 1/sec = ft/sec². If the two time units are different, the acceleration is usually expressed in the form, mi/hr/sec, rather than $\frac{mi/hr}{sec}$.

When an automobile is brought to a stop, it may have velocities of 8 ft/sec, 6 ft/sec, 4 ft/sec, and 2 ft/sec at the end of each of four successive seconds. In this case *the value of the acceleration is negative;* this is an example of negatively accelerated motion, also called retarded or *decelerated motion.* In each second 2 ft/sec is subtracted from the velocity. The vehicle's motion is uniformly retarded.

We may also have variably retarded motion. In stopping an automobile we

first exert a gentle brake pressure. Then we push harder on the brake pedal until the car slows down. Finally we ease up on the brake pedal so that the car comes to a smooth stop.

6. Equations for uniformly accelerated motion. Acceleration and its effect on the motion of objects was first clearly explained by Galileo Galilei (1564–1642). He performed many experiments to determine the rate at which objects fall and the rate at which balls roll down an inclined plane.

Let us repeat one of Galileo's experiments. We raise one end of a board so that it is just steep enough to allow a ball to roll down it at the rate of 1 foot in the first second. The apparatus is shown in Fig. 4-9. As the ball rolls down the board, we determine its position at one-second intervals. The data we obtain are shown in the following table:

Elapsed Time (sec)	Total Distance (ft)	Distance Each Second (ft)	Final Velocity (ft/sec)
1	1	1	2
2	4	3	4
3	9	5	6
4	16	7	8
5	25	9	10

The motion of a ball rolling down an inclined plane is uniformly accelerated motion. The distance rolled each second

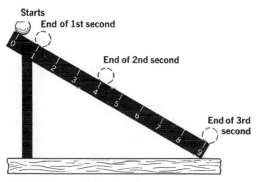

Fig. 4-9. The ball rolls down the plane with uniformly accelerated motion.

is 2 ft greater than that rolled the second before. Thus the acceleration is 2 ft/sec².

The initial velocity of the ball is zero. Its acceleration, or gain in velocity, is 2 ft/sec². Therefore, its velocity at the end of *the first second* is 2 ft/sec. (If at that instant the ball ceased to be accelerated, it would continue to move with a constant velocity of 2 ft/sec.) At the end of the next second, its velocity is 4 ft/sec. In five seconds, 5 × 2 ft/sec, or 10 ft/sec is added to its original velocity. Its velocity at the end of the fifth second is 10 ft/sec. Thus we find that *the final velocity of an object starting from rest equals the product of the acceleration by the time. If an object does not start from rest, its final velocity will equal the sum of its initial* *velocity and the increase in velocity produced by the acceleration.*

We may arrive at this same conclusion by mathematical reasoning also. We know the equation defining acceleration is

$$a = \frac{v_f - v_i}{t}$$

Multiplying both sides of the equation by t,

$$at = v_f - v_i$$

Isolating the term v_f yields

$$v_f = v_i + at \quad \text{(Equation 1)}$$

> If the object starts from rest, $v_i = 0$, and
> $$v_f = at$$

Sample Problem

A ball with an initial velocity of 10.0 ft/sec rolls down an inclined plane with uniformly accelerated motion. If its acceleration is 20.0 ft/sec², find: (*a*) its velocity at the end of the tenth second; (*b*) the distance it rolls in 10.0 sec; and (*c*) the distance it rolls in the eighth second.

Solution

(*a*) $v_f = v_i + at$
$v_f = 10.0 \text{ ft/sec} + 20.0 \text{ ft/sec}^2 \times 10.0 \text{ sec}$
$v_f = 210. \text{ ft/sec}$

Note: $\dfrac{\text{ft}}{\text{sec}} + \dfrac{\text{ft}}{\text{sec} \times \text{sec}} \times \text{sec} = \dfrac{\text{ft}}{\text{sec}}$

(*b*) $s = v_i t + \tfrac{1}{2}at^2$
$s = 10.0 \text{ ft/sec} \times 10.0 \text{ sec} + \tfrac{1}{2} \times 20.0 \text{ ft/sec}^2 \times (10.0 \text{ sec})^2$
$s = 1.10 \times 10^3 \text{ ft}$

Note: $\dfrac{\text{ft}}{\text{sec}} \times \text{sec} + \dfrac{\text{ft}}{\text{sec}^2} \times \text{sec}^2 = \text{ft}$

(*c*) $s/\text{sec} = v_i + \tfrac{1}{2}a(2t - 1 \text{ sec})$
$s/\text{sec} = 10.0 \text{ ft/sec} + \tfrac{1}{2} \times 20.0 \text{ ft/sec}^2 [(2 \times 8.0 \text{ sec}) - 1 \text{ sec}]$
$s/\text{sec} = 160. \text{ ft/sec}$

Note: $\dfrac{\text{ft}}{\text{sec}} + \dfrac{\text{ft}}{\text{sec}^2} \times \text{sec} = \dfrac{\text{ft}}{\text{sec}}$

In Section 3 we learned that

$$v_{av} = \frac{s}{t}$$

or

$$s = v_{av}t \qquad \text{(Equation 2)}$$

With uniform acceleration, the average velocity for any given number of seconds equals one-half the sum of the initial and final velocities.

$$v_{av} = \frac{v_i + v_f}{2} \qquad \text{(Equation 3)}$$

By substituting the value of v_f obtained in Equation 1 in Equation 3,

$$v_{av} = \frac{v_i + (v_i + at)}{2} \qquad \text{(Equation 4)}$$

We now substitute the value of v_{av} obtained in Equation 4 in Equation 2. This gives us

$$s = v_it + \tfrac{1}{2}at^2 \qquad \text{(Equation 5)}$$

If an object undergoes uniform acceleration, its displacement equals the sum of its initial velocity times the elapsed time and one-half the acceleration times the square of the elapsed time.

If the object starts from rest, $v_it = 0$, and
$$s = \tfrac{1}{2}at^2$$

From this equation we see that if an object starts from rest and travels with uniformly accelerated motion, the acceleration equals twice the distance the object travels during the first second.

Now let us solve Equation 1 for t, and substitute this value of t in Equation 5. From Equation 1,

$$t = \frac{v_f - v_i}{a}$$

Substituting in Equation 5,

$$s = v_i\left(\frac{v_f - v_i}{a}\right) + \tfrac{1}{2}a\left(\frac{v_f - v_i}{a}\right)^2$$

Multiplying by $2a$ and expanding terms,

$$2as = 2v_iv_f - 2v_i^2 + v_f^2 - 2v_iv_f + v_i^2$$

Combining terms,

$$2as = v_f^2 - v_i^2$$

Solving for v_f,

$$v_f = \sqrt{v_i^2 + 2as} \qquad \text{(Equation 6)}$$

With uniform acceleration, the final velocity equals the square root of the sum of the square of the initial velocity and twice the acceleration times the displacement.

If the object starts from rest, $v_i^2 = 0$, and
$$v_f = \sqrt{2as}$$

The equation

$$s/\text{sec} = v_i + \tfrac{1}{2}a(2t - 1 \text{ sec})$$

may be used to find the distance traveled by an object *in any given second.* If we wish to find the distance traveled in the eighth second, for instance, we let $t = 8$ sec.

We may use Equation 1 to find v_f, v_i, a, or t, if three of these quantities are known. We may use Equation 5 to find s, v_i, t, or a, if three of these are known. We may use Equation 6 to find v_f, v_i, a, or s, if three of these are known. See the Sample Problem on the opposite page.

7. Equations for uniformly retarded motion. The equations given in Section 6 also apply to uniformly retarded motion. They may be used to find out how far an automobile will travel after the brakes are applied, or to find the length of time required to bring the car to a stop. See the Sample Problem on page 76.

8. Equations for freely falling bodies. In the experiments with a ball rolling down an inclined plane, the acceleration was produced by a component of the force of gravity. If the plane is steeper, this component is increased. When the plane is vertical, the acceleration is the result of the action of the entire force of gravity. The ball becomes a freely falling body.

If a body falls freely from rest at the latitude and altitude of New York City, the force of gravity gives it a velocity of 9.80 m/sec in one second of time. Since $a = v_f/t$, the acceleration of gravity equals 9.80 m/sec² at this location. We must consider the location since the value of the acceleration of gravity varies with different locations on the earth's surface. The value given is approximately true for most locations in the United States. Corresponding values for the acceleration of gravity are 980. cm/sec² and 32.16 ft/sec². In computations this last value is usually rounded to 32 ft/sec².

The equations for accelerated motion apply to freely falling bodies also. Since the acceleration of gravity, g, is the same for all objects at a given location, we may substitute g for a in these equations. These now become

$$v_f = v_i + gt$$
$$s = v_i t + \tfrac{1}{2}gt^2$$
$$v_f = \sqrt{v_i^2 + 2gs}$$
$$s/sec = v_i + \tfrac{1}{2}g(2t - 1 \text{ sec})$$

Commonly, freely falling bodies start from rest, and thus are not likely to have an initial downward velocity other than zero.

$$\boxed{\begin{aligned} &\text{If } v_i = 0 \\ v_f &= gt \\ s &= \tfrac{1}{2}gt^2 \\ v_f &= \sqrt{2gs} \\ s/sec &= \tfrac{1}{2}g(2t - 1 \text{ sec}) \end{aligned}}$$

In the case of freely falling bodies, s is always a vertical distance. Vector quantities in these equations are customarily assigned plus signs if they are directed downward and minus signs if they are directed upward.

9. The effect of the atmosphere on freely falling bodies. When Galileo performed his experiments with falling bodies, he discovered that dense objects fell slightly faster than those of lower density. Since there was very little difference, he concluded that the unequal rate of descent must be caused by the resistance of the air. He believed that all objects would fall at the same rate in a vacuum.

Sample Problem

An automobile is traveling 30. mi/hr. Its brakes retard it at the rate of 20. ft/sec². (*a*) How long will it take to stop the car? (*b*) What distance will the car travel after the brakes are applied?

Solution

(*a*) $a = \dfrac{v_f - v_i}{t}$

$t = \dfrac{v_f - v_i}{a}$

$t = \dfrac{0 - \left(30.\ \text{mi/hr} \times \dfrac{88\ \text{ft/sec}}{60.\ \text{mi/hr}}\right)}{-20.\ \text{ft/sec}^2}$ The value for acceleration is negative since deceleration is involved.

$t = 2.2 \text{ sec}$

(*b*) $s = v_i t + \tfrac{1}{2}at^2$

$s = \left(30.\ \text{mi/hr} \times \dfrac{88\ \text{ft/sec}}{60.\ \text{mi/hr}}\right) \times 2.2 \text{ sec} +$

$\qquad\qquad\qquad \tfrac{1}{2}(-20.\ \text{ft/sec}^2)(2.2 \text{ sec})^2$

$s = 48 \text{ ft}$

With the invention of the vacuum pump, it became possible to test Galileo's idea. The classic coin-and-feather-tube experiment does this nicely. We invert a long glass tube filled with air, containing a feather and a coin. The feather flutters down slowly, striking the bottom long after the coin. See Fig. 4-10(A). As air is pumped from the tube, the rates of fall of the coin and feather become almost the same. If we could pump all the air from the tube, both the coin and feather would fall at the same rate. See Fig. 4-10(B).

The equations given in Section 8 do not take into consideration the resistance of the air, and therefore apply only to objects falling freely in a vacuum. They apply with reasonable accuracy to dense and compact objects, such as baseballs or lead shot, falling through the air. Of course, they do not apply to leaves or feathers dropping through the air, nor to a descending parachutist.

10. Terminal velocity. A freely falling object is acted on by the downward force of gravity and the upward force of fluid friction of the air. Since the force of fluid friction increases with velocity, a body which is falling freely through the atmosphere eventually attains a velocity at which the magnitude of the force of fluid friction equals that of gravity. When this occurs, the body moves downward with a constant velocity, called the *terminal velocity.* An airman falling without opening his parachute may reach a terminal velocity of about 120 mi/hr. When he opens his parachute, the parachute increases the air resistance tremendously; and his terminal velocity may be reduced to about 14 mi/hr, allowing him to strike the earth without harm.

11. The altitude reached by objects projected upward. An object thrown upward is uniformly retarded by the force of gravity until it finally stops rising. Then, as it falls, it is uniformly accelerated by the force of gravity. If we know the initial

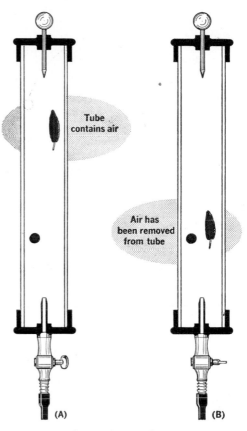

Tube contains air

Air has been removed from tube

(A)   (B)

Fig. 4-10. Objects fall at the same rate in a vacuum.

velocity with which it is projected upward, we may apply the equations in Section 8 to find how high it will rise and how long it will take for the ascent. See the Sample Problem on page 78.

12. The path of a projectile. The path of a projectile is determined principally by two types of motion. Neglecting air resistance, the horizontal component of the muzzle velocity of a projectile is a constant. The projectile is also acted on by the force of gravity, which pulls it toward the earth. This downward acceleration also acts on the vertical component of the muzzle velocity. The vertical acceleration and the horizontal velocity act independently on the moving body. This may be demonstrated by means of the apparatus shown in Fig. 4-11. If balls are placed at A and B

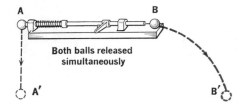

Fig. 4-11. Even though ball B has a horizontal velocity, the force of gravitational attraction acts in the same way on both balls
A and B, causing them to strike the floor at
the same time, as shown by A' and B'.

and the trigger released, both balls are
acted upon by gravity. Ball A merely drops
to the floor. Ball B is given a horizontal
velocity. Since both balls strike the floor
at the same time, we may conclude that
the action of gravity is independent of the
horizontal velocity of ball B.

Suppose a rifle bullet is fired horizontally with a velocity of 3000. ft/sec. Neglecting the air resistance, the bullet will

travel 3000. ft by the end of the first second.
But gravity begins acting on the bullet
immediately after it leaves the muzzle of
the gun. During the first second, a freely
falling body drops 16 ft. Consequently
this bullet will drop 16 ft while traveling
to a target 3000. ft away. In 2 seconds the
bullet will travel 6000. ft, but it will also
drop 64 ft. The path of a high-velocity
projectile approximates a straight line,

Sample Problem

An object is projected upward with a velocity of 100. m/sec.
(a) To what height will it rise? (b) How long will it take to reach
that height? (c) What will be the total time elapsed until it strikes
the earth?

Solution

(a) $v_f = \sqrt{v_i^2 + 2gs}$

$s = \dfrac{v_f^2 - v_i^2}{2g}$

$s = \dfrac{0 - (-100.\ \text{m/sec})^2}{2 \times 9.80\ \text{m/sec}^2}$ (The value for v_i is negative
because the velocity is upward.)

$s = -510.\ \text{m}$ (The negative value obtained
for s indicates an upward dis-
placement.)

(b) $v_f = v_i + gt$

$t = \dfrac{v_f - v_i}{g}$

$t = \dfrac{0 - (-100.\ \text{m/sec})}{9.80\ \text{m/sec}^2}$

$t = 10.2\ \text{sec}$

(c) Neglecting the effect of the atmosphere, the same amount of
time is required for the object to fall as to rise. Thus, the total
time elapsed will be 2 × 10.2 sec = 20.4 sec.

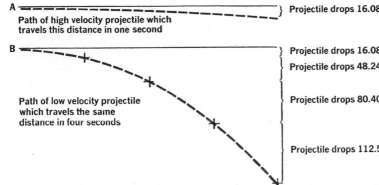

A } Projectile drops 16.08 ft during first second

Path of high velocity projectile which travels this distance in one second

B } Projectile drops 16.08 ft during first second

} Projectile drops 48.24 ft during second second

Path of low velocity projectile which travels the same distance in four seconds

} Projectile drops 80.40 ft during third second

} Projectile drops 112.56 ft during fourth second

Fig. 4-12. The effect of the force of gravitational attraction on high velocity and low velocity projectiles.

but the path of a slow-moving projectile is quite noticeably curved. Figure 4-12 compares the paths of high- and low-velocity projectiles.

A rifle is generally fired at a small upward angle to counteract the effect of gravity on the bullet after it is fired. The size of this angle is determined by adjusting the rear sight to the proper range marking. Then, when the rifle is aimed, its muzzle is directed upward at the correct angle. This gives the velocity of the bullet a slight upward component that is enough to overcome the effect of gravity while the bullet is on its way to its distant target.

The muzzle of a field gun is elevated

Fig. 4-13. In order to counteract the action of the force of gravity on the bullet, a rifle is aimed the necessary distance above the target by raising the rear sight. (National Rifle Association)

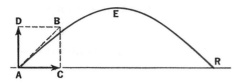

Fig. 4-14. Neglecting air resistance, the path of a projectile fired upward at an angle is a parabola.

so that the projectile is fired at an angle with the horizontal. The path such a projectile might take is shown in Fig. 4-14. The angle *BAC* is the angle of elevation; *AC* and *AD* are the horizontal and vertical components of the velocity; *AR* is the range. The path of the projectile, *AER*, is the *trajectory*.

QUESTIONS

A 1. (*a*) What is acceleration? (*b*) Why is a unit of time used twice in a unit of acceleration?
2. Why is acceleration a vector quantity?
3. Distinguish between (*a*) uniformly accelerated motion; (*b*) variably accelerated motion; (*c*) uniformly decelerated motion; (*d*) variably decelerated motion.
4. What effect does the force of gravity have on a baseball thrown directly upward?
5. (*a*) What motions govern the path of a projectile? (*b*) What effect does each have on its path?

B 6. What equation relates final velocity to initial velocity, acceleration, and time?
7. What equation would you use to calculate displacement when the initial velocity, final velocity, and time are known?
8. (*a*) What opposing forces act on a body falling freely through the atmosphere? (*b*) Why does the velocity of such a body ultimately become constant?
9. (*a*) What adjustment is made on the rear sight of a rifle when the distance to the target is increased? (*b*) How would the use of a higher velocity bullet affect the adjustment?

PROBLEMS

Note: Use $g = 9.80$ m/sec², or 32 ft/sec². Ignore the effect of the atmosphere.

A 1. If a ball is dropped and attains a velocity of 29.31 m/sec in 3.00 sec, what is the acceleration of gravity?
2. An automobile can be accelerated from 45 mi/hr to 65 mi/hr in 8.1 sec. What is the acceleration?
3. Derive a formula which yields the time required for a body to undergo a given decrease in velocity if the deceleration is known.
4. Derive a formula by which you can calculate the total time which elapses from when you throw a ball directly upward until you catch it, assuming you know the height it reaches.
5. A large rock is dropped from a bridge into the river below. (*a*) If the time required for it to drop is 1.7 sec, with what velocity, in m/sec, does it hit the water? (*b*) What is the height, in meters, of the bridge above the water?
6. (*a*) How many seconds does it take for a metal ball to drop 400. ft from rest? (*b*) What velocity does it attain?
7. An object with an initial velocity of 20.0 cm/sec is accelerated at 8.0 cm/sec² for 5.0 sec. (*a*) What is the total displacement? (*b*) What is the displacement during the fifth second?
8. How many feet will a bomb which is dropped from an airplane fall in the tenth second after it is released?
9. What velocity is attained by an object which is accelerated at 0.30 m/sec² for a distance of 50. m, if its initial velocity was 0.50 m/sec?
10. (*a*) If the brakes of an automobile can decelerate it at 10.0 ft/sec², what time is required to reduce the velocity of the automobile from 70.0 mi/hr to 35.0 mi/hr? (*b*) How many feet does the car travel during this deceleration?

B 11. A bomb is dropped from an airplane flying at an altitude of 1.00×10^4 m. With what velocity will it strike the earth?
12. A baseball player sends a fly ball to a height of 144 ft. After the bat strikes the ball, how much time will there be for a fielder to get into position to make the catch?
13. A boy throws a stone from the ground to the top of the school flagpole. If it returns to the ground after 4.0 sec, how many meters high is the flagpole?

14. A stone is dropped from a balloon which is ascending at the rate of 15 ft/sec when the balloon is 1000. ft above the ground. What time is required for the stone to reach the ground?

15. A baseball is thrown vertically downward from the top of a 150. m tower with an initial velocity of 20. m/sec. (a) With what velocity does it reach the ground? (b) What time is required?

16. The barrel of a field gun is elevated at an angle of 45.0°. The velocity of the projectile leaving the muzzle of the gun is 1.00×10^3 ft/sec. Calculate (a) the vertical and horizontal components of the muzzle velocity; (b) the

height of the trajectory; (c) the time which elapses before the projectile returns to earth; (d) the range of the gun.

17. A shell is fired from a gun the barrel of which is elevated 20.0° above the horizontal. The muzzle velocity of the projectile is 250. m/sec. Calculate (a) the vertical and horizontal components of the muzzle velocity; (b) the height of the trajectory; (c) the time the projectile is in flight; (d) the range.

18. A bomb is dropped from an airplane flying horizontally at 2.00×10^4 ft at 325 mi/hr. Neglecting the effect of the air, how many feet short of the point directly above the target must the bomb be released?

3 NEWTON'S LAWS OF MOTION

13. The three laws of motion. Sir Isaac Newton (1642–1727) formulated three laws of motion that help to explain some very important principles of physics. While some of Newton's laws could be proved only under ideal conditions, actual observations and experiments make us sure that they are true. Newton's laws may be applied to objects on the earth and to the earth itself, or even to the sun, moon, and stars. We have been discussing some simple ways in which objects move. Newton's laws tell us why these objects move by describing the relationship between force and motion.

14. Newton's first law of motion—the law of inertia. Suppose you bring your car to a stop on a perfectly level street and you forget to set the hand brake or leave the car in gear. What will happen to your car? If no force is applied to it, it will not move. Suppose, however, that someone pulls into the parking space behind and carelessly bumps your car. What happens? Your car moves and then gradually comes to a stop. Why? The bump against your car is a force acting on it. The force moves your car; that is, increases its velocity from zero to perhaps one mile per hour. A change in velocity is acceleration. Therefore an unbalanced

force produces acceleration. The car eventually stops, however. What forces produce the deceleration? The friction of its moving parts and of the tires on the street brings the car to rest. If there were no friction, it is logical to assume that the car would continue to roll at constant speed.

We may state *Newton's first law of motion: A body continues in its state of rest*

Fig. 4-15. Sir Isaac Newton (1642–1727) formulated three important laws of motion which describe how forces act on matter. (Bettmann Archive)

Fig. 4-16. The inertia of the coin enables us to flick the card from beneath it. The coin then drops directly into the glass.

or *uniform motion unless an unbalanced force acts on it.* Since the first condition for equilibrium (Chapter 3, Section 12) is that there be no unbalanced force acting on a body, Newton's first law of motion tells us the characteristics of the motion of a body in equilibrium. A body in equilibrium is at rest or in uniform motion. In Section 3 of this chapter we learned that uniform motion involves constant velocity. Therefore a moving object is in equilibrium if its velocity is constant.

15. Inertia. When a body is at rest, or when it is moving at a constant speed in a straight line, its velocity is constant. The velocity of a body cannot change unless an unbalanced force acts on it. When we change the velocity of an object, we accelerate it. Consequently, *an unbalanced force accelerates an object.*

The property of an object which requires us to exert a force in order to accelerate it is called the **inertia** *of the body.* Thus, if a body is stationary, we say that its inertia tends to keep it stationary; we have to overcome the inertia in order to move the body. The inertia of a coin placed on a card over the mouth of a tumbler enables us to flick away the card so that the coin then drops into the tumbler. If a body is in motion, its inertia tends to keep it in motion. If you are standing in a crowded bus and the driver makes a sudden stop, your body continues to move forward because of its inertia. In order to swing a

stone attached to a cord in a circular path, you must exert a continual force on the cord. The inertia of the stone resists the continual change of direction as the stone is swung around. *The measure of inertia of a body is the* **mass** *of the body.*

16. Newton's second law of motion— the law of acceleration. In our discussion of inertia, we mentioned three quantities which are evidently related to one another: force, acceleration, and mass. In order to find out how they are related, we shall perform two imaginary experiments. These experiments are imaginary in the sense that they cannot be performed exactly as described. Real experiments show that if we could provide these imaginary conditions, we would obtain the results given. For the experiments we need a spring balance, some brass weights of equal mass, and a smooth horizontal surface on which the weights can move without friction.

1. We exert successive forces of 1 lb, 2 lb, 3 lb, and so on, on one brass weight, and measure the acceleration produced. The forces are measured by the spring balance. A stop watch and meter stick are used to measure the accelerations. See Fig. 4-17. We find that, for the *constant mass* of one brass weight, *the acceleration is directly proportional to the force applied.* The acceleration is in the same direction as the applied force.

$$a \propto F \quad (m \text{ is constant})$$

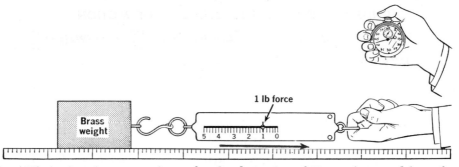

Fig. 4-17. An imaginary experiment for the derivation of Newton's second law of motion—measuring the acceleration of a brass weight when acted on by a force of one pound.

The symbol ∝ is read "varies as." This is another way of saying that a is directly proportional to F.

2. Next, we take a second brass weight and verify that its mass is the same as that of the first. We may do this by observing whether equal forces produce equal accelerations on both weights. Now we determine the acceleration produced by a certain force acting on one weight. Then, using the two brass weights together, we determine the acceleration produced by this same force. We may take three brass weights of equal mass and repeat the experiment. When we do this, we find that the acceleration produced by the same force each time is inversely proportional to the mass being accelerated.

$$a \propto \frac{1}{m} \quad \text{(F is constant)}$$

Since we have found that the acceleration varies directly with the force and inversely with the mass, we may combine the two statements and obtain

$$a \propto \frac{F}{m}$$

The acceleration of a body is directly proportional to the force exerted on the body, is inversely proportional to the mass of the body, and is in the same direction as the force. This is a statement of **Newton's second law of motion.**

17. Units of force and mass. We may convert the proportional expression of Newton's second law into an equation by inserting the constant k, and solving for F,

$$F = kma$$

It would be convenient to let $k = 1$, for then F would equal ma. We may do this only if we are willing to define one of the quantities in the equation in terms of the other two. This is what physicists have done. Consequently, in terms of the units we are about to define,

$$F = ma$$

In the MKS system, the unit of mass is the kilogram, and the unit in which acceleration is expressed is the meter per second². (See Section 5.) The force required to accelerate 1 kilogram of mass at the rate of 1 meter per second² is *1 kg-m/sec²*. This force is called a *newton* (nt).

In the CGS system, the unit of mass is the gram, and the unit of acceleration is the centimeter per second². The force required to accelerate 1 gram of mass at the rate of 1 centimeter per second² is *1 g-cm/sec²*. This force is called a *dyne*. One newton equals 10⁵ dynes.

In the English system, the unit of *force* is the pound, and the unit of acceleration is the foot per second². The *mass* of a body which will be accelerated at the rate of

UNITS FOR NEWTON'S SECOND LAW OF MOTION

	Mass	Acceleration	Force (Weight)
MKS	kilogram (kg)	$\dfrac{\text{meter/second}}{\text{second}}$ (m/sec^2)	newton (nt)
CGS	gram (g)	$\dfrac{\text{centimeter/second}}{\text{second}}$ (cm/sec^2)	dyne
FPS	slug	$\dfrac{\text{foot/second}}{\text{second}}$ (ft/sec^2)	pound (lb)

Units in red are composed of basic units; those in black are derived units.

1 foot per second² when 1 pound of force acts upon it is a *slug*.

This is the origin of the derived units of force in the metric system and of the derived unit of mass in the English system described in Chapter 2, Sections 7 and 9. See the Sample Problem below.

18. Forces on bodies of known weights. In the experiments we used to derive the equation, $F = ma$, we learned that the acceleration acquired by a particular object was directly proportional to the amount of force applied. We may express this as the proportion

$$\frac{F}{F'} = \frac{a}{a'}$$

In the case of a freely falling body, one of the forces is known because it equals the weight, w, of the body. The acceleration, g, is also known. It is the acceleration due to gravitational attraction, 32 ft/sec². Making these substitutions, the proportion becomes

$$\frac{F}{w} = \frac{a}{g}$$

and

$$F = \frac{wa}{g}$$

By using this formula, we can calculate the force needed to impart any desired acceleration to a body of known weight. See the Sample Problem opposite.

Sample Problem

What force, in newtons, is required to accelerate a small cart with a mass of 10. kg at the rate of 5.0 m/sec² in an eastward direction?

Solution

$F = ma$
$F = 10.\ \text{kg} \times 5.0\ \text{m/sec}^2.$
$F = 50.\ \text{kg-m/sec}^2 = 50.\ \text{nt, eastward}$
(This force must act eastward because this is the direction in which the cart is accelerated.)

Since $F = \dfrac{wa}{g}$ and $F = ma$, we can derive two other useful relationships,

$$m = \frac{w}{g} \quad \text{and} \quad w = mg$$

See the Sample Problems on page 86.

★ 19. Impulse and momentum. We have already defined acceleration as the rate of change of velocity. This may be expressed as

$$a = \frac{v_f - v_i}{t}$$

If we substitute this expression for a in the equation $F = ma$, we get

$$F = \frac{mv_f - mv_i}{t}$$

Multiplying by t,

$$Ft = mv_f - mv_i$$

This equation defines and gives the relationship between two important quantities, *impulse* and *change of momentum*. *The product of a force and the length of time it acts is called* **impulse**. *The product of the mass of an object and its velocity is called* **momentum**. *We see that impulse and change of momentum are equal. A force, F, acting on an object for time, t, will change its momentum by an amount, $mv_f - mv_i$.*

Suppose you place your hand flat on the table, palm upward. If a 1-lb weight is lowered gradually on your hand, the impact is bearable. Since the 1-lb weight is gently lowered onto your hand, only a small force acts on the weight to move it in the direction of your palm. The time during which this force acts is also small. These quantities combine to produce a small impulse. Consequently, the weight lowered onto your hand loses only a small amount of momentum, and you find the impact bearable.

Now, suppose the 1-lb weight is dropped from a height of 1 ft onto your hand. You can imagine that the effect would be unpleasant. The weight might injure your hand. In this case the full force of gravity acts on the mass of the 1-lb weight. If we assume that the time during which this force acts is the same as in the first case, you can easily see that the falling weight on being stopped loses much more momentum than the gently lowered weight did. The impact of the falling weight is greater because of its greater loss of momentum. See Fig. 4-18.

The mass of a body is a scalar quantity, but its velocity is a vector quantity. Consequently the product, momentum, is also a vector quantity. The direction of momentum of an object is the same as the direction of the velocity of the object.

A ferryboat docking moves very slowly,

Sample Problem

A car weighs 4000. lb. What force is needed to give it an acceleration of 10.0 ft/sec²?

Solution

$$F = \frac{wa}{g}$$

$$F = \frac{4000.\ \text{lb} \times 10.0\ \text{ft/sec}^2}{32.2\ \text{ft/sec}^2}$$

$$F = 1.24 \times 10^3\ \text{lb}$$

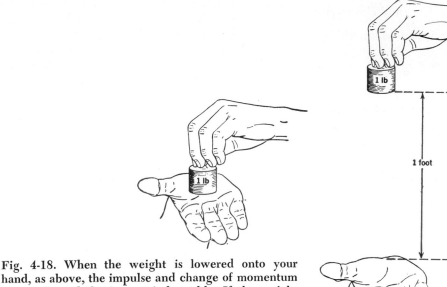

1 lb

1 foot

1 lb

Fig. 4-18. When the weight is lowered onto your hand, as above, the impulse and change of momentum are small, and the impact is bearable. If the weight is dropped onto your hand from a height of one foot, as at the right, the impulse and change of momentum are much larger; the impact may injure your hand.

Sample Problem

The acceleration of gravity is 9.80 m/sec². What is the weight, in newtons, of a mass of 25.0 kg?

Solution

$w = mg$
$w = 25.0 \text{ kg} \times 9.80 \text{ m/sec}^2$
$w = 245 \text{ nt}$

Sample Problem

What is the mass, in slugs, of a 10.-lb bag of sugar?

Solution

The acceleration of gravity is 32 ft/sec².
$m = w/g$
$m = 10. \text{ lb} \div 32 \text{ ft/sec}^2$
$m = 0.31 \text{ slug}$

yet because of its great mass, it undergoes a large change of momentum. If you catch your foot between the slowly moving boat and the dock, it will surely be crushed by the great force exerted by the boat, since the time involved is short. A rifle bullet has a terrific impact against the object it strikes. Its velocity may be from 1500 to 3000 ft/sec. Its small mass of only a fraction of a slug multiplied by such a large velocity gives it the large momentum. See the Sample Problem below.

20. Newton's third law of motion— the law of interaction. Let us describe some of the forces which are exerted when you put this book on the top of a level table. The weight of the book is a downward force, but because the book does not move, there can be no unbalanced forces acting on it. The table top, therefore, must exert an upward force on the book equal to the downward force the book exerts on the table. In order to walk forward, you exert a force against the floor with your feet, while the floor pushes against your feet with a force of equal magnitude.

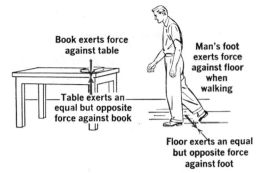

Book exerts force against table

Table exerts an equal but opposite force against book

Man's foot exerts force against floor when walking

Floor exerts an equal but opposite force against foot

Fig. 4-19. When one body exerts a force upon a second body, the second body exerts an equal and opposite force upon the first.

In each of these situations we have two objects. In the first instance, the objects are the book and the table. In the second, they are the foot and the floor. Two forces are involved in each situation. In the first, they are the force of the book against the table and the force of the table against the book. In the second, they are the force of the foot against the floor and the force of the floor against the foot. In cases such as these, one force may be called the

---

Sample Problem

The mass of an automobile is 1800. kg. (a) If its velocity is 15.0 m/sec northward, what is its momentum? (b) How long must a force of 1350. nt act on the automobile to give it this momentum?

Solution

(a) Momentum equals the product mv.
    1800. kg $\times$ 15.0 m/sec = 2.70 $\times$ 10^4 kg·m/sec northward

(b) $Ft = mv_f - mv_i$

$$t = \frac{mv_f - mv_i}{F}$$

$$t = \frac{1800.\ \text{kg} \times 15.0\ \text{m/sec} - 1800.\ \text{kg} \times 0\ \text{m/sec}}{1350.\ \text{nt}}$$

$t = 20.0$ sec

Fig. 4-20. Both balances show the same reading because the action force equals the reaction force.

action, while the second force may be called the *reaction*. **Newton's third law of motion** states: *Whenever one body exerts a force upon a second body, the second exerts an equal and opposite force upon the first.* In other words, *for every action there is an equal and opposite reaction.*

We have been considering action and reaction in fixed bodies, but the same law holds true if the bodies are free to move. A boy rows a boat toward the shore of a lake and when he is three or four feet from shore, he attempts to leap ashore. He exerts a force against the boat and the boat exerts an equal but opposite force against him. However, since both objects are free to move, the boy's force against the boat accelerates it in one direction and the boat's force against the boy accelerates him in the opposite direction. The amount of acceleration of each object is inversely proportional to its mass. The boy probably judges the force he must exert to reach shore on the basis of his experience in jumping the same distance from a fixed object. Consequently, when he jumps from the boat, he probably does not reach shore but instead falls into the water.

Suppose we fasten one spring balance to a table leg and hook another spring balance to it, as shown in Fig. 4-20. Now, if we pull steadily, we find that both balance readings are the same. The pull of the first balance on the second equals the pull of the second on the first. The action is equal but opposite to the reaction.

You may try to argue that motion cannot occur if action and reaction are equal. If two boys pull with equal force but in opposite directions upon a lightweight wagon, the wagon will not move. But this is not an example of action and reaction. There are two forces, it is true, *but they are both exerted on the same object.* Action and reaction are shown in the force which each boy's feet exert against the ground and the equal but opposite force the ground exerts against the feet.

21. Applications of Newton's third law of motion. There are many everyday happenings in which Newton's third law of motion plays an important part. When we row a boat, the oars exert a force against the water and the water exerts an opposite force against the oars. Air reacts against the propellers of an airplane, so that the propellers pull the airplane through the air.

Water reacts against the nozzle of a garden hose. If the hose is not held in place, it will be driven backward by reaction force. This same reaction force is used to drive a rotary lawn sprinkler.

22. Reaction motors. Suppose we have a machine gun mounted on wheels so that it may move along a track, as shown in Fig. 4-21. Bullets fired from the gun leave the barrel with a muzzle velocity, v_f. Since the bullets have a total mass, m, the combined momentum of these bullets will be

Reaction force of bullets on gun accelerates the gun toward the right

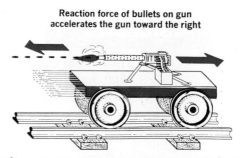

Fig. 4-21. The unbalanced force of the bullets on the gun causes the gun to move toward the right with increasing velocity.

Fig. 4-22. The unbalanced forward force of expanding gases accelerates a jet airplane. (United States Air Force)

mv_f and since the original velocity of the bullets was zero, their change of momentum is also mv_f. From Section 19, we know this change of momentum to be equal to the impulse of the gun, Ft. The force exerted by the gun will equal the combined momentum of the bullets divided by the time required to fire them, $F = mv_f/t$. According to Newton's third law of motion, this force equals the reaction force of the bullets on the gun. The reaction force acts in the opposite direction. It accelerates the machine gun, which then moves backward with increasing velocity.

Jet and rocket engines exert force in a similar manner. Instead of a mass of bullets leaving the muzzle of the gun in a certain time, we have a mass of hot gases issuing from the jet exhaust in a given time. In place of the muzzle velocity of the bullets, we have the jet velocity of the gases relative to the engine. The product of these two quantities, mass/time and velocity, gives the reaction force which drives the jet or rocket forward. This forward reaction force is called the *thrust*. Since the magnitude of the force depends upon the exhaust velocity of the gases, this velocity should be as high as possible.

QUESTIONS

A **1.** If you place a steel ball in the center of the top of a level table, the ball will remain there. (*a*) What forces are acting in this situation? (*b*) Are there any unbalanced forces acting on the ball? (*c*) Why does it remain at rest?
2. (*a*) If you give the steel ball of Question 1 a slight push, what happens to the ball? (*b*) Why? (*c*) What forces act on the ball after it has been pushed? (*d*) Are any of these unbalanced forces? (*e*) What is the effect of the various forces on the motion of the ball?
3. Suppose you fasten one end of an 0.5-m length of cord to the ball and the other end to a nail driven into the table top. (*a*) Now, when you push the ball, what path does it follow? (*b*) What forces act in this situation? (*c*) Are any of these unbalanced forces? (*d*) What effect do the various forces have on the motion of the ball?
4. (*a*) State Newton's first law of motion. (*b*) Describe the motion of a body in equilibrium.
5. (*a*) Which property of matter makes it necessary for us to exert a force on matter in order to accelerate it? (*b*) How is this property measured?

6. (a) If other conditions are constant, how does the acceleration of a body vary with the amount of force applied? (b) How does the direction of the acceleration compare with the direction of the applied force?

7. How does the acceleration which is produced on different bodies by identical forces vary with the mass of the body?

8. (a) State Newton's second law of motion. (b) What is the equation which expresses the relationship of force to mass and acceleration?

9. Why is it necessary, in the MKS and CGS systems, to define the units of force in terms of the units of mass and acceleration?

10. Why is it necessary, in the FPS system, to define the unit of mass in terms of the units of force and acceleration?

11. How can we calculate the amount of force required to produce a certain acceleration of an object of known weight?

12. Suppose you suspend a brick from a rigid support by means of a suitable length of cord. (a) What downward force acts on the brick? (b) If this force is the action force, what force is the reaction force?

13. (a) What upward force acts on the suspended brick of Question 12? (b) If this force is the action force, what is the corresponding reaction force?

14. (a) What force acts on the rigid support from which the brick of Question 12 is suspended? (b) If this force is the action force, what is the corresponding reaction force?

15. (a) State Newton's third law of motion. (b) How many forces are involved? (c) How many bodies are involved?

B 16. Why does a falling object undergo constant acceleration?

17. In the operation of a rotary lawn sprinkler (a) what two bodies are involved; (b) what two forces are involved; (c) which force produces the rotation? (d) Why?

18. (a) What is impulse? (b) What is momentum? (c) How are impulse and change of momentum related?

19. Why will a slowly docking ferryboat and a speeding rifle bullet both have a large amount of momentum?

20. (a) What name is given to the force which accelerates a reaction motor? (b) What is the origin of this force? (c) What conditions determine its magnitude?

PROBLEMS

Note: Use $g = 9.80$ m/sec^2, 980. cm/sec^2, or 32 ft/sec^2.

A 1. What force is required to accelerate an object having a mass of 3.0 kg at 5.0 m/sec^2?

2. What is the mass of an object which is accelerated 10.0 ft/sec^2 by a force of 25.0 lb?

3. A force of 6.5×10^3 dynes is applied to a body with a mass of 130. g. What is the acceleration?

4. What acceleration does an object which has a mass of 10. slugs undergo when a force of 50. lb acts on it?

5. What is the weight of a 20.-kg block of stone?

6. What is the mass of a 94-lb bag of cement?

7. What force is required to give a projectile weighing 500. nt an acceleration of 3.00×10^3 m/sec^2?

8. A truck weighs 10. tons. What force will give it an acceleration of 4.0 ft/sec^2?

B 9. (a) If a force of 3.0 nt acts on a body for 5.0 sec, what is the change of momentum of the body? (b) If the mass of the body is 2.5 kg, what is the increase in its velocity?

10. The jet velocity of a rocket is 6.0×10^3 ft/sec. If 1.3×10^3 lb of gas issue from the exhaust per second, what is the thrust of the rocket?

11. A ball, mass 0.10 kg, rolls from rest down an inclined plane 2.0 m long which makes an angle of 20.0° with the horizontal. (a) What force accelerates the ball down the plane? (b) What is the velocity of the ball when it reaches the bottom of the plane? (c) How long does it take the ball to roll down the plane?

12. An automobile weighing 3000. lb crashes into a wall with a velocity of 15.0 ft/sec. If the car moves 0.500 ft. before coming to a stop, what average force does the car exert on the wall?

13. A safe, mass 250. kg, rolls down an inclined plane 5.00 m long onto a horizontal surface. The inclined plane makes an angle of 25.0° with the horizontal. The coefficient of friction between the safe and the surfaces over which it rolls is 0.100. (a) What net force accelerates the safe down the plane? (b) What is the velocity of the safe at the bottom of the plane? (c) How far does the safe roll on the horizontal surface before coming to a stop?

4 UNIVERSAL GRAVITATION

23. The force of gravitational attraction. You know from experience that objects fall toward the earth. They do this because they are acted on by the **force of gravitational attraction,** *the mutual force of attraction between bodies.*

The force of gravitational attraction is a property *of all bodies,* but the effects of gravitation which we most readily observe are those caused by massive bodies like the earth, the moon, and the sun. A falling apple is attracted to the earth, but the apple attracts the earth as well. The earth attracts the moon, and the moon attracts the earth.

Newton formulated the following **law of universal gravitation:** *Every body in the universe attracts every other body with a force that is directly proportional to the product of their masses and inversely proportional to the square of the distance between their centers.* This law tells us that the magnitude of the force of gravitational attraction depends upon only two things: (*1*) the masses of the bodies; and (*2*) the square of the distance between their centers. The formula for this law is

$$F = G \frac{m_1 m_2}{s^2} \qquad \text{(Equation 1)}$$

in which m_1 and m_2 are the masses of the bodies, s is the distance between their centers, F is the force of attraction between them, and G is a proportionality constant called the *gravitational constant.* In the MKS system, G has the value 6.67×10^{-11} nt-m²/kg².

From Equation 1, we see that doubling the mass of one of the bodies doubles the force of attraction. In terms of the earth's attraction, a body having twice the mass of another will weigh twice as much as the other, provided the distances between the centers of the objects and the center of the earth are the same.

An object on the surface of the earth is

about 4000 mi from its center. If the object were taken up to a height of 4000 mi, it would be 8000 mi from the earth's center. From Equation 1, we learn that doubling the distance between the centers of the bodies reduces the attraction to one-fourth as much. A person who weighs 144 lb on the earth's surface would weigh only 36 lb at a height of 4000 mi above the surface of the earth. At a height of 8000 mi, 12,000 mi from the earth's center, he would weigh only 16 lb. See Fig. 4-23.

24. The mass of the earth. We may use the formula for the force of gravitational attraction, Equation 1 above, to calculate the mass of the earth. In the equation, let us use M, the mass of the earth, for m_1. For m_2, let us use m, the mass of a body on the earth's surface. In this case s will be the radius of the earth. The force of attraction F will be the weight of the body, so we shall replace F by w.

$$w = G \frac{Mm}{s^2} \qquad \text{(Equation 2)}$$

Dividing both sides of the equation by m,

$$\frac{w}{m} = \frac{GM}{s^2} \qquad \text{(Equation 3)}$$

But

$$w = mg \qquad \text{(Equation 4)}$$

Or

$$\frac{w}{m} = g \qquad \text{(Equation 5)}$$

Substituting Equation 5 in Equation 3,

$$g = \frac{GM}{s^2} \qquad \text{(Equation 6)}$$

Since both G and M are constants, Equation 6 shows that the acceleration of gravity in a given location depends only on the square of the distance from the center of the earth.

Equation 6 may be used to determine the mass of the earth. Solving for M,

$$M = \frac{gs^2}{G}$$

Substituting 9.80 m/sec² for g, 6.37 × 10⁶ m for s, and 6.67 × 10⁻¹¹ nt-m²/kg² for G, $M = 5.96 \times 10^{24}$ kg, the mass of the earth.

We can now use this value of M in Equation 6 to determine the theoretical value for the acceleration of gravity at any given location on or above the earth's surface. Such factors as local variations in the composition of the earth's crust and the effect of the earth's rotation must be

considered to obtain the actual value of the acceleration of gravity at a particular location.

25. The variation of the weight of an object with its location. Equation 2, above, tells us that the weight of a body is the earth's attraction for that body. When we say that a man weighs 200. lb, we mean that the earth attracts him with a force of 200. lb and he attracts the earth with a force of 200. lb. Equation 4, above, tells us that the weight of a body is also the product of its mass and the acceleration of gravity. The mass of a body is constant. But Equation 6, above, indicates that the acceleration of gravity is inversely proportional to the square of the distance from the center of the earth. All parts of the earth's surface are not the same distance from its center, the variations ranging from 1286 ft below sea level at the shore of the Dead Sea to 29,028 ft above sea level at the top of Mount Everest. Therefore a body at the top of a mountain, where the acceleration of gravity is less, will weigh less than it does at sea level. Also, since the earth is slightly flattened at the poles, and the weight-lowering effect of the earth's rotation is small, a man weighs a little more at the North Pole than he does at the Equator. A man who weighs 189 lb at the Equator weighs about 190 lb at either pole.

If we sink a shaft down into the earth and are lowered into it, our weight does not keep increasing as we are lowered beneath the surface. It is true that we get nearer the earth's center, but the gravitational attraction of the material above us causes us to weigh less when we are beneath the surface. A body weighs most on that part of the surface of the earth which is nearest the earth's center. Its weight is less if it is carried above the surface or lowered beneath it.

26. An equal-arm balance is used to compare masses. In Fig. 4-24, AB represents the beam of an equal-arm balance.

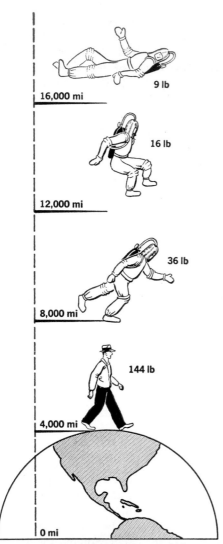

Fig. 4-23. The weight of a man decreases as his distance from the center of the earth increases.

This beam is carefully constructed so that it is light in weight yet rigid enough so that it will not bend when a load is applied at its ends. It rests on a knife-edged agate bearing located exactly at the mid-point of the beam, C. When balance pans of equal weight are attached at each end, the center of gravity of the beam lies directly below this point of suspension.

Now let us put an object of unknown *mass* on the left-hand balance pan. The earth attracts this object with a force which is its *weight*. This force, acting on the arm of the balance AC, creates a counterclockwise torque. If we place known masses from a set of weights on the right-hand balance pan, we can bring the beam of the balance into equilibrium. The attraction of the earth for these known masses is a force which acts on the right-hand portion of the beam of the balance to produce a clockwise torque. When equilibrium is attained, the clockwise torque is equal to the counterclockwise torque.

In constructing the balance, the balance arms were made of equal length. This means that when the balance is in equilibrium, *the forces on the ends of the beam are equal.* Furthermore, *the acceleration due to gravity is the same on the objects placed on the balance pans.* (For practical purposes they are at the same spot on the surface of the

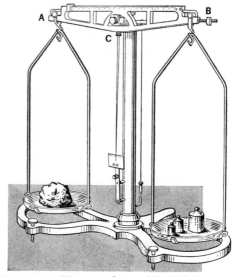

Fig. 4-24. **The equal-arm beam balance is used for comparing masses. The mass of the stone on the left-hand balance pan equals the combined masses of the weights on the right-hand balance pan.**

earth.) Since the forces are equal, and the acceleration of gravity is equal, *the masses must be equal.* We know the masses of the individual weights because the weights were made in comparison with the standard kilogram. Consequently, the mass of the object on the left-hand balance pan equals the sum of the individual masses on the right-hand pan. An equal-arm balance is therefore a means of comparing masses.

5 CIRCULAR MOTION AND ROTARY MOTION

27. Circular motion. From Newton's first law of motion, we learned that a body which has acquired velocity continues to move in a straight line. If a constant force acts on the moving body at right angles to its path, the body will be deflected from its straight line, and its motion will become circular. *Circular motion is motion of a body along a curved path*

of constant radius. Suppose we tie one end of a string to a ball and hold the other end of the string firmly. We may swing the ball in a circle with our hand as a center. The pull of the hand upon the cord constantly deflects the ball from its linear path toward the center, as shown in Fig. 4-25. As the ball moves along the circumference from B to A, the pull toward the center has deflected it a distance equal to *OA*. *The force that deflects a body from its linear path and compels it to move along a curve is called the* **centripetal** *(sen-trip-uh-tul)* **force.** *Centripetal* means acting toward a center.

According to Newton's third law of motion, to every action there is an equal and opposite reaction. We have seen that the string exerts a centripetal force on the ball, causing it to move in a curved path. However, the ball exerts on the string an equal but opposite force, due to its tendency to continue along a straight path. *This reaction force that is equal in magnitude to the centripetal force but acts in the opposite direction is called the* **centrifugal** *(sen-trif-yuh-gul)* **reaction.** *Centrifugal* means acting away from a center. The centripetal force is the force exerted by the string on the ball. The centrifugal reaction is the force exerted by the ball on the string. If the string breaks, the ball will continue to move in a straight line tangent to the curved path. This agrees with Newton's first law of motion, because when the string is broken, the centripetal force no longer acts on the ball. With no centripetal force, there can be no centrifugal reaction. In circular motion the centripetal force is the primary one since it acts on the

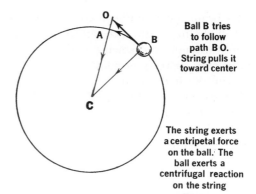

Ball B tries to follow path B O. String pulls it toward center

The string exerts a centripetal force on the ball. The ball exerts a centrifugal reaction on the string

Fig. 4-25. The force of the string on the ball results in circular motion of the ball.

object and causes it to move in the circular path.

28. Calculating centripetal force. We can use a device to measure the pull which the string in Fig. 4-25 exerts on the ball. Then if we use a ball which has double the mass, but the same speed, we find that the pull the string must exert to keep the ball in its circular path is twice as great. We conclude that the centripetal force is directly proportional to the mass of the object in circular motion. If we shorten the string but do not change the speed of the ball, the string must exert a greater force because it pulls the ball from its path more rapidly. Careful measurements show

Sample Problem

A ball having a mass of 0.050 kg is attached to the end of a cord 1.5 m long. The ball is swung in a circular path at the end of the cord with a velocity of 8.0 m/sec. What is the force in newtons which the string exerts on the ball?

Solution

$$\text{C.F.} = \frac{mv^2}{r}$$

$$\text{C.F.} = \frac{0.050 \text{ kg} \times (8.0 \text{ m/sec})^2}{1.5 \text{ m}}$$

$$\text{C.F.} = 2.1 \text{ nt}$$

that centripetal force is inversely proportional to the radius of curvature. As we swing any ball faster, its velocity along the curve increases, and the string must pull more strongly on the ball. Accurate measurements show that the centripetal force is directly proportional to the square of the velocity of the body in circular motion. If m is the mass of the body, v is its velocity, and r is the radius of its path,

$$\text{Centripetal Force} = \frac{mv^2}{r}$$

See the Sample Problem on the opposite page.

29. Increasing centripetal force. We are all too familiar with the damage caused by the unbalanced force that sends an automobile into the ditch if the driver attempts to round a sharp curve too fast. Modern highways have curves of large radius which are banked. To bank a curve is to make the outside edge of the curve higher than the inside edge. This increases the horizontal component of the force exerted by the road on the automobile and enables the road to exert a greater centripetal force. Consequently a car may safely round the curve at a higher speed. When you ride a bicycle or a motorcycle, or when you skate, you lean toward the center when rounding a curve. This also increases the centripetal force upon you.

30. The motion of earth satellites. Since 1957, a number of artificial earth satellites have been launched by the United States and the Soviet Union. The purpose of the satellite launching is to learn more about the atmosphere and the region of outer space near the earth. The satellites are equipped with a variety of instruments to measure temperature, pressure, cosmic-ray intensity, and the density of meteoric matter in their orbits. The information they gather is transmitted to the earth by radio.

The motion of a satellite, if it has a circular orbit about the earth, is rather

Fig. 4-26. The launching of this Jupiter-C rocket from Cape Canaveral, Florida, placed the first United States artificial earth satellite in orbit. Satellites have since been launched from California as well. The narrow cylinder at the top of the rocket is the satellite. (U.S. Army)

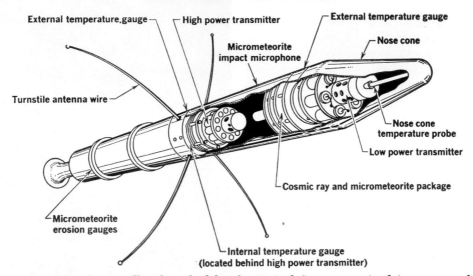

External temperature gauge

High power transmitter

External temperature gauge

Micrometeorite impact microphone

Nose cone

Turnstile antenna wire

Nose cone temperature probe

Low power transmitter

Cosmic ray and micrometeorite package

Micrometeorite erosion gauges

Internal temperature gauge
(located behind high power transmitter)

Fig. 4-27. The first satellite launched by the United States contained instruments for measuring temperatures, cosmic ray intensity, and micrometeorite intensity, together with radio transmitters for relaying the measurements back to earth. (Jet Propulsion Laboratories, California Institute of Technology)

easy to describe, since it involves only what we have already learned about centripetal force and the acceleration of gravity. The only force acting on a satellite which moves at constant speed in a circular orbit about the earth is the earth's attraction for the satellite. This, of course, is the weight of the satellite, a force directed toward the center of the earth. This is the centripetal force which is necessary for the satellite's circular motion. Thus, using w to represent the weight of a satellite in a circular orbit,

$$w = \frac{mv^2}{r} \qquad \text{(Equation 1)}$$

in which m is the mass of the satellite, v is its velocity, and r is its distance from the center of the earth.

Substituting $w = mg$ in Equation 1,

$$mg = \frac{mv^2}{r}$$

and

$$v = \sqrt{rg} \qquad \text{(Equation 2)}$$

Note that in Equation 2, the value of g is the acceleration of gravity at the distance r from the center of the earth. Since the acceleration of gravity at a given location depends on the distance from the center of the earth, the velocity which a satellite must have to remain in orbit depends only on the radius of its orbit. This velocity is called the *orbiting velocity*.

Let us assume that a satellite is moving at a constant speed in a circular path 500 mi above the earth. Since the average radius of the earth is 3960 mi, the radius of the orbit of the satellite is 4460 mi or 2.35×10^7 ft or 7.18×10^6 m. To calculate the acceleration of gravity at this distance from the earth, we use Equation 6, Section 24:

$$g = \frac{6.67 \times 10^{-11} \text{ nt-m}^2/\text{kg}^2 \times 5.96 \times 10^{24} \text{ kg}}{(7.18 \times 10^6 \text{ m})^2}$$

$$g = 7.71 \text{ m/sec}^2 \text{ or } 25.3 \text{ ft/sec}^2$$

Now using Equation 2 of this section,

$$v = \sqrt{2.35 \times 10^7 \text{ ft} \times 25.3 \text{ ft/sec}^2}$$

$$v = 2.44 \times 10^4 \text{ ft/sec}$$

This velocity is about 1.66×10^4 mi/hr. One revolution in such an orbit would require 1.69 hr or 101 min.

A satellite is launched by a rocket which consists of several stages. The first stage may lift the rocket to an altitude of about 50 miles and then fall away while the remainder of the rocket coasts to an altitude of about 300 mi. At the top of this trajectory, when the rocket is horizontal, the second and third stages may be fired, one following the other, increasing the horizontal velocity of the rocket to that required for orbiting at this altitude (approximately 18,000 mi/hr). After the final stage has burned out, the satellite is separated from it.

Once the satellite goes into orbit, the plane of the orbit is fixed in space. However, as the satellite goes around the earth, the earth spins on its axis beneath it. Thus each circuit of the satellite is over a different part of the earth's surface.

The orbit of a satellite is usually not a circle. During launching, variations from the precise calculations of elevation, altitude, and velocity are practically impossible to eliminate. The orbit is then elliptical. Sometimes scientists deliberately plan for a satellite to enter an elliptical orbit so that it will probe a range of altitudes. An elliptical path may bring a satellite periodically into the upper atmosphere. The friction of the atmosphere on the satellite causes its speed to decrease gradually. It is then drawn closer to the earth, and may be ultimately heated to incandescence and vaporized as it enters the lower portions of the earth's atmosphere.

Fig. 4-28. Conditions at launching have a great effect on the orbit of a satellite. (A) Suitable speed and horizontal path at required altitude; orbit is circular. (B) Speed and altitude suitable, but satellite is tilted up slightly at launching. (C) Speed and altitude suitable, but satellite is tilted down slightly at launching. (D) Launching altitude suitable, but speed slightly under requirements; orbit is an ellipse with highest point at launching. (E) Launching altitude suitable, but speed slightly high; orbit is a large ellipse with lowest point at launching. (Mobil Oil Co.)

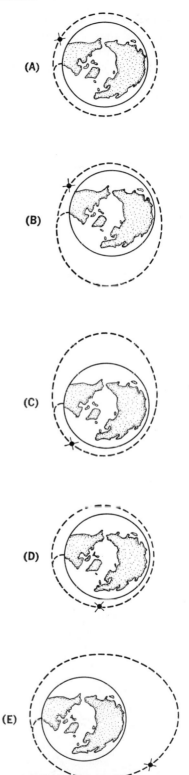

31. A rocket to the moon. We have already learned that a satellite which has been given an initial horizontal velocity of about 18,000 mi/hr will orbit in a circular path about the earth at an altitude of about 300 mi. If this horizontal velocity is increased, the orbit becomes elliptical. If the initial horizontal velocity is raised still further, to about 25,000 mi/hr, the rocket escapes from the earth's pull of gravity entirely, and continues on out into space. The initial horizontal velocity which an object must have in order to escape from the earth's gravitational attraction is called the *escape velocity*. See Fig. 4-29. The first rocket to escape the earth's gravitational attraction was launched by the Soviet Union in 1959.

If an instrument-carrying rocket is to be sent on a path that will enable it to circle the moon, about 240,000 mi away, and return to the earth's atmosphere before being destroyed, several important factors must be considered. These are (*1*) the attraction of the earth, (*2*) the attraction of the moon, and (*3*) the attraction of the sun.

In order to overcome the attraction of the earth, the rocket must have sufficient speed to reach that point in space where the gravitational attractions of the earth and the moon are equal. Scientists estimate that the initial horizontal velocity which such a rocket must have is 23,900 mi/hr.

The rocket must be carefully aimed and the time of firing accurately determined so that the rocket will come into the vicinity of the moon as the moon revolves around the earth.

The gravitational attraction of the moon will begin to accelerate a rocket from the earth when the rocket gets about 40,000 miles from the moon. If the rocket does not approach the moon too closely, the gravitational attraction of the moon will alter the elliptical orbit of the rocket somewhat, but not enough to prevent its return to the earth. If the rocket approaches within about 2000 mi of the moon, however, the moon's gravitational attraction is strong enough to change the course of the rocket more drastically, accelerating it to the escape velocity, and sending it on into outer space, where it may become a solar satellite. If the rocket approaches still closer to the moon, the moon's attraction may cause the rocket to swing around the moon sharply and return to the earth, or may cause it to fall on the moon.

The effect of the sun is slight, but it becomes significant over the long distance the rocket must travel. The attraction of the sun makes possible an orbit in which the rocket loops around the moon at a distance of less than 1500 miles and returns to the earth. It is calculated that such a trip would require about 157

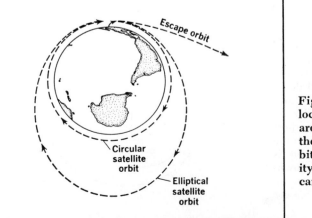

Fig. 4-29. A satellite with an initial velocity of about 18,000 mi/hr will go around the earth in a circular orbit. If the velocity is somewhat higher, the orbit will be elliptical. If the initial velocity is about 25,500 mi/hr, a satellite can escape from the earth entirely.

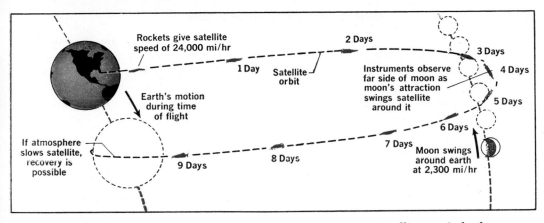

Fig. 4-30. A proposed flight path for an instrument-carrying satellite to circle the moon and return to the earth's atmosphere.

hours, almost 50 of which would be spent near enough to the moon to allow close observation. See Fig. 4-30.

The successful performance of an instrument-carrying rocket on such a flight requires very careful calculation, and exact adherence by the rocket to the planned orbit. The information obtained by such a flight might include photographs of the far side of the moon and data on any magnetism possessed by the moon. Such data can be radioed to earth while the rocket is in flight.

32. Rotary motion. *Rotary motion is the motion of a body turning about an axis.* Rotary motion occurs in a turning bicycle wheel, the rotating crankshaft of an automobile engine, and a pulley wheel attached to the spinning shaft of an electric motor. Note the difference between circular and rotary motion. In circular motion, the object as a whole travels along a circular path. In rotary motion, the object simply spins. While a bicycle wheel spinning on a stationary axle undergoes rotary motion, a part of the wheel, say the valve stem of the tire, experiences circular motion.

For rotary motion to be *uniform,* the object must spin about a fixed axis at a definite rate. The movements of the hands of an electric clock are examples of uniform rotary motion. If either the direction of the axis or the rate of spin varies, the rotary motion is *variable.* The movements of automobile wheels as the car is driven at different speeds, and the movements of a spinning top as it falls down, are examples of variable rotary motion.

The rate of rotary motion is called **angular velocity.** For an object in uniform rotary motion, angular velocity equals the angle through which the object turns divided by the time required for this rotation. Angular velocity may be measured in revolutions per minute. However, it includes not only the rate of rotation, but also the direction of the axis of rotation. Thus, angular velocity is a vector quantity, represented by a vector parallel to the axis of rotation. The length of the vector indicates the magnitude of the angular velocity, while the direction of the vector is the direction the thumb of the right hand points if the fingers of the right hand encircle the vector in the direction in which the body is rotating. See Fig. 4-31.

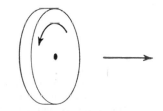

Fig. 4-31. Angular velocity is represented by a vector parallel to the axis of rotation.

An object spinning on an axis has a high degree of stability. We have already learned from our study of linear motion that a change of velocity involves acceleration, and to produce acceleration requires the application of a force. The same principles are true for rotary motion. A force must be applied to change either the rate of rotation or the direction of the axis. Both of these changes involve a change of angular velocity, which requires *angular acceleration*. The stability of a rotating body allows the rider to balance easily a moving bicycle or motorcycle. The same principles apply to a rolling automobile tire.

33. Precession. If angular velocities in the same or opposite directions are added, the result is either an increase or decrease in the rate of spin about the same axis. But *if angular velocities about two different axes are added geometrically, motion about a third axis results. This motion is called* **precession.**

To explain why precession occurs, we must refer to Fig. 4-32. Here we have a wheel spinning in the direction indicated by the arrow about axis *A*. One end of the axle is free; the other end *O* is pivoted, but may turn in any direction. The force

of gravitational attraction on the wheel and axle exerts a force tending to pull the free end of the axle down. This force produces an acceleration which gives the wheel and axle an angular velocity about axis *B*. In the vector diagram, Fig. 4-33, the angular velocity of the wheel spinning on the axle is represented by the vector *OA'*. The angular velocity produced by gravity about axis *B* is represented by the vector *OB'*. Note that both of the vectors *are in the horizontal plane*. Vector addition gives us the resultant angular velocity *OR*. As a result of the addition of these two velocities, we find that the axle turns counterclockwise when viewed from above to the position of the resultant *OR*. *Note that the axle remains in the horizontal plane*. Actually this precession continues, because when the axle reaches the direction *OR*, the force of gravitational attraction still exerts a downward force on the free end of the axle. The continuous addition of the angular velocity thus produced to that possessed by the rotating wheel results in circular motion of the axle about the vertical axis *C*.

34. The gyroscope. *A gyroscope is a wheel and axle mounted in such a way that it is*

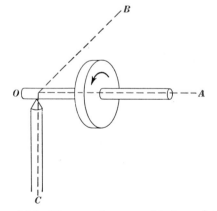

Fig. 4-32. The continuous addition of the angular velocity about horizontal axis *B*, produced by the force of gravitational attraction, to the angular velocity of the wheel about horizontal axis *A* produces circular motion about vertical axis *C*.

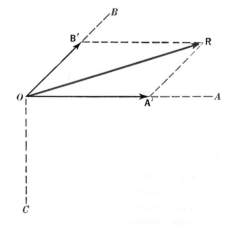

Fig. 4-33. The vector addition of the angular velocities about separate axes in one plane produces an angular velocity about an axis perpendicular to the plane. This motion is called precession.

free to turn in any direction. See Fig. 4-34. Consequently, once the wheel is set spinning, the base of the mounting may be turned in any direction without changing the direction of the axis of rotation. If, however, a force which acts at right angles to the axis of rotation is applied to one of the inner mountings, precession will occur as described in Section 33.

A gyroscope may serve as the heart of such instruments as the gyrocompass, gyropilot, directional gyro, and the gyrohorizon. In these devices, a gyroscope turned by an electric motor is set in motion in a definite direction. As a ship or airplane moves with respect to the fixed direction of the gyroscope, electric signals are sent to motors which operate the controls of the ship or airplane. This adjustment of the controls corrects for the change in motion and keeps the ship or airplane on course. A gyrocompass is mounted in such a way that unless its axis stays parallel to the axis of rotation of the earth, there will be a torque on it which causes it to precess to this position.

Fig. 4-34. A gyroscope is a wheel and axle mounted so that it is free to turn in any direction. (W. M. Welch Mfg. Co., Chicago)

Gyroscopes are also used in missile guidance systems and as stabilizers to reduce the rolling motion of ships.

6 SIMPLE HARMONIC MOTION

35. Simple harmonic motion. We have already studied several types of motion: uniform linear, accelerated linear, circular, and rotary. Now we are ready to describe the last type of motion we shall consider—*simple harmonic motion.* Simple harmonic motion is a special type of *periodic motion.* **Periodic motion** *occurs when an object continually moves back and forth over a definite path in equal intervals of time.*

In Fig. 4-35 we have represented a mass m attached to a spring supported from a horizontal beam. If we pull down on the mass and then let it go, it will vibrate up and down in periodic motion. Let us investigate this periodic motion quantitatively.

If we exert a force F acting downward on mass m we can displace it a distance d. We also find by experiment that if we exert a force $2F$ we displace the mass a distance $2d$. Thus the downward force we exert is directly proportional to the downward displacement from the equilibrium position.

In exerting this force downward we pull against the spring, and the spring also pulls against our hand with a force $-F$ (third law of motion). When we release the mass, the force of the spring produces an upward acceleration which is directly proportional to the force (second law of motion).

As the mass m is returning to its equilibrium position, less and less force is exerted on it by the spring. (Why?) Consequently, the acceleration becomes less. The force is zero when the mass is at its equilibrium position. The acceleration is also zero. The mass *m* has acquired its maximum velocity at this point, however, and its inertia carries it past the equilibrium position. As this occurs, the spring becomes compressed and exerts a downward force on the mass. This gradually decelerates it, stops it when its upward displacement from the equilibrium position equals its original downward displacement (why?), and accelerates it downward again. As a consequence of the upward and downward forces exerted by the spring on the mass, the mass describes an up-and-down motion.

The mass goes up above the equilibrium position as far as it goes down, and it completes each up-and-down cycle in the same amount of time. At each point in the up-and-down cycle, the force exerted on the mass, and therefore the resulting acceleration, are directly proportional to the displacement of the mass from the equilibrium position. Both the force and the acceleration are directed toward the equilibrium position. Periodic motion with these particular characteristics is **simple harmonic motion.**

Obviously not all back-and-forth or up-and-down motion is simple harmonic motion. The motion of a mass vibrating up-and-down on a spring, the motion of the prongs of a vibrating tuning fork, and the

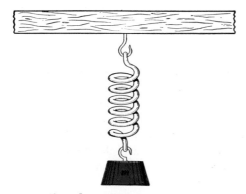

Fig. 4-35. When mass *m* is pulled downward and released, it vibrates up and down in simple harmonic motion.

motion of a swinging pendulum are examples of motion that is simple harmonic motion or very nearly so.

36. The relationship between circular motion and simple harmonic motion. It is sometimes quite helpful to analyze simple harmonic motion in terms of circular motion. Let us see how this is done. We shall also be interested in certain definitions relating to simple harmonic motion.

In Fig. 4-36, point *P* is moving with uniform speed in a circular path around point *O*. Point *P'* is the perpendicular projection of point *P* along line *MN*. When point *P* is at *a*, its projection is at *a'*; when it is at *b*, its projection is at *b'*, and so on. As point *P* makes a complete revolution of the reference circle, point *P'* describes a *complete vibration* in simple harmonic motion along *MN*. When *P'* is at *b'*, the *displacement* of *P'* is the distance *b'O'*—its distance from the midpoint of its vibration at that particular instant. The *amplitude* of the vibration is the maximum displacement *O'M* or *O'N*—it equals the radius of the reference circle. The *period* is the time required for a complete vibration—it is the time required for the point to make one revolution of the reference circle. The *frequency* of a vibratory motion is the number of vibrations per second—the number of revolutions per second of the point on the reference circle. *The frequency is the reciprocal of the period.* The *equilibrium position* of a body in simple harmonic motion is the midpoint of its path, *O'*.

37. The pendulum. *A body suspended so that it can swing to and fro about a horizontal axis is called a* **pendulum.** Pendulums have been used for many years as timekeepers, controlling the movement of the hands of clocks. A pendulum can also be used to demonstrate the rotation of the earth on its axis or to determine the value of the acceleration of gravity. The motion of a pendulum, if the displacement is small, is very nearly simple harmonic motion.

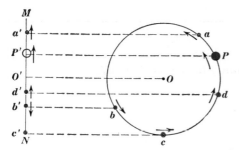

Fig. 4-36. Simple harmonic motion can be analyzed in terms of circular motion.

The simple pendulum used in physics laboratories is a small dense mass suspended by a cord whose mass is so small that it may be neglected. Usually it consists of a wooden or metal ball suspended by a light-weight thread as shown in Fig. 4-37. The point, or axis, about which the pendulum vibrates is called the *center of suspension.* The other definitions relating to pendulums are taken from those for simple harmonic motion. For example, as the ball, or pendulum bob, moves from *A* to *B* and back again to *A*, it makes a complete vibration. The time required for a complete vibration is the period of the pendulum. The number of complete vibrations per second is the frequency. The displacement is the distance of the bob at any instant from the equilibrium position *C*. The amplitude is the maximum displacement.

38. The period of a pendulum. Galileo was probably the first to study the motion of a pendulum. When he was a medical student about twenty years old, Galileo observed the gentle swaying of a sanctuary lamp in the cathedral at Pisa. Using his pulse as a timer, he found that successive vibrations were made in equal lengths of time, regardless of the amplitude of the vibrations of the lamp. He later verified his observations by experiment and then suggested that a pendulum be used to time the pulse rate of medical patients.

The facts about the period of a pendulum are summarized as follows:

1. The period of a pendulum is independent of the mass or material of the pendulum. This is strictly true only if the pendulum vibrates in a vacuum. Air resistance has more effect on a ball of cotton used as a pendulum bob than it does on a ball of lead.

2. The period of a pendulum is independent of the amplitude if the arc is small. A pendulum usually swings through an arc of 10° or less.

3. The period of a pendulum is directly proportional to the square root of its length. We may express this algebraically as

$$T : T' = \sqrt{l} : \sqrt{l'}$$

If we have two pendulums, one 25 cm long and the other 100. cm long, the period of the longer one will be twice that of the shorter one. The square roots of 25 and 100. are 5 and 10. respectively. Thus the periods are in the ratio of 5 to 10., or 1 to 2.

4. The period of a pendulum is inversely proportional to the square root of the acceleration due to gravity. A pendulum vibrates slightly faster at the North Pole than at the Equator. If we use the letter *l* to denote the length of a pendulum and *g* to denote the acceleration due to gravity, the period *T* is

$$T = 2\pi \sqrt{\frac{l}{g}}$$

See the Sample Problem on the following page.

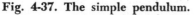

Fig. 4-37. The simple pendulum.

Sample Problem

Find the length of a pendulum which has a period of 1.00 sec for a complete vibration at a location where $g = 9.80$ m/sec².

Solution

$$T = 2\pi\sqrt{l/g}$$

$$l = \frac{gT^2}{4\pi^2}$$

$$l = \frac{9.80 \text{ m/sec}^2 \times (1.00 \text{ sec})^2}{4 \times (3.14)^2}$$

$$l = 0.248 \text{ m}$$

Note: The Standard Seconds Pendulum has a period of two seconds for a complete vibration, or a period of one second for a *single* (half of a complete) vibration.

QUESTIONS

A 1. (a) What force acts on an artificial satellite in orbit around the earth? (b) What force is the satellite exerting?
2. On what two factors does the magnitude of the force of gravitational attraction depend?
3. Why must we exert five times as much force to lift a mass of 5 kg as we must to lift a mass of 1 kg?
4. Assuming your mass remains constant, how will your weight vary as you go from Colorado Springs, elevation 5900 ft, to the top of Pikes Peak, elevation 14,110 ft?
5. Even though your mass remains constant, what happens to your weight as you drive from the entrance to Death Valley National Monument, elevation 5250 ft, down to the lowest spot in Death Valley, which is 280 ft below sea level?
6. When we weigh an object on an equal-arm balance, what are we actually doing?
7. (a) What is circular motion? (b) What force causes circular motion? (c) What force is equal and opposite to this?
8. What factors determine the magnitude of a centripetal force?
9. (a) Define *orbiting velocity*. (b) Define *escape velocity*.
10. (a) What is rotary motion? (b) Give examples of uniform and variable rotary motion.
11. Name some useful applications of the gyroscope.

12. What are the special characteristics of simple harmonic motion?
13. Define the following terms: (a) complete vibration; (b) displacement; (c) amplitude; (d) period; (e) frequency.
14. What factors determine the period of a pendulum?

B 15. What is meant by the statement "the aviator experienced a force of 2.5 g's in pulling out of that dive"?
16. (a) Why is a body which moves at constant speed in a circular path undergoing acceleration? (b) What force produces this acceleration?
17. (a) Explain why angular velocity is a vector quantity. (b) How is the vector representing an angular velocity drawn?
18. What is the result of the geometric addition of two angular velocities about different axes?
19. How should a pendulum clock which loses time be adjusted?
20. How could a pendulum be used to measure the value of g, the acceleration of gravity?
21. (a) What recent missile and satellite launchings have been carried out by the United States? (b) At which launching sites did they occur? (c) What new knowledge has been obtained from each of these launchings?
22. Describe some of the problems involved in sending a man to the moon and returning him safely to earth.

PROBLEMS

A **1.** What is the force of attraction between two 100.-kg masses whose centers are 2.00 m apart?

2. The acceleration of gravity on the moon has been calculated to be 6.5 ft/sec². If a man weighs 160. lb on the earth, what will be his weight on the moon?

3. A mass of 5.00 kg and a mass of 10.0 kg are 0.300 m apart. Calculate the force of attraction between them.

4. The instrument-carrying payload of a rocket weighs 200. lb on the earth's surface. What does it weigh at an altitude of 1.60×10^4 miles above the earth?

5. The acceleration of gravity at Hartford, Connecticut, is 980.336 cm/sec². What is the force of gravitational attraction in dynes on a mass of 250.000 g at this location?

6. A ball which has a mass of 2.5×10^{-2} kg is swung at a velocity of 5.0 m/sec at the end of a string 2.0 m long. What force does the string exert on the ball?

7. A pendulum 25 cm long describes a complete vibration in 1.0 sec. What is the period of a pendulum 100. cm long?

8. What is the period of a pendulum 1.5 m long? Use $g = 9.8$ m/sec².

B **9.** An automobile weighs 3000. lb. If this car is driven around a curve which has a radius of 500. ft at the rate of 66 ft/sec, what is the centripetal force of the road on the automobile?

10. What is the orbiting velocity of a satellite moving at a constant speed in a circular path 1.00×10^3 mi above the earth?

11. What is the length, in feet, of a pendulum which has a period of 5.0 sec? Use $g = 32$ ft/sec².

12. If a pendulum 1.0000 m long has a period of 2.0065 sec at Denver, Colorado, what is the value of the acceleration of gravity in that location?

# Summary

Motion is a continuing change of place or position, velocity is the rate of displacement, and acceleration is the rate of change of velocity. The relationships between initial and final velocity, acceleration, time, and displacement may be expressed mathematically for uniformly accelerated motion.

Newton's laws of motion are (1) a body continues in its state of rest or uniform motion unless an unbalanced force acts on it; (2) the acceleration of a body is directly proportional to the force exerted on the body, is inversely proportional to the mass of the body, and is in the same direction as the force; (3) for every action there is an equal and opposite reaction.

The force of gravitational attraction is the mutual force of attraction between bodies. Newton's law of universal gravitation states that every body in the universe attracts every other body with a force that is directly proportional to the product of their masses and inversely proportional to the square of the distance between their centers.

Circular motion is produced by a centripetal force which gives rise to a centrifugal reaction. Rotary motion is the motion of a body turning about an axis. The rate of rotary motion is called angular velocity. If angular velocities about two different axes are added geometrically, motion about a third axis, or precession, results.

Periodic motion occurs when an object continually moves back and forth over a definite path in equal intervals of time. Simple harmonic motion is a special type of periodic motion.

TERMS TO DEFINE

acceleration
action force
amplitude
angular acceleration
angular velocity
center of suspension
centrifugal reaction
centripetal force
circular motion
complete vibration
decelerated motion
displacement
dyne
equilibrium position
escape velocity
first law of motion
force of gravity

frequency
gravitational constant
gyroscope
impulse
inertia
linear motion
mass
momentum
motion
newton
orbiting velocity
pendulum
period
periodic motion
precession
reaction force
reaction motors

resultant velocity
rotary motion
second law of motion
simple harmonic motion
slug
speed
terminal velocity
third law of motion
thrust
trajectory
uniform acceleration
uniform motion
uniform rotary motion
variable acceleration
variable motion
variable rotary motion
velocity

RESEARCH ON YOUR OWN

1. Secure two similar carts of the type used in inclined-plane experiments. Connect the two with a rubber band. Pull them apart and release them quickly, noting the place where they collide. Compare your findings with the results obtained when one cart is double or triple the other cart's weight. Explain your results.
2. In advanced texts, look up the formula for measuring the speed of a bullet by means of a ballistic pendulum. Can you modify the procedure, so that you can find the velocity of much slower bodies, such as a pendulum at the bottom of its swing or a pellet from a rubber-band sling shot?
3. Spin a hard-boiled egg about its long axis. Try the same experiment using a fresh egg. Momentarily stop each egg from spinning, and then release it. Explain any differences in the motion of the eggs.
4. Report on Galileo's experiments with accelerated motion.
5. Get a golf ball, a rubber ball of about the same size, and a table tennis ball. By numerous trials, determine the average distance that you can throw each ball. Explain any resulting differences in the distances.
6. Get a strong horseshoe magnet and a steel ball. Lay the magnet on a flat level surface and roll the ball so that it passes near the poles of the magnet at varying speeds and distances from the poles. Write a report explaining the results obtained.

CHAPTER 5 — WORK, POWER, ENERGY, MACHINES

1 WORK

1. The scientific meaning of work. In everyday language we use the word *work* to describe any activity in which we exert muscular or mental effort. In physics, the word *work* has a very special meaning. In Chapter 1, Section 12, we learned that *work is done when a force acts on a body and moves it.* No matter how long you hold a 50-lb load on your shoulder, you are not doing any work in a scientific sense; you are merely exerting an upward force which counteracts the downward force of the load. You do work in a scientific sense when you raise the load to your shoulder, when you carry it up a flight of stairs, or when you drag it across the floor. In these cases, *you exert a force which moves the object.*

2. Units of work. Two factors must be considered in measuring work: (*1*) the force applied, and (*2*) the distance through which the force acts. *The amount of work, W, equals the product of the force, F, and the distance, s, through which it acts.*

$$W = Fs$$

From this formula, we see that if either the force or the distance is zero, no work is done.

VOCABULARY

Actual mechanical advantage. The ratio of the resistance force to the effort force.
Efficiency. The ratio of the actual mechanical advantage to the ideal mechanical advantage; the ratio of the output to the input.
Energy. The capacity for doing work.
Ideal mechanical advantage. The ratio of the distance the effort force moves to the distance the resistance force moves.
Input. The product of the effort force and the distance through which it acts.
Kinetic energy. The energy due to the motion of a mass.
Output. The product of the resistance force and the distance through which it acts.
Potential energy. Stored energy, or energy due to the position of a mass.
Power. The time rate of doing work.
Work. The product of a force and the distance through which it acts.

1 JOULE

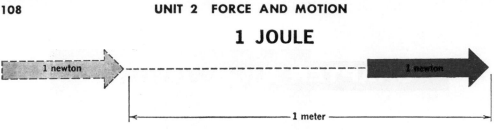

Work = Force X Distance

Fig. 5-1. One joule of work is done when a force of one newton acts through a distance of one meter.

1. Metric system—MKS units. When the force is measured in newtons and the distance is measured in meters, the work is expressed in joules. *A force of one newton, acting through a distance of one meter, does one joule (jool or jowl) of work.* This unit of work was named for the English physicist, James Prescott Joule (*jool*) (1818–1889). Note that *a joule is a newton-meter.* See Fig. 5-1.

On the earth, we must exert a force of about 9.8 nt to lift a mass of 1.0 kg. If we lift this mass to a height of 10. m, we do 9.8 nt × 10. m = 98 joules of work.

If we merely slide the 1.0 kg mass along a horizontal board with a coefficient of friction of 0.30, the force we exert is 0.30 × 9.8 nt = 2.9 nt. The work done in sliding this mass horizontally for a distance of 10. m is 2.9 nt × 10. m = 29 joules. In both instances, the force is applied to the object in the direction in which the object moves.

Suppose, however, that the force is applied to the object in a direction other than that in which it moves. Then, only that component of the applied force which acts in the direction the object moves is

Sample Problem

A trunk weighs 150. lb. (*a*) How much work is done in carrying it up a flight of stairs 20. ft high? (*b*) How much work is done in sliding it 20. ft across a horizontal platform? The coefficient of friction is 0.30.

Solution

(*a*) $W = Fs$
  $W = 150.\ \text{lb} \times 20.\ \text{ft}$
  $W = 3.0 \times 10^3\ \text{ft-lb}$

(*b*) $\mu = \dfrac{F}{N}$
  $F = \mu \times N$
  $F = 0.30 \times 150.\ \text{lb}$
  $F = 45\ \text{lb}$
  $W = Fs$
  $W = 45\ \text{lb} \times 20.\ \text{ft}$
  $W = 9.0 \times 10^2\ \text{ft-lb}$

used in computing the work done on the object.

2. *Metric system—CGS units.* When the force is measured in dynes and the distance is measured in centimeters, the work is expressed in ergs. *A force of one dyne, acting through a distance of one centimeter, does one erg of work.* One erg equals 10^{-7} joule.

3. *English system.* When the force is measured in pounds and the distance is measured in feet, the work is expressed in foot-pounds. *A force of one pound, acting through a distance of one foot, does one foot-pound of work.* The unit of work is called the foot-pound to distinguish it from the English system unit of torque, the pound-foot. See the Sample Problem opposite.

PROBLEMS

A 1. A man weighing 750. nt climbs a flight of stairs that is 5.0 m high. What work does he do?

2. A force of 50. lb is needed to push a loaded wheelbarrow along a horizontal walk. If the wheelbarrow is pushed 175 ft along this walk, how much work is done?

3. How much work must be done to raise a block weighing 9.80×10^5 dynes through a height of 35.4 cm?

4. The coefficient of friction between a large packing case and the floor is 0.25. If the packing case weighs 250. lb, how much work must be done in order to move it 20.0 ft across a level floor?

5. What work is done when a man lifts a 2.5-kg package and places it on a shelf 2.2 m high?

6. How much work must be done to roll a metal safe, mass 100. kg, a distance of 15.0 m across a level floor? The coefficient of friction is 0.050.

B 7. A boy pulls a loaded sled by means of a rope which makes an angle of 45.0° with the horizontal. If the mass of the sled is 60.0 kg and the coefficient of friction is 0.020, how much work is done in pulling the sled along a level road for a distance of 1.000 km?

8. A loaded trunk has a mass of 35 kg. The coefficient of friction between the trunk and the floor is 0.20. How much work will be done in moving the trunk 8.0 m across a level floor and then lifting it into the back of a truck 1.3 m above the floor?

9. A crate, mass 75.0 kg, is to be pushed up an inclined plane 3.00 m long, which makes an angle of 20.0° with the horizontal. If the coefficient of friction between the crate and the inclined plane is 0.150, how much work must be done?

10. An unbalanced force of 5.0 nt acts on a mass of 2.0 kg which is initially at rest. How much work is done (*a*) during the first two seconds; (*b*) during the tenth second?

2 POWER

3. The meaning of power. Like the term *work*, the term *power* has a scientific meaning that differs from its everyday meaning. When we say a person has great power, we usually mean he has great strength, or he wields great authority. In physics, the term *power* means *the rate of doing work*.

A man does the same amount of work when he climbs a flight of stairs in one minute as he does when he climbs the same flight of stairs in one hour, but he does not use the same amount of power.

Power depends upon three factors: (*1*) the force exerted, (*2*) the distance the force moves, and (*3*) the time required.

4. Units of power. Since power is the time rate of doing work,

$$P = \frac{W}{t}$$

in which P represents power, W is work, and t is time. Or, because $W = Fs$,

$$P = \frac{Fs}{t}$$

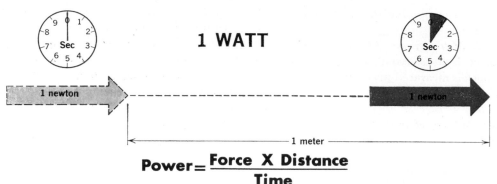

Fig. 5-2. One watt of power is expended when a force of one newton acts through a distance of one meter in one second of time.

1. Metric system—MKS units. When work is measured in joules and time is measured in seconds, power is expressed in *watts. A watt is a joule per second.* See Fig. 5-2. This unit is named in honor of James Watt (1736–1819), the inventor of the steam engine. Since the watt is an inconveniently small unit, power is more commonly measured in units of 1000 watts, called kilowatts (kw).

Because you have heard the terms watt and kilowatt used frequently in connection with electricity, you may think that these terms are applied only to electric power. This definitely is not so. The watt is the basic unit of power in the MKS system and may be used to express quantities of mechanical as well as electric power. See the Sample Problem below.

2. Metric system—CGS units. The power unit in this system is one erg per second. It has no special name.

3. English system. If one foot-pound of work is done in one second of time, the power is one foot-pound per second. However, this unit is too small to be used conveniently. The common unit of power in the English system is the horsepower (hp), *exactly* 550 ft-lb/sec or 33,000 ft-lb/min.

Sample Problem

A boy's mass is 75 kg. If he walks up a flight of stairs 12 m high in 30. sec, what power has he used?

Solution

$w = mg$

$w = 75 \text{ kg} \times 9.8 \text{ m/sec}^2$

$w = 7.4 \times 10^2 \text{ nt}$

But w equals the force F which must be exerted. So

$P = \dfrac{Fs}{t}$

$P = \dfrac{7.4 \times 10^2 \text{ nt} \times 12 \text{ m}}{30. \text{ sec}}$

$P = 3.0 \times 10^2 \text{ watts}$

$$P \text{ (in hp)} = \frac{W \text{ (in ft-lb)}}{550 \text{ ft-lb/sec/hp} \times t \text{ (in sec)}}$$

This unit was originated by James Watt, who found by a series of experiments that a horse pulling a heavy wagon could continue to work, for a reasonable length of time, at the rate of 550 ft-lb/sec.

One horsepower equals 746 watts or 0.746 kilowatt. It is useful to remember that 1 hp = about $\frac{3}{4}$ kw. See the Sample Problem below.

Sample Problem

What horsepower engine is required to hoist 100. tons of coal per hour from a mine 200. ft deep?

Solution

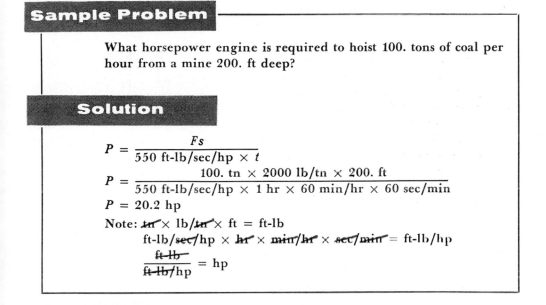

$$P = \frac{Fs}{550 \text{ ft-lb/sec/hp} \times t}$$

$$P = \frac{100. \text{ tn} \times 2000 \text{ lb/tn} \times 200. \text{ ft}}{550 \text{ ft-lb/sec/hp} \times 1 \text{ hr} \times 60 \text{ min/hr} \times 60 \text{ sec/min}}$$

$$P = 20.2 \text{ hp}$$

Note: t̶n̶ × lb/t̶n̶ × ft = ft-lb

ft-lb/s̶e̶c̶/hp × h̶r̶ × m̶i̶n̶/h̶r̶ × s̶e̶c̶/m̶i̶n̶ = ft-lb/hp

$$\frac{\text{f̶t̶-̶l̶b̶}}{\text{f̶t̶-̶l̶b̶}/hp} = hp$$

PROBLEMS

A 1. How many kilowatts of power are required to raise a mass of 50. kg to a height of 10. m in 15 sec?

2. A power shovel raised 500. lb of earth to a height of 12.0 ft in 7.00 sec. What horsepower was developed?

3. The loaded cage of an elevator has a mass of 2.5×10^3 kg. If it is raised in 10. sec to a height of 50. m, how many kilowatts of power are required?

4. An elevator in the Empire State Building in New York City makes the ascent to the 80th floor in 50.0 sec. If the height is 989 ft, what horsepower must be developed in order to lift 12 persons averaging 150. lb each to this floor?

5. The mass of a large steel ball is 1500 kg. What power is used in raising this steel ball to a height of 30. m if the work is performed in 30.0 sec?

6. An elevator in a garage can raise an automobile weighing 1.5 tons to a height of 30.0 ft in 2.0 min. What horsepower is used?

B 7. A pump can deliver 20.0 l of gasoline per minute. What power, in kilowatts, is expended by the pump in raising gasoline a distance of 6.0 m? One liter of gasoline has a mass of 0.700 kg.

8. If the effective coefficient of friction is 0.0050, what horsepower is required to move a train of fifty railroad cars, each weighing 50. tons, at the rate of 60. mi/hr along a level track?

9. A motor is rated to deliver 10.0 kw. At what speed in m/min can this motor raise a load which has a mass of 2.75×10^4 kg?

10. What horsepower is required to move an automobile weighing 1.75 tons up a grade which rises 2.0 ft for each 100. ft of roadway, at 50.0 mi/hr, if the frictional force opposing the motion is 500. lb?

11. How many kilowatts of power will be required to move a locomotive weighing 1.00×10^6 nt up a grade which rises 1.50 m for each 100. m of track, at 40.0 km/hr, if the frictional force opposing the motion is 2.00×10^3 nt?

3 ENERGY

5. The meaning of energy. In Chapter 1 we described energy as the ability to do work. An object acquires energy when work is done against gravity in raising it to an elevated position or when work is done to set it in motion. The energy thus acquired can be used to do work. The water impounded behind a dam has energy and can be used to turn a water wheel. Winds possess energy, too, and can drive windmills or push sailboats. The destruction caused by waves shows that they also have energy.

6. Kinetic and potential energy. In mechanics there are two kinds of energy, *kinetic energy* and *potential energy*. **Kinetic energy** *is energy due to the motion of a mass.* A moving automobile, a bullet leaving the muzzle of a gun, strong winds, and falling or running water all possess kinetic energy.

Potential energy *is stored energy, or energy due to the position of a mass.* A rock resting on the edge of a cliff has potential energy. This energy becomes kinetic if the rock falls over the edge. The coiled mainspring of a watch has potential energy, because work was done in winding it. Its potential energy becomes kinetic as the spring unwinds. If we pull a heavy pendulum bob to one side, we store up potential energy by raising the bob against the force of gravity. As the bob swings downward, the potential energy becomes kinetic. This kinetic energy is sufficient to carry the bob upward again on the opposite side where the kinetic energy changes back into potential energy. We see from this and other examples that it is possible to change potential energy into kinetic energy, and also possible to change kinetic energy into potential energy.

7. The measurement of potential energy. Since energy is the capacity for doing work, we may use work units for measuring both potential and kinetic energy.

The potential energy acquired by a body equals the work done on the body against gravity or other forces to place it in position. The formula for calculating work is

$$W = Fs$$

Therefore

$$P.E. = Fs$$

In lifting an object, F is its weight, which from Newton's second law of motion equals mg, and s is the vertical distance h through which it is lifted, so

$$P.E. = mgh$$

1. Metric system—MKS units. The mass of the object is given in kilograms, the acceleration of gravity is 9.8 m/sec², and the height is given in meters. The potential energy is expressed in joules.

2. Metric system—CGS units. In this system, the mass of the object is given in grams; the acceleration of gravity is 980 cm/sec²; and the height is measured in centimeters. The calculated energy is expressed in ergs.

3. English system. When using this formula with English-system units, remember that the product mg equals the force required to lift the object. That is, mg equals the weight of the object, w. So,

$$P.E. = wh$$

If w is measured in pounds and h is given in feet, the potential energy is expressed in foot-pounds. See the Sample Problems on the opposite page.

8. The measurement of kinetic energy. The velocity of a freely falling body starting from rest, in terms of the acceleration of gravity and the distance traveled, is given by the formula

$$v = \sqrt{2gs}$$

CHAPTER 5 WORK, POWER, ENERGY, MACHINES   113

Solving for s, we obtain

$$s = \frac{v^2}{2g}$$

Since s in this equation means the same quantity as h in the formula P.E. = mgh, let us substitute for h the expression we have just derived for s. Since this object is moving with velocity v, it possesses kinetic energy. We then obtain

$$K.E. = mg \times \frac{v^2}{2g}$$

or, $$K.E. = \tfrac{1}{2}mv^2$$

1. Metric system—MKS units. The mass m must be given in kilograms and v in meters per second. Then K.E. is expressed in joules.

2. Metric system—CGS units. The mass m must be given in grams and v in centimeters per second. Then K.E. is expressed in ergs.

3. English system. In using this equation with English units, m must be given in slugs and v in feet per second. It may be helpful to substitute w/g for m when using English units. Then,

$$K.E. = \frac{wv^2}{2g}$$

K.E. is expressed in foot-pounds. See the Sample Problems on page 114.

9. Mass and energy. In Chapter 1 we stated that matter and energy were interchangeable. The Einstein equation for the relation between matter and energy is $E = mc^2$, where E is energy in joules, if m is mass in kilograms, and c is the velocity of light, 3×10^8 m/sec.

★ One of the basic steps in the reasoning which results in the Einstein equation is the idea that the mass of an object varies with its velocity. Up to this point we have assumed that the mass of an object

Sample Problem

What potential energy is acquired by a block of steel whose mass is 50. kg, when it is raised 5.0 m?

Solution

P.E. — mgh
P.E. = 50. kg × 9.8 m/sec² × 5.0 m
P.E. = 2.5 × 10³ joules

Sample Problem

What is the potential energy of a block which weighs 40. lb, when it is lifted from the floor to a table 3.0 ft high?

Solution

P.E. = wh
P.E. = 40. lb × 3.0 ft
P.E. = 1.2 × 10² ft-lb

does not vary with its location or condition, and at the velocities attained by matter as we normally deal with it, the variation of mass is so slight we cannot detect it. However, at velocities near that of light, the increase in mass is appreciable, as experiments on rapidly moving electrons show.

★ The mass of a body increases as its velocity increases according to the formula

$$m = \frac{m_0}{\sqrt{1 - (v^2/c^2)}}$$

In this formula, m is the mass of the object at velocity v; m_0 is the mass of the object when its velocity is zero; and c is the velocity of light.

The table (right) shows how the mass of a body varies with velocity. The velocity is expressed as a percentage of the velocity of light. That is, a velocity of 50 percent is half the velocity of light. The mass is expressed as the ratio between the mass at velocity v and the mass at velocity zero. In other words, at a velocity 50 percent of the velocity of light, a body has 1.15 times the mass it had at velocity zero.

Velocity of Object (percent of velocity of light)	Mass (m/m_0)
0	1.00
25	1.03
50	1.15
75	1.51
80	1.67
85	1.88
90	2.30
95	3.16
99	7.07
99.9	22.4

Sample Problem

A baseball has a mass of 0.14 kg. If it is thrown with a velocity of 7.5 m/sec, what is its kinetic energy?

Solution

K.E. = $\frac{1}{2}mv^2$
K.E. = $\frac{1}{2}$ × 0.14 kg × (7.5 m/sec)^2
K.E. = 3.9 joules

Sample Problem

Find the kinetic energy of a bullet weighing 0.10 lb if its velocity is 2.0 × 10^3 ft/sec.

Solution

K.E. = $\dfrac{wv^2}{2g}$

K.E. = $\dfrac{0.10 \text{ lb} \times (2.0 \times 10^3 \text{ ft/sec})^2}{2 \times 32 \text{ ft/sec}^2}$

K.E. = 6.3 × 10^3 ft-lb

UNITS IN MECHANICS

	Length	Mass	Time	Velocity	Acceleration	Force	Work	Power
	s	m	t	$v = s/t$	$a = v/t$	$F = ma$	$W = Fs$	$P = W/t$
MKS	meter (m)	kilo-gram (kg)	second (sec)	m/sec	m/sec^2	$\dfrac{\text{kg-m}}{\text{sec}^2}$ newton (nt)	nt-m joule	joule/sec watt
CGS	centi-meter (cm)	gram (g)	second (sec)	cm/sec	cm/sec^2	$\dfrac{\text{g-cm}}{\text{sec}^2}$ dyne	dyne-cm erg	erg/sec 10^{-7} watt
FPS	foot (ft)	$\dfrac{\text{lb-sec}^2}{\text{ft}}$ slug	second (sec)	ft/sec	ft/sec^2	pound (lb)	ft-lb	$\dfrac{\text{ft-lb}}{\text{sec}}$ $550 \dfrac{\text{ft-lb}}{\text{sec}} = 1 \text{ hp}$

The basic units in each system are shown in red.

QUESTIONS

A **1.** What conditions must be met before "work," as the term is used in physics, is done?
2. How is the term "power" used in physics?
3. (*a*) What is "energy"? (*b*) What are the two important kinds of energy? (*c*) Differentiate between them.

B **4.** (*a*) What is Einstein's equation relating mass and energy? (*b*) Identify each of the terms used in this equation. (*c*) In what units are they usually expressed?
★ **5.** What effect does velocity have on the mass of a body?

PROBLEMS

A **1.** A man lifts a mass of 2.00 kg from the floor to a table 0.80 m high. What potential energy, in joules, does this mass now have by virtue of its change of position?
2. By virtue of its position, what potential energy is possessed by 10.0 ft^3 of water at the top of Niagara Falls? The weight of 1.00 ft^3 of water is 62.4 lb and Niagara Falls is 167 ft high.
3. What potential energy, in ergs, is acquired by a mass of 25 g raised through a height of 55 cm?
4. A large rock has a mass of 10.0 slugs. If it rests at the top of a steep cliff 135 ft high, what potential energy does it have?
5. What is the kinetic energy of a baseball, mass 0.14 kg, if it is thrown with a velocity of 18 m/sec?
6. The weight of a bomb is 500. lb. If it strikes the earth with a velocity of 150. ft/sec, what is its kinetic energy?

B **7.** A stone having a mass of 50.0 kg is dropped from a height of 200. m. What is the potential energy and the kinetic energy of the stone (*a*) at $t = 0$ sec; (*b*) at $t = 1.00$ sec; (*c*) at $t = 5.00$ sec; (*d*) when the stone strikes the ground?
8. An automobile is accelerated on a level road from 30. mi/hr to 50. mi/hr in 11.0 sec. The car weighs 3600. lb. (*a*) What is the increase in kinetic energy of the car? (*b*) What force is producing the acceleration? (*c*) What horsepower is developed?
9. What is the kinetic energy in ergs of an electron, mass 9.1×10^{-28} g, moving at a speed of 1.0×10^9 cm/sec?
10. Assuming 1.0 g of matter is completely transformed into energy, how many joules of energy are produced?
11. What is the m/m_0 ratio of a body moving (*a*) with 40.0% of the velocity of light; (*b*) with 99.99% of the velocity of light?

4 MACHINES

10. Uses of machines. From the very earliest times man has used machines to help him in his work and now is dependent on machines in almost every task.

We use machines to *transform energy.* A generator transforms mechanical energy into electric energy. A steam turbine or gas turbine transforms heat energy into mechanical energy.

We use machines to *transfer energy* from one place to another. The connecting rods, crankshaft, drive shaft, and rear axle transfer energy from the combustion in the cylinders of an automobile to the tires on the rear wheels.

Another use of machines is to *multiply force.* If a garage mechanic wishes to lift the engine out of an automobile, he may use a system of pulleys. The pulley system enables a mechanic to raise the engine by exerting a force which is smaller than the weight of the engine. But he must exert this smaller force over a greater distance than the height through which the engine is raised. Thus, the engine moves more slowly than the chain on which the mechanic pulls. A machine enables us to gain force, but only at the expense of speed.

Machines may also be used to *multiply speed.* A bicycle is a machine by which we gain speed, but only by exerting a greater force. No machine can be used to gain both force and speed at the same time.

Finally, machines are used to *change the direction of a force.* The single pulley at the top of a flag pole enables one end of the rope to exert an upward force on the flag as a downward force is exerted on the other end.

11. There are six simple machines. These are the *lever,* the *pulley,* the *wheel and axle,* the *inclined plane,* the *screw,* and the *wedge.* Other machines are either modifications of one of these simple machines

or combinations of two or more of them. The pulley and the wheel and axle are fundamentally levers, however, while the wedge and screw are modified inclined planes.

12. Mechanical advantage. The mechanical advantage of force of a machine may be defined in two ways.

1. The *ideal mechanical advantage,* IMA, is the ratio of the distance the effort force moves, s_E, to the distance the resistance force moves, s_R.

$$IMA = \frac{s_E}{s_R}$$

2. The *actual mechanical advantage,* AMA, is the ratio of the resistance force, F_R, to the effort force, F_E.

$$AMA = \frac{F_R}{F_E}$$

13. Efficiency of machines. The efficiency of any machine is the ratio of its actual mechanical advantage to its ideal mechanical advantage, converted to a percentage.

$$efficiency = \frac{AMA}{IMA} \times 100\%$$

Because force is required to move the parts of a machine and to overcome friction in the machine, the AMA is never as great as the IMA; the efficiency of a machine is always less than 100 percent.

Another useful relationship for determining the efficiency of a machine may be derived as follows. From the definitions of AMA and IMA,

$$\frac{AMA}{IMA} = \frac{F_R/F_E}{s_E/s_R}$$

Simplifying the complex fraction yields

$$\frac{AMA}{IMA} = \frac{F_R s_R}{F_E s_E}$$

The product $F_R s_R$ is the work done by the machine, or the *output*, W_{output}, and the product $F_E s_E$ is the work put into the machine, or the *input*, W_{input}. As a consequence,

$$\frac{AMA}{IMA} = \frac{W_{output}}{W_{input}}$$

and

$$\text{efficiency} = \frac{W_{output}}{W_{input}} \times 100\%$$

The Sample Problems below illustrate the method by which efficiency is calculated.

14. The lever. When we row a boat through the water, we are using the oars as levers. *A lever is a rigid bar which is free to turn about a fixed point called the fulcrum.* The fulcrum is the pivot point. The effort force is exerted upon one lever arm and tends to rotate the lever in one direction. The resistance force is exerted upon the other lever arm and tends to rotate the lever in the opposite direction. When we use oars as levers to move a boat through water, the blades are fulcrums, the effort forces are exerted on the handles, and the resistance forces are exerted on the oarlocks. In studying the lever, we apply the principles learned in Chapter 3 for producing equilibrium.

Sample Problem

A machine has an ideal mechanical advantage of 5.0, but an actual mechanical advantage of 4.0. What is the efficiency of this machine?

Solution

$$\text{efficiency} = \frac{AMA}{IMA} \times 100\%$$

$$\text{efficiency} = \frac{4.0}{5.0} \times 100\%$$

$$\text{efficiency} = 80.\%$$

Sample Problem

A force of 40. nt moves through a distance of 20. m in lifting a weight of 180. nt to a height of 4.0 m. What is the efficiency?

Solution

$$\text{efficiency} = \frac{W_{output}}{W_{input}} \times 100\%$$

$$\text{efficiency} = \frac{180. \text{ nt} \times 4.0 \text{ m}}{40. \text{ nt} \times 20. \text{ m}} \times 100\%$$

$$\text{efficiency} = 90.\%$$

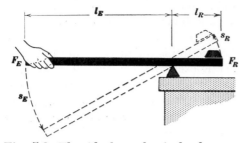

Fig. 5-3. The ideal mechanical advantage of a lever is the length of the effort arm divided by the length of the resistance arm.

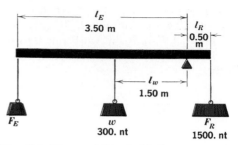

Fig. 5-4. The weight of this lever acts as a counterclockwise force and aids the effort force.

In the lever shown in Fig. 5-3, the effort force, F_E, acts upon the arm l_E, and tends to produce counterclockwise rotation. The resistance force, F_R, acts upon the arm l_R, and tends to produce clockwise rotation. If the effort force moves through the distance s_E, the resistance force moves through the distance s_R. We can use the formula

$$\frac{s_E}{s_R} = \frac{l_E}{l_R}$$

because arcs of circles subtended by equal central angles are directly proportional to the radii of the circles. Consequently the distances moved by the effort force and the resistance force are proportional to the lengths of the lever arms upon which the forces act. We have seen that

$$IMA = \frac{s_E}{s_R}$$

Therefore, for all kinds of levers,

$$IMA = \frac{l_E}{l_R}$$

The ideal mechanical advantage of any lever equals the length of the effort arm divided by the length of the resistance arm. If l_E is 2 m long, and l_R is only 0.67 m long, the ideal mechanical advantage is 2 m ÷ 0.67 m = 3.

In the preceding discussion, we have ignored the weight of the lever. Often we cannot do this in practical situations. The weight of a lever may be considered to be concentrated at the center of gravity of the lever. See Chapter 3, Section 19. This weight thus aids either the effort force or the resistance force, depending on how the lever is used. See the Sample Problems opposite.

15. The pulley. *A pulley is a wheel that turns readily on an axle, which in turn is mounted in a frame.* One or more pulleys enclosed in a frame is usually called a *block;* a series of pulleys with the attached rope or chain is known as a *block and tackle.*

Figure 5-6(*A*) shows a single fixed pulley. This pulley acts like a lever in which l_E equals l_R, and the ideal mechanical advantage is one. If we neglect friction, an effort force of 1 lb, pulling downward through a distance of 1 ft, raises a resistance force of 1 lb through a distance of 1 ft. A single fixed pulley gains neither force nor speed. It merely changes the direction in which a force is applied.

A single movable pulley is shown in Fig. 5-6(*B*). The force F_E acts upon the arm l_E, which is the diameter of the pulley; F_R acts upon the arm l_R, which is the radius of the pulley. Since the diameter is twice the radius, the ideal mechanical advantage of a single movable pulley is two. When the effort force moves 2 ft, the resistance force is lifted 1 ft.

Many different combinations of fixed and movable pulleys are possible. We shall consider only two, each consisting of one fixed and one movable block. In both, the cord or rope is continuous; the effort force is applied to one end of the cord,

Sample Problem

The uniform bar shown in Fig. 5-4 is 4.00 m long. It weighs 300. nt. The force F_R, 1500. nt, acts on one end of the bar, 0.50 m from the fulcrum. If F_E is applied at the other end of the bar, what must be its magnitude to produce equilibrium?

Solution

Clockwise torque = counterclockwise torque

$$F_R \times l_R = F_E \times l_E + w \times l_w$$

$$F_E = \frac{F_R \times l_R - w \times l_w}{l_E}$$

$$F_E = \frac{1500.\ nt \times 0.50\ m - 300.\ nt \times 1.50\ m}{3.50\ m}$$

$$F_E = 86\ nt$$

Sample Problem

Figure 5-5 represents a lever 12.0 ft long. The lever is uniform and weighs 60. lb. What upward effort force must be applied at the end of the lever to balance a resistance force of 300. lb which acts 2.0 ft from the fulcrum?

Solution

Clockwise torque = counterclockwise torque

$$F_E \times l_E = F_R \times l_R + w \times l_w$$

$$F_E = \frac{F_R \times l_R + w \times l_w}{l_E}$$

$$F_E = \frac{300.\ lb \times 2.0\ ft + 60.\ lb \times 6.0\ ft}{12.0\ ft}$$

$$F_E = 80.\ lb$$

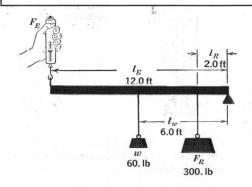

Fig. 5-5. The weight of this lever acts as a counterclockwise force and hinders the effort force.

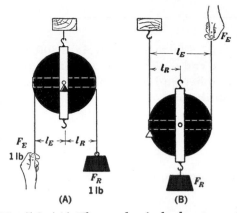

F_E ←l_E→←l_R→
1 lb

F_R
1 lb

(A)   (B)

Fig. 5-6. (*A*) **The mechanical advantage of a single fixed pulley is one.** (*B*) **The mechanical advantage of a single movable pulley is two.**

while the other end of the cord may be attached either to the movable block or to the fixed block.

1. Cord attached to the movable block. The arrangement of the pulleys is shown in Fig. 5-7(*A*). The force F_E must pull downward a distance of 5 ft to lift F_R 1 ft. Therefore *the ideal mechanical advantage,* s_E/s_R, is 5, which *equals the number of strands supporting the movable block.* The strand of cord on which the effort force acts does not support the movable block. It does not increase the mechanical advantage, but merely changes the direction of the effort force.

2. Cord attached to the fixed block. In Fig. 5-7(*B*), one end of the cord is attached to the fixed block. In this arrangement, the number of strands supporting the movable block is four. The last strand, on which the effort force acts, does not support the movable block; this block merely changes the direction of the effort force. The mechanical advantage of this pulley system is four.

If we let the letter *n* represent the number of strands which support the movable block in a pulley system which uses a single continuous cord, the pulley formula becomes

$$IMA = n$$

16. The wheel and axle. *A wheel and axle is a wheel or crank rigidly attached to an axle.* Both the wheel and the axle have the same angular velocity.

In Fig. 5-8 we have two wheels of unequal diameter, fastened so they turn together about the same axis. In one revolution, F_E moves a distance equal to the circumference, C, of the wheel. During this time, F_R will travel a distance equal to the circumference, c, of the axle. Since $s_E = C$, and $s_R = c$,

$$IMA = \frac{C}{c}$$

We may also use the following equations for the ideal mechanical advantage of the wheel and axle:

$$IMA = \frac{D}{d} \quad or \quad IMA = \frac{R}{r}$$

In these, D is the diameter of the wheel, d is the diameter of the axle, R is the radius of the wheel, and r is the radius of the

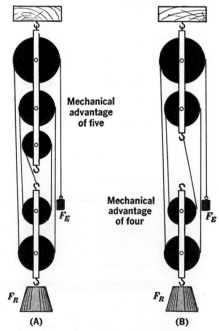

Mechanical advantage of five

Mechanical advantage of four

F_E F_E

F_R F_R

(A)   (B)

Fig. 5-7. (*A*) **Five strands support the movable block.** (*B*) **Four strands support the movable block.**

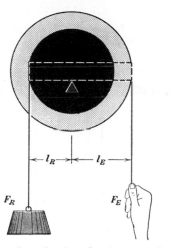

Fig. 5-8. The wheel and axle is similar to a lever with unequal arms.

effort force is required because we move the object up a slanted surface rather than lifting it vertically. (See Chapter 3, Section 14.) However, the effort force must be applied over the entire length of the plane in order to raise the load through the height of the plane, *if the force is applied parallel to the plane.* See Fig. 5-9. Since s_E is the length, l, of the plane, and s_R is the height, h,

$$IMA = \frac{l}{h}$$

See the Sample Problem on the following page.

axle. We may use these equations because the diameter or radius of a wheel is directly proportional to its circumference.

See the Sample Problem below.

17. The inclined plane. When we wish to increase the height or elevation of an object without lifting it vertically, we may use an *inclined plane.*

When an inclined plane is used, less

Fig. 5-9. The ideal mechanical advantage of this inclined plane is the length of the plane divided by its height.

Sample Problem

A wheel having a diameter of 0.70 m is attached to an axle which has a diameter of 0.10 m. What force must be applied to the rim of the wheel to raise a weight of 3000. nt attached to the axle? The efficiency is 75%.

Solution

$$efficiency = \frac{AMA}{IMA} \times 100\%$$

$$efficiency = \frac{F_R/F_E}{D/d} \times 100\%$$

$$F_E = F_R \times \frac{d}{D} \times \frac{100\%}{eff.}$$

$$F_E = 3000. \ nt \times \frac{0.10 \ m}{0.70 \ m} \times \frac{100\%}{75\%}$$

$$F_E = 5.7 \times 10^2 \ nt$$

Fig. 5-10. We must apply the principles of resolution of forces and coefficient of friction to calculate the efficiency of this inclined plane.

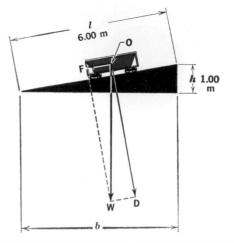

Sample Problem

An inclined plane is 6.00 m long and 1.00 m high. (*a*) If the coefficient of friction is 0.050, what force will be required to roll a weight of 10,000. nt up the plane? (*b*) What is the efficiency?

Solution

(*a*) Construct the diagram to scale as shown in Fig. 5-10. Use the formula for a right triangle to calculate *b*.

$b = 5.92$ m

Resolve the 10,000. nt weight into components acting against the plane and down the plane, using the method of Chapter 3, Section 14.

$$\overrightarrow{OF} = 1.67 \times 10^3 \text{ nt}$$

$$\overrightarrow{OD} = 9.84 \times 10^3 \text{ nt}$$

Using $\overrightarrow{OD}$ and the coefficient of friction, calculate the force required to overcome friction, F_f, using the method of Chapter 3, Section 28.

$$F_f = 4.92 \times 10^2 \text{ nt}$$

$$F_E = \overrightarrow{OF} + F_f$$

$$F_E = 1.67 \times 10^3 \text{ nt} + 4.92 \times 10^2 \text{ nt}$$

$$F_E = 2.16 \times 10^3 \text{ nt}$$

(*b*) efficiency $= \dfrac{\text{AMA}}{\text{IMA}} \times 100\%$

efficiency $= \dfrac{F_R/F_E}{l/h} \times 100\%$

efficiency $= \dfrac{10,000. \text{ nt}/2.16 \times 10^3 \text{ nt}}{6.00 \text{ m}/1.00 \text{ m}} \times 100\%$

efficiency $= 77.2\%$

Fig. 5-11. The wedge is a double inclined plane.

In certain cases, the force may be applied *parallel to the base of the plane.* If *b* represents the base of the plane, then,

$$IMA = \frac{b}{h}$$

18. The wedge. *The wedge is really a double inclined plane.* See Fig. 5-11. There is so much friction in using a wedge that an ideal mechanical advantage is of little significance. A wedge which is long in proportion to its thickness is easier to drive. Consequently, we may say that its mechanical advantage depends upon the ratio of its length to its thickness.

19. The screw. Let us cut a sheet of paper in the shape of a right triangle and wind it on a pencil, as shown in Fig. 5-12. This reveals that *a screw is really an inclined plane wound upon a cylinder.* The distance between the threads is called the *pitch* of the screw. The effort force is often applied at one end of a lever which is set in the head of the screw or to a wrench which is attached to the head of the screw. It may also be applied tangentially to the handle of a screwdriver set in a groove in the head of the screw. While the effort force describes a complete circle, the head and axis of the screw make one complete turn, and the resistance force moves a distance equal to the pitch of the screw. If *r* is the length of the lever arm upon which F_E acts, then, for one revolution, s_E equals $2\pi r$. As F_E moves this distance, F_R moves the distance *d*, which is the pitch of the screw. But *d* is s_R. Consequently,

$$IMA = \frac{2\pi r}{d}$$

As in the case of the wedge, the ideal me-

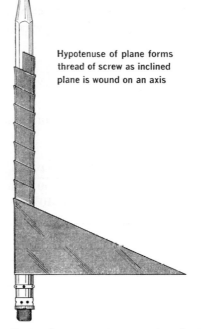

Hypotenuse of plane forms thread of screw as inclined plane is wound on an axis

Fig. 5-12. The screw is an inclined plane wound on an axis.

chanical advantage of most screws is much greater than the actual mechanical advantage because of the friction involved in their use. The Sample Problem on page 124 illustrates the calculation of IMA for a screw.

Bolts, nuts, and screws of all kinds are examples of this simple machine. For measuring the thickness of paper and foil, for finding the diameter of a wire, or for measuring precisely machined parts, a fine-threaded screw is used. Such a screw is contained in a *micrometer* (my-*krom*-uh-ter) *caliper.* The handle of the caliper, which is actually the head of the screw, may be divided into 50 parts, as shown in Fig. 5-13. The threads of the screw of this micrometer are 0.050 in apart. Consequently, when the head is turned from one division to the next, the caliper is opened or closed by 0.001 in.

20. The efficiency of the simple machines. It is impossible to make any

Sample Problem

The lever of a screw is 0.60 m long. If the screw has 2 threads to the centimeter, what is the ideal mechanical advantage?

Solution

Since there are 2 threads to the centimeter, the pitch of the screw is 0.50 cm = 0.0050 m.

$$IMA = \frac{2\pi r}{d}$$

$$IMA = \frac{2 \times 3.14 \times 0.60 \text{ m}}{0.0050 \text{ m}}$$

$$IMA = 7.5 \times 10^2$$

machine 100 percent efficient because we cannot totally eliminate either the friction or the weight of the parts of the machine. In certain levers the efficiency may be nearly 100 percent; friction is small, but the weight of the lever may lower the efficiency. The efficiency of a block and tackle is usually not more than 60 percent; the rigidity of the ropes, the friction of the wheels, and the weight of the movable block all tend to reduce the efficiency of this simple machine. If the surface of an inclined plane is very smooth and hard, the efficiency of the plane may be as high as 80 percent. The friction of the wedge

is so great that it is almost impossible to estimate its efficiency. While the jackscrew has a high mechanical advantage, friction may reduce its efficiency to no more than 25 percent.

21. Compound machines. Many complicated machines are merely combinations of simple machines. The crank of a food chopper works on the principle of the wheel and axle. The crank turns a screw which forces the food through small holes, where it is chopped off by the wedge action of a cutting disk. *Such a combination of two or more simple machines is called a* **compound machine.**

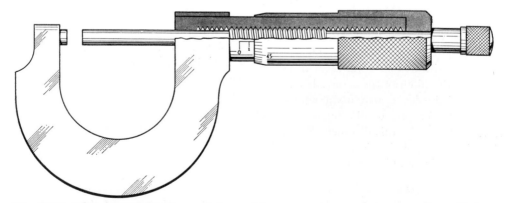

Fig. 5-13. The micrometer is used for making accurate measurements of small distances. Its accuracy depends on a precisely threaded screw.

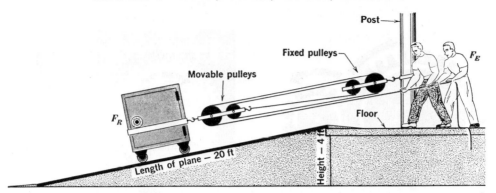

Fig. 5-14. The ideal mechanical advantage of a compound machine is usually the product of the ideal mechanical advantages of the simple machines that compose it. What is the ideal mechanical advantage of this compound machine?

Figure 5-14 shows a safe which weighs 4000 lb. We wish to move it onto a raised floor 4 ft above the lower level. An inclined walk 20 ft long leads onto the raised floor. The ideal mechanical advantage of the inclined plane is 20 ft ÷ 4 ft — 5; however, even neglecting friction, we still have to exert a force of 4000 lb ÷ 5 = 800 lb to pull the safe up the walk. If we attach the movable block of a block and tackle to the safe, and the fixed block to the post, we have a pulley system which has a mechanical advantage of 5. (Five strands support the movable block.) Now, neglecting friction and the weight of the block and tackle, a force of 800 lb ÷ 5 — 160 lb must be applied to the rope to pull the safe up the incline. The combined ideal mechanical advantage of the two machines is 5 × 5, or 25. *In nearly all cases of compound machines, the total ideal mechanical advantage is the product of the separate ideal mechanical advantages.*

22. Combinations of gear wheels. Figure 5-15 shows some gear wheels in combination. This device is usually called a train of gears. It has a high mechanical advantage. The effort force is applied on the circumference of the gear wheel A, which makes one revolution in the same time as its axle B. Wheel C, however, makes only that fraction of a revolution

which is equal to

$$\frac{\text{number of cogs in } B}{\text{number of cogs in } C}$$

The wheel F, too, will revolve only a fraction as rapidly as D. The wheels A and G are essentially a wheel and axle. Therefore, the total ideal mechanical advantage equals

$$\frac{\text{radius of } A}{\text{radius of } G} \times \frac{\text{no. of cogs in } C}{\text{no. of cogs in } B}$$

$$\times \frac{\text{no. of cogs in } F}{\text{no. of cogs in } D}$$

Gear wheels are used to vary the speed or direction of a twisting force. Suppose a wheel that has 32 gear teeth is meshed with a wheel that has only 16 teeth, as

Fig. 5-15. A train of gear wheels.

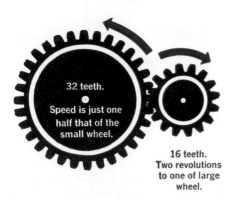

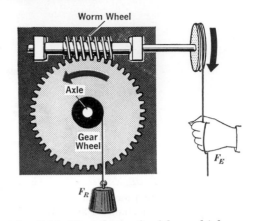

Fig. 5-16. Combinations of gear wheels of different diameters are used to increase or decrease speed.

Fig. 5-18. The worm wheel has a high mechanical advantage, but friction may lower its efficiency.

shown in Fig. 5-16. If we apply the effort force to the first wheel, we gain speed, since the second wheel will make two revolutions while the first is making one. If we apply the effort force to the second wheel, we gain force, and have an ideal mechanical advantage of 2.

In a bicycle, the sprocket wheels on separate shafts are connected by a chain. In Fig. 5-17 the front sprocket wheel has 28 teeth and the rear one only 7. During one complete revolution of the pedals, the rear wheel of this bicycle will make four complete revolutions.

23. The worm wheel. A worm wheel is shown in Fig. 5-18. It is a screw which

is meshed with a gear wheel. The effort force is used to turn the worm wheel. If there are 50 teeth in the gear wheel, one complete turn of the worm will turn the gear through 1/50 of a revolution. The resistance force acts on the axle of the gear wheel. If we let l represent the length of the lever arm upon which the effort force acts, and n the number of teeth in the gear wheel, with r the radius of the axle,

$$\text{IMA} = \frac{nl}{r}$$

24. The differential pulley. This compound machine has two wheels of unequal

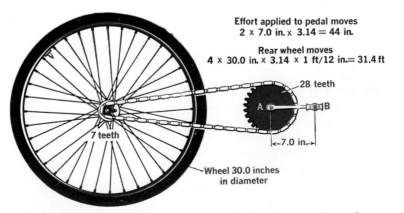

Fig. 5-17. The bicycle has a mechanical advantage of speed.

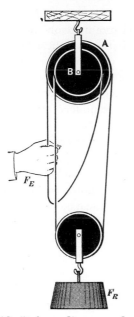

Fig. 5-19. Left, a diagram of a differential pulley; right, a commercial chain hoist.

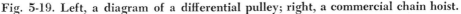

diameter which are fastened together and turn on the same axle. An endless chain connects the two wheels with a movable pulley, shown in Fig. 5-19. The endless chain is made of links which fit into notches in the rims of the pulley wheels so that the chain cannot slip on the wheels.

Suppose F_R shortens the chain by winding on the wheel A a length of chain equal to its circumference, C. While this is being done, a length of chain equal to the circumference, c, of the wheel B will be unwound. The chain is thus shortened a distance equal to $C - c$, and F_R, which is attached to the movable pulley, is lifted a distance equal to $\frac{1}{2}(C - c)$. Therefore s_E equals C, and s_R equals $\frac{1}{2}(C - c)$, and then

$$\text{IMA} = \frac{2C}{C - c}$$

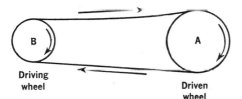

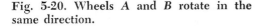

Fig. 5-20. Wheels A and B rotate in the same direction.

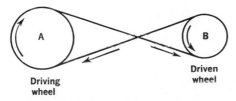

Fig. 5-21. Wheels A and B rotate in opposite directions.

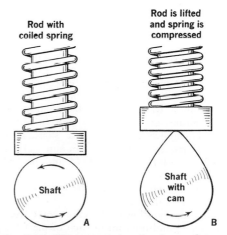

Fig. 5-22. Rotary motion is changed to reciprocating motion by means of a cam.

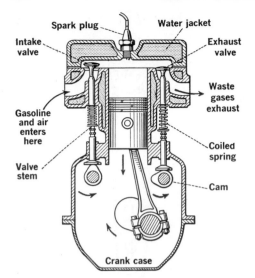

Fig. 5-23. In this sectional view of a gaso-line engine, the rotary motion of the cam-shafts is changed into the reciprocating mo-tion of the valves by means of cams, while the reciprocating motion of the piston is transformed into the rotary motion of the crankshaft by means of an eccentric bear-ing.

★ **25. The transmission of mechanical power.** In a home workshop several machines are commonly driven by the same electric motor, the power being transmitted by means of a belt and pulleys. Usually the belt is connected as shown in Fig. 5-20. Then the driven wheel will rotate in the same direction as the drive wheel mounted on the motor shaft. If the belt is twisted, the wheels will turn in opposite directions, as in Fig. 5-21. The ratio of the angular velocities of the wheels is inversely proportional to the ratio of the circumferences, diameters, or radii of the wheels.

★ **26. Rotary motion and reciprocating motion.** Rotary motion can be changed into reciprocating (back-and-forth) motion by the method shown in Fig. 5-22. If the circular shaft shown at (A) rotates, it slides around under the vertical rod, but does not move the rod up and down. As the shaft at (B), with a projection, or *cam*, on one side rotates, the rod is lifted. The spring which presses the rod against the shaft pushes the rod down again after the cam has passed. The shaft on which the cam is mounted is called a *camshaft*. The intake and exhaust valves of automobile engines are often controlled by cams and cam-shafts.

The reciprocating motion of the pistons of an automobile engine is transformed into rotary motion by means of the con-necting rods and the "off-center" bearings of the crankshaft. These off-center bearings are sometimes called eccentrics. See Fig. 5-23.

QUESTIONS

A   **1.** Explain which of the following machines transform energy from one form to another, and which merely transfer energy from one spot to another: (a) electric motor; (b) gear wheels in a watch; (c) fan belt and pulleys in an automobile engine; (d) gasoline engine on a lawnmower; (e) the drive shaft, differ-ential gears, and rear axle of an automobile.
2. Distinguish between the IMA and the AMA of a machine.
3. In what two ways may the efficiency of a machine be calculated?
4. Give the position of the effort force, resist-ance force, and fulcrum in each of the follow-ing: (a) a claw hammer used for pulling nails; (b) the oar of a rowboat; (c) forceps handling small weights; (d) your lower jaw; (e) an equal-arm balance; (f) a pair of scissors; (g) a wheelbarrow.
5. (a) Draw a diagram of a lever in which the weight of the lever aids the effort force. (b) Draw a diagram of a lever in which the weight of the lever hinders the effort force.
6. Show by a diagram how you would connect two double-sheave pulleys to obtain the highest mechanical advantage.
7. How heavy a load can a man lift with a single fixed pulley?
8. Why are sloping ramps easier to climb than flights of stairs?
9. Why is it impractical to calculate an IMA for the wedge?

10. (*a*) How is friction an advantage in the use of a jackscrew? (*b*) In what way is it a disadvantage?

11. How is the IMA of a compound machine calculated?

B   12. The IMA of a wheel and axle is the ratio of the circumference of the wheel to the circumference of the axle. Prove: (*a*) the IMA of a wheel and axle is the ratio of the diameter of the wheel to the diameter of the axle; (*b*) the IMA of a wheel and axle is the ratio of the radius of the wheel to the radius of the axle.

13. What trigonometric function gives the relationship between the angle an inclined plane makes with the horizontal and the IMA of the plane?

14. Show how the wedge and the screw are actually applications of the inclined plane.

15. What will be the ratio between the number of teeth in the gear wheel attached to the second hand of a watch and the number of teeth in the gear wheel attached to the minute hand?

PROBLEMS

A   1. A plank 5.0 m long is used as a lever with the effort force placed between the effort force and the resistance force. The fulcrum is 2.0 m from the resistance force. (*a*) What is the IMA of this machine? (*b*) What force is needed to counterbalance a 10.-kg mass which acts as a resistance?

2. John must use a force of 50. lb in order to lift the handles of a loaded wheelbarrow. The distance from the wheel to the handles is 4.0 ft, and the loaded wheelbarrow weighs 150. lb. How far is the center of gravity of the wheelbarrow from the wheel?

3. A block and tackle is to be used to raise a load weighing 2.00×10^3 nt. If the maximum force which can be exerted is 600. nt, at least how many strands of rope must support the movable block?

4. A force of 100. lb is exerted on the rope of a block and tackle, and the rope is pulled in 30.0 ft. This work causes a weight of 500. lb to be raised 5.0 ft. What is the efficiency of this machine?

5. Robert and Paul are using a windlass to raise a mass of 750. kg. The radius of the wheel is 0.50 m and the radius of the axle is 0.040 m. (*a*) What is the IMA? (*b*) If the efficiency of the machine is 60.% and each boy exerts an equal force, how much force must each apply?

6. The length of the crank handle on a windlass is 10. in. The diameter of the axle is 1.0 in. If a force of 50. lb on the crank handle can raise a load of 600. lb, what is the efficiency of the windlass?

7. The raised end of an inclined plane 4.0 m long is 0.90 m high. Neglecting friction, what force is required to roll a steel drum weighing 750. nt up this plane?

8. A plank 13 ft long is used as an inclined plane to a platform 5.0 ft high. What force must be used to push a block of ice weighing 195 lb up the plank if the coefficient of friction is 0.0050?

9. A jackscrew has a lever arm 0.75 m long. The screw has 1.5 threads to the centimeter. If 300. nt of force must be exerted in order to raise a load of 6.00 metric tons, calculate the efficiency.

10. A housemover's jackscrew, exerting a force of 11 tons on a house, can raise one corner 0.50 ft in 10. min. If the efficiency of the jackscrew is 30.%, what is the horsepower input?

B   11. The large wheel of a differential pulley has a circumference of 0.60 m. The small wheel has a circumference of 0.55 m. (*a*) What is the IMA of this differential pulley? (*b*) If a force of 375 nt is required in order to raise a motor block weighing 5000. nt, what is the AMA? (*c*) Calculate the efficiency.

12. What is the mechanical advantage of the train of gears shown in Fig. 5-15? The radius of *A* is twice that of *G*. *B* and *D* each have 16 teeth, while *C* and *F* each have 36 teeth.

13. A worm drive, like that shown in Fig. 5-18, has 90 teeth in the gear wheel. If the radius of the drive wheel is 0.40 m, and the radius of the axle is 0.020 m, what load can be lifted by a force of 50. nt, if the efficiency is 65%?

14. A gangplank is 25.0 ft long and weighs 200. lb. It is resting on the end of a pier with 5.0 ft of its length extending out over the water. A man who weighs 175 lb walks out on the gangplank and stands at the far end. Now suppose another man, weighing 175 lb, walks out on the plank to join the first man. How far out from the pier can he walk before the gangplank starts to tip over?

15. (*a*) What horsepower must be developed

in order to pull 100. ft of rope from a block and tackle with a force of 50.0 lb in 5.5 sec? (*b*) If four strands support the movable block, and the weight raised is 125 lb, what is the efficiency of the machine?

16. The handle of a crank can opener is 4.0 in. long. Attached to the same axle as this crank is a toothed wheel which presses against the rim of the can and causes the can to turn while being opened. The diameter of the toothed wheel is 0.50 in. (*a*) If a force of 5.0 lb is applied to the crank, how much work must be done in opening a can which has a top 3.0 in. in diameter? (*b*) If the work is done in 5.0 sec, what horsepower is expended?

17. A safe weighing 2.00 tons is to be pulled up an inclined plane 20 ft long onto a platform 4.0 ft high. A block and tackle having an IMA of 5.0 is attached to the safe. If two men, each pulling with a force of 125 lb, move the safe, what is the efficiency of the machine?

18. A scaffold 4.0 m long has a mass of 50. kg.

Each end is supported by a block and tackle in which four strands support the movable block. If a painter, mass 75 kg, stands 0.75 m from one block, with what force must he pull to raise the end of the scaffold if the efficiency is 40.%?

19. The crank handle of the hoist on a wrecking truck is 18 in. long. On the same shaft there is a gear wheel which has 25 teeth. This gear wheel meshes with another one having 100. teeth, which is fastened to the axle shaft. This axle, on which the chain is wound, is 2.0 in. in diameter. The chain passes over a single fixed pulley at the end of the boom, through a single movable pulley to which the hoisting block is attached, and is fastened to the top of the boom. This hoist operates at 60.% efficiency. What effort applied to the crank handle is required to raise the front of an automobile 18 ft long and weighing 3700. lb? The center of gravity of the car is 8.0 ft from the front.

 **ummary**

Work is the product of a force and the distance through which it acts; power is the time rate of doing work; and energy is the capacity for doing work. Energy may be either potential or kinetic. Matter and energy are interchangeable. The mass of a body increases as its velocity increases, the effect being significant at velocities near that of light.

Man uses machines to transform energy, transfer energy, multiply force, multiply speed, or change the direction of a force. The six simple machines are the lever, the pulley, the wheel and axle, the inclined plane, the screw, and the wedge. The ideal mechanical advantage of a machine is the ratio of the distance the effort force moves to the distance the resistance force moves. The actual mechanical advantage is the ratio of the resistance force to the effort force. The efficiency of a machine is the ratio of its AMA to its IMA or the ratio of its output to its input. Compound machines are combinations of simple machines.

TERMS TO DEFINE

AMA	IMA	pulley
block	inclined plane	screw
compound machine	input	train of gears
differential pulley	joule	uses of machines
efficiency	kinetic energy	variation of mass with
energy	lever	velocity
erg	micrometer caliper	watt
erg/sec	output	wedge
foot-pound	pitch	wheel and axle
fulcrum	potential energy	work
horsepower	power	worm wheel

RESEARCH ON YOUR OWN

1. Time yourself running up as many flights of stairs as you can. Calculate your maximum horsepower.
2. If your school owns a hand-cranked electric generator, measure your power in watts. This is the product of volts and amperes.
3. A "Rube Goldberg" device is one by which a simple event like lighting a match sets off a long chain of events which ends in another simple event, such as the turning on of a light. Invariably energy is wasted in this sequence. Devise such a system of events, describing or contriving the simple machines to accomplish the end in view.
4. Using a piece of string, a support, and a set of metric weights, find the mass of a meter stick.
5. Examine one room in your home, the kitchen for example, and identify all the devices which are applications of one or more of the machines studied in this chapter. Make a list of these devices.
6. Make a list of the devices visible on an automobile, without lifting the hood, which are applications of one or more simple machines.
7. Report on types of automatic transmissions. Explain their similarities of operation and their differences.
8. Visit a large garage or machine shop and examine the various devices used for exerting large forces with little expenditure of effort.

UNIT **3**

Structure of matter

CHAPTER 6

ATOMIC STRUCTURE

VOCABULARY

Ångström. A unit of linear measure; 1×10^{-8} cm.

Atom. The smallest particle of an element that can enter into combination with other elements.

Atomic mass. The mass of an atom expressed in atomic mass units of 1.660×10^{-24} g.

Atomic number. The number of protons in the nucleus of an atom.

Chemical change. A change in which new substances with new properties are formed.

Electron. A negatively charged particle found in an atom and having a rest mass of 9.1083×10^{-28} g.

Electron volt. The energy required to move an electron between two points which have a potential difference of one volt.

Isotopes. Atoms whose nuclei contain the same number of protons but different numbers of neutrons.

Mass defect. The amount by which the mass of a nucleus is less than the combined mass of its constituent particles.

Mass number. The integer nearest to the atomic mass; the sum of the number of protons and neutrons in the nucleus.

Molecule. The smallest particle of any substance which can exist free and still exhibit all the properties of the substance.

Neutron. A neutral particle found in an atom and having a mass of 1.675×10^{-24} g.

Nuclear change. A change which involves changes in the identity of the atoms themselves.

Nucleus. The positively charged dense central part of an atom.

Physical change. A change in which the identifying properties of a substance remain unchanged.

Physicist's atomic weight. The weighted average of the atomic masses of isotopes based on their relative abundance.

Proton. A positively charged particle found in an atom and having a mass of 1.67239×10^{-24} g.

Fig. 6-1. Very large molecules, like these poliomyelitis virus molecules, can be photographed by means of the electron microscope. (Drs. C. E. Williams and R. C. Schwerdt)

1. Matter is made up of molecules. Suppose, in imagination, we were to take a crystal of sugar and divide it into two pieces. Next, we might divide one of these pieces in two, and then divide one of the resulting pieces in two. We might expect to continue this process indefinitely, getting smaller and smaller fragments each time. However, ultimately we would reach a limit because we would get two particles of sugar, each of which, if further divided, would yield smaller particles that no longer had the properties of sugar. The subdivision of other kinds of matter would give us the same result; a point is reached in the division of matter beyond which the identity and properties of that matter change. *The smallest particle of any substance which has the properties of that substance is called a* **molecule.**

Ordinary molecules like those of sugar or water have never been seen. They are far too small to be revealed by even the most powerful microscope. It has been estimated that if a drop of water could be magnified until it became as large as the earth, its molecules would be about one meter in diameter. Simple molecules, like those of water, are about 3×10^{-8} cm in diameter. A convenient unit to use for expressing molecular dimensions is the *Ångström, Å, which equals 10^{-8} cm.* Thus, water molecules are about 3 Å in diameter. Large virus molecules, which can be magnified by an electron microscope and photographed, are nearly 100 times this diameter (about 230 Å). In addition to the direct photographic evidence for the existence of very large molecules, there is much indirect evidence for the existence of smaller ones. Some of this indirect evidence will be described in Chapter 8.

2. Atoms. We are now ready to continue, in imagination, with the division of a molecule of sugar. We know that this molecule is the smallest particle which still retains the properties of sugar, but when we divide the sugar molecule, we find that it is made of three different kinds of matter. The simple kinds of matter of which molecules are composed are the *chemical elements.* The three chemical elements in sugar are carbon, hydrogen, and oxygen. The particles of these or any other elements are called atoms. *An* **atom** *is the smallest particle of an element that can enter into combination with other elements.*

Scientists have learned much about the way in which atoms are arranged in molecules. For example, they believe that the atoms of hydrogen and oxygen are arranged in a water molecule as shown at the upper left in Fig. 6-2. At the lower left of the figure is shown the probable structure of a molecule of ethyl alcohol composed of atoms of carbon, oxygen, and hydrogen. At the right is a representation of a molecule of simple sugar.

Since atoms make up molecules, we would expect atoms to be smaller in size than molecules. The smallest atom, the hydrogen atom, is about 0.6 Å in diameter. The largest atoms are slightly more than 5 Å in diameter. The hydrogen atom is also the lightest atom, having a mass of 1.67330×10^{-24} g. One of the heaviest atoms, though not one of the largest, is a

Fig. 6-2. Molecular models of water (upper left), ethyl alcohol (lower left), and glucose (right). The carbon atoms are black, the oxygen atoms are light blue, and the hydrogen atoms are orange. (Felix Cooper)

uranium atom. Its mass is 3.96×10^{-22} g. Thus, there is a 10-fold range in the diameters of atoms and about a 250-fold range in the masses of atoms.

To express conveniently the masses of individual atoms in grams requires the use of scientific notation, but even this is awkward for routine computations. Consequently, scientists usually express the *atomic mass* of an atom in *atomic mass units* (amu) of 1.660×10^{-24} g. This unit is exactly $\frac{1}{16}$ of the mass of the most abundant kind of oxygen atom. In atomic mass units, the atomic mass of the most abundant kind of hydrogen atom is 1.008145, while that of the most abundant kind of uranium atom is 238.125223. Observe the accuracy with which atomic masses are known. *The mass number of an atom, represented by the symbol A, is the integer nearest to the atomic mass.* Thus, for the hydrogen atom just mentioned, $A = 1$, while for the uranium atom $A = 238$.

Recently the field ion microscope has made it possible for scientists to photograph the arrangement of atoms in metals. Figure 6-3 shows the lattice pattern of the atoms

at the end of a very fine-pointed spherical tungsten needle tip, 6.5×10^{-6} cm in radius, magnified over a million times. This color photograph, taken by Dr. E. W. Müller of The Pennsylvania State University, was made by superimposing a red and a green copy of two consecutive photographs of the same surface. Minor surface

Fig. 6-3. A field ion microscope picture of the arrangement of atoms on the tip of a very fine-pointed tungsten needle. (E. W. Müller)

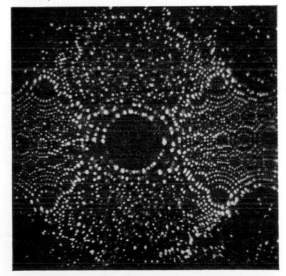

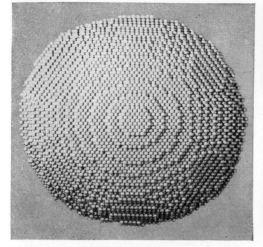

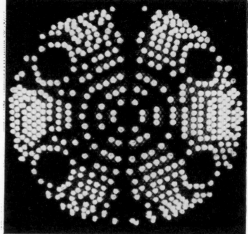

Fig. 6-4. A model of the tungsten needle tip used in the field ion microscope. This model is made of small cork balls representing the atoms in the close-packed lattice characteristic of the metal. (E. W. Müller)

Fig 6-5. When the balls at the corners of the layers of the model in Fig. 6-4 were coated with luminescent paint and photographed in the dark, this picture resulted. Compare it with Fig. 6-3. (E. W. Müller)

changes, due to the evaporation and condensation of a few tungsten atoms, are shown by this technique. The newly deposited atoms appear green, while those removed during the experiment appear red. The unchanged atoms appear yellow. (The reason for such a color-combining effect will be explained in Chapter 17.) In some parts of the photograph the arrangement of atoms is less perfect than in others. These imperfections are important in determining the strength of a metal, the growth of its crystals, and many other physical and chemical properties.

Figure 6-4 shows a cork-ball model of the tip of the tungsten needle photographed in Fig. 6-3. The balls at the corners of the layers of atoms in the model are coated with luminous paint. Figure 6-5 is a photograph of the model taken in the dark. Compare it with the picture of the actual needle tip.

Figure 6-6 is a simplified diagram of a field ion microscope. The fine-pointed needle is given a high positive charge of from 5000 to 30,000 volts, and a small amount of helium gas is introduced into the high-vacuum microscope tube through

a gun at the side of the tube. When a helium atom comes close to the tip of the needle, a negatively charged particle (electron) is stripped from it by the strong positive charge on the needle, and the resulting positively charged helium atom is repelled toward the screen of the tube. The screen is coated with a fluorescent material which glows where charged helium atoms strike it. The temperature of the microscope tube is maintained at about −252° C by liquid hydrogen. Under this low-temperature condition, helium atoms are most likely to be stripped of an electron and repelled from the atoms at the corners of the various planes of the needle. The photograph thus shows the position of these particular atoms.

Field ion microscope photographs give direct evidence of the existence of atoms. Indirect evidence is found in the study of chemical reactions. In a chemical reaction the atoms composing the molecules of two or more kinds of matter become rearranged to form molecules of other kinds of matter. The same number of the same kinds of atoms are present, but in different molecular arrangements.

3. Smaller particles of matter. Late in the nineteenth century, certain experiments showed that atoms were not the indivisible particles they had been assumed to be, but were composed of still smaller particles. Since that time, scientists have been conducting experiments and accumulating evidence about atomic structure. Even today, our understanding is not complete. What we do know indicates that atoms are composed of several different kinds of smaller particles arranged in a rather complex way. In the next few sections, we shall study some of the experiments which provided the evidence on which scientists base our present concepts of atomic structure.

4. The discovery of the electron. Late in the nineteenth century, some physicists were experimenting with the conduction of electricity through gases. One of these experiments led to the discovery of the electron. A glass tube containing air was fitted with electrodes (electric terminals) as in Fig. 6-7, page 138. When a source of high voltage electricity, about 10,000

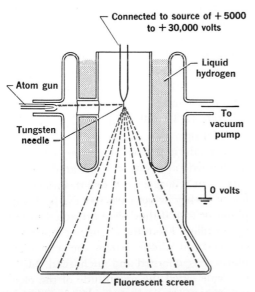

Fig. 6-6. A simplified diagram of a field ion microscope.

Connected to source of + 5000
to + 30,000 volts

Liquid
hydrogen

Atom gun

Tungsten
needle

To
vacuum
pump

0 volts

Fluorescent screen

volts, was connected to the electrodes, no electricity flowed between them. If, however, some of the air was removed from the tube, electricity began to flow from one electrode to another through the rarefied air, and the air in the tube gave off light. (This is the principle of operation of modern neon signs.) When still more air was removed from the tube, the light emitted by the air faded, and the glass walls of the tube glowed with a greenish fluorescence.

The evacuated tube in Fig. 6-8(A), page 139, is fitted with electrodes and has a metal cross inserted in it. When the electrodes of this tube are connected to a source of high voltage electricity, the glass walls glow green everywhere except in the area of the shadow cast by the cross. Apparently, the cause of the green fluorescence is a radiation traveling in straight lines from the negative electrode. Since the negative electrode is called the cathode, the rays producing the green fluorescence in the glass are called *cathode rays*. (The positive terminal in such discharge tubes is called the anode.)

In 1895, the French scientist Jean Perrin (1870-1942) was investigating the nature of these cathode rays. He devised an evacuated discharge tube, fitted with electrodes, which also contained a slit and a screen. When the tube was in operation, the slit produced a narrow beam of cathode rays. The screen fluoresced when struck by cathode rays and thus showed the path taken by the rays. The rays normally took a horizontal path through the tube, as shown in Fig. 6-8(B), but when Perrin placed a magnet near the beam of cathode rays, as shown in Fig. 6-8(C), the beam was deflected downward.

As you know, a magnet can attract pieces of iron and steel. It can also exert a force which alters the course of a beam of *electrically charged particles*. Now, only radiations consisting of moving *negatively charged* particles are affected in the way

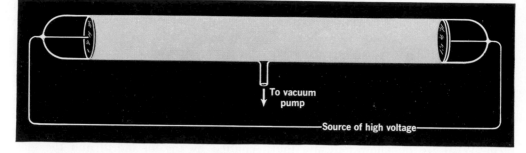

Fig. 6-7. Electricity passing through the low pressure air in this tube causes it to glow with a purplish-pink color.

that Perrin observed. Radiations similar to light are not affected by a magnet. So Perrin showed, by this experiment, that cathode rays were actually a stream of negatively charged particles.

Although many experimenters such as Perrin and Sir William Crookes (1832–1919) investigated the properties of cathode rays, credit is usually given to J. J. Thomson (1856–1940) for identifying this radiation with the particle we now call the electron. He studied the deflection of cathode rays under the influence of magnetism and of electrically charged plates, using a tube like that in Fig. 6-9, page 140, and showed that cathode-ray particles are much lighter than atoms. He also concluded that these particles are present in all forms of matter, since the nature of the radiation did not change when he changed the composition of the cathode or of the gas in the tube. Thus Thomson is credited with the discovery of one type of particle found in atoms—the *electron*.

Today we know that electrons are negatively charged particles with a *rest* mass of 9.1083×10^{-28} g. (In Chapter 5, Section 9, we learned that the mass of particles such as electrons, which can move with speeds which approach that of light, undergoes a significant increase as their speed increases.) The atomic mass of an electron is 0.0005486, $\frac{1}{1837}$ of the mass of an atom of hydrogen. The electron is a very small particle; while its size is not

precisely known, its diameter is believed to be about 10^{-12} cm, or 10^{-4} Å.

5. The magnitude of the charge on an electron. After the discovery of the electron, many scientists tried to determine its electric charge. By 1911 the American physicist R. A. Millikan (1868–1953) had determined the value of the electronic charge within one percent of the presently accepted value. His oil-drop experiment is one of the classic experiments of physics.

Millikan's apparatus was substantially that shown in Fig. 6-10. Fine drops of oil were sprayed into a closed vessel containing air at a low pressure. The friction in the atomizer caused some of the oil drops to acquire an electric charge. Occasionally, a charged drop of oil would pass through the hole in the uncharged top capacitor plate and become visible in the telescope. Millikan watched this drop fall under the influence of gravity. He used the rate of its fall to determine the size of the drop.

When the capacitor plates were charged, uncharged oil drops still fell at the same rate, but charged oil drops either fell faster if they were attracted to the lower plate, or rose if they were attracted to the upper plate. From the change of motion of charged oil drops when the capacitor plates were charged and uncharged, Millikan calculated the magnitude of the electric charge on each drop. He found that the charges were always a certain value

or a multiple of this value, and thus concluded that the smallest charge found on
an oil drop must be the same as the charge
on an electron. The present value for this
charge is -1.6019×10^{-19} coulomb. The
coulomb as a unit of electric charge is
explained in Chapter 18, Section 9.

6. The discovery of the atomic nucleus.
Another experiment of great importance
to our understanding of atomic structure
was carried out in 1911 by Ernest Rutherford (1871–1937), an English physicist.
He bombarded a thin metal foil with a
stream of alpha particles (tiny positively
charged particles emitted by the radioactive element radium). Most of the alpha
particles passed straight through the
metal foil, showing that the foil was very
porous to such tiny particles. A few alpha
particles were deflected slightly from their
path, while a few others were deflected
either at right angles to the foil or back
in the direction from which they had
come. See Fig. 6-11, page 141. Several years
later, Rutherford described the unexpected
result of this experiment as follows: "It
was about as credible as if you had fired
a 15-inch shell at a piece of tissue paper
and it came back and hit you."

Apparently the few greatly deflected
alpha particles had been turned from
their course by interaction with some part
of the atoms of the metal foil. Since alpha
particles are positively charged and have
a speed of about 20,000 mi/sec, their
marked deflection could be explained by
assuming that they were repelled by
massive, positively charged parts of the
atoms of the foil. (This assumption is

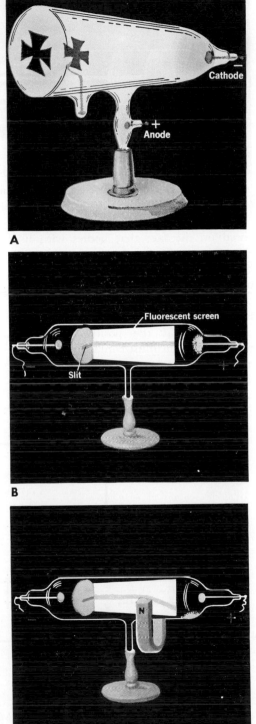

Fig. 6-8. (A) The radiation causing the
green fluorescence of the walls of an evacuated discharge tube travels in straight lines
from the cathode. (B) The slit in the metal
disk permits only a narrow beam of cathode
radiation to strike the fluorescent screen.
(C) The action of a magnet on a beam of
cathode radiation shows that it consists of
negatively charged particles.

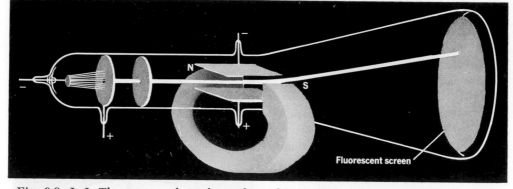

Fig. 6-9. J. J. Thomson used a tube such as this to show that cathode radiation particles are much lighter than atoms and are present in all forms of matter.

based on the fact that bodies with like electrostatic charges repel one another.) However, the infrequency of the deflections indicated that this massive, positively charged part of an atom is very small. From his experimental data, Rutherford concluded that the positively charged part of an atom must contain most of the mass of the atom, and yet be only 10^{-4} the diameter of the atom itself. Rutherford called this part of the atom the *atomic nucleus*. An atomic nucleus is about 10^{-4} Å in diameter, which is of the same order of magnitude as the diameter of an electron.

7. The discovery of the proton. Since atoms are electrically neutral, the discovery of electrons spurred the hunt for the positively charged particle in atoms. Significant progress had been made in this direction even before Rutherford's discovery of the atomic nucleus. If a perforated disk is used as a cathode in a discharge tube, luminous rays appear in straight lines coming through the hole

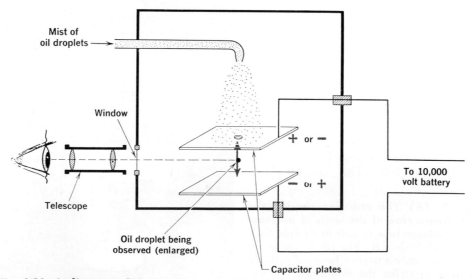

Fig. 6-10. A diagram of the apparatus for Millikan's oil-drop experiment. When the oil droplet is stationary, the upward force of attraction of the charged plates just equals the downward force of gravitational attraction.

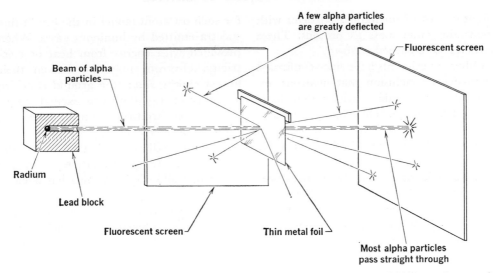

Fig. 6-11. A diagram showing the scattering effect of thin metal foil on a beam of alpha particles from radium.

on the side opposite the anode. In 1895 Perrin tested this radiation with magnets and with electrically charged plates and showed that it consists of particles with a positive charge. In 1907 Thomson named them *positive rays*.

It was found that the properties of positive rays, unlike those of cathode rays, depend on the nature of the gas in the tube. The charge-to-mass ratio of the particles composing positive rays showed that they were charged particles formed from atoms of the gas in the tube. No positive particles with a charge-to-mass ratio similar to that of the electron were found. The lightest particle found in positive rays had the mass of a hydrogen atom, and carried a charge equal in magnitude but opposite in sign to that carried by an electron. This positive particle was assumed to be a hydrogen atom from which one electron had been removed. Other experiments shortly indicated that this positively charged hydrogen atom is an important part of the structure of other atoms. The name *proton* was given to this particle in 1920.

Protons are positively charged particles with a mass of 1.67239×10^{-24} g, which is $\frac{1836}{1837}$ of the mass of a hydrogen atom. On the atomic mass scale, the mass of a proton is 1.007596. Since a hydrogen atom consists of a proton and an electron, most of the mass of a hydrogen atom is that of its proton. While a proton has much more mass than an electron, it is believed to be somewhat smaller, having a diameter of $2.5 - 3.0 \times 10^{-5}$ Å. A proton has one unit of positive electric charge, equal in magnitude but opposite in sign to that of the electron. Since atoms are electrically neutral, they must have an equal number of protons and electrons.

8. The discovery of the neutron. In 1930 physicists found that when certain elements such as beryllium or boron are bombarded with alpha particles from the radioactive element polonium, a radiation with very high penetrating power is obtained. Two years later, it was shown that this radiation could cause the emission of high-speed protons from a hydrogen-containing material like paraffin. In order to explain the nature and properties of this radiation, James Chadwick (1891–   ), an English physicist, suggested that it might consist of uncharged particles with about the same mass as protons. These particles were named *neutrons*.

Other experiments have since confirmed Chadwick's conclusion that neutrons are fundamental atomic particles that have no electric charge. They have a mass of 1.675×10^{-24} g (roughly the same mass as a proton). On the atomic mass scale, the mass of a neutron is 1.008986.

9. Early ideas about atomic structure. A short time after Thomson discovered that electrons were a part of all matter, he made a proposal about the possible structure of atoms. His idea was that an atom was a collection of electrons gathered into a spherical space, that this space acted as if it had a charge of positive electricity equal in amount to the negative electricity of the electrons, and that the electrons were arranged in a series of concentric shells. While Thomson's idea of the positive part of an atom was very indefinite, his concept of the arrangement of electrons was significant.

We have already learned how Rutherford's work on the scattering of alpha particles showed that an atom does not consist of a uniform sphere. Instead, the positive part is concentrated at the center of the atom in a very small nucleus, approximately 10^{-4} Å in diameter. Rutherford believed that the electrons form a spherical grouping around the nucleus so that the atom as a whole has a diameter of about 1 Å.

An explanation of the possible arrangement of electrons in an atom was made in 1913 by Niels Bohr (1885–   ), a Danish physicist, who suggested that electrons move in circular orbits around the nucleus. Bohr believed that there are several possible orbits about a nucleus, and that electrons in each orbit have a characteristic amount of energy; electrons in orbits close to the nucleus have low energy, while those in orbits farther from the nucleus have higher energy. Bohr found evidence

for such an atom model in the bright-line spectra emitted by luminous gases. When provided with energy from heat or electricity, electrons may move from their lowest energy state (the ground state) to a higher energy state (an excited state). When an electron returns from an excited state to a lower energy state, it emits energy as radiation of a characteristic wavelength. If the radiation is in the range of visible light, it also has a characteristic color.

According to Bohr, a hydrogen atom has a proton nucleus, with one electron moving about it in a circular orbit. If the proton were the size of a pinhead, the electron, somewhat larger, would revolve about it in an orbit with a radius of 40 ft. Later, modifications of Bohr's ideas were proposed by Arnold Sommerfeld (1868–1951), a German physicist, who suggested the possibility of elliptical electron orbits as well as circular ones.

10. The wave properties of atomic particles. So far we have described electrons and protons as particles. However, in 1927 physicists discovered that under certain conditions, a beam of electrons behaves in ways previously associated only with radiations such as light and radio waves. For example, the direction of an electron beam can be altered by its passage through a narrow slit, a phenomenon characteristic of waves. The electron microscopes we use today are applications of this wave property of electrons.

Physicists have since shown that protons and neutrons, as well as electrons, exhibit wave properties.

11. The uncertainty principle. The discovery that matter exhibits both particle and wave properties led Werner Heisenberg (1901–   ) in 1927 to develop the *uncertainty principle: it is impossible simultaneously to determine **exactly** both the position of an object and its momentum*—or any quantity related to its momentum, such as velocity or energy. The expected error in any such simultaneous determination has been calculated to be of the order of 10^{-26} erg-sec. Thus, for bodies of ordinary mass, this error is smaller than errors in measurement, and the uncertainty effect is not observable. With electrons, however, which have a mass of about 10^{-27} g, the effect is pronounced.

Thus, applying the uncertainty principle, we may be able to determine where an electron is, but we cannot at the same time determine its speed or direction. This is because the method (short wavelength radiation) which we must use to determine the position of the electron changes its momentum. Likewise, to determine an electron's momentum, we must use an instrument which changes the electron's direction of motion, and thus prevents us from determining its position. The same situation exists with respect to other atomic particles.

12. The present concept of atomic structure. Past discoveries have shown that an atom consists of a nucleus containing protons and usually neutrons, with electrons moving about the nucleus in paths dictated by their energies.

1. The nucleus. The nucleus of an atom is about 10^{-4} the diameter of the atom, yet the nucleus contains virtually all the mass of the atom. The number of protons in known nuclei varies from 1 to 102, the number of known chemical elements at the time of this writing. The number of protons in the nucleus is characteristic of the atoms of a particular element. Thus, all atoms of hydrogen have 1 proton in their nuclei, while all oxygen atoms have 8 protons, and all uranium atoms have 92 protons. *The number of protons in the nucleus of an atom is the **atomic number** of the atom.* The atomic number of an atom is represented by Z. Thus, for hydrogen, $Z = 1$, for oxygen, $Z = 8$, and for uranium, $Z = 92$. The concept of atomic numbers was developed by Henry Moseley (1887–1915), an English scientist, as a

result of studying the X-ray spectra of the chemical elements.

The greater the number of protons in a nucleus, the greater the number of neutrons also. While in light-weight nuclei the ratio of protons to neutrons is nearly 1:1, in heavier nuclei it rises to 1:1.6. The nucleus of the most abundant type of hydrogen atom is the only one which does not contain neutrons. The nucleus of the most abundant type of oxygen atom contains 8 protons and 8 neutrons, and the nucleus of the most abundant type of uranium atom contains 92 protons and 146 neutrons. The number of neutrons in a nucleus is represented by N. For the hydrogen atom described, $N = 0$, while for the oxygen and uranium atoms described, $N = 8$ and 146, respectively. Because the mass of a proton or a neutron is so nearly 1 amu, *the **mass number** of an atom is also the sum of the number of protons and neutrons in its nucleus,* or

$$A = Z + N$$

(Compare this definition with the one given in Section 2.) Thus, the mass numbers determined in this manner for the hydrogen, oxygen, and uranium nuclei just described are $1 + 0 = 1$, $8 + 8 = 16$, and $92 + 146 = 238$, respectively. Protons and neutrons are spoken of collectively as *nucleons*.

It is possible for two atoms of the same element to have nuclei containing the same number of protons but different numbers of neutrons. These atoms are *isotopes*. **Isotopes** *are atoms whose nuclei contain the same number of protons but different numbers of neutrons.* The element hydrogen exists in three isotopic forms: *protium*, 1 proton, no neutron; *deuterium*, 1 proton, 1 neutron; and *tritium*, 1 proton, 2 neutrons. Isotopes of all the chemical elements are known to occur naturally or have been produced artificially.

In general, nuclei with odd atomic numbers exist naturally in only one or two isotopic forms. Those with even atomic numbers exist in several isotopic forms, some elements having as high as eleven.

Isotopes have the same atomic number, but have different atomic masses, and therefore different mass numbers. The following table gives these data for the naturally occurring isotopes of hydrogen, oxygen, and uranium.

★ The elements as they occur naturally are mixtures of isotopes in quite definite proportions. *The physicist's atomic weight is the weighted average of the atomic masses of the isotopes based on their relative abundance.* The physicist's atomic weight scale is based on the weight of the oxygen isotope with mass number 16 as 16.0000.

Some unfamiliar type of force must hold the protons and neutrons together in the nucleus. They cannot be held by electrostatic attraction, because the similarly charged protons would repel each other; and neutrons, being neutral, are not subject to electrostatic attraction. The force

cannot be gravitational either, because calculations show that it would be too weak. The forces between nuclear particles have very short range, somewhat smaller than the diameter of a nucleus. The type of force acting in the nucleus is believed to be an *exchange force*, which binds the protons and neutrons together by means of a continuous exchange of a third particle between them. This third particle is believed to be a π meson (*messon* or *mee*-son). The mass of a π meson is about 275 times that of an electron. A meson may be positive, negative, or neutral. It can exist as an independent particle for only about 10^{-8} sec. This exchange force idea involving π mesons is not entirely satisfactory, but it has been sufficiently useful to lead scientists to believe that it is at least partly correct.

Although we are not certain of the nature of the binding force, we can determine rather accurately the *binding energy* which holds the particles of a nucleus together. *The mass of a nucleus is always less*

Isotope	Nuclear particles	Atomic number	Atomic mass	Mass number
Protium	1 proton	1	1.008145	1
Deuterium	1 proton 1 neutron	1	2.014740	2
Tritium	1 proton 2 neutrons	1	3.017005	3
Oxygen-16	8 protons 8 neutrons	8	16.00000 (by definition)	16
Oxygen-17	8 protons 9 neutrons	8	17.004534	17
Oxygen-18	8 protons 10 neutrons	8	18.004855	18
Uranium-234	92 protons 142 neutrons	92	234.114064	234
Uranium-235	92 protons 143 neutrons	92	235.117496	235
Uranium-238	92 protons 146 neutrons	92	238.125223	238

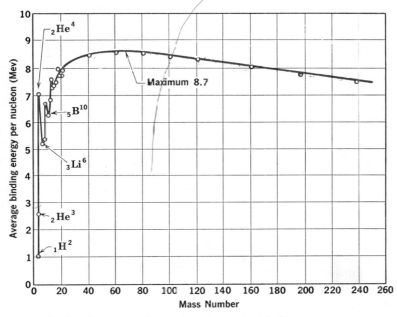

Fig. 6-12. Graph showing the relationship between binding energy per nucleon and mass number.

than the combined mass of its constituent parti-cles by an amount called the mass defect, which is equivalent to the nuclear binding energy. Let us take the formation of a helium nucleus, 2 protons and 2 neutrons, as an example. The mass of a proton is 1.007596 amu, while that of a neutron is 1.008986 amu; 2×1.007596 amu $+ 2 \times 1.008986$ amu $= 4.033164$ amu. The mass of a helium nucleus is 4.002777 amu. The difference, 4.033164 amu $- 4.002777$ amu $= 0.030387$ amu, the mass defect. Converting this to grams,

0.030387 amu $\times 1.660 \times 10^{-24}$ g/amu
$= 5.045 \times 10^{-26}$ g

and substituting in Einstein's equation, $E = mc^2$,

$E = 5.045 \times 10^{-26}$ g $\times (3 \times 10^{10}$ cm/sec$)^2$
$E = 4.54 \times 10^{-5}$ erg

It is this energy, liberated during the for-mation of a helium nucleus, which holds it together.

An erg is an inconveniently large unit to use in measuring nuclear binding ener-gies. Nuclear physicists use an electron volt (ev) instead. *An electron volt is the energy required to move an electron between two points which have a potential difference of one volt.* The million electron volt (Mev) is also used. The following approximate equivalents are useful:

1 amu = 931 Mev
1 erg = 6.24×10^5 Mev

The binding energy of a helium nucleus is therefore

0.030387 amu $\times 931$ Mev/amu $= 28.3$ Mev

By calculating the nuclear binding ener-gies for many of the elements, physicists have learned that this binding energy is proportional to the number of nucleons. This agrees with the exchange force theory of nuclear bonding. If the nuclear binding energy is divided by the number of nu-cleons, the binding energy per nucleon may be determined. For helium, this is 28.3 Mev ÷ 4 nucleons = 7.1 Mev/nu-cleon. The graph in Fig. 6-12 shows the variation of binding energy per nucleon

with mass number. Note that elements of
low or high mass number have lower binding energies per nucleon than those of
intermediate mass number. These data
will be considered more fully in Chapter 7.

2. The electron shells. Since atoms are
electrically neutral, they must contain
equal numbers of protons and electrons.
Thus, *Z* also equals the number of electrons in an atom. The electrons move
about the nucleus, each electron having a
definite amount of energy which determines the *orbital* in which it moves. An
orbital is not an orbit or path in the physical sense, but is a probable pattern of
movement characteristic of the energy of
the particle. Groups of orbitals are called
shells or *energy levels* in an atom and are
frequently designated by letters of the al-
phabet beginning with K and running sequentially to Q in the most complex elements. They are also sometimes numbered
from 1 to 7. The number of orbitals in a
shell is the square of the shell number
(1st shell, 1 orbital; 2nd shell, 4 orbitals;
3rd shell, 9 orbitals, etc.). The maximum
number of electrons which can occupy an
orbital is 2; thus the maximum number of
electrons which can occupy a shell is two

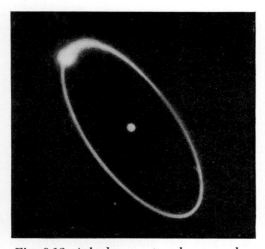

Fig. 6-13. A hydrogen atom has a nucleus
consisting of one proton. One electron
moves about this nucleus in the K shell.

times the number of orbitals in the shell.

While atoms may be pictured as in Figs.
6-13 and 6-14, you should remember that
the paths of electrons are not so definite
as these diagrams show. Each path diagram merely represents the region in which
the probability of finding a particular
electron is greatest. This lack of precision
in our physical picture of an atom is, of
course, explained by the uncertainty
principle.

The motion of electrons in shells about
the nucleus enables them to occupy, in
effect, the vast empty space about the
nucleus. The aggregate of electrons is referred to as the *electron cloud*. The electron
cloud is held near the nucleus by electrostatic attraction, while the electrons themselves mutually repel one another because
of their similar charge. The electron cloud
forms an electronic field about an atom
which gives it volume and prohibits the
interpenetration of one atom by another.

13. The mass spectrograph. We have
already learned that a magnet can alter
the course of a beam of moving charged
particles. If all the particles in the beam
have the same velocity, the same charge,
and the same mass, they will be equally
deflected by the action of the magnet.
However, if they differ in mass, the magnet
will have more effect on the less massive
particles. The magnet exerts a definite
force, which produces an acceleration in
the particle inversely proportional to its
mass (Newton's second law of motion).
If this acceleration produces a change in
the direction of the particle, the less massive and therefore more highly accelerated
particle will undergo a greater change of
direction. If these highly accelerated particles are ions produced from the naturally
occurring mixture of isotopes of an element, it should be possible to use the magnetic method to separate an element into
its isotopic forms and thus determine their
relative abundance. An apparatus of this
sort was constructed by F. W. Aston

Fig. 6-14. An oxygen atom has a nucleus consisting of 8 protons and 8 neutrons. Two electrons are in the K shell and 6 electrons are in the L shell.

(1877–1945), an English physicist, in 1919. It is called a *mass spectrograph*.

Figure 6-15 is a simplified diagram of a mass spectrograph. A beam of ions passes between electrically charged plates, which attract ions that are not of the desired charge. Ions that are of the desired charge are deflected by the plates toward the magnet. The magnet deflects the ions again, causing those of different masses to take separate paths. The ions then strike a photographic plate. When the plate is developed, dark bands appear where the ions struck the plate. From the intensity of these bands and their spacing, it is possible to determine the isotopic masses and their relative abundance.

By replacing the photographic plate with collecting vessels, it is possible to separate mechanically the isotopes of an element.

14. The bonding of atoms. Atoms may combine in several ways. We shall describe three distinct types of bonding.

1. Ionic bonding. When atoms combine by ionic bonding, one or more electrons *are transferred* from the outer shell of one atom to the outer shell of a second atom.

By this process, both atoms usually attain outer shells with a very stable structure. The K shell is very stable when it contains 2 electrons. The other shells are stable when they contain 8 electrons.

When sodium reacts with chlorine to form common salt, sodium chloride, the single electron in the M shell of the sodium atom is transferred to the M shell of the chlorine atom. The sodium particle, now deficient by 1 electron, has an outer shell of 8 electrons, but 1 excess positive charge; this particle is no longer a neutral sodium atom but is a positively charged sodium *ion*. Likewise, the chlorine particle has an outer shell of 8 electrons but 1 excess negative charge; this particle is a chloride *ion*. *An ion is an atom or a group of atoms with an unbalanced electrostatic charge.* Because

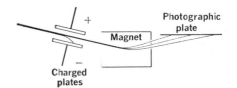

Fig. 6-15. A simplified diagram of a mass spectrograph.

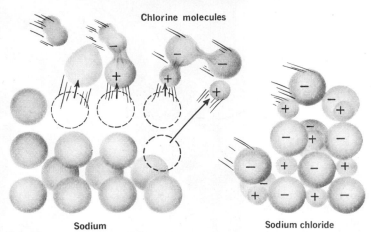

Fig. 6-16. When sodium reacts with chlorine to form common salt, an electron is transferred from the outer shell of each sodium atom to the outer shell of each chlorine atom. The particles composing the salt are sodium ions and chloride ions.

energy is emitted in the process of electron transfer, the resulting ions are more stable than the original atoms.

2. Covalent bonding. Atoms may also *share* outer shell electrons in an attempt to attain stable configurations. Two hydrogen atoms each share an electron in forming a hydrogen *molecule*. Thus, the K shell of each atom in effect contains two electrons. In a water molecule, the oxygen atom shares one of its outer shell electrons with each of two hydrogen atoms. Each of the hydrogen atoms shares its single electron

with the oxygen atom. In this way, the outer L shell of the oxygen atom contains in effect 8 electrons and the outer K shell of each hydrogen atom contains in effect 2 electrons. Energy is usually emitted in the process of electron sharing and the molecule thus produced is more stable than the original atoms. In a few cases energy must be absorbed to produce a molecule from its constituent atoms. These molecules have more energy than their constituent atoms and are consequently unstable.

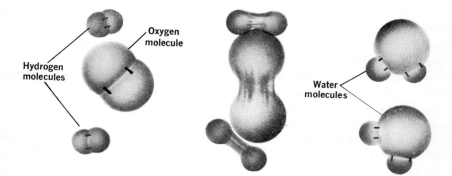

Fig. 6-17. In the water molecules which result from the reaction of hydrogen and oxygen, the oxygen atom shares an outer shell electron with each of two hydrogen atoms, while each of the hydrogen atoms shares its single electron with the oxygen atom. This is an example of covalent bonding.

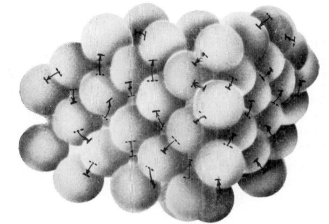

Fig. 6-18. The atoms of a metal are held together by exchange forces caused by the continual interchange of outer shell electrons among "near neighbor" atoms.

3. Metallic bonding. In solid metals, the atoms are packed as closely together as possible. This means that in most metals, each atom has 12 other atoms surrounding it. The outer shell electrons of all these atoms are loosely held and are continually being *exchanged*. The exchange process produces the attraction between the like atoms in a metal. Energy is given off when a solid metal is formed from its vapor, and thus the atoms bonded together in a solid are more stable than the independent atoms which exist in a metallic vapor.

15. Changes in matter. Iron rusts, water freezes, sugar dissolves in water, milk sours, radium disintegrates and eventually produces lead. These are just some of the changes which occur daily. Changes in matter are of three kinds: (1) *physical,* (2) *chemical,* and (3) *nuclear.*

When a physical change occurs, the identity of the substance is not lost. When water freezes and forms ice, its composition is not changed; if we heat the ice, it changes back into water. When sugar dissolves in water it undergoes a physical change; if the water evaporates, the sugar remains behind. *In a physical change the composition of the substance is not changed.* The substance consists of the same molecules, or atoms, or ions as it did before.

However, when chemical changes occur, new substances having their own distinct properties are formed, using the ions or atoms of the original substances. The rusting of iron produces a new material, iron oxide. Sour milk certainly has different properties from the sweet milk it was originally. *In a chemical change the composition of the substance is changed, and new substances with new properties are produced.* We still have the same atoms or ions, as well as the same number of atoms or ions, but they are rearranged to form new substances.

Still another important change occurs in matter. A nuclear change is like a chemical change because new substances with new properties are formed. *But in a nuclear change, the new materials are formed by changes in the identity of atoms themselves.* In nature some of these changes take place spontaneously. One example is the gradual change of radium atoms into lead atoms. Under man's direction, other nuclear changes are being brought about. Atomic and hydrogen bombs owe their destructive force to nuclear changes, while the creative results of nuclear changes include the production of power, the improved treatment of disease, and a new understanding of plant and animal life.

Summary

The smallest particle of any substance which has the properties of that substance is a molecule. Molecules are composed of atoms, which are the smallest particles of the chemical elements that can enter into combination with other elements. Atoms, in turn, have a dense, central nucleus, which contains protons and (except for protium) neutrons, and which is surrounded by a cloud of electrons arranged in shells or energy levels.

Under certain conditions atomic particles exhibit wave characteristics. The uncertainty principle states that it is impossible simultaneously to determine exactly both the position of an object and its momentum.

Isotopes are atoms whose nuclei contain the same number of protons but different numbers of neutrons. The mass spectrograph makes possible the separation and determination of the relative abundance of isotopes. The physicist's atomic weight is the weighted average of the atomic masses of the isotopes based on their relative abundance.

The mass of a nucleus is always less than the combined mass of its constituent particles by an amount called the mass defect, which is equivalent to the nuclear binding energy. Binding energies are conveniently expressed in million electron volts.

Atoms may be bonded by ionic bonding, covalent bonding, or metallic bonding. Changes in matter are physical, chemical, or nuclear.

TERMS TO DEFINE

Ångström	electron	neutron
atom	electron cloud	nuclear change
atomic mass	electron shell	nucleon
atomic mass unit	electron volt	nucleus
atomic number	energy level	oil-drop experiment
binding energy	exchange force	orbital
Bohr atom	ion	physical change
bombardment of metal foil	ionic bonding	physicist's atomic weight
with alpha particles	isotope	π meson
cathode rays	mass defect	positive rays
chemical change	mass number	proton
chemical element	mass spectrograph	uncertainty principle
covalent bonding	metallic bonding	wave properties of atomic
electrode	molecule	particles

QUESTIONS

A 1. What is the smallest particle of a substance that can exist free and still exhibit all the properties of the substance?
2. What is an atom?
3. (a) What is the range of atomic diameters? (b) What is the range of masses of atoms?

4. How did cathode rays receive their name?
5. What effect do cathode rays have on the glass of an evacuated tube?
6. (a) What are positive rays? (b) What are the particles of lowest mass found in positive rays?

7. Compare the masses, diameters, and charges of protons and electrons.

8. What device is an application of the wave behavior of electrons?

9. (a) What name is given to the number of protons in the nucleus of an atom? (b) How does the proton-neutron ratio vary with atomic mass?

10. What is the relationship between the mass number, the atomic number, and the number of neutrons in an atom?

11. What are nucleons?

12. (a) What do isotopes have in common? (b) In what ways do they differ?

13. What information may be obtained through the use of a mass spectrograph?

14. What are the differences between ionic, covalent, and metallic bonding?

15. Give examples of physical, chemical, and nuclear changes.

B 16. (a) What is the size of molecules which may be photographed with the aid of an electron microscope? (b) What is the size of ordinary molecules, like those of water?

17. (a) What is the magnitude of an atomic mass unit? (b) How was this value determined?

18. (a) What did Perrin discover about the nature of cathode rays? (b) Who identified them as a stream of what are now called electrons? (c) What was the scope of his investigations?

19. (a) Who determined the value of the electronic charge by means of the oil-drop experiment? (b) On what principle is the oil-drop experiment based?

20. Describe the experiment by which Rutherford showed that an atom has a very small, massive, positively charged nucleus.

21. What was the nature of the experiments which led to the discovery of the neutron?

22. (a) What was Thomson's concept of atomic structure? (b) What was Rutherford's contribution? (c) How were these ideas refined by Bohr and Sommerfeld?

23. (a) What is the uncertainty principle? (b) What is the magnitude of the uncertainty? (c) Why is it significant only for atomic particles?

24. What relationship generally exists between the atomic number of an atom and the number of its isotopes?

25. What is believed to be the nature of the force holding protons and neutrons together in the nucleus of an atom?

26. (a) What is the mass defect of an atom? (b) What is the nuclear binding energy? (c) How are they related?

27. (a) What is an electron volt? (b) What is a Mev?

28. How does the binding energy per nucleon vary with the mass number of an atom?

★ 29. What is the standard on which the physicist bases his system of atomic weights?

PROBLEMS

A 1. A hydrogen atom is 0.6 Å in diameter. What is its diameter in centimeters?

2. Moderately high speed electrons have a radiation wave length of 1.67×10^{-8} cm. Express this value in Ångström units.

3. (a) Calculate the mass in grams of an atom of an isotope of iron which has an atomic mass of 55.95332. (b) What is the mass number of this isotope?

4. The mass of an atom of an unstable isotope of neon is 3.818×10^{-23} g. (a) What is its atomic mass? (b) What is its mass number?

5. A calcium ion has 20 protons, 20 neutrons, and 18 electrons. What is the magnitude of its charge in coulombs?

6. (a) What is the atomic number of a zinc atom composed of 30 protons, 34 neutrons, and 30 electrons? (b) What is the mass number of the atom?

7. What particles, and how many of each, make up an atom of silver, atomic number 47, mass number 109?

★ 8. Calculate the mass of an electron which is moving with 80.0% of the speed of light.

B 9. Calculate the binding energy per nucleon in Mev for carbon-12. This isotope consists of 6 protons, 6 neutrons, and 6 electrons. Its atomic mass is 12.00386.

10. Calculate the binding energy per nucleon in Mev for sulfur-32 which consists of 16 protons, 16 neutrons, and 16 electrons, if its atomic mass is 31.98085.

★ 11. Calculate the physicist's atomic weight for chlorine if naturally occurring chlorine consists of 75.4% Cl-35 and 24.6% Cl-37. The respective atomic masses are 34.97867 and 36.97750.

★ 12. Naturally occurring magnesium consists of 78.6% Mg-24, 10.1% Mg-25, and 11.3% Mg-26. If their respective atomic masses are 23.9924, 24.9938, and 25.9898, calculate the physicist's atomic weight.

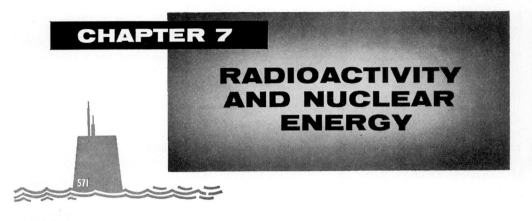

CHAPTER 7

RADIOACTIVITY AND NUCLEAR ENERGY

VOCABULARY

Alpha (α) particle. Particle identical with a helium nucleus emitted from the nucleus of a radioactive atom.

Beta (β) particle. Particle identical with an electron emitted from the nucleus of a radioactive atom.

Chain reaction. A reaction in which the material or energy which starts the reaction is also one of the products.

Cosmic rays. High energy particles which apparently come from beyond our solar system.

Critical size. The amount of radioactive material required to sustain a chain reaction.

Curie. A unit of radioactivity; one curie is the quantity of radioactive material giving 3.70×10^{10} disintegrations per second.

Fission. The disintegration of a nucleus into two medium-weight parts.

Fusion. The combination of two light-weight nuclei to form a heavier, more stable nucleus.

Gamma (γ) ray. High energy X ray emitted from the nucleus of a radioactive atom.

Half life. The length of time during which half of a given number of atoms of a radioactive element will disintegrate.

Moderator. A material which slows neutrons.

Nuclear disintegration. The emission of a proton or a neutron from a nucleus as a result of its bombardment with alpha particles, protons, deuterons, or neutrons.

Nuclear reactor. A device in which the controlled fission of radioactive material produces new radioactive substances and energy.

Radioactive decomposition. A radioactive change in which a nucleus emits a particle and rays, forming a lighter, more stable nucleus.

Radioactivity. The spontaneous, uncontrollable disintegration of the nucleus of an atom with the emission of particles and rays.

Transmutation. A change in the identity of a nucleus because of a change in its number of protons.

1. The discovery of radioactivity. In 1896 Henri Becquerel (1852–1908), a French scientist, discovered radioactivity. He found that the uranium ore, pitchblende, gives off an invisible radiation, and that this radiation affects an unexposed photographic plate in the same way that light affects the plate during exposure. Substances which emit such radiation are *radioactive*, and have the property called *radioactivity*. We now know that the emission of this radiation accompanies the spontaneous breakdown of the nuclei of the atoms of the radioactive material.

2. Naturally occurring radioactive elements. All of the naturally occurring elements with atomic numbers greater than 83 are radioactive. A few naturally radioactive isotopes of elements with atomic numbers smaller than 83 are also known. Of the natural radioactive elements, uranium and radium are probably better known to you than others such as thorium, radon, and polonium.

3. General properties of radioactive elements. All radioactive elements have been found to possess certain common characteristics.

1. They affect the light-sensitive emulsion on a photographic plate. Even though the photographic plate is wrapped in heavy black paper and kept in the dark, the radiation from radioactive materials penetrates the wrapping and affects the plate. When the plate is developed, a black spot shows up on the negative where the invisible radiation struck it. The radiation penetrates paper, wood, flesh, and *thin* sheets of metal.

2. They ionize the surrounding air. The emitted radiation strips electrons from the gas molecules in the air about the radioactive material. The gas molecules which have thus lost electrons are ions.

3. They produce fluorescence in certain other compounds. The radiation from radioactive materials produces a series of bright flashes when it strikes certain compounds. The combined effect of these flashes is a glow or fluorescence given off by the affected material. Radium bromide added to zinc sulfide causes the zinc sulfide to glow, and since the glow is visible in the dark, the mixture is useful as an ingredient of luminous paint.

4. They have pronounced physiological effects. Radiation from natural radioactive sources can kill plant seeds, bacteria, and even small animals. It can produce flesh burns that heal with great difficulty. Controlled radiation is used to destroy diseased tissue in the treatment of cancer and certain skin diseases.

5. They emit energy continuously. In highly radioactive materials some energy may be given off as visible light. In the dark, such materials glow with a pale phosphorescence. All radioactive materials give off some energy as heat. This energy emission is due to loss of mass as the nuclei of the radioactive material break down.

4. The nature of the radiation from radioactive materials. The radiation from the nuclei of the atoms of radioactive materials consists of

1. Alpha (α) particles. These are composed of two protons and two neutrons. They are the nuclei of helium atoms, with two positive electric charges and a mass about four times that of the hydrogen atom. Since their range of speeds is only from 10,000 to 20,000 mi/sec, their penetrating power is not very great. They can be stopped by a few centimeters of air, a thin piece of aluminum foil, or a thin sheet of paper. Alpha particles easily ionize gas molecules in the air.

2. Beta (β) particles. These are electrons, just as cathode rays are; they have a single negative electric charge and about $\frac{1}{1837}$ the mass of a hydrogen atom. Beta particles are much more penetrating than alpha particles, since their speed is from 60,000 to 160,000 mi/sec.

3. Gamma (γ) rays. These are high energy X rays—the same kind of radiation

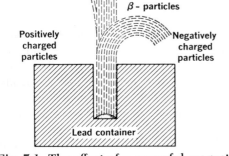

Fig. 7-1. The effect of a powerful magnetic field on the radiation from a radioactive material.

the paper and the south pole is below the paper. The heavy alpha particles are deflected slightly in one direction, the lighter beta particles are deflected more markedly in the other direction, and the gamma rays, being uncharged, are not deflected at all. By the use of such a magnetic field, Rutherford learned the nature of the radiation from radioactive materials.

5. The detection of radioactivity. Since the discovery of radioactivity, many methods have been developed for detecting it and measuring its intensity. These methods are based on the various properties of the radiation—the ability to produce fluorescence, to ionize the surrounding molecules, and to affect photographic plates. We shall describe several of the more important methods of detecting radioactivity.

1. The electroscope. One of the first instruments to be used in detecting and measuring radioactivity was the electroscope. A simple electroscope is shown in Fig. 7-2. A negatively charged electroscope becomes discharged when ions in the air take electrons from the electroscope disk. Similarly, a positively charged electroscope becomes discharged as it takes up electrons from the ions in the air. The rate at which an electroscope is discharged, then, is a measure of the number of ions in the air near the electroscope; and since radioactive materials produce ions in propor-

as visible light, but of much shorter wavelength and higher frequency. Gamma rays are believed to be produced by transitions in energy levels in the nucleus, and are the most penetrating radiations given off by radioactive elements. They produce phosphorescence and affect photographic plates.

Figure 7-1 shows the effect of a strong magnetic field, perpendicular to the plane of the paper, on the radiation from a small amount of radioactive material. Imagine that the north pole of the magnet is above

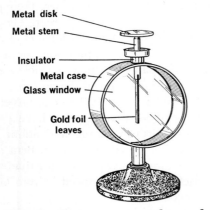

Fig. 7-2. An electroscope may be used to detect and measure radioactivity.

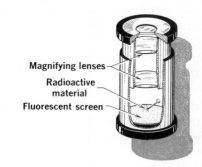

Fig. 7-3. A spinthariscope. Alpha and beta particles produce flashes of light on the fluorescent screen which may be observed through the magnifying lenses.

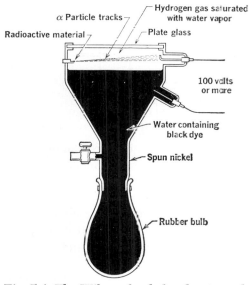

Fig. 7-4. The Wilson cloud chamber is used to study radioactive materials.

tion to their radioactivity, their effect on an electroscope is one way in which radioactivity may be measured.

2. *The spinthariscope.* The spinthariscope is another instrument which was used in the early studies of radioactivity. In this device, alpha and beta particles from radioactive materials strike a zinc sulfide screen; where they strike the screen they produce a momentary flash of light which can be observed through a magnifier. From a count of the number of flashes observed in a given period of time, the intensity of the radiation may be determined. See Fig. 7-3.

3. *The cloud chamber.* In 1911, C. T. R. Wilson (1869–1959) devised a cloud chamber apparatus similar to the one in Fig. 7-4. The lower part of the inverted cone and rubber bulb is filled with water, dyed black. The hydrogen gas above the dyed water becomes saturated with water vapor. In the upper compartment of the apparatus is a glass capsule containing a tiny bit of the radioactive material being studied, perhaps radium chloride. A potential difference of 100 volts or more is maintained across the illuminated space in the upper compartment.

When the rubber bulb is squeezed, the saturated hydrogen is compressed. As the bulb is released, the hydrogen expands, cools, and becomes supersaturated with water vapor. Tracks of alpha particles can now be seen through the glass against the dark background, because the alpha particles ionize some of the hydrogen molecules, causing particles of fog to condense on the molecules. The alpha particle tracks come out from the tip of the capsule in which the radioactive material is enclosed. Using such a cloud chamber, physicists can identify the fragments of atoms by means of the tracks made by the particles produced when the atoms disintegrate. See Fig. 7-5.

4. *The photographic method.* Charged particles such as alpha particles, beta particles, protons, and deuterons (deuterium nuclei) affect the emulsion of a photographic plate. When the plate is carefully

Fig. 7-5. Tracks of alpha particles photographed in a Wilson cloud chamber. (W. D. Harkins, University of Chicago)

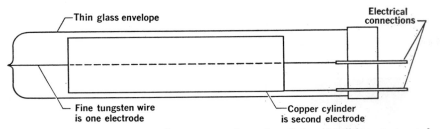

Fig. 7-6. A diagram showing the construction of a Geiger-Müller counter tube.

developed, the actual tracks of these particles through the emulsion become visible. Measurements of these tracks make it possible for scientists to determine the mass and charge of the particles.

5. *The Geiger counter.* A Geiger counter consists of a thin-walled glass tube called a *Geiger-Müller tube*, containing two electrodes and a gas at low pressure, connected with a suitable electronic counting circuit. One of the electrodes of the Geiger-Müller tube is a metal cylinder; the other is a fine wire. See Fig. 7-6. The potential difference between the electrodes is maintained at a level that is just below that necessary for discharging the tube. When a charged particle passes through the counter, it ionizes the gas in the tube. This lowers the resistance of the gas between the two electrodes, and allows current momentarily to pass. This passage may be registered as a "click" in a loudspeaker.

6. *The bubble chamber.* In a bubble chamber, Fig. 7-7, a transparent liquid such as ether, ethyl alcohol, or pentane is heated under pressure to a temperature well above its normal boiling point. When the pressure is released quickly, the liquid is in a highly unstable, superheated condition; it is ready to boil violently. An ionizing particle passing through the liquid at this instant leaves a trail of tiny bubbles which may be photographed. See Fig. 7-8.

6. The nuclear stability of the elements. In Chapter 6, Section 12, we discussed

Fig. 7-7. A bubble chamber. (D. Glaser, Lawrence Radiation Laboratories)

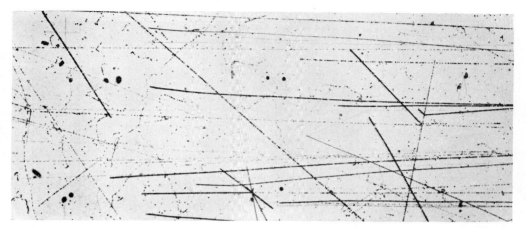

Fig. 7-8. This photograph shows the tracks of protons and π mesons through a propane bubble chamber. The heavy tracks stopping in the chamber are those of protons; the light tracks passing entirely through the chamber are those of π mesons. A number of interactions between particles are evident. (Brookhaven National Laboratory)

the binding energy which holds the protons and neutrons together in the nucleus of an atom, stating that the lightest and heaviest nuclei have the smallest binding energy per nucleon, while nuclei of elements of intermediate mass have the greatest binding energy per nucleon. Since the binding energy per nucleon is an indication of nuclear stability, we see that the nuclei of the lightest and heaviest atoms are less stable than the nuclei of elements of intermediate atomic mass. Factors other than mass are associated with the stability of atomic nuclei. These are (1) the ratio of neutrons to protons; and (2) the even-odd relationship of the number of neutrons to the number of protons.

Many properties of nuclear particles indicate that there are energy levels in the atomic nucleus, just as there are electron energy levels in the atom. In the most stable nuclei, the ratio of protons to neutrons is 1:1 but nuclei with a greater number of neutrons than protons have lower binding energy and are less stable. In nuclei with an equal number of protons and neutrons, these particles occupy the lowest energy levels in the nucleus and give it stability. However, in nuclei that contain an excess of neutrons over protons

some of the neutrons must occupy higher energy levels, reducing the binding energy and consequently lowering the stability of the nucleus.

The frequency of occurrence of stable nuclei gives evidence that the even-odd relationship of the number of protons to the number of neutrons affects the stability of a nucleus. By far the greatest number of stable nuclei have an even number of protons and an even number of neutrons. Less frequent in occurrence are stable nuclei with an even number of protons and an odd number of neutrons, or vice versa. Only a few stable nuclei are known which have an odd number of protons and an odd number of neutrons.

7. Types of nuclear reactions. Because of the differences in nuclear stability, nuclear reactions in which energy may be released are of four types. In each case a small amount of the mass of the reacting particles is converted into energy and the products have greater stability than the original particles.

1. A nucleus undergoes *radioactive decomposition,* forming a slightly lighter, more stable nucleus by emitting an alpha particle or a beta particle, and gamma rays.

THE URANIUM DISINTEGRATION SERIES

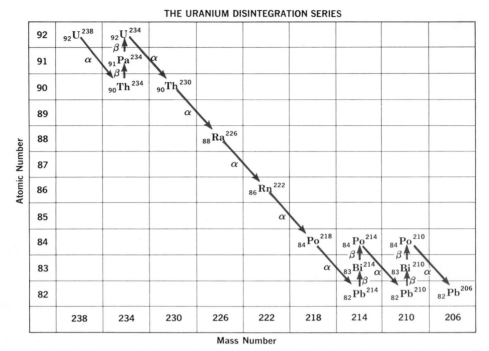

Fig. 7-9. The Uranium Disintegration Series is one of four known series of nuclear disintegrations.

2. A nucleus is bombarded with alpha particles, protons, deuterons, or neutrons. The unstable nucleus that is formed emits a proton or a neutron and becomes more stable. This process is called **nuclear disintegration.**

3. A very heavy nucleus is split and forms two medium-weight nuclei. This process is known as *fission.*

4. Light-weight nuclei combine to form heavier, more stable nuclei. This process is known as *fusion.*

We shall briefly describe each of these types of reactions, and give certain associated information, in the remaining sections of this chapter.

Fig. 7-10. The lower end of the Van de Graaff generator at the Massachusetts Institute of Technology. Here electric charges are put on the 48-in. rubber belts by repulsion from strongly negative, many-pointed electrodes. The charges ride up on the belt to the top of the generator, where they are picked off by a collector and transferred to the top terminal. See also the diagram of a Van de Graaff generator, Fig. 18-31. (Fay Photo)

Fig. 7-11. The insulating supporting columns and the top terminals of the Van de Graaff generator at the Massachusetts Institute of Technology. The supporting columns, made of layers of paper cemented with special shellac, are 6 ft in diameter and 25 ft high. The terminals are aluminum spheres 15 ft in diameter. The generator is capable of developing a potential difference of 2 million volts. (Fay Photo)

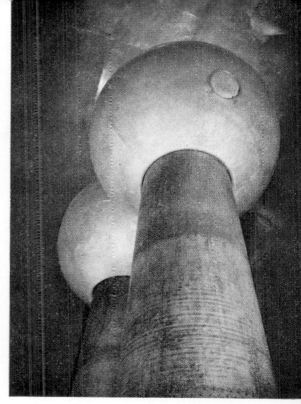

8. Radioactive decomposition. The nuclei of uranium, radium, and other radioactive elements are continually disintegrating. See Fig. 7-9. The alpha and beta particles emitted are products of spontaneous atomic disintegration in which certain heavy atoms break down into slightly lighter atoms. After an average life of 2500 years, for example, a radium atom disintegrates. This atom has an atomic mass of 226.095999. When it disintegrates, it loses an alpha particle, which becomes a neutral helium atom, mass 4.003873, upon gaining two electrons. The remainder of the atom, mass 222.-086899, is a gas known as radon. Thus two gases, helium and radon, are formed when an atom of radium disintegrates. The nuclear equation representing this change is

$$_{88}Ra^{226} \longrightarrow {}_{86}Rn^{222} + {}_2He^4 + energy$$

Only the nuclei are represented in this equation. The superscript is the mass number of the nucleus. The subscript is the atomic number. The letter symbols are the chemical symbols for the elements with the given atomic numbers. Alpha particles, since they are helium nuclei, are represented as $_2He^4$. The change represented by the equation is a nuclear change, since the identity of the nuclei of the radium atoms changes. It is also called a **transmutation,** *which is a change in the identity of a nucleus because of a change in the number of protons.*

The mass change in this reaction is $226.095999 - (222.086899 + 4.003873) = 0.005227$. This loss of mass indicates that

0.005227 amu $\times$ 931 Mev/amu $= 0.486$ Mev of energy is evolved, and that the products are more stable than the nucleus which underwent decomposition.

A more important concept than average life of a radioactive nucleus is its *half life. The half life of a nucleus is the length of time during which half of a given number of this type of radioactive nucleus will disintegrate.* The half life of $_{88}Ra^{226}$ is about 1620 years. This means that radium disintegrates at such a rate that of 1.00 g of radium which existed 1620 years ago, only 0.50 g remains today; and 1620 years from now, only half of this present amount, or 0.25 g, will remain. The average life of any nucleus is 1.44 times its half life.

If the half life of a nucleus is known, its *disintegration constant* (the ratio between the number of nuclei disintegrating per second and the total number of nuclei) can be calculated from

$$\lambda = \frac{0.693}{T_{\frac{1}{2}}}$$

In this formula λ (Greek letter lambda) is the disintegration constant in 1/sec if the half life $T_{\frac{1}{2}}$ is given in seconds. (The derivation of the formula is beyond the scope of high school physics.) For $_{88}Ra^{226}$

$$\lambda = \frac{0.693}{1620 \text{ yr} \times 365 \text{ da/yr} \times 86{,}400 \text{ sec/da}}$$

$$\lambda = 1.36 \times 10^{-11}/\text{sec}$$

In 1.000 g of radium there are 2.665×10^{21} nuclei; thus 2.665×10^{21} nuclei $\times 1.36 \times 10^{-11}/\text{sec} = 3.62 \times 10^{10}$ nuclei/sec disintegrating.

The commonly used unit of radioactivity is the *curie*. One **curie** is the quantity *of a radioactive material giving* 3.70×10^{10} *disintegrations per second.* Thus the radioactivity of 1 g of radium is approximately 1 curie.

The energy evolved per second from 1 g of radium will be 3.62×10^{10} nuclei/sec $\times 0.486$ Mev/nucleus $= 1.76 \times 10^{10}$ Mev/sec or 1.76×10^{10} Mev/sec $\times \frac{1 \text{ erg}}{6.24 \times 10^5 \text{ Mev}}$ $= 2.82 \times 10^4$ ergs/sec.

Radon atoms are much less stable than radium atoms, the half life of $_{86}Rn^{222}$ being only 3.82 days. When radon disintegrates by emitting an alpha particle, it forms polonium.

$$_{86}Rn^{222} \longrightarrow {}_{84}Po^{218} + {}_2He^4 + \text{energy}$$

Polonium, in turn, emits an alpha particle, forming an isotope of lead.

$$_{84}Po^{218} \longrightarrow {}_{82}Pb^{214} + {}_2He^4 + \text{energy}$$

This lead isotope emits a beta particle as it decomposes.

$$_{82}Pb^{214} \longrightarrow {}_{83}Bi^{214} + {}_{-1}e^0 + \text{energy}$$

Further changes as shown in Fig. 7-9 finally result in a lead isotope, $_{82}Pb^{206}$. Since this isotope is stable, the radioactive decomposition stops.

Figure 7-9 shows the steps in one series of nuclear disintegrations, that beginning with $_{92}U^{238}$. Three other series are also known, those beginning with $_{92}U^{235}$, $_{90}Th^{232}$, and $_{93}Np^{237}$.

9. Nuclear disintegration. Rutherford produced the first nuclear disintegration in 1919 by bombarding nitrogen with alpha particles from radium. He obtained protons (hydrogen nuclei) and an isotope of oxygen.

$$_7N^{14} + {}_2He^4 \longrightarrow {}_8O^{17} + {}_1H^1$$

This was also the first artificial transmutation produced, and the first evidence of protons as products of nuclear reactions.

A second important nuclear disintegration is that by which J. D. Cockcroft (1897–) and E. T. S. Walton (1903–), English scientists, verified Einstein's equation $E = mc^2$ in 1932. They bombarded lithium with high speed protons, producing alpha particles and energy.

$$_3Li^7 + {}_1H^1 \longrightarrow {}_2He^4 + {}_2He^4 + \text{energy}$$

The mass change is $(7.018232 + 1.008145) - 2(4.003873) = 0.018631$. This mass change is equivalent to 0.018631 amu $\times 931$ Mev/amu $= 17.32$ Mev of energy. Cockcroft and Walton measured the actual energy emitted by the reaction and found that it agreed very closely with this calculated energy.

A nuclear disintegration also carried out in 1932 led to the discovery of the neutron. See Chapter 6, Section 8. The reaction which occurs when beryllium is bombarded with alpha particles from polonium is

$$_4Be^9 + {}_2He^4 \longrightarrow {}_6C^{12} + {}_0n^1 + \text{energy}$$

This reaction is still employed for the production of neutrons for nuclear bombardment experiments.

10. Particle accelerators. Alpha particles from radioactive elements such as radium and polonium were not very effective in bringing about changes in the nuclei of atoms because they had little penetrating power. Consequently scientists looked for a new source of particles with which to bombard the nucleus. They wanted particles that would have greater velocity and more energy. One of the devices constructed to secure such particles was the Van de Graaff generator.

From Fig. 7-10, we see that a Van de Graaff generator is a kind of escalator for electrons. Electrons are put on the insulated moving belt by repulsion from a strongly negative electrode. They ride up on the belt to the top of the generator, where they are picked off by a collector and transferred to the top terminal. Thus a large negative charge can be built up on the top terminal. See Fig. 7-11. The large difference of electric potential thus obtained can be used to accelerate charged particles, electrons or protons, making them effective atomic bullets. Since the high charge on a Van de Graaff generator can leak off into the atmosphere if the air is humid, such generators are sometimes built under a large, pear-shaped shell which can be filled with dry air under pressure to keep the charge on the top terminal.

Dr. E. O. Lawrence (1901–1958), formerly of the University of California, invented an "atom smasher" which operates on a different principle from the Van de Graaff generator. Dr. Lawrence called it a *cyclotron*. See Fig. 7-12. *The cyclotron consists of a large cylindrical box, shaped like a pill box, placed between the poles of a huge electromagnet and used for accelerating charged particles.* The box is exhausted until a very high vacuum exists inside. The protons or deuterons used as bullets are fed into the center of the box. Inside the box are two hollow, D-shaped electrodes, called *dees*, which are connected to a source of very high voltage through an oscillator. When the cyclotron is in operation, the electric charge on these dees is reversed very rapidly by the oscillator. The combination of the high voltage alternating potential and the action of the field of the electromagnet causes the ions inside to take a spiral course. They move faster and faster as they near the outside of the box and acquire more and more energy. When they reach the outer rim of the box, they are deflected toward the target. The energy

of the particles accelerated in a cyclotron may reach 15 Mev. By means of the cyclotron, scientists have learned much about the structure of the atom, and about the products formed when atoms disintegrate.

Physicists, however, were still not satisfied with the energy of the ions from a cyclotron. They wanted to give more energy to the protons and deuterons than the highest practical energy which a cyclotron could provide (about 15 Mev). When physicists tried to make the particles go faster to give them more energy, the mass of the particles increased. (See Chapter 5, Section 9.) This increased mass slowed them down to such an extent that they could not reach the gap between the dees when the oscillating voltage reversed. The first change in the design of the particle accelerator to overcome this difficulty was to make the oscillator of variable frequency. Then, as the mass of the particles increased and their velocity dropped off,

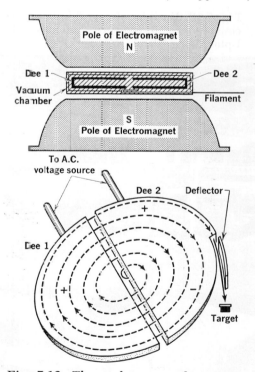

Fig. 7-12. The cyclotron accelerates protons or deuterons to 15 Mev energies.

the frequency of the oscillator could be reduced. The changes in the voltage of the field were timed to coincide with the slower acceleration of the more massive particles. This type of machine is called a *synchro-cyclotron*. In a synchro-cyclotron, the energy of the particles can be boosted to about 600 Mev.

A newer type of particle accelerator is the *synchrotron*. It also operates on the principle of accelerating particles by making them move in a circular path with increasing velocity. However, because both the oscillating voltage and the magnetic field are variable and controllable, the path of the particles is made to be a narrow circle of large diameter. The cosmotron at the Brookhaven National Laboratory, Upton, New York, and the bevatron at the University of California are the newest of these devices. They can impart energies of 3 to 6.5 billion electron volts to the accelerated protons.

The *betatron* is a device which accelerates electrons in much the same way as a cyclotron accelerates protons or deuterons. The accelerated electrons may be used as "bullets" for bombardment, or for producing high energy X rays. A powerful betatron is capable of giving electrons an energy of 250 Mev.

Still another particle accelerator is the *linear accelerator*. In this device, particles travel in a straight line through many stages of relatively small potential difference, each of which acts to accelerate the particles. Energies of 630 Mev have been obtained.

11. Advantages of neutrons as "bullets." Before neutrons were discovered in 1932, alpha particles and protons were used for the study of atomic nuclei. However, alpha particles and protons have a positive electric charge. Great quantities of energy, such as those imparted to these particles by cyclotrons and synchrotrons,

Fig. 7-13. Energies of over 3 billion electron volts can be imparted to protons by the cosmotron at Brookhaven National Laboratory. (Brookhaven National Laboratory, Upton, Long Island, New York)

Fig. 7-14. The interior of the heavy ion linear accelerator at the University of California Radiation Laboratory. This device is designed to accelerate the nuclei of atoms ranging up to argon, $_{18}A^{40}$, in mass. (University of California)

are required to "fire" these charged "bullets" into a nucleus, because their positive charge causes them to be repelled by the positive nuclear charge.

Neutrons have no charge and can easily penetrate the nucleus of an atom, since no force of repulsion is acting. Fast neutrons with energies up to about 1 Mev may either go right through an atom without causing any change in it, or cause the disintegration of a nucleus. On the other hand, slow neutrons, with energies of the order of 10 ev, are sometimes trapped by a nucleus, which then becomes unstable and may disintegrate. Fast neutrons may be slowed by passage through materials composed of elements of low atomic weight such as deuterium oxide or graphite. Such materials are called *moderators.* Neutrons are produced by an atom smasher when the accelerated positively charged particles strike a target material, usually beryllium. (See Section 9.)

12. Artificial radioactivity. It is possible to prepare radioactive atoms artificially.

In 1934 Irène Joliot-Curie (1897–1956), working with her husband, Frédéric (1900–1958), discovered that stable atoms can be made artificially radioactive by bombardment with deuterons or neutrons. It is now possible to produce radioactive isotopes of all the elements. Many radioactive isotopes are manufactured by slow neutron bombardment in the nuclear reactor at Oak Ridge, Tennessee. The equation showing the formation of radioactive $_{27}Co^{60}$ from naturally occurring nonradioactive $_{27}Co^{59}$ by slow neutron bombardment is

$$_{27}Co^{59} + _0n^1 \longrightarrow _{27}Co^{60}$$

The radiation from $_{27}Co^{60}$ consists of beta particles and gamma rays.

Radioactive $_{15}P^{32}$ is prepared by bombardment of $_{16}S^{32}$ with slow neutrons:

$$_{16}S^{32} + _0n^1 \longrightarrow _{15}P^{32} + _1H^1$$

The radiation from $_{15}P^{32}$ consists only of beta particles. Radioactive phosphorus and radioactive cobalt are used in the treatment of various forms of cancer. Also,

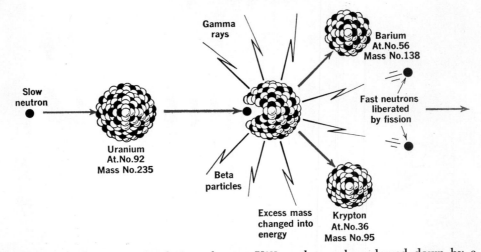

Fig. 7-15. Neutrons from the fission of one $_{92}U^{235}$ nucleus, when slowed down by a moderator, can cause fission in a second $_{92}U^{235}$ nucleus. This makes a chain reaction possible.

many radioactive isotopes are used as tracers to determine the course of chemical reactions, the wearing ability of various products, the efficiency of fertilizers, and the flow of fluids through pipelines.

13. The unusual nuclear properties of uranium. The element uranium, atomic number 92, exists in nature in three isotopic forms, $_{92}U^{234}$, $_{92}U^{235}$, and $_{92}U^{238}$. By far the most abundant is $_{92}U^{238}$, which forms 99.3 percent of naturally occurring uranium; $_{92}U^{235}$ exists to the extent of 0.7 percent, while only traces of $_{92}U^{234}$ have been found.

When $_{92}U^{238}$ is bombarded with slow neutrons, its nucleus may capture a neutron. This process results in formation of an unstable isotope of uranium, $_{92}U^{239}$, which emits a beta particle and forms a man-made radioactive element, neptunium, with atomic number 93.

$$_{92}U^{238} + _{0}n^{1} \rightarrow _{92}U^{239}$$
$$_{92}U^{239} \rightarrow _{93}Np^{239} + _{-1}e^{0}$$

Neptunium is also an unstable element. It ejects a beta particle from its nucleus, forming a second man-made element, plutonium, atomic number 94.

$$_{93}Np^{239} \rightarrow _{94}Pu^{239} + _{-1}e^{0}$$

Neptunium and plutonium were the first transuranium elements (those with more than 92 protons in their nuclei). At this writing, ten transuranium elements have been artificially prepared by bombarding the nuclei of uranium or more complex elements with neutrons, alpha particles, or other "nuclear bullets."

The $_{92}U^{235}$ also captures slow neutrons, producing a highly unstable nucleus. However, instead of emitting alpha or beta particles or gamma rays, this nucleus can split into two medium-weight parts. During this *fission*, neutrons are given out, and a small amount of mass is converted to a tremendous burst of energy.

One equation for the fission of $_{92}U^{235}$ is

$$_{92}U^{235} + _{0}n^{1} \rightarrow$$
$$_{56}Ba^{138} + _{36}Kr^{95} + 3 _{0}n^{1} + \text{energy}$$

The isotopic mass of $_{92}U^{235}$ is slightly greater than 235 (235.1170), and that of the neutron is slightly greater than 1 (1.008986). The isotopic masses of the unstable isotopes of barium and krypton are slightly less than 138 (137.948700) and 95 (so unstable that its value is only known to be less than 95.000000). So instead of the masses of the reactants equal-

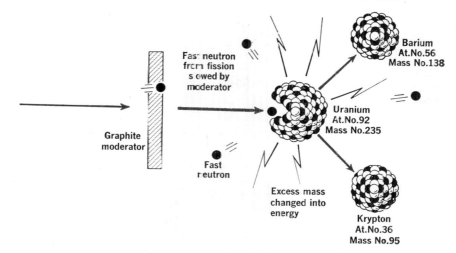

Fast neutron from fission slowed by moderator

Graphite moderator

Fast neutron

Barium
At.No.56
Mass No.138

Uranium
At.No.92
Mass No.235

Excess mass changed into energy

Krypton
At.No.36
Mass No.95

ing the masses of the products, there is a conversion of about 0.2 amu into energy. The equivalent amount of energy is 0.2 amu × 931 Mev/amu = 186 Mev.

It was later discovered that plutonium, made from $_{92}U^{238}$, acts the same way $_{92}U^{235}$ does when bombarded with slow neutrons; it undergoes fission and produces more neutrons.

14. Chain reactions. *A reaction in which the material or energy which starts a reaction is also one of the products is a* **chain reaction.** The fissions of $_{94}Pu^{239}$ and $_{92}U^{235}$ are

such reactions. Neutrons initiate these reactions and also are one of the products. One neutron causes one atom of $_{92}U^{235}$ to undergo fission, as shown in Fig. 7-15. Suppose that two neutrons are produced (the average yield is 2.5 neutrons). Each neutron can now strike a $_{92}U^{235}$ nucleus and produce fissions in which four neutrons are liberated. These four can strike four more $_{92}U^{235}$ nuclei, causing them to undergo fission. In an extremely small fraction of a second, billions of neutrons can be produced to act as bullets. This is

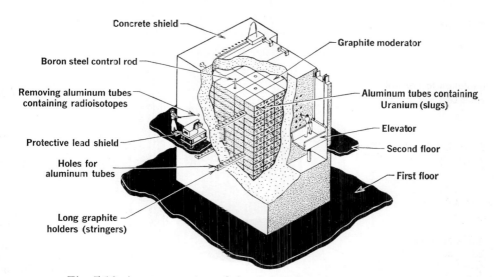

Concrete shield

Boron steel control rod

Removing aluminum tubes containing radioisotopes

Protective lead shield

Holes for aluminum tubes

Long graphite holders (stringers)

Graphite moderator

Aluminum tubes containing Uranium (slugs)

Elevator

Second floor

First floor

Fig. 7-16. A cutaway view of the Oak Ridge, Tennessee, reactor.

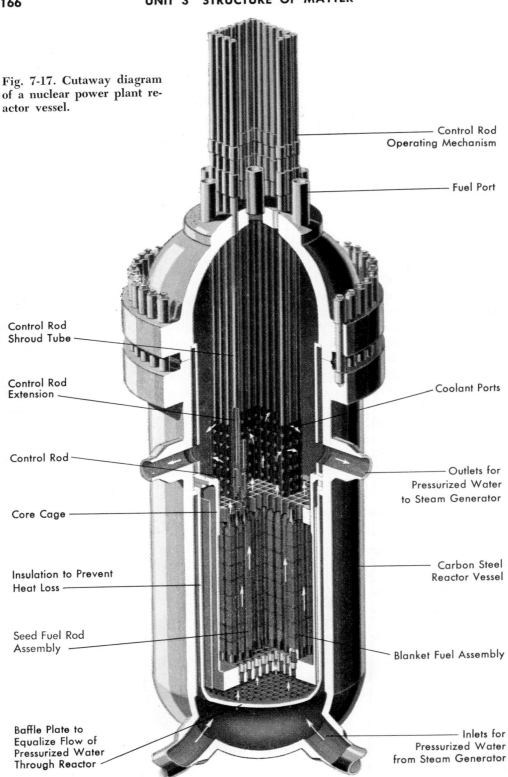

Fig. 7-17. Cutaway diagram of a nuclear power plant reactor vessel.

Control Rod Operating Mechanism

Fuel Port

Control Rod Shroud Tube

Control Rod Extension

Control Rod

Core Cage

Insulation to Prevent Heat Loss

Seed Fuel Rod Assembly

Baffle Plate to Equalize Flow of Pressurized Water Through Reactor

Coolant Ports

Outlets for Pressurized Water to Steam Generator

Carbon Steel Reactor Vessel

Blanket Fuel Assembly

Inlets for Pressurized Water from Steam Generator

what happens in an uncontrolled chain reaction, such as the explosion of an atomic bomb.

15. Nuclear reactors contain controlled chain reactions. *A nuclear reactor is a device in which the controlled fission of radioactive material produces new radioactive substances and energy.* One of the earliest reactors containing natural uranium as a fuel was built at Oak Ridge, Tennessee, in 1943. This reactor has a lattice-type construction with blocks of graphite forming the framework and acting as a moderator. (Fast neutrons are a product of fission; slow neutrons are needed to cause fission.) The rods of uranium are enclosed in aluminum cans and placed between the blocks of graphite. Control rods of neutron-absorbing boron steel are inserted in the lattice to regulate the number of free neutrons. A definite amount of uranium must be in the reactor to sustain the chain reaction, a quantity of uranium called the *critical size.*

Two types of reactions occur in the fuel in this reactor. Neutrons cause $_{92}U^{235}$ nuclei to undergo fission. The fast neutrons from this fission are slowed down by passage through the graphite. Some strike other $_{92}U^{235}$ nuclei and continue the chain reaction while others strike $_{92}U^{238}$ nuclei and initiate the changes which produce plutonium. Great quantities of heat energy are liberated, so the reactor has to be cooled continuously by air blown through tubes in the lattice. The rate of the nuclear reactions is controlled by insertion or removal of the neutron-absorbing control rods. This reactor is being used at present to produce radioactive isotopes.

Several specialized types of reactors are now in operation. One is the Oak Ridge reactor just described. The Hanford, Washington, reactors primarily produce $_{94}Pu^{239}$ for atomic weapons. Near Arco, Idaho, there are a materials testing reactor and a breeder reactor. A materials testing reactor is just what its name implies—a

reactor used for testing the behavior of various materials under very high radioactivity. A breeder reactor is one in which one fissionable material, $_{94}Pu^{239}$, for example, is produced at a greater rate than the $_{92}U^{235}$ used as a fuel is consumed.

16. Electric power production from a nuclear reactor. A nuclear reactor can serve as a source of heat energy, just as a coal, oil, or gas fire does. The great amount of energy available from the world supply of nuclear fuels as compared with the diminishing supply of coal and petroleum makes nuclear fuels worth developing for future use.

Several nuclear power plants for the generation of electricity are planned or operating in the United States, as well as in Canada, Great Britain, Russia, and several other countries. The first large nuclear power plant in the United States is located at Shippingport, near Pittsburgh, Pennsylvania.

This power plant uses a reactor containing natural uranium enriched with $_{92}U^{235}$ as fuel. The fuel rods are surrounded by a blanket of rods of natural uranium oxide. The control rods are of hafnium metal. The moderator and heat transfer fluid is pressurized water, which is circulated between the reactor core and the steam generators. The operating temperature of the reactor is approximately 525° F, with a pressure of about 2000 lb/in.²

Figure 7-17 is a cut-away diagram of the reactor vessel. The vessel is made of steel plates, and is about 30 ft high and about 10 ft in diameter. At the top are the control rod operating mechanisms and the ports for inserting or removing fuel rods. Midway down the sides of the reactor vessel are the outlets for the heated pressurized water, while at the bottom are the inlets for the pressurized water.

The fuel rods in the reactor vessel are supported in the core cage. There are two types of fuel rods: (1) seed fuel rods, and (2) blanket fuel rods.

The seed fuel rod assemblies are arranged in the reactor vessel in a hollow square. Each assembly consists of four boxes holding plates of enriched $_{92}U^{235}$ alloyed with zirconium, as shown in Fig. 7-18. The cross-shaped space between the boxes contains a hafnium control rod which may be raised or lowered in the seed fuel rod assembly to regulate the rate of the reactions taking place in it. Pressurized water is pumped up between the plates in the fuel rod assemblies to absorb the heat of the reaction.

The remainder of the core cage is filled with blanket fuel rod assemblies. See Fig. 7-19. A blanket fuel rod is a zirconium alloy tube filled with pellets of uranium oxide. These fuel rods are grouped into blanket bundles, which are held together by end plates with coolant flow holes. Thus the pressurized water coolant may flow upward around each fuel rod. The blanket bundles are fastened together in blanket fuel rod assemblies. Both the blanket fuel rod assemblies and the seed fuel rod assemblies are held in the core cage by a locking collar, which also provides a means by which the rod may be inserted or removed from the reactor vessel.

The fission of $_{92}U^{235}$ in the seed assemblies furnishes energy at the start of reactor operation. Neutrons from these reactions cause reactions in the uranium oxide in the blanket assemblies. They promote the fission of $_{92}U^{235}$ and the transmutation of $_{92}U^{238}$ to plutonium, which may then undergo fission and provide additional energy. Thus the operation of this reactor depends upon both fission and breeder reactions.

The hot pressurized water from the reactor is pumped through the steam generators, in which the heat of the pressurized water converts other water to steam under pressure. The pressurized water, cooled by the transfer of its heat to produce steam, is returned to the reactor for reheating. The steam formed in the steam generators is used to drive turbines, which in turn drive electric generators. The steam, after passage through the turbines, is condensed and returned to the steam generators to be converted to steam once again.

17. Fusion reactions. In Section 7 we learned that increased nuclear stability

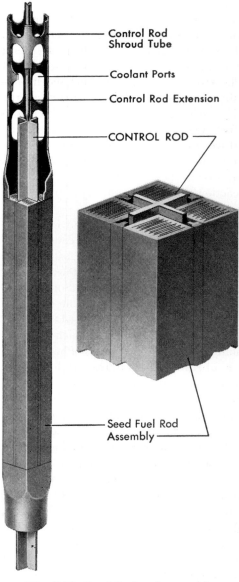

Control Rod
Shroud Tube

Coolant Ports

Control Rod Extension

CONTROL ROD

Seed Fuel Rod
Assembly

Fig. 7-18. Seed fuel rod assembly.

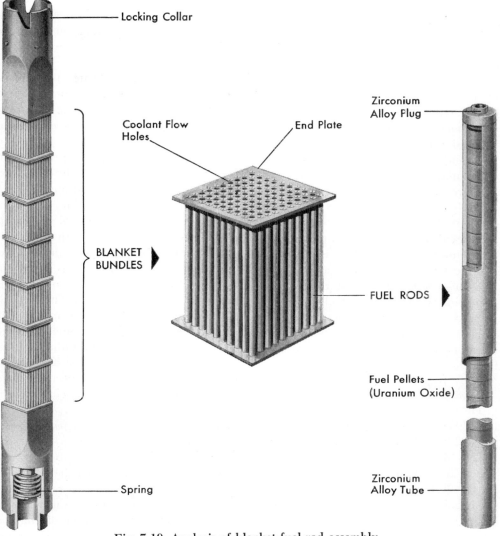

Locking Collar

Coolant Flow
Holes

End Plate

Zirconium
Alloy Plug

BLANKET
BUNDLES

FUEL RODS

Fuel Pellets
(Uranium Oxide)

Spring

Zirconium
Alloy Tube

Fig. 7-19. Analysis of blanket fuel rod assembly.

and consequent evolution of energy could be produced by combining light-weight nuclei to form heavier nuclei. This process was defined as fusion.

Fusion reactions are believed to be the source of the sun's energy. There are probably two fusion reactions taking place in the sun. One of these occurs in the very hot central region of the sun, while the other goes on in the outer region which is at a slightly lower temperature. Although these two reactions have a different sequence of intermediate reactions, the net effect is the combination of four hydrogen nuclei to form a helium nucleus and two positrons, with a loss of mass and corresponding production of energy.

$$4 \; _1H^1 \longrightarrow \; _2He^4 + 2 \; _{+1}e^0 + \text{energy}$$

A positron, $_{+1}e^0$, is a positively charged particle with the mass of an electron. Positrons were discovered in 1932 by C. D. Anderson (1905–   ), an American physicist. They are very short-lived, usually existing for less than a microsecond.

The mass and energy changes in this

reaction are $4(1.008145) - [4.003873 + 2(0.000548)] = 0.027611$; 0.027611 amu $\times$ 931 Mev/amu $= 25.7$ Mev.

The thermonuclear bomb, sometimes called the hydrogen bomb or H-bomb, produces energy by a fusion reaction. A hydrogen bomb can be made much more destructive than an atomic bomb because correspondingly more energy is liberated in a fusion reaction than in a fission reaction, and the quantities of reacting materials may be made much larger; in fact, they are theoretically unlimited.

One possible reaction in a hydrogen bomb is the formation of alpha particles and tremendous energy from a compound of lithium and hydrogen. This compound may be formed from $_3Li^6$ and $_1H^2$. Such a fusion reaction can be started only by subjecting $_3Li^6_1H^2$ to extremely high temperature and pressure. These conditions are met by using an atomic bomb as the necessary detonator to set off the hydrogen bomb.

$$_3Li^6_1H^2 \rightarrow 2\ _2He^4 + \text{energy}$$

The mass and energy changes are $(6.017034 + 2.014740) - 2(4.003873) = 0.024028$; 0.024028 amu $\times$ 931 Mev/amu $= 22.4$ Mev.

Let us compare the energy produced by the fission of $_{92}U^{235}$ with the energy produced by the fusion of an equal mass of $_3Li^6_1H^2$. In the fission reaction (Section 13) 236 amu of reactants produce 186 Mev of energy. In the fusion reaction 8 amu of reactant produce 22.4 Mev of energy. Therefore 236 amu of this react-

ant undergoing fusion would produce 236 amu/8 amu $\times$ 22.4 Mev = 660 Mev of energy, almost 30 times as much as the fission reaction for an equal mass of reactant.

Current research indicates that fusion reactions may be carried out at lower temperatures. If so, fusion reactions may be another possible source of energy for power generation.

18. Cosmic rays. An electroscope, if left out in the air, will slowly discharge. A Geiger counter will continue to click at an infrequent, yet definite rate even though no radioactive material is present. These observations indicate that there is some slight ionization in the air, and experiments have shown that this ionization is caused by particles coming into our atmosphere from outer space. These particles are nuclei of elements of low atomic weight, protons (hydrogen nuclei) being the most abundant type. Other nuclei, however, ranging up to those of elements as heavy as iron, have also been detected in the upper atmosphere. Their source is not definitely known. *These high energy particles apparently come from beyond our solar system,* hence they have been given the name **cosmic rays.** A few of these cosmic rays from outer space reach the surface of the earth, but most cosmic rays collide with the gas particles in the upper atmosphere and produce a shower of charged particles. A study of the variation of cosmic ray intensity with altitude is one of the primary objectives of the earth satellite programs now being conducted.

Summary

Radioactivity is the spontaneous breakdown of the nuclei of atoms with the emission of particles and rays; it is a property of all elements with atomic numbers greater than 83. Common properties of radioactive elements include effect on the light-sensitive emulsion on a photographic plate, ionization of the surrounding air, production of fluorescence in certain compounds, pronounced physiological effects, and continuous emission of energy.

The radiation from radioactive elements consists of alpha particles (helium nuclei), beta particles (electrons), and gamma rays (high energy X rays). Radioactivity may be detected by an electroscope, a spinthariscope, a cloud chamber, photographic methods, a Geiger counter, or a bubble chamber.

Differences in the nuclear stability of elements make possible four types of energy-producing nuclear reactions: radioactive decomposition, nuclear disintegration, fission, and fusion. More energy can be produced from equal masses of fuel by fusion reactions than by fission reactions. Among the devices used as particle accelerators are Van de Graaff generators, cyclotrons, synchrocyclotrons, synchrotrons, betatrons, and linear accelerators. Atoms may be made artificially radioactive. Cosmic rays are high energy particles which come from outer space.

TERMS TO DEFINE

alpha particle	cyclotron	nuclear disintegration
artificial radioactivity	disintegration constant	nuclear reactor
beta particle	electroscope	nuclear stability
betatron	fission	radioactive
bubble chamber	fusion	radioactive decomposition
chain reaction	gamma ray	spinthariscope
cloud chamber	Geiger counter	synchro-cyclotron
cosmic rays	half life	synchrotron
critical size	linear accelerator	transmutation
curie	moderator	Van de Graaff generator

QUESTIONS

A 1. (a) Who discovered radioactivity? (b) How did he make his discovery?
2. (a) What is radioactivity? (b) What naturally occurring elements are radioactive?
3. Compare the composition, charge, and speed of alpha and beta particles.
4. (a) How are gamma rays believed to be produced? (b) What are their important properties?
5. In order for energy to be evolved in a nuclear reaction, how must the combined masses of the reactants compare with the combined masses of the products?
6. In a nuclear equation, (a) what do the letter symbols represent; (b) what do the subscripts indicate; (c) what do the superscripts indicate?
7. What is a *curie*?
8. What important conclusion was drawn from the experimental work of Cockcroft and Walton?
9. Compare the various particle accelerators with respect to the energies which they impart to the particles they accelerate.

10. What is the difference in the movement of the particles being accelerated in a cyclotron and those in a synchrotron?
11. Why are neutrons more effective than other particles for bombarding nuclei?
12. What are some important uses for radioactive isotopes?
13. What is the function of a moderator?
14. Why is a fusion reaction more desirable as a source of energy than a fission reaction?
15. (a) What is a chain reaction? (b) Why can the fission of $_{92}U^{235}$ produce a chain reaction?
16. (a) What is a materials testing reactor? (b) What is a breeder reactor?
17. What characteristic must a reactor control rod have?
18. (a) What is the nature of cosmic rays? (b) What do we know about their source?

B 19. Describe five properties which radioactive elements have in common.

20. How does a powerful magnetic field affect the radiation from a radioactive material?
21. What property of the radiation from radioactive materials is used to detect it by (a) an electroscope; (b) a spinthariscope; (c) a cloud chamber; (d) the Geiger counter; (e) the bubble chamber?
22. How does the stability of a nucleus vary with (a) mass; (b) the proton-neutron ratio; (c) the even-odd relationship of the number of protons to the number of neutrons?
23. Describe the four types of nuclear reactions in which energy may be released.
24. (a) What is the difference between the average life of a radioactive atom and its half life? (b) What is the relationship between the average life of a nucleus and its half life?

25. Write nuclear equations for the radioactive decomposition of (a) $_{90}Th^{234}$; (b) $_{92}U^{234}$; (c) $_{83}Bi^{214}$; (d) $_{84}Po^{210}$.
26. Write a nuclear equation for the production of neutrons by bombarding beryllium with alpha particles.
27. How are particles accelerated in (a) a Van de Graaff generator; (b) a cyclotron; (c) a linear accelerator?
28. Write nuclear equations showing the preparation of $_{94}Pu^{239}$ from $_{92}U^{238}$.
29. Trace the energy transformations in the production of electric energy from nuclear energy at the Shippingport atomic power plant.
30. (a) What are positrons? (b) By whom were they discovered? (c) What is their length of life?

PROBLEMS

Note: The atomic mass in grams of any isotope contains 6.0238×10^{23} atoms of that isotope.

A   1. How much energy in Mev is evolved in the disintegration of an $_{86}Rn^{222}$ nucleus? Atomic masses: $_{86}Rn^{222}$—222.0869; $_{84}Po^{218}$—218.0768; $_2He^4$—4.0039.
2. Calculate the energy evolved when an $_{82}Pb^{214}$ nucleus disintegrates. Atomic masses: $_{82}Pb^{214}$—214.0663; $_{83}Bi^{214}$—214.0653; $_{-1}e^0$—0.0005.
3. What is the disintegration constant of $_{86}Rn^{222}$ which has a half life of 3.82 da?
4. Determine the disintegration constant of $_{92}U^{238}$ if its half life is 4.49×10^9 years.

B   5. (a) What is the radioactivity in millicuries of 100. g of pure $_{90}Th^{232}$? Half life:

1.4×10^{10} yr; atomic mass: 232.1103. It disintegrates to $_{88}Ra^{228}$, atomic mass, 228.1026. (b) What is the rate of energy evolution?
6. (a) Calculate the radioactivity of 5.00 $\times 10^{-3}$ g of $_{86}Rn^{222}$. (b) What is the rate of energy evolution?
7. Compare the energy evolved from equal masses of fuel elements in the following reactions:
(a) fission: $_{94}Pu^{239} + _0n^1 \rightarrow _{52}Te^{137} + _{42}Mo^{100} + 3 \, _0n^1 +$ energy; (b) fusion: $2 \, _1H^2 \rightarrow _2He^4 +$ energy. Atomic masses: $_{94}Pu^{239}$—239.1265; $_0n^1$—1.0090; $_{52}Te^{137}$—not accurately known, use 137.0000, its maximum atomic mass; $_{42}Mo^{100}$—99.9383; $_1H^2$—2.0147; $_2He^4$—4.0039.

RESEARCH ON YOUR OWN

1. The "cloud" of the Wilson cloud chamber can be simply demonstrated. Put a few cubic centimeters of water or alcohol into a liter flask or similar container. Increase the pressure in the flask considerably. (A simple rubber bulb pump fitted to a stopper may be used for this purpose.) Then release the pressure suddenly. Occasional tracks of alpha particles may be seen in the flask. If you have an old watch with a luminous dial, hang the dial (or a part of it) in the flask. Repeat the experiment and explain any differences in the results.
2. Try taking a picture in the dark of a watch or clock with a luminous dial. Lay a piece of photographic print paper on the watch dial and put the watch and print paper in a dark place for a few days. Develop the print and explain the results.
3. Construct one of the kit-type Geiger counters now on the market, or design a circuit of your own for the purpose.
4. Investigate the construction of the betatron, cyclotron, and synchrotron. Write a report on any one of these, or on the fundamental differences in the construction of the three.
5. Prepare a chart or model of one of the experimental devices developed to obtain thermonuclear energy by the fusion process.

CHAPTER 8

THE KINETIC THEORY OF MATTER

VOCABULARY

Adhesion. The force of attraction between unlike molecules.

Buoyant force. The upward force which any fluid exerts on a body placed in it.

Capillarity. The elevation or depression of liquids in small diameter tubes.

Cohesion. The force of attraction between like molecules.

Diffusion. The penetration of one type of particle into a mass consisting of a second type of particle.

Elasticity. The property of matter that requires a force to produce distortion, and causes it to resume its original shape when the force is removed.

Elastic limit. The smallest stress which produces permanent distortion.

Elastic modulus. The ratio of stress to strain.

Ideal gas. A gas consisting of infinitely small molecules which exert no forces on each other.

Kinetic theory. A theory of matter which assumes that the molecules of matter are in constant motion and obey Newton's laws of motion.

Pressure. The force applied to a unit area.

Specific gravity. The ratio of the density of a substance to the density of a standard.

Standard pressure. The pressure exerted by a column of mercury exactly 760 mm high.

Standard temperature. The temperature of melting ice, 0° C.

Strain. The amount of distortion.

Streamline flow. The smooth flow of a fluid through a tube.

Stress. The distorting force.

Surface tension. The tendency of a liquid surface to contract.

Tensile strength. The force required to break a rod or wire of unit cross-sectional area.

Theory. A probable explanation for observed phenomena which is supported by abundant data.

Total force. The force acting against the entire area of a particular surface.

Viscosity. The internal friction of a fluid.

173

1. The kinetic theory. In Chapter 1 we learned that matter exists in three physical states—solid, liquid, and gaseous. Then in Chapter 6, we found that the particles composing various substances are atoms, molecules, or ions. Now we are ready to consider how the forces between these particles of matter and the energy they possess determine the properties of solids, liquids, and gases. In this chapter we shall use the term "molecule" in a general sense to mean a particle of a substance, often including atoms and ions along with true molecules.

Scientists continually search for explanations of what they observe and develop theories to explain their observations. *A theory is a probable explanation for observed phenomena, supported by abundant data.* The *kinetic theory* helps explain the properties of matter in terms of the forces between molecules and the energy they possess. Most of the data that supports the kinetic theory results from indirect observation. It is almost impossible to observe the behavior of individual molecules, and even if we could make such observations easily, they would not mean very much. Scientists, however, can observe the behavior of large groups of molecules, and from the results of these experiments, describe the average behavior of molecules.

The three basic assumptions of the *kinetic theory* are

1. Matter is composed of very tiny particles called molecules. The chemical properties of molecules depend on their composition. Their physical properties, however, depend on the forces the molecules exert on each other and the distance separating them.

2. Molecules are in constant motion. The average kinetic energy of molecules depends on the temperature.

3. Molecules obey Newton's laws of motion. In collisions between molecules, their momentums and kinetic energies are not changed. Such collisions are said to be *elastic.*

2. Forces acting between molecules. Considerable force is required to pull a solid apart; obviously, the forces between the molecules of a solid must be very great. Liquids separate into drops very easily, indicating that molecular forces in liquids are not as great as those in solids. Even though the size of a molecule of a substance does not change appreciably with the physical state of the substance, most liquids occupy a larger volume than the same mass of solid. Thus, molecules of liquids must be farther apart than those of solids. In a gas, which occupies a volume of the order of 10^3 times that of an equal mass of liquid, molecules separate from each other spontaneously, showing that the forces between molecules of gases are negligible. We may conclude, then, that forces between molecules decrease as the distance between the molecules increases.

Solids and liquids are not easily compressed. Apparently when molecules are closer together than their normal spacing in solids and liquids, there are repulsive forces between them, and the closer molecules are pushed together, the greater these repulsive forces become.

The graph in Fig. 8-1 shows this variation of force with the distance between molecules. We see that when molecules are far apart the force of attraction between them is slight. As molecules come closer together, the force of attraction between them increases, reaches a maximum, and then decreases to zero at their normal spacing. As the distance between the molecules is further decreased, the force between them becomes one of repulsion; this force increases rapidly as the molecules come closer to each other.

3. The relationship between mass density and weight density. One of the properties exhibited by matter in each of its three states is density. In Chapter 1,

Section 9, we defined mass density as mass per unit volume:

$$D_m = \frac{m}{V}$$

Similarly, weight density was defined as weight per unit volume:

$$D_w = \frac{w}{V}$$

From Newton's second law of motion (Chapter 4, Section 18) we know that

$$w = mg$$

so

$$D_w = D_m g$$

While either weight density or mass density may be expressed in each of the three systems of measurement, weight density is usually expressed in FPS units, lb/ft³, and mass density is usually given in CGS units, g/cm³. Mass density in g/cm³

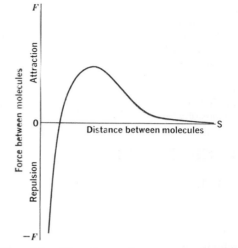

Fig. 8-1. The force between molecules varies with the distance separating them.

must be multiplied by $10^3 \ \frac{kg/m^3}{g/cm^3}$ to give the equivalent mass density in MKS units, kg/m³.

QUESTIONS

A 1. (a) What are the physical states of matter? (b) Of what types of particles are substances composed?
2. What are the three basic asumptions of the kinetic theory?
3. Why are molecular collisions said to be elastic?
4. (a) Under what circumstances are the forces between molecules attractive? (b) Under what circumstances are they repulsive?
5. (a) Distinguish between mass density and weight density. (b) How are they related to each other?

B 6. (a) What is a scientific theory? (b) How does it differ from a scientific law?
7. What does the volume occupied by a given mass of matter as a solid, liquid, and gas indicate about the spacing between molecules in the three physical states?
8. How does the magnitude of the force between molecules vary with the physical state of a substance?
9. On what does the average kinetic energy of the molecules of a substance depend?
10. What direct evidence do we have that matter is composed of molecules?

PROBLEMS

Note: Additional data needed for the following problems will be found in Tables 1 and 2, Appendix B.

A 1. What is the mass density of a piece of rock which has a volume of 150. cm³ and a mass of 420. g?
2. Determine the weight density of a 5.00 lb brass weight if its volume is 9.44×10^{-3} ft³.
3. The mass density of water at 50° C is 0.988 g/cm³. What is its weight density in dynes/cm³?

4. The weight density of maple is 45 lb/ft³. What is the weight of a block 12.0 in. long, 4.0 in. wide, and 4.0 in. thick?
5. A bar of silver is 6.0 cm long, 2.0 cm wide, and 1.5 cm thick. The mass density of silver is 10.5 g/cm³. What is the weight of the bar in newtons?

B 6. Mercury is 13.6 times as dense as water. How many cubic inches does 5.00 lb of mercury occupy?

7. A swimming pool is 25 m long, 10. m wide, and is filled to an average depth of 1.5 m. (a) How many kilograms of water does it contain? (b) How many newtons of water does it contain?

8. A cylindrical tank for gasoline is 10.0 ft long and 4.00 ft in diameter. The density of gasoline is 0.700 that of water. How many pounds of gasoline will the tank hold?

9. A cylindrical water tank is 5.00 m in diameter and 5.00 m high. If the tank is exactly three-quarters full at 15° C, (a) how many kilograms of water does it contain; (b) how many metric tons of water does it contain?

10. The mass density of granite is 2.65 g/cm³. Calculate (a) its mass density in kg/m³; (b) its weight density in nt/m³; (c) its weight density in lb/ft³.

1 SOLIDS

4. The nature of a solid. Solids are characterized by a definite shape and a definite volume. Scientists usually describe solids as *crystalline* or *amorphous;* those which are crystalline have a regular arrangement of particles, while those which are amorphous have a completely random particle arrangement.

Crystalline solids may be classified as consisting of atomic, molecular, ionic, or macromolecular crystals, depending on the particles of which they are composed. Atomic crystals consist of atoms in a regular arrangement; metals are examples of atomic crystals. The force holding the atoms together in an atomic crystal is an electronic exchange force, the motion of the loosely held outer shell electrons among neighboring atoms bonding them together. The nonmetallic chemical elements and many compounds form molecular crystals in which the molecules are arranged in a regular pattern; sulfur crystals and sugar crystals are examples. The forces which hold molecules together in crystals are called *Van der Waals forces.* They arise from the ability of the varying electric field of the atoms of one molecule to cause a similar variation in the electric field of the atoms of another molecule, resulting in an attraction between the molecules. Ionic crystals are composed of ions; in Chapter 6, Section 14, we described sodium chloride as an example of this type of solid. The forces holding ions in a regular pattern are electrostatic. Macromolecular crystals do not contain

small molecular units, and the entire crystal can be considered to be a molecule. A diamond is an example of a macromolecule; the force holding the carbon atoms together in a diamond originates in the sharing of pairs of electrons by adjacent atoms.

In amorphous solids the particles are usually large long chain molecules which are entangled. These solids are held together by a combination of Van der Waals forces and the physical entangling of the molecules.

In addition to the forces which bind the particles of a solid together, the motion of the particles of a solid must also be considered. Particles of a solid are held in relatively fixed positions by the forces which bind them together. However, they do have a weak vibratory motion back and forth about their fixed positions. The amplitude of their vibration, and therefore their kinetic energy, is related to the temperature of the solid; at low temperatures the kinetic energy is small, while at higher temperatures it is larger. See Fig. 8-2.

Evidence for this weak vibratory motion comes from experiments which demonstrate *diffusion* in solids. **Diffusion** is the *penetration of one type of particle into a mass consisting of a second type of particle.* If a lead plate and a gold plate are placed in close contact and left in this condition for several months, particles of gold may be detected in the lead, showing that even solids diffuse. The slowness of diffusion in solids is a result of the limited motion of the particles and of their close-packed, orderly arrangement.

5. Cohesion and adhesion. *The general term for the force of attraction between molecules of the same kind is* **cohesion.** We know from Fig. 8-1 that this is a close-range force. Cohesion holds the closely packed molecules of a solid together. If a solid is broken, a layer of molecules of the gases in the air on the broken surfaces prevents us from reconstructing the solid so that its molecules are close enough together to have sufficient attraction to hold. However, if we polish the surfaces of two like solids and slide them together, we can bring the cohesive forces into action and cause the solids to stick together. This may be demonstrated with carefully ground glass plates or metal gauge blocks.

Molecules of different kinds sometimes attract each other strongly: chewing gum sticks to the leather of shoes, glue sticks to wood, and when we write on a blackboard, some of the chalk particles adhere to the slate. *The force of attraction between molecules of different kinds is called* **adhesion.** When two different substances are in contact, both cohesion and adhesion exist; the characteristics of the particles of the sub-

Fig. 8-3. A machine which determines the tensile strength of metal rods. The metal rod shown has been pulled with such force that it is about to break. Notice the decrease in diameter at the point where the break will occur. (American Iron and Steel Institute)

stances involved determine which force controls the action at their contact surface.

6. Tensile strength. Several properties of solids depend on the cohesive force between molecules. One of these properties is tensile strength. Suppose two wires of the same diameter, one copper and one steel, are put in a special machine which pulls on them until they break. When tested in this manner, the steel wire proves stronger than a copper wire of the same diameter. Therefore we say that steel has a higher tensile strength than copper. *The* **tensile strength** *of a material is the force required to break a rod or wire of that material having a unit cross-sectional area.* This area may be 1 in.^{2} or 1 cm^2. (See Table 4, Appendix B.) Tensile strength is a measure of the cohesive force between adjacent molecules over the entire cross-sectional area.

7. Ductility and malleability. If a metal rod can be drawn through a die to produce a wire, the metal is said to be *ductile* (*duk*-til), or to possess *ductility*. As the metal is pulled through the die, its diameter is decreased but its length is increased, and the rod becomes a wire. See Fig. 8-4 (*A*).

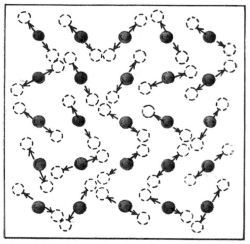

Fig. 8-2. The molecules of a solid vibrate about fixed positions.

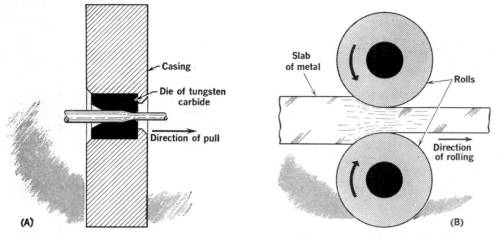

Fig. 8-4. During drawing (*A*) and rolling (*B*), the atoms of a metal are forced to move over each other from one position in the crystal pattern to another.

Metals which may be hammered or rolled into sheets are said to be *malleable* (*mal*-ee-uh-bul) or to have *malleability*. During the hammering or rolling, the shape or thickness of the metal is greatly changed. See Fig. 8-4(*B*).

During hammering, rolling, or drawing, the atoms of a metal are forced to move over each other from one position in the crystal pattern to another. However, since the cohesive forces are strong, and the atoms do not become widely separated

from each other during the process of re-arrangement, the metal holds together while its shape is being changed. Metals such as silver, gold, platinum, copper, aluminum, and iron are highly malleable and ductile.

8. Elasticity. *A solid*, such as a steel spring, *which requires a certain amount of force to distort (stretch) it and then tends to resume its original shape when the distorting force is removed has the property of* **elasticity.** The elasticity of solids depends on molecular

KINDS   OF   ELASTICITY

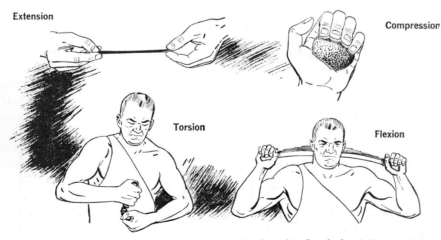

Fig. 8-5. Examples of each of the four kinds of elasticity.

forces. *The force which acts on a body and tends to distort it is called a* **stress.** *The change, or distortion, which is produced is called the* **strain.** If we squeeze a tennis ball, it becomes distorted. However, it tends to recover its original shape and size when the stress is removed. This is an example of *elasticity of compression.* The type of elasticity illustrated by the stretching of a coiled spring is called *elasticity of extension*, while the twisting of the same spring is an example of *elasticity of torsion.* An illustration of the *elasticity of flexion* is the bending of a strip of steel. In all these cases the material tends to resume its original form when the stress is removed. The stress changes the distances between the molecules, either pulling them farther apart or pushing them closer together; when the stress is removed, the molecular forces restore the molecules to their normal spacing.

9. Hooke's law and the elastic modulus. The beams and girders used in buildings and bridges are often acted on by varying forces or stresses. It is important for engineers to know what distortion or strain these forces will produce, and in order to do this, they must have some way to measure the elasticity of materials.

If we stretch a coiled spring, as shown in Fig. 8-6(*A*), it probably will return exactly to its original form after the removal of the stress. If it does, it is said to be *perfectly elastic.* If the spring is stretched too far, so that it remains permanently distorted, its *elastic limit* has been exceeded. *The* **elastic limit** *is the smallest stress which produces permanent distortion.* At the elastic limit the molecular forces have been overcome to such an extent that the particles move over one another, shifting places in the crystal pattern, and altering the shape of the material. Such a drastic change cannot be restored by the molecular forces. Every material has a certain range of perfect elasticity through which it may be distorted and yet return to its original condition, before its elastic limit is reached.

Suppose we fasten one end of a steel wire to a beam, as in Fig. 8-6(*B*). Now let us add 100-g brass weights to the hanger attached to the lower end. The wire is stretched gradually as weights are added one by one. We find that one brass weight stretches the wire 1 mm, and when the weight is removed, the wire returns to its original length. Two brass weights stretch the wire 2 mm; again the wire returns to its original length when the weights are removed. The wire is stretched 3 mm by three brass weights, once more returning to its original length when we take the weights off. If we continue, applying more and more weights, eventually we reach the elastic limit. Then when we remove the weights, the wire remains distorted; it does not return to its original length.

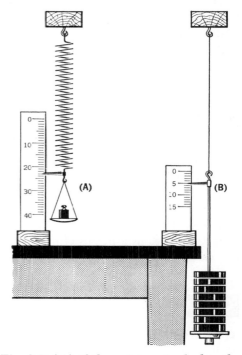

Fig. 8-6. (*A*) If the pointer attached to the spring returns to the zero mark after the weight is removed, the spring is perfectly elastic. (*B*) If the weights stretch the wire to its elastic limit, the pointer will not return to zero when the weights are removed.

Sample Problem

A steel bar 30. ft long, with a cross-sectional area of 3.0 in.² is supporting a load of 1.5 tons. How much does the bar stretch?

Solution

From Table 5, Appendix B, we find that the elastic modulus for steel is 29×10^6 lb/in.²

$$Y = \frac{Fl}{\Delta l A}$$

$$\Delta l = \frac{Fl}{YA}$$

$$\Delta l = \frac{1.5 \text{ tons} \times 2000 \text{ lb/ton} \times 30. \text{ ft}}{29 \times 10^6 \text{ lb/in.}^2 \times 3.0 \text{ in.}^2}$$

$$\Delta l = 1.0 \times 10^{-3} \text{ ft}$$

By such a method Robert Hooke (1635–1703) found that the amount of distortion in elastic materials is directly proportional to the distorting force, provided the elastic limit is not exceeded. *Hooke's law* states that *within the limits of perfect elasticity, strain is directly proportional to stress.* This is the principle upon which a spring balance operates; the amount by which the spring is stretched is directly proportional to the force applied.

The value of the ratio, stress/strain, is different for different materials. It is, however, reasonably the same for a given material, even though the material may be fashioned in different shapes and sizes. This ratio gives us a means of comparing the elasticity of various materials. It is

called the *elastic modulus*, and is defined by the equation

$$Y = \frac{Fl}{\Delta l A}$$

where Y is the elastic modulus, F is the applied stress, A is the cross-sectional area of the material, Δl is the strain, and l is the original length of the material. In the CGS system the elastic modulus is expressed in dynes/cm². In the FPS system the elastic modulus is expressed in lb/in.² (The unit lb/in.² is used rather than lb/ft² because in.² is a more practical unit for the cross-sectional area of structural materials.) Values of the elastic modulus for various materials are given in Table 5, Appendix B. See the Sample Problem above.

QUESTIONS

A 1. (*a*) Into what two classes may solids be divided? (*b*) What is the particle arrangement in each?
2. (*a*) Describe the motion of the particles of a solid. (*b*) What experimental evidence supports this description?
3. (*a*) What name is given to the force of attraction between molecules of the same kind?

(*b*) What name is given to the force of attraction between molecules of different kinds?
4. (*a*) What is *tensile strength?* (*b*) In what units is it usually expressed?
5. (*a*) What is *ductility?* (*b*) What is *malleability?* (*c*) What must be true of the cohesive forces in ductile and malleable metals?
6. (*a*) Define *elasticity.* (*b*) Name the four types

of elasticity, giving an example of each.

7. Distinguish between *stress* and *strain*.

8. What is the statement of Hooke's law?

9. (*a*) What is the *elastic modulus?* (*b*) What is the formula by which it is defined? (*c*) Identify each term in the formula.

B 10. (*a*) Of what particles may crystalline solids be composed? (*b*) Give an example of a crystalline solid composed of each kind of particle. (*c*) What type of bonding force exists in each of these solids?

11. (*a*) Of what type of particle is an amorphous solid usually composed? (*b*) What is the nature of the bonding in such solids?

12. What determines which force, cohesion or adhesion, controls the action at the contact surface between two different substances?

13. What happens to the crystal pattern of an elastic material when its elastic limit is exceeded?

PROBLEMS

A 1. A coiled spring is stretched to 0.050 m when a weight of 0.50 nt is hung from one end. (*a*) How much work was done? (*b*) What is the potential energy of the spring? (*c*) How far will the spring be stretched by a 1.00 nt weight? (*d*) What weight will stretch the spring 0.030 m?

2. The hook of a spring balance is pulled down 2.0 in. by a 10.-lb weight. (*a*) What is the potential energy of the spring in footpounds? (*b*) If a 25-lb weight is substituted for the 10.-lb weight, how far is the hook pulled down? (*c*) How far apart are the 1.0-lb graduations?

3. Two wires are identical except that one is 100. cm long and the other is 200. cm long. The first wire is broken by a force of 500. nt. What force is needed to break the second wire?

4. What force is needed to break a wire having a cross-sectional area of 5.0×10^{-4} in.^{2} and a tensile strength of 375,000 lb/in.^{2}?

5. The cross-sectional area of a wire is 2.5×10^{-3} cm^2; its tensile strength is 1.00×10^{10} dynes/cm^2. What force is required to break the wire?

6. What is the increase in the length of an annealed steel wire 15 ft long and 1.0×10^{-2} in.^{2} in cross-sectional area when subjected to a force of 100. lb?

7. A brass wire 200. cm long and 5.0×10^{-2} cm^2 in cross-sectional area supports a weight of 1.00×10^5 dynes. How much is the wire stretched?

B 8. Calculate the conversion factor by which tensile strength in lb/in.^{2} must be multiplied to give tensile strength in dynes/cm^2.

9. The tensile strength of platinum wire is 5.00×10^4 lb/in.^{2} (*a*) Calculate its tensile strength in dynes/cm^2. (*b*) What force is required to break a platinum wire 0.50 mm in diameter?

10. A hollow metal post 12.0 ft long supports a load of 30.0 tons. If the cross-sectional area of the metal is 3.0 in.^{2} and the load decreases the length of the post 0.012 ft, calculate the elastic modulus.

11. A rod is 6.0 mm in diameter and is composed of a material having an elastic modulus of 9.0×10^{11} dynes/cm^2. What force in dynes will stretch it by 0.20% of its length?

2 LIQUIDS

10. The nature of a liquid. The particles of most substances which are liquid at room temperature (20° C) are molecules. Most metals, ionic compounds, and macromolecular substances remain solid at this temperature. The kinetic energy of the molecules of many molecular substances at room temperature is great enough to overcome partially the Van der Waals forces which produce the orderly pattern of molecular crystals. Thus the molecules of these substances have mobility and the substances are liquids. While molecules of a liquid are almost as close together as those of a solid, a liquid does not have the regular structure characteristic of a solid. In a liquid, small groups of molecules may still cling together; but the molecules can move over one another easily, enabling the liquid to flow or take the shape of its container. See Fig. 8-7. Even though the Van der Waals forces in liquids are somewhat weakened, they are still strong enough to give a liquid one free surface and thus a definite volume.

In 1827 an English botanist, Robert Brown (1773–1858), made an important discovery. He placed some pollen grains in water and dropped a bit of this suspension on a small glass slide. When he examined the suspension with a microscope, he found that the pollen vibrated in a very haphazard way, the path of one particle resembling that shown in Fig. 8-8. This Brownian movement is caused by the ceaseless bombardment of the suspended particles by the molecules of the suspending liquid. It shows us that liquid molecules are in continuous rapid, random vibration.

Molecules of liquids also diffuse. To demonstrate this, we pour enough concentrated copper sulfate solution into a tall cylinder to form a layer of blue liquid several centimeters deep. Next we float a flat cork on the surface of the solution, and pour water carefully through a funnel tube onto the top of the cork, as shown in Fig. 8-9. The water spreads out over the surface of the blue liquid, resulting in the formation of two distinct layers because the water has a much lower density than the copper sulfate solution. After the cylinder stands for a few days the boundary between the layers becomes less distinct. Some of the blue solution diffuses into the water above, while some of the water molecules diffuse into the copper sulfate solution below. Even though weeks may pass before the diffusion is complete, we see that diffusion does occur in liquids in spite of the force of gravity. The rate of diffusion of liquids is somewhat faster than that of solids because of the slightly more open molecular arrangement and greater molecular mobility.

11. Cohesion and adhesion in liquids. If you stick your finger into thick molasses and then pull it out, you discover that a certain amount of force is needed to pull

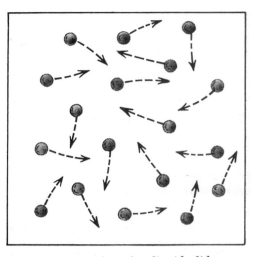

Fig. 8-7. Molecules of a liquid slide over one another freely.

apart the molecules of the molasses. If you try to lick the molasses off your fingers, you realize that force is required to pull the molasses molecules away from the molecules of your fingers. This shows that cohesion occurs in liquids and that adhesion occurs between liquids and solids. The relative strength of these forces determines what occurs at the surface of a liquid and a solid.

If we dip a clean glass rod into water and remove it, some of the water clings to the glass rod; we say that the water wets the glass. The adhesion of water molecules to glass must therefore be greater than the cohesion between water molecules.

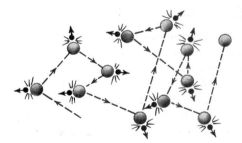

Fig. 8-8. The haphazard movement of the large particle is the result of its bombardment by the molecules of the liquid in which it is suspended.

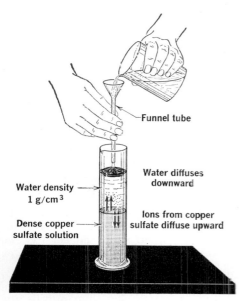

Funnel tube

Water diffuses
downward

Water density
1 g/cm^3

Dense copper
sulfate solution

Ions from copper
sulfate diffuse upward

Fig. 8-9. The diffusion of liquids proceeds slowly.

If we dip the glass rod into mercury, the mercury does not cling to the glass. The cohesion of mercury molecules is greater than their adhesion to glass.

Cohesive forces vary in different liquids. They are usually smaller in liquids than in solids.

12. Surface tension. Have you ever floated a sewing needle or a safety-razor blade on the surface of a glass of water? If you place them carefully on the surface they float, even though they are about seven times as dense as water. A close look at the water surface shows that the needle or razor blade floats in a hollow in the water surface. *The water acts as though it has a thin elastic surface film.* The weight of the needle or razor blade is counterbalanced by the upward force exerted by the surface film. This property of liquids is due to *surface tension.*

All liquids show surface tension. Mercury has a very high surface tension. However, in many liquids the surface film is not as strong as that of water or mercury. The cleaning action of some detergents is due to their ability to lower the surface tension of water, making it possible for the water and detergent to penetrate more readily between the fibers or into the pores of the substance being cleaned.

By studying Fig. 8-10, we can understand why a liquid has surface tension. A molecule at A is attracted equally in all directions by the cohesion of the surrounding molecules. A molecule at B is attracted equally on all sides, but more strongly downward than upward. The molecule at C is not attracted in an upward direction at all. We see that there is an unbalanced force tending to pull such surface molecules toward the interior of the liquid and keep the free surface of the liquid as small as possible. This unbalanced contracting force causes a liquid surface to act like an elastic film. *The tendency of a liquid surface to contract is called* **surface tension.** When a force acts on a liquid surface film and distorts it, the cohesion of the liquid molecules exerts an equal and opposite force tending to restore the horizontal surface. Thus the weight of a floating needle produces a depression in the water surface film which increases the area of the film. The cohesion of the water molecules exerts a counterbalancing upward force on the needle by tending to restore the surface of the liquid to its original horizontal condition.

Surface tension causes liquid films to be elastic. A liquid film has two free surfaces

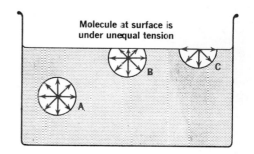

Molecule at surface is
under unequal tension

Fig. 8-10. The unbalanced downward force on molecules near the surface of a liquid causes surface tension.

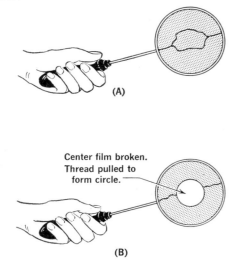

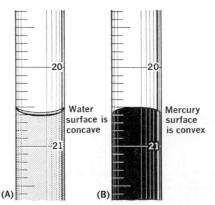

Fig. 8-13. (A) Liquids which wet the surfaces of their containers have concave surfaces. (B) Liquids which do not wet the surfaces of their containers have convex surfaces.

Center film broken. Thread pulled to form circle.

(B)

Fig. 8-11. (A) A soapy-water film is formed across the ring. (B) When the center of the film is broken, the outer portion of the film contracts and pulls the loop of thread into a circle.

on which molecules are subject to an unbalanced force toward the center of the film. Thus both free surfaces tend to assume a minimum area. The contraction of the film may be demonstrated by the device shown in Fig. 8-11. If we dip a wire ring containing a loop of thread, Fig. 8-11(A), into a dish of soapsuds, a film is formed across the ring. If we break the film inside the loop of thread with a

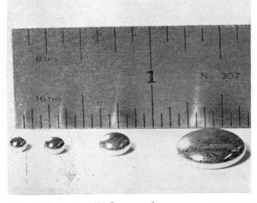

Fig. 8-12. Small drops of mercury assume a spherical shape because of surface tension. (Felix Cooper)

hot wire, the unbroken film outside the loop contracts and pulls the thread equally on all sides to form a circle, as shown in Fig. 8-11(B).

Surface tension causes a free liquid to assume a spherical shape. A free liquid is one which is not acted upon by any force. This is an ideal condition, but is approximated by small drops of mercury on a table top. From geometry you learned that a sphere has the smallest surface area for a given volume. The unbalanced force acting on liquid surface molecules tends to pull them toward the center of the liquid, reducing the surface area and causing the liquid to assume a spherical shape. Since the cohesive force between mercury molecules is great and mercury has a very high surface tension, small drops of mercury are spherical in shape. Larger drops of mercury, on which the effect of the force of gravity is appreciable, are noticeably flattened.

13. The shape of liquid surfaces. If you examine the surface of water in a glass container, you will find that it is not exactly level. It is very slightly concave when viewed from above. The edge of the surface where it comes in contact with the glass is lifted a little above the general

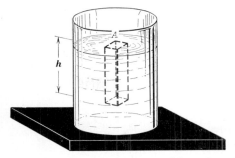

Fig. 8-14. The pressure exerted by a liquid depends upon its depth and weight density.

level, as shown in Fig. 8-13(A). *The crescent-shaped surface of a liquid column is called the* **meniscus** (meh-*niss*-kus). The water at the edge is lifted above the normal level because the adhesion of water to the glass is greater than the cohesion between water molecules.

If the container is filled with mercury instead of water, the edges of the liquid are depressed and the surface is *slightly convex.* See Fig. 8-13(B). In this case the cohesion between mercury molecules is greater than their adhesion to glass.

14. The pressure exerted by a liquid. *Pressure is the force applied to a unit area.* It may be defined by

$$p = \frac{F}{A}$$

where p represents the pressure, when a force F is applied to an area A. Pressure

may be expressed in newtons/meter^2, dynes/centimeter^2, pounds/inch^2, or pounds/foot^2.

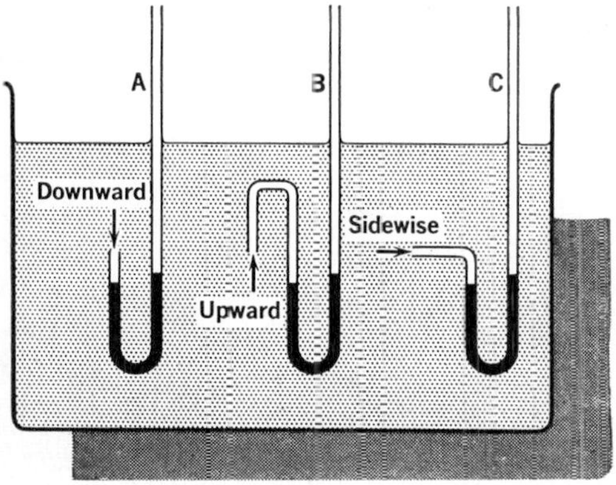

It is obvious that a liquid exerts a downward force because of its weight. Since a liquid is not easily compressed and its molecules can flow over one another readily, a liquid also always exerts a sidewise force and an upward force. Thus a liquid exerts a force, and therefore a pressure, in all directions.

From the weight density formula, the weight of a given volume of a liquid is

$$w = VD_w$$

Suppose we consider a volume of liquid having a uniform cross-sectional area A and depth h, as in Fig. 8-14, then

$$w = AhD_w$$

But the weight w is the force F exerted by the liquid on area A. Therefore

$$F = AhD_w \qquad \text{(Equation 1)}$$

We have already learned that

$$p = \frac{F}{A} \qquad \text{(Equation 2)}$$

So by substituting the expression for F in Equation 1 in Equation 2

$$p = \frac{AhD_w}{A}$$

and simplifying,

$$p = hD_w$$

Thus the pressure exerted by a liquid due to its weight depends on two factors, the depth of the liquid and its weight density.

To show the effect of direction on liquid pressure, we use the apparatus shown in Fig. 8-15. Three tubes of the same diameter contain the same amount of mercury. We lower the tubes into water so that all the open ends are at the same depth. The water pressure causes the mercury to rise in the long arm of each tube. At A the water presses *downward;* at B the water presses *upward;* at C the water presses *sidewise.* The difference between the mercury

Fig. 8-15. The pressure exerted by a liquid at a given depth is independent of direction.

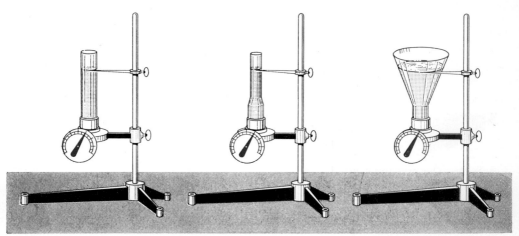

Fig. 8-16. The gauges show that the pressure caused by equal depths of liquid is the same at the bottom of each vase, even though the volume of liquid in each vase is different.

levels in the two arms of each tube is the same. This indicates that all the pressures are equal, and that *the pressure exerted by a liquid due to its weight is independent of direction.*

To show the effect of the *shape and volume* of the container on liquid pressure, we use the apparatus shown in Fig. 8-16. The vases of this apparatus are called *Pascal's* (pass-*kals*) *vases* because they were devised by the French physicist, Blaise Pascal (1623–1662). The area of the diaphragm at the bottom of each vase is the same, and the pointers, which show the increase in pressure as water is poured into these vases, all indicate the same pressure. The pressure at the bottom of each vase is the same, even though the shapes are different and the amount of water in each one is different. Therefore, *liquid pressure is independent of the shape and volume of the container.* Because of this, liquids stand at the same height in connecting containers of large diameter, regardless of their shape. See Fig. 8-17. See the Sample Problems on the opposite page.

15. Capillarity. In Section 14 we learned that liquids stand at the same level in connecting tubes. This is true only if the tubes have large enough diameters so that

the centers of the liquid surfaces are relatively flat. Experiments show that *water does not stand at the same level in connecting tubes of varying small diameters.* The height to which it rises increases as the diameter of the tube decreases. See Fig. 8-18(A). When mercury is used, the depression of the surface is greater as the diameter of the tube is reduced. See Fig. 8-18(B). *This elevation or depression of liquids in small diameter or capillary (hairlike) tubes is called capillarity.*

Capillarity depends on both adhesion and surface tension. The adhesion of water to glass causes the water to creep up the glass walls and produce a concave surface; surface tension tends to flatten this surface by contraction. The combined action of these two forces raises the water

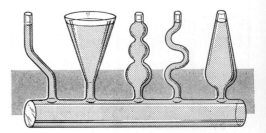

Fig. 8-17. A liquid stands at the same height in connecting containers of large diameter.

above its surrounding level. The water level rises until the two forces are counterbalanced by the weight of the elevated liquid. Why is a liquid like mercury depressed in capillary tubes?

Several conclusions about capillarity have been verified by experiment. (1) *Liquids rise in capillary tubes if they wet the tubes; liquids that do not wet the tubes are depressed.* (2) *The elevation or depression is inversely proportional to the diameter of the tube.* (3) *The amount of elevation or depression decreases as the temperature increases.*

16. The total force exerted by liquids.

Total force is the force acting against the entire area of a particular surface. A liquid exerts a total force against the entire area of the bottom and sides of its container. Since liquid pressure equals force per unit area, total force will equal the product of the average pressure on the area by the entire area.

$$F = Ap_{av}$$

And since $p_{av} = h_{av}D_w$,

$$F = Ah_{av}D_w$$

For the total force against the horizontal bottom of a container, h_{av} is the depth of

---

Sample Problem

A diver descends to a depth of 50.0 m in sea water, which has a mass density of 1.025 g/cm³. What is the pressure on his body in newtons/meter²?

Solution

$$p = hD_w$$
$$p = hD_m g$$
$$p = 50.0 \text{ m} \times 1.025 \text{ g/cm}^3 \times 10^3 \frac{\text{kg/m}^3}{\text{g/cm}^3} \times 9.80 \text{ m/sec}^2$$
$$p = 5.02 \times 10^5 \text{ nt/m}^2$$

Sample Problem

The water pressure in a certain city is 150. lb/in.² How many feet above the city must a reservoir be to supply this pressure? The weight density of water is 62.4 lb/ft³.

Solution

$$p = hD_w$$
$$h = \frac{p}{D_w}$$
$$h = \frac{150. \text{ lb/in.}^2}{62.4 \text{ lb/ft}^3} \times \frac{144 \text{ in.}^2}{\text{ft}^2}$$
$$h = 346 \text{ ft}$$

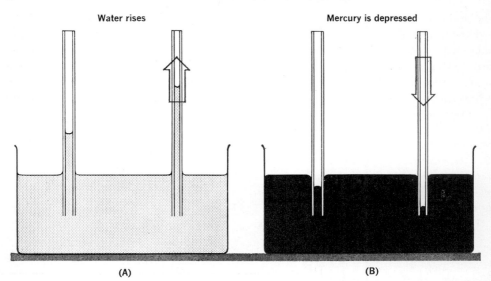

Fig. 8-18. (*A*) Capillary action of water. (*B*) Capillary action of mercury.

the liquid in the container. For the total force against the rectangular vertical side of a container, h_{av} is one-half the depth of the liquid in the container. See the Sample Problem below.

17. Measuring water pressure. The pressure in the mains of a water supply system should be great enough to provide an adequate flow to all the users, and meet emergency water needs, as for fire fighting. An *open manometer* (muh-*nom*-eh-ter), shown in Fig. 8-19, is one device

which may be used to measure water pressure. In this manometer the water pressure is balanced against the pressure of a column of mercury. The manometer, which is partially filled with mercury, is attached to the faucet, and when the water is turned on, the pressure of the water is measured by the height reached by the mercury column *AB*.

A more convenient type of pressure gauge is the *Bourdon* (*boor*-dun) *gauge*, shown in Fig. 8-20. The pressure of the

---

Sample Problem

Find the force in newtons against the end of a swimming pool 10.0 m wide if the water is 3.00 m deep. The mass density of water is 1.00 g/cm³.

Solution

$F = Ah_{av}D_w$

$F = Ah_{av}D_mg$

$F = 10.0 \text{ m} \times 3.00 \text{ m} \times 1.50 \text{ m} \times 1.00 \text{ g/cm}^3 \times 10^3 \dfrac{\text{kg/m}^3}{\text{g/cm}^3}$
$$\times 9.80 \text{ m/sec}^2$$

$F = 4.41 \times 10^5 \text{ nt}$

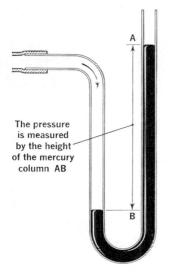

The pressure
is measured
by the height
of the mercury
column AB

Fig. 8-19. An open manometer is used to measure pressure.

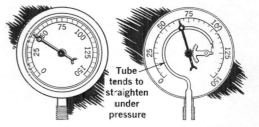

Tube
tends to
straighten
under
pressure

Fig. 8-20. The Bourdon pressure gauge. The internal mechanism is shown at the right.

water tends to straighten out the flat, curved tube; the motion of the end of the tube is transmitted to a shaft by means of a lever and gear mechanism. The pointer on the shaft then moves across the dial, which is calibrated to read pressure directly in $lb/in.^2$

18. Pressure transmission by liquids. Suppose we put a stopper in one end of an iron pipe completely filled with a liquid. As we push a second stopper into the open end of the pipe, the first stopper is pushed out, showing that the liquid in the pipe transmits the pressure that was exerted on the second stopper to the first stopper. Liquids are not easily compressed because of the enormous repulsive forces which arise between molecules when they are pushed closer than their normal spacing. Thus liquids transmit pressure readily.

Now let us drill several small holes in the pipe and repeat the experiment. As the second stopper is pushed into the pipe, the liquid squirts out through the holes. This shows that the pressure applied to the confined liquid is transmitted throughout the liquid. Liquids transmit pressure in all directions because their molecules

move freely and slide over one another readily.

19. Pascal's principle. Pascal, who devised the vases described in Section 14, also devised an experiment to study the transmission of external pressure by liquids. As shown in Fig. 8-21, he put tightly fitted pistons into openings in a container filled with water, the area of one opening being 100 times as large as the other. Pascal stated that *one man*, pushing against the small piston, could hold it against the force of *100 men* pushing against the larger piston. Such an apparatus is *a machine which multiplies force.*

Pascal realized that the transmission of pressure by the water produced the results he noted. This principle of mechanics, ***Pascal's principle,*** may be stated as follows: *Pressure applied anywhere on a confined fluid is transmitted undiminished in every direction. The force thus exerted by the confined fluid acts at right angles to every portion of the surface of the container, and is equal upon equal areas.* Note that fluids may be either

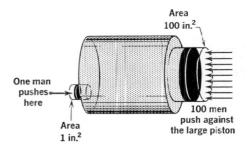

Area
100 in.^{2}

One man
pushes
here

Area
1 in.^{2}

100 men
push against
the large piston

Fig. 8-21. Pascal discovered that a container like this, filled with water, was actually a machine for multiplying force.

Fig. 8-22. The uniform pattern of spray from the entire length of this perforated hose is proof of Pascal's principle that pressure is transmitted undiminished in all directions through a confined fluid. (Supplex Corp.)

liquids or gases; Pascal's principle applies to both.

20. The hydraulic press. Figure 8-23 is similar to Fig. 8-21, except that the pistons are arranged so that they move vertically. Assume that A, Fig. 8-23, has an area of 1.00 in.^{2} and B has an area of 100. in.^{2} Then a weight of 1.00 lb on piston C will just balance a weight of 100. lb on piston D. The *pressure* produced by the weight on piston C is 1.00 lb/in.^{2} According to Pascal's principle, this pressure is transmitted undiminished through the liquid and is exerted on the lower surface of the large piston D. This piston has an area of 100. in.^{2} Consequently, the total force which acts upward on the large piston is 100. in.$^2 \times 1.00$ lb/in.$^2 = 100.$ lb. This force supports the 100.-lb weight on piston D. A force *slightly* in excess of 1.00 lb acting downward on the small piston would lift the weight of 100. lb on the large piston. We can see from this example how it is possible to develop this apparatus

into a machine to multiply force; this is the principle of the *hydraulic press*. If we make the large piston 1000. times the area of the small one, the force on the small piston is multiplied by 1000.

In this machine, as in the others we have studied, we must remember that *as*

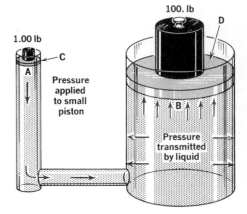

Fig. 8-23. A 1.00-lb weight placed on the small piston can balance a 100-lb weight on the large piston because the large piston has an area 100 times that of the small piston.

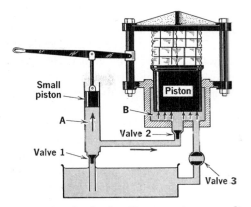

Fig. 8-24. The hydraulic press is an application of Pascal's principle.

we multiply force, we decrease correspondingly the distance and speed of the load. Suppose we push piston C down 10. in. Then 10. in.³ of water will be forced from A into B. This 10. in.³ of water must spread over an area of 100. in.² Therefore it raises the water level and lifts the large piston 10. in.³ ÷ 100. in.², or 0.10 in. If C moves 10. in., D moves only 0.10 in., $\frac{1}{100}$ as far as C. The force of 1.00 lb is multiplied 100 times by this device, but the object to be lifted on the large piston moves only $\frac{1}{100}$ as fast as the small piston. For any machine,

$$IMA = \frac{s_E}{s_R}$$

But in the cylinders of a hydraulic press,

$$A_E \times s_E = A_R \times s_R \quad \text{(Why?)}$$

where A_E is the area of the effort piston and A_R is the area of the resistance piston. Solving for s_E/s_R,

$$\frac{s_E}{s_R} = \frac{A_R}{A_E}$$

Therefore, $\quad IMA = \frac{A_R}{A_E}$

And since the areas of circles are proportional to the squares of their diameters, or the squares of their radii,

$$IMA = \frac{d_R{}^2}{d_E{}^2} = \frac{r_R{}^2}{r_E{}^2}$$

Figure 8-24 is a simplified diagram of a hydraulic press. It consists of two cylinders, one much larger than the other. In each there is a piston which fits tightly, so that the liquid cannot pass between the piston and the cylinder wall. A lever is attached to the small piston. As the small piston is pushed down, some of the liquid from the small cylinder A is forced into the large cylinder B. This raises the large piston a small amount. As the lever is worked up and down, it pumps the liquid from the reservoir and forces it into the cylinder B. When the pressure is to be released, Valve 3 is opened to let the liquid flow from B back into the reservoir.

A hydraulic press is used for baling cotton, squeezing the juice from apples and other fruits, punching holes in steel plates, shaping metal body parts for automobiles, and lifting enormous weights.

Other devices in which liquids are used to transmit pressure are the hydraulic brakes on automobiles, and the hydraulic lifts used on dentists' and barbers' chairs and for raising automobiles at service stations and garages.

21. The buoyant force of liquids. Cork and wood float on water; if you fill your lungs with air, it is usually possible for you to float on water. These examples show that water exerts an upward force on objects placed in it; an object floats if the upward force of the water on it is greater than the weight of the object itself. Objects denser than water, even though they sink readily, appear to lose a part of their weight when submerged. A man can lift a larger stone under water than he can possibly lift in air; the upward force of the water lifts part of the weight for him. *The upward force which any liquid exerts upon a body placed in it is called the **buoyant force.***

22. Archimedes' principle. Let us perform the following experiment. The overflow can shown in Fig. 8-25 is filled with water up to the spout. A heavy metal cylinder is weighed in air and is then

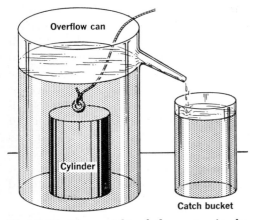

Fig. 8-25. The weight of the water in the catch bucket equals the buoyant force of the water on the cylinder.

weighed while completely immersed in water. The difference between the two weights is the buoyant force of the water. Next, the cylinder is lowered into the overflow can and all the water that overflows is caught. The volume of water which overflows equals the volume of the cylinder. If the work is carefully done, the weight of the water displaced by the metal cylinder equals the buoyant force of the water.

Similar experiments were performed by Archimedes (ark-ih-*mee*-deez) (287–212 B.C.), and resulted in the discovery that *the buoyant force which a fluid exerts on a body placed in it is equal to the weight of the fluid the body displaces.* Today we call this statement *Archimedes' principle.*

To test Archimedes' principle, let us now consider a cubic block, 10.0 cm on a side, submerged in water so that its upper surface *A* is just 10.0 cm below the surface of the water. We have shown this in Fig. 8-26. Let us calculate the total *downward* force on the upper surface of the block.

$$F = Ah_{av}D_m \, g$$

$$F = 100. \text{ cm}^2 \times 10.0 \text{ cm} \times 1 \text{ g/cm}^3$$
$$\times \, 980. \text{ cm/sec}^2$$

$$F = 9.80 \times 10^5 \text{ dynes}$$

The total *upward* force on the lower surface *B* is similarly calculated to be 19.60×10^5 dynes. The upward force at *B* exceeds the downward force at *A* by 9.80×10^5 dynes. Thus the buoyant force of the water on the block is 9.80×10^5 dynes.

The volume of a cubic block 10.0 cm on a side is 1.00×10^3 cm³. Since the block and the water cannot occupy the same space at the same time, the block must displace 1.00×10^3 cm³ of water. We know that 1.00 cm³ of water weighs 980. dynes. Therefore, the block displaced 9.80×10^5 dynes of water, which is equal to the buoyant force of the water on the block. These facts about total force in liquids prove Archimedes' principle. See the Sample Problem on the opposite page.

(To check your understanding, calculate the buoyant force when the *upper* surface of the block is 20.0 cm below the surface of the water.)

When a solid floats partially submerged in a liquid, the volume of liquid displaced is less than the volume of the solid. A comparison of these volumes gives us a relationship between the density of the solid and the density of the liquid in which it floats.

The formulas for density are

$$D_m = \frac{m}{V} \quad \text{and} \quad D_w = \frac{w}{V}$$

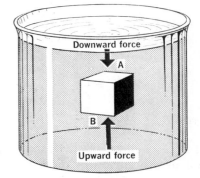

Fig. 8-26. The buoyant force equals the difference between the upward force and the downward force.

Sample Problem

A person whose volume is 2.00 ft³ weighs 130. lb. (*a*) If he jumps into sea water, weight density 64.0 lb/ft³, will he sink or float? (*b*) If he uses a cork life preserver, volume 1.00 ft³, weight density 15.0 lb/ft³, will he float?

Solution

(*a*) Weight of body = 130. lb
Buoyant force of sea water = 2.00 ft³ × 64.0 lb/ft³ = 128 lb
The buoyant force is less than the weight of the body. The person will sink.

(*b*) Total weight = 130. lb + 1.00 ft³ × 15.0 lb/ft³ = 145 lb
Buoyant force of sea water = (2.00 ft³ + 1.00 ft³) × 64.0 lb/ft³ = 192 lb
The buoyant force is greater than the total weight; the person will float.

Solving for m and w,

$$m = D_m V \quad \text{and} \quad w = D_w V$$

When a solid floats in a liquid the weight of the liquid displaced equals the weight of the solid. Also the mass of the liquid displaced equals the mass of the solid. (Why?) Thus, for either weight density or mass density,

$$D_s V_s = D_l V_l$$

where D_s is the density of the solid, V_s is its volume, D_l is the density of the liquid, and V_l is the volume of the liquid. Solving for $\dfrac{D_s}{D_l}$,

$$\frac{D_s}{D_l} = \frac{V_l}{V_s}$$

For a uniform cross-sectional area, $V = Ah$, where A is the cross-sectional area and h is the height, so

$$\frac{D_s}{D_l} = \frac{A_l h_l}{A_s h_s}$$

But for a solid floating in a liquid $A_l = A_s$, and h_l is the height of the solid submerged,

h_{sub}. The relationship then becomes

$$\frac{D_s}{D_l} = \frac{h_{\text{sub}}}{h_s}$$

Thus the fractional part of the solid which is submerged equals the ratio of the density of the solid to the density of the liquid in which it floats. See the Sample Problem on page 194.

Archimedes' principle is applied in the design of ships, pontoon bridges, floating dry docks, and buoys.

23. Specific gravity. In our study of the properties of liquids we have used the weight densities of various substances several times. Frequently it is helpful to compare the density of one substance with that of another. However, in order to make our comparisons meaningful, we need a standard. *Water is the standard* which physicists have chosen for comparing the densities of all *solids* and *liquids*. *The ratio of the density of a solid or liquid to the density of water is called its* **specific gravity.**

$$\text{Sp. gr.} = \frac{D_{\text{substance}}}{D_{\text{water}}}$$

The mass density of copper in CGS units is 8.9 g/cm³, while that of water is 1.0 g/cm³. Copper is thus 8.9 times as dense as water, and *the specific gravity of copper is 8.9.*

If we use FPS units, the weight density of copper is 555 lb/ft³, while that of water is 62.4 lb/ft³. Dividing 555 lb/ft³ by 62.4 lb/ft³, we obtain the specific gravity 8.9, as before.

In Appendix B you will find tables showing the specific gravities of various substances.

24. Measuring specific gravity. Specific gravity has been defined as

$$\text{Sp. gr.} = \frac{\text{density of substance}}{\text{density of water}}$$

If equal volumes of the substance and of water are considered,

$$\text{Sp. gr.} = \frac{\text{weight of substance}}{\text{weight of an equal volume of water}}$$

By using Archimedes' principle, we can easily find the *weight of an equal volume of water*, since a body submerged in water is buoyed up by a force equal to the weight of the water displaced. Therefore,

$$\text{Sp. gr.} = \frac{\text{weight of substance in air}}{\text{buoyant force of water}}$$

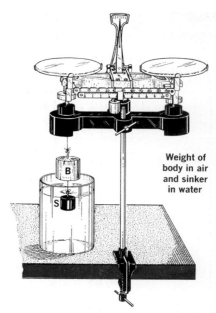

Weight of body in air and sinker in water

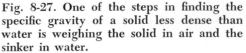

Fig. 8-27. One of the steps in finding the specific gravity of a solid less dense than water is weighing the solid in air and the sinker in water.

1. Solids. Case a. Solids denser than water. If the solid is insoluble, the difference between its weight in air and its weight in water can be found by weighing, and equals the buoyant force of the water. See the Sample Problem on page 195, top.

Sample Problem

The mass density of ice is 0.92 g/cm³. The mass density of sea water is 1.025 g/cm³. What fractional part of an iceberg is above the surface?

Solution

$$\frac{h_{sub}}{h_s} = \frac{D_s}{D_l}$$

$$\frac{h_{sub}}{h_s} = \frac{0.92 \text{ g/cm}^3}{1.025 \text{ g/cm}^3}$$

$$\frac{h_{sub}}{h_s} = 0.90, \text{ the fraction submerged}$$

$$1.00 - 0.90 = 0.10, \text{ the fraction above the surface}$$

Sample Problem

A stone weighs 3.0×10^4 dynes in air, and 2.0×10^4 dynes in water. What is its specific gravity?

Solution

$$\text{Sp. gr.} = \frac{\text{weight of substance in air}}{\text{buoyant force of water}}$$

$$\text{Sp. gr.} = \frac{3.0 \times 10^4 \text{ dynes}}{3.0 \times 10^4 \text{ dynes} - 2.0 \times 10^4 \text{ dynes}}$$

$$\text{Sp. gr.} = 3.0$$

Case b. Solids less dense than water. A solid must float if the buoyant force becomes equal to the weight of the solid before it is completely submerged. Therefore we use an indirect method employing a dense sinker to find the buoyant force on such solids. See Fig. 8-27. The difference between the combined weight of the solid in air and the sinker in water, and the combined weight of both the solid and the sinker in water, is the buoyant force on the low-density solid. The Sample Problem below illustrates the method of computation employed.

2. Liquids. There are several methods for comparing the weight of a liquid with the weight of an equal volume of water.

a. The bottle method. The bottle shown in Fig. 8-28 is called a *pycnometer* (pik-*nom-eh*-ter). Because of the tiny hole in the stopper, the pycnometer can be easily filled with exactly the same volume of liquid each time it is used. By comparing the weight of liquid of unknown specific gravity it can hold with the weight of water it can hold, we may determine the specific gravity of the liquid. See the Sample Problem on page 196, top.

Sample Problem

A piece of cork weighs 5.0×10^4 dynes. A sinker submerged in water weighs 2.10×10^5 dynes. The combined weight of the cork and sinker when both are submerged is 1.0×10^4 dynes. What is the specific gravity of the cork?

Solution

$$\text{Sp. gr.} = \frac{\text{weight of substance in air}}{\text{buoyant force of water}}$$

$$\text{Sp. gr.} = \frac{5.0 \times 10^4 \text{ dynes}}{(5.0 \times 10^4 \text{ dynes} + 2.10 \times 10^5 \text{ dynes}) - 1.0 \times 10^4 \text{ dynes}}$$

$$\text{Sp. gr.} = 0.20$$

Sample Problem

A pycnometer weighs 2.2×10^4 dynes. When filled with water it weighs 7.2×10^4 dynes. When filled with alcohol, it weighs 6.2×10^4 dynes. Find the specific gravity of the alcohol.

Solution

$$\text{Sp. gr.} = \frac{\text{weight of liquid}}{\text{weight of an equal volume of water}}$$

$$\text{Sp. gr.} = \frac{6.2 \times 10^4 \text{ dynes} - 2.2 \times 10^4 \text{ dynes}}{7.2 \times 10^4 \text{ dynes} - 2.2 \times 10^4 \text{ dynes}}$$

$$\text{Sp. gr.} = 0.80$$

b. Loss-of-weight method, or *bulb method*. The denser a liquid is, the greater the buoyant force it can exert. We can find the relative weights of two liquids by comparing their buoyant forces upon the same solid. A glass bulb or a platinum ball is most often used. Then

$$\text{Sp. gr.} = \frac{\text{buoyant force of liquid}}{\text{buoyant force of water}}$$

See the Sample Problem below.

c. The hydrometer method. A wooden rod, loaded at one end so that it will float vertically, sinks in water until the weight of the water it displaces exactly equals its own weight. If it is placed in a liquid of unknown specific gravity, it again sinks until it displaces a weight of the unknown liquid equal to its own weight. If the rod is uniform, the densities of the liquids displaced will be inversely proportional to the depths to which the rod sinks. For example, if the rod sinks to a depth of 10.0 cm in water and to a depth of 8.0 cm in the unknown liquid, then the unknown liquid is $\frac{10.0 \text{ cm}}{8.0 \text{ cm}}$, or 1.25 times as dense as water.

$$\text{Sp. gr.} = \frac{\text{depth rod sinks in water}}{\text{depth rod sinks in liquid}}$$

Sample Problem

A ball weighs 4.0×10^4 dynes in air, 3.2×10^4 dynes in water, and 2.8×10^4 dynes in a liquid of unknown specific gravity. Find the specific gravity of the liquid.

Solution

$$\text{Sp. gr.} = \frac{\text{buoyant force of liquid}}{\text{buoyant force of water}}$$

$$\text{Sp. gr.} = \frac{4.0 \times 10^4 \text{ dynes} - 2.8 \times 10^4 \text{ dynes}}{4.0 \times 10^4 \text{ dynes} - 3.2 \times 10^4 \text{ dynes}}$$

$$\text{Sp. gr.} = 1.5$$

25 cm³

Fig. 8-28. The volume of liquid a pycnometer contains may be duplicated precisely.

The commercial *hydrometer* (hy-*drom*-eh-ter), Fig. 8-29, has a scale graduated in such a way that the specific gravity of the liquid in which it floats may be read directly. The purpose of the upper bulb is to increase the volume of the hydrometer. The lower bulb is filled with shot or mercury so that the hydrometer will float in a vertical position. Some hydrometers are designed so that they are suitable for determining the specific gravity of liquids less dense than water; others are designed for use with liquids of greater density.

The determination of specific gravity has many practical applications. The specific gravity of rocks and minerals is a means for their identification. The specific gravity of metals and alloys is particularly important in aircraft construction, since structural parts of airplanes and missiles must be strong yet light in weight. The specific gravity of a liquid is an indication of its purity. The specific gravity of the liquid in an automobile storage battery indicates how fully the battery is charged. The liquid in a fully charged battery has a higher specific gravity than that in a battery which has lost most of its charge. The battery fluid, a solution of sulfuric acid in water, may have a specific gravity of 1.300 in a fully charged battery, while

in a discharged battery it may have a specific gravity of only 1.150.

Special hydrometers have been designed for particular purposes. Acidimeters are used in testing the concentration of acids. The alcoholometer is a special hydrometer for measuring the amount of alcohol in various alcohol-water mixtures. A special hydrometer called a lactometer is used to indicate the specific gravity of milk. Since the specific gravity of cow's milk usually lies between 1.027 and 1.035, the lactometer is calibrated over this range, the scale having numerical graduations running from 20 to 40.

A service station attendant estimates the freezing point of the mixture of antifreeze and water in an automobile radiator by using a special hydrometer to check the specific gravity of the mixture.

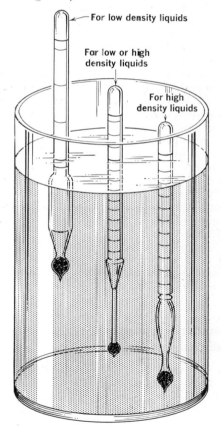

For low density liquids

For low or high density liquids

For high density liquids

Fig. 8-29. Different types of hydrometers.

QUESTIONS

A **1.** What characteristic of liquid molecules did Brown's experiment reveal?

2. Describe a demonstration which shows that molecules of liquids diffuse.

3. Why does alcohol cling to a glass rod while mercury does not?

4. What is the effect of adding a detergent to the water on which a needle is floating?

5. Why is a soap bubble floating through the air spherical in shape?

6. What determines whether a meniscus is concave or convex when viewed from above?

7. (*a*) What is pressure? (*b*) In what units is it commonly expressed? (*c*) To which system of measurement does each of these units belong?

8. On what two factors does the magnitude of the pressure exerted by a liquid due to its weight depend?

9. Water rises to a certain height in a capillary tube of given diameter. What is the effect on the amount of rise if (*a*) the tube is lengthened; (*b*) the diameter of the tube is decreased; (*c*) the temperature of the water is raised?

10. On what factors does the total force exerted by the water against the side wall of a swimming pool depend?

11. (*a*) What two devices are commonly used to measure liquid pressure? (*b*) Explain each.

12. (*a*) Why can liquids be used to transmit pressure? (*b*) Why do they transmit pressure in all directions?

13. State Pascal's principle.

14. For what purposes may a hydraulic press be used?

15. (*a*) What is the buoyant force? (*b*) What is the magnitude of the buoyant force?

16. Why is it possible for a person to float more readily in Great Salt Lake than in Lake Michigan?

17. Define specific gravity.

18. How is specific gravity converted to density in (*a*) the CGS system; (*b*) the MKS system; (*c*) the FPS system?

B **19.** Describe the characteristics of the particles of a substance which is liquid at room temperature.

20. (*a*) What is the nature of the action force when a safety-razor blade floats on water? (*b*) What is the nature of the reaction force?

21. Why can lead shot be made by allowing melted lead to fall through a column of cool air?

22. Describe an experiment which shows that the magnitude of the pressure exerted by a liquid due to its weight is (*a*) independent of direction; (*b*) independent of the shape and volume of the container.

23. Why is mercury depressed in capillary tubes?

24. (*a*) What are the action forces which cause water to rise in a capillary tube? (*b*) What is the reaction force?

25. Using Fig. 8-24, explain the operation of a hydraulic press.

26. Derive the formula for the IMA of a hydraulic press in terms of the areas of the pistons.

27. (*a*) Why is it important to keep the weight of a conventional submarine as nearly constant as possible despite the consumption of food and fuel? (*b*) How is this done?

28. An overflow can containing some water is suspended from the hook of a spring balance. Explain how the balance reading is affected if (*a*) a small block of wood floats on the water; (*b*) a brass weight is suspended in the water.

29. (*a*) Will a ship that is wrecked in mid-ocean sink to the bottom or float submerged at a certain depth? (*b*) Explain.

30. What relationship exists between the fractional part of a solid which is submerged, the density of the solid, and the density of the liquid in which it floats?

31. A fisherman ties a piece of lead to his line near the hook, and a cork to the line a foot or two from the hook. Why?

PROBLEMS

A **1.** What pressure in dynes/cm² is exerted by a column of mercury 72.0 cm high if the mass density of mercury is 13.6 g/cm³?

2. The surface of Lake Mead, formed behind Hoover Dam, is 530. ft above the base of the dam. What is the pressure at the base of the dam?

3. What pressure in dynes/cm² is indicated by an open manometer in which the difference in water levels is 25.0 cm?

4. The difference in mercury levels in the arms of an open manometer is 10.0 in. What is the indicated pressure in lb/in.²? Mercury is 13.6 times as dense as water.

5. The cross-sectional area of the mouth of a jug is 5.0 cm²; the area of the bottom of the jug is 200. cm². The jug is filled with water. What additional total force will be exerted on the bottom of the jug if 5.0×10^6 dynes of force is applied to a stopper fitted into the mouth of the jug?

6. A hydraulic press has pistons with areas of 10.0 in.² and 1.00×10^3 in.² respectively. What force must be applied to the small piston to produce a force of 2.5 tons on the large piston?

7. A rod 25.0 cm long floats vertically in carbon tetrachloride with 15.0 cm submerged. If the mass density of carbon tetrachloride is 1.60 g/cm³, what is the mass density of the rod?

8. A wooden rod 12.0 in. long is weighted so that it floats vertically in water with 2.0 in. above the surface. What is the weight density of the rod in lb/ft³?

9. The specific gravity of gold is 19.3. What is its weight density in nt/m³?

10. What is the specific gravity of silver if its weight density is 655.2 lb/ft³?

11. A block of copper weighs 1.00×10^5 dynes in air and 8.88×10^4 dynes in water. What is its specific gravity?

12. A large lump of coal weighs 25 lb in air and 7.2 lb in water. What is the specific gravity of the coal?

13. A piece of maple weighs 1.75×10^5 dynes in air. The maple in air and the sinker in water have a combined weight of 3.50×10^5 dynes. When both are immersed in water, their weight is 6.0×10^4 dynes. Calculate the specific gravity of the maple.

14. A piece of cork weighs 0.50 lb in air; a sinker weighs 2.20 lb in water. The weight of both cork and sinker in water is 0.60 lb. Determine the specific gravity of the cork.

15. An empty pycnometer has a mass of 23.2 g. When filled with water its mass is 58.3 g. When filled with olive oil, its mass is 55.4 g. Calculate the specific gravity of the olive oil.

16. A pycnometer weighs 2.47×10^4 dynes. When filled with water, the combined weight is 4.98×10^4 dynes. What is the combined weight after the pycnometer is emptied of water and then filled with mercury?

17. A glass bulb loses 3.50×10^4 dynes when immersed in water and 5.25×10^4 dynes when immersed in chloroform. What is the specific gravity of chloroform?

18. A glass bulb has a mass of 50.2 g in air and 27.2 g in water. When immersed in nitric acid, its apparent mass is 17.6 g. What is the specific gravity of nitric acid?

19. A hydrometer sinks to a depth of 6.00 inches in water. To what depth will it sink in a salt solution, specific gravity 1.09?

B   20. A tank is 5.0 m long, 3.0 m wide, and filled with alcohol to a depth of 2.0 m. The mass density of alcohol is 0.80 g/cm³. Calculate (a) the total force in newtons on the bottom of the tank; (b) the total force against each side; (c) the total force against each end.

21. A swimming pool is 50.0 ft long and 20.0 ft wide. If the water is 8.0 ft deep, calculate (a) the pressure in lb/in.² on the bottom of the pool; (b) the total force in lb on the bottom of the pool; (c) the total force against each side; (d) the total force against each end.

22. A cylindrical tank 12.0 ft long, radius 2.5 ft, is buried on its side in the ground. If the tank is full of gasoline, specific gravity 0.70, what is the total force against one of the circular ends of the tank?

23. The lever of a hydraulic press has an IMA of 5.0. The cross-sectional area of the small piston is 5.0 cm² and that of the large piston is 75.0 cm². What load can be supported by the large piston when a force of 3.0×10^7 dynes is applied to the lever?

24. The lever of a hydraulic press has an IMA of 7.5. The diameter of the small piston is 2.5 in and that of the large piston is 15 in. What force is exerted by the large piston when a force of 50. lb is applied to the lever?

25. A piece of pine, mass density 0.500 g/cm³, has a piece of silver, mass density 10.5 g/cm³, imbedded in it. When immersed, it displaces 1000. cm³ of water and has an apparent mass of 250. g. What are the mass and volume of the piece of pine and of the silver imbedded in it?

26. A flat-bottomed river barge is 20.0 ft wide and 75.0 ft long. It is floating empty in a river. How much deeper will it sink into the water if a load of 200. tons of sand is placed in it?

27. Scientists have estimated that the density of some stars is so great that one cubic inch weighs a ton. Determine the specific gravity of such a material.

28. What is the specific gravity of the matter of which a proton is composed? Assume the diameter of a proton is 3.0×10^{-5} Å and its mass is 1.67×10^{-24} g.

29. A person's body, specific gravity 1.07, displaces 2.50 ft³ of water when completely submerged. If the person is kept afloat by a cork life preserver which is totally submerged and which displaces 1.00 ft³ of water, what fraction of the person's volume is kept out of water?

3 GASES

25. The nature of a gas. The particles of substances which are gases at room temperature are molecules; some of these molecules consist of a single atom, many consist of two atoms, while others consist of several atoms. Since matter in the gaseous state occupies a volume of the order of 10^3 times that which it does in the liquid state, molecules of gases are much farther apart than those of liquids. Even so, 1 cm^3 of a gas contains about 3×10^{19} molecules. Many ordinary molecules have diameters of the order of 4×10^{-8} cm. In gases, these molecules are about 4×10^{-7} cm or about 10 diameters apart. The kinetic energy of the molecules of a gas is sufficient to overcome entirely the Van der Waals forces between them. The molecules are thus essentially independent particles, traveling at a rather high rate of speed, about 5×10^4 cm/sec. See Fig. 8-30. At this speed, they travel about 10^{-5} cm before colliding with other molecules or with the walls of the container, and undergo about 5×10^9 collisions per second. Evidence for this concept of the nature of a gas comes from observing several properties of gases: (*1*) expansion, (*2*) pressure, and (*3*) diffusion.

1. The fact that a gas does not have a definite shape or a definite volume, but will expand and completely fill any container into which it is introduced, shows that gas molecules are rapidly moving independent particles. When someone accidentally leaves a gas valve open in the laboratory, you can soon smell the gas, no matter where you are in the room. The gas molecules move in random fashion in all directions until they become thoroughly mixed with the molecules of the air.

2. A toy balloon may burst from the pressure which the air inside it exerts on its inside surface. This pressure is caused by the constant bombardment of the inside surface by many billions of moving molecules. If we increase the number of molecules within the balloon by blowing more air into it, the number of collisions against the inside surface and therefore the pressure on the inside surface increases.

3. Hydrochloric acid is a water solution of a dense gas called hydrogen chloride; ammonia water is a water solution of a low density gas, ammonia. When these gases combine, they form a cloud of fine, white particles of a solid, ammonium chloride. Suppose we put a few drops of hydrochloric acid in a warm bottle, and an equal amount of ammonia water in a second warm bottle. Then we cover the mouth of each bottle with a glass plate, and invert the bottle containing ammonia over the one containing hydrogen chloride, as shown in Fig. 8-31(*A*). After letting the bottles stand for a minute or two, we slide out the glass plates and leave the bottles mouth-to-mouth. We can tell from the white smoke produced that the less dense ammonia descends and mixes with the more dense hydrogen chloride. The hydrogen chloride also rises and mixes

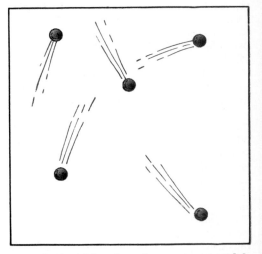

Fig. 8-30. Molecules of a gas are widely separated and move rapidly.

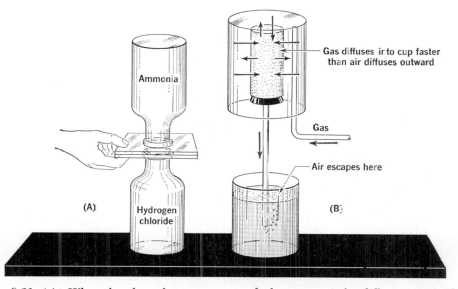

Fig. 8-31. (A) When the glass plates are removed, the gases mix by diffusion. (B) The more rapid diffusion of gas into the cup increases the pressure within the cup. As a result, some of the air is forced down the tube and bubbles through the liquid.

with some of the ammonia remaining in the upper bottle. The movement of each of these gases is the opposite of that which would be caused by gravity, and must be due to molecular motion. Thus the diffusion of gases is another evidence of the constant movement of gas molecules.

Gases diffuse through porous solids. In the apparatus shown in Fig. 8-31(B), an unglazed earthenware cup is closed with a rubber stopper through which passes a glass tube, which dips into a colored liquid. When a large beaker is placed over the cup, and gas from the gas valve is led into the beaker, air immediately begins to bubble through the colored liquid. Evidently the lighter molecules of gas move through the porous walls of the cup faster than do the heavier molecules in the air. Thus there is an accumulation of molecules inside the cup which increases the pressure of the gas there and pushes the liquid down the tube, forcing some of the air in the tube to escape. If a dense gas like carbon dioxide is led into the beaker, molecules from the air flow out through the porous cup faster than the

carbon dioxide molecules enter. This reduces the pressure inside the cup and the colored liquid rises in the tube. Thus we see that there is an inverse relation between the rate of diffusion of a gas and its density.

The diffusion of gases through porous solids is an important process. Such diffusion occurs through the membranes of plants, animals, and man, allowing oxygen to reach living cells and carbon dioxide to escape. Uranium isotopes may be separated by means of the different rates of diffusion of $_{92}U^{235}F_6$ and $_{92}U^{238}F_6$, two gaseous hexafluorides of uranium, through a suitable porous barrier.

Scientists frequently find it desirable when dealing with the behavior of gases to consider what they call an *ideal gas*. An *ideal gas* is one consisting of infinitely small molecules which exert no forces on each other. Real gases within the usual experimental ranges of temperature and pressure conform very well to the theoretical behavior of an ideal gas, even though they consist of molecules of finite size which do exert forces on each other. Under the usual

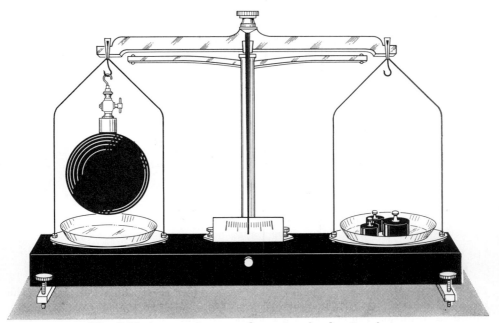

Fig. 8-32. An experiment to determine the density of air.

temperatures and pressures, spaces separating the molecules are large enough so that the actual size of the molecules and the forces between them have little effect.

26. Measurement of gases. Physicists generally measure quantities of solids and liquids in mass units, but the densities of gases are so small that volume units are more convenient for measurement. Unlike solids and liquids, whose volumes vary only slightly with temperature and pressure changes, gas volumes vary greatly with such changes. When we measure quantities of gases we must always state the temperature and pressure at which the volume measurement is made, because only then is the amount of matter definitely specified.

For convenience in comparing quantities of gases, scientists have selected certain standard conditions for the measurement of gas volumes. *The standard temperature is the temperature of melting ice, 0° C. The standard pressure is the pressure exerted by a column of mercury exactly 760 mm*

high. The abbreviation S.T.P. means standard temperature and pressure.

27. The density and specific gravity of gases. We are not usually conscious of the fact that air has mass, since we move so easily through it. However, in the laboratory, we may determine the mass of a given volume of air and find its density. For this experiment a metal globe like that shown in Fig. 8-32 is used. First, the globe is weighed when it is full of air. Then the air is pumped out and the globe is weighed again. We find that the globe now weighs less than it did the first time; the difference we observe is the mass of the air removed. If we determine the volume of air removed, its mass density can be calculated. The mass density of dry air at S.T.P. is 1.293 g/l; the weight density of dry air at S.T.P. is 1.30 oz/ft³. Air is commonly used as the standard for determining the specific gravity of gases. The specific gravities of common gases are given in Table 8, Appendix B.

28. Air pressure. Since air has weight,

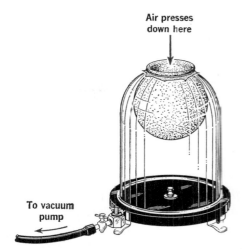

Air presses
down here

To vacuum
pump

Fig. 8-33. As air is pumped out of the bell jar, the higher air pressure outside pushes the membrane down into the jar.

it must exert pressure. Suppose we tie a thin rubber membrane over the open top of a bell jar, as shown in Fig. 8-33. We put the bell jar on a pump plate, connect it to a vacuum pump, and begin to remove the air. The rubber membrane is pressed farther and farther down into the jar as the air is gradually removed. Finally, the membrane may burst. As air from the inside of the bell jar is removed, the *upward force* which the air inside exerts decreases. The *unbalanced downward force* finally bursts the membrane.

Although we live at the bottom of a layer of air hundreds of miles deep, we do not feel the pressure which it exerts because the pressure is nearly equal from all directions. However, we certainly notice the enormous force the air can exert when we see wind breaking the limbs of trees, uprooting trees bodily, or damaging buildings.

29. Liquids rise in evacuated tubes. Every time we drink through a straw we show that a liquid rises in an evacuated tube; the liquid rises in the straw because it is forced up by the pressure of the atmosphere. We reduce the air pressure on the surface of the liquid within the straw

by the action of our lips and cheeks. See Fig. 8-34. Fundamental experiments on the pressure of the atmosphere were performed by Evangelista Torricelli (toh-reh-*chel*-ee) (1608–1647), an Italian physicist. About the middle of the seventeenth century, men were trying to find out why water from deep wells would not rise more than 32 ft in the tubes of the pumps they were using. Torricelli knew that air had weight, and he suspected that it was the pressure of the surrounding air that forced the water up the tube of a pump. If this were so, he reasoned, mercury, which is 13.6 times as dense as water, would be forced up only $\frac{1}{13.6}$ times as high in an exhausted tube. Torricelli took a glass tube about 3 ft long and, after closing one end, filled the tube with mercury. Placing his finger over the open end of the tube, he then inverted the tube in a bowl of mercury, as shown in Fig. 8-35(A). When he removed his finger from the opening, only a little of the mercury flowed out from the tube. The mercury column, AB, stood at a height of approximately 30 in. above the level of the mercury in the bowl. Torricelli thus proved that the atmospheric pressure at sea level just counterbalances a column of mercury about 30 in. high. It is not strictly correct to say that liquids

Air pressure is
reduced here

Air pushes down on the
liquid surface with one
atmosphere pressure

Fig. 8-34. When you reduce the air pressure within the straw by the action of your cheeks and lips, the higher air pressure outside forces the liquid up through the straw into your mouth.

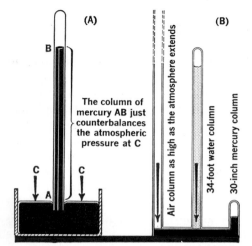

Fig. 8-35. (A) The air at sea level exerts a pressure which may be counterbalanced by a column of mercury 76 cm, or about 30 in., high. (B) Pressure exerted by a column of air as high as the atmosphere is the same as that exerted by a 34-ft water column or a 30-in. mercury column.

"rise" in evacuated tubes; they are *forced up* by the pressure of the air on the surface of the liquid outside the tube.

Torricelli's belief in the pressure of the atmosphere was confirmed by Pascal, who reasoned that if the mercury column in a Torricellian tube was actually sustained by the pressure of the atmosphere, the height of the column would be less at higher altitudes. Pascal arranged to have a Torricellian apparatus carried to the top of a 3000-ft mountain in central France. When the apparatus was assembled at the top of the mountain, the mercury column was found to be about 3 in. shorter than it was at the base of the mountain.

We know that water pressure increases with depth. Consequently, we expect to find that the pressure of the atmosphere in a valley is greater than it is on the top of a nearby mountain. Air is so compressible, however, that its density varies greatly at different altitudes, and it is difficult to calculate the pressure due to its depth.

30. The pressure of the atmosphere. The experiments of Torricelli and Pascal

proved conclusively that the height to which a liquid will rise in an evacuated tube depends on the pressure of the air on the surface of the liquid outside the tube. The air at sea level normally exerts a pressure which counterbalances a mercury column 76.0 cm, or 29.9 in., high. We know how to calculate liquid pressure, so we can find the pressure exerted by the atmosphere.

$$p = hD_m$$
$$p = 76.0 \text{ cm} \times 13.6 \text{ g/cm}^3$$
$$p = 1.03 \times 10^3 \text{ g/cm}^2$$

This equals the normal pressure of the atmosphere at sea level.

In the English system the height of the mercury column is 29.9 in., or 2.49 ft. The density of mercury is 62.4 lb/ft³ × 13.6 (its specific gravity), or 849 lb/ft³. Then,

$$p = hD_w$$
$$p = 2.49 \text{ ft} \times 849 \text{ lb/ft}^3$$
$$p = 2.12 \times 10^3 \text{ lb/ft}^2$$

or, more commonly

$$p = 2.12 \times 10^3 \text{ lb/ft}^2 \times \frac{1 \text{ ft}^2}{144 \text{ in.}^2}$$
$$p = 14.7 \text{ lb/in.}^2$$

This is known as a "pressure of one atmosphere." "Two atmospheres pressure" is twice this, or 29.4 lb/in.²

If we make a Torricellian tube using water, it must be 13.6 times as long as one filled with mercury (13.6 × 29.9 in. = 407 in. or 33.9 ft). If the atmospheric pressure at sea level can support a column of water only 34 ft high, we can understand why seventeenth-century pumps would not lift water more than 32 ft, since no pump produces a perfect vacuum. The three tubes shown in Fig. 8-35(B) represent the relative heights of columns of mercury, water, and the atmosphere which produce the same pressure. In addition to making possible the operation of pumps for water and other liquids, atmospheric pressure causes a liquid to flow through a siphon.

31. The mercurial barometer. A *barometer* is used to measure the pressure of the *atmosphere*. A mercurial barometer is simply a Torricellian apparatus, mounted in a frame, and having a device for measuring the height of the mercury column. Sometimes the tube and bowl are attached to a board on which a scale is mounted. In Fig. 8-36(*A*), a metal tube is used as a frame to support the glass tube and bowl and to protect them from breakage. The scale, in inches or centimeters, is etched on the metal tube, which has a vertical slot cut in it near the top, as shown in Fig. 8-36(*B*), so the level of the mercury in the glass tube can be seen and measured.

If the air pressure decreases, some of the mercury flows out of the tube into the bowl; if the air pressure increases, the mercury flows back into the tube. These changes in the level of the mercury in the bowl produce an error in the measurements of the height of the mercury column to be read from the fixed scale. Consequently, each barometer has a fixed point, usually an ivory peg, from which to measure the height of the column. This peg is mounted on the frame of the barometer just inside the bowl; the point of the peg is used as the zero mark of the scale. By means of a flexible membrane and a thumbscrew, as shown in Fig. 8-36(*C*), the surface of the mercury in the bowl can be adjusted to coincide with the tip of the ivory peg. This should be done before any readings are taken.

Mercury is a suitable liquid for use in a barometer because it has a high specific gravity and a comparatively low freezing point. However, mercury does expand with an increase in temperature, and readings taken with a mercurial barometer should be corrected for changes in temperature.

32. The aneroid barometer. Since a mercurial barometer is at least 3 ft in length and contains a liquid, it is awkward to handle and inconvenient to carry from one place to another; in fact, extreme care must be used when one is moved.

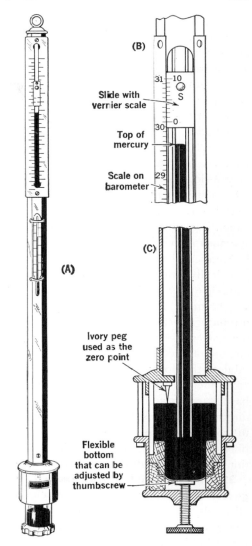

Fig. 8-36. (*A*) A mercurial barometer. (*B*) A vernier scale is used to enable us to read a barometer more accurately. (*C*) The mercury level in the bowl of a barometer must be adjusted to the zero point before each reading is taken.

Furthermore, a mercurial barometer must be mounted in a vertical position. An *aneroid* (*an-er-oid*) *barometer*, like that shown in Fig. 8-37, avoids these difficulties *by not containing a liquid*, but it is not as accurate as a mercurial barometer. It consists essentially of a shallow box with a thin, corrugated metal cover, as shown in Fig. 8-38. The base of the metal box is fastened to the base of the barometer. Because the air has been partially removed from the box, the elastic cover, or diaphragm, is very sensitive to changes in atmospheric pressure, moving up or down in response to these changes. The motion of the diaphragm is communicated by a system of levers and a chain to a shaft with a pointer that moves across a graduated scale. This system of levers multiplies the small movement of the diaphragm so that it may be measured on the scale, which is graduated by comparison with a standard mercurial barometer.

An aneroid barometer may be made in practically any size. Some are small enough to be carried in a pocket, like a watch; many have a dial the size of an ordinary clock face. A good aneroid barometer is so sensitive that it shows a change of pressure when lowered from a table to the floor.

Altimeters in airplanes are aneroid barometers graduated to read altitudes directly. They must be adjusted frequently to compensate for variations in atmospheric pressure caused by weather conditions encountered during a flight.

33. The buoyant force exerted by gases. Archimedes' principle applies to all fluids, gases as well as liquids; just as water exerts a buoyant force on submerged objects, air exerts a buoyant force on objects submerged in it. An object which displaces exactly one liter of air, mass 1.293 g, will weigh 1.293 g $\times$ $\frac{980.\text{ dynes}}{g}$ = 1.267 $\times$ 10^3 dynes more in a vacuum than it does in air at S.T.P. This shows that the buoyant force of air under standard conditions is 1.267 $\times$ 10^3 dynes/liter, and an object accordingly rises in air if the buoyant force which the air exerts on it is greater than the weight of the object.

A balloon is essentially a strong, airtight bag filled with a gas less dense than

Fig. 8-37. An aneroid barometer. (Taylor Instrument Co.)

air. It rises if its weight plus the weight of the gas it contains is less than the weight of the air it displaces. If the balloon is filled with hydrogen (a gas which weighs only 88 dynes/liter), every liter of air the balloon displaces exerts a lifting force equal to the difference between the weight of one liter of air and one liter of hydrogen; that is, 1.267 $\times$ 10^3 dynes − 88 dynes = 1.179 $\times$ 10^3 dynes. While it is the buoyant force of the air displaced that actually causes a balloon to rise, we commonly speak of it as the *lifting force* of hydrogen, a lifting force of 1.179 $\times$ 10^3 dynes/liter.

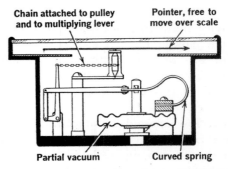

Fig. 8-38. Cross section of an aneroid barometer showing the corrugated box and the system of levers.

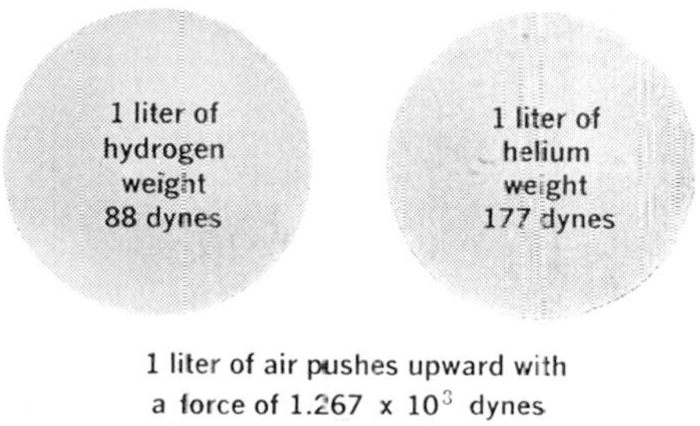

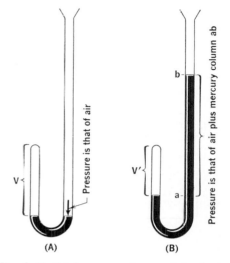

1 liter of
hydrogen
weight
88 dynes

1 liter of
helium
weight
177 dynes

1 liter of air pushes upward with
a force of 1.267 x 10³ dynes

Fig. 8-39. The upward force of the air is the same in both cases, but the helium weighs more than the hydrogen, so its lifting power is less.

Since there are 10³ liters in a cubic meter, the lifting force of hydrogen is equal to 1.179×10^6 dynes/m³ or approximately 1.2 oz/ft³. See Fig. 8-39.

Hydrogen is the gas of lowest density, but it burns and is consequently dangerous to use for filling balloons. Helium gas is twice as dense as hydrogen, but it does not burn; it is more often used for filling balloons and airships in the United States. The lifting force of one liter of helium is 1.267×10^3 dynes $-$ 177 dynes $= 1.090 \times 10^3$ dynes, 93 percent that of hydrogen.

34. Boyle's law. An English scientist, Robert Boyle (1627–1691), was the first person to perform experiments on what he called the "springiness of the air." No doubt other scientists living at that time knew about compressed air, but none of them had performed experiments to learn how the volume of a gas is affected by the pressure exerted on it.

In his experiments, Boyle used a J-shaped tube similar to that shown in Fig. 8-40. He poured just enough mercury into the tube to fill the bent portion and then adjusted the mercury levels so that they would be at the same height in both arms of the tube. In this way, Boyle trapped a volume of air, V, in the short arm of the tube. Next he measured the length of the tube so that he could determine the volume of the confined gas. He knew that this gas must be under atmospheric pressure, because the mercury levels

Fig. 8-40. J-tube apparatus used to demonstrate Boyle's law.

were the same. See Fig. 8-40(A). By reading the barometer, Boyle found the exact pressure exerted on the volume of gas, V. Let us call that pressure p.

Next he added more mercury to the long arm of the tube, as shown in Fig. 8-40(B). By measuring the length of the column of air in the short arm he could determine its new volume, V'. He could find the new pressure, p', on this volume of gas by measuring the length of the mercury column ab, and adding that length to the barometer reading. As a result of several trials with this type of apparatus, Boyle found that increasing the pressure on a volume of confined gas reduced its volume correspondingly. Doubling the pressure reduced the volume to one-half; tripling the pressure reduced the volume to one-third.

Boyle's law may be stated as follows: *The volume of a dry gas varies inversely with the pressure exerted on it, provided the temperature remains constant.*

35. A graph of Boyle's law. Suppose we take 2000. cm³ of a gas measured at a pressure of 200. mm of mercury. Let us subject it to each of the pressures indicated at the left in the table on page 208. We then find by experiment the volume occupied by this gas at each pressure.

Pressure (mm)	Volume (cm³)
200.	2000.
250.	1600.
333.	1200.
400.	1000.
500.	800.
800.	500.
1000.	400.
1200.	333.
1600.	250.
2000.	200.

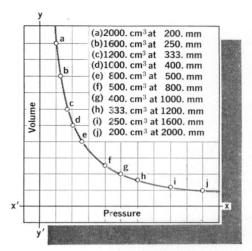

Fig. 8-41. The graph shows the relationship between the pressure on a gas and its volume. This is the graph of two quantities which are inversely proportional.

We have plotted these data in Fig. 8-41, using the pressures as abscissas, and the volumes as ordinates. This is a graph of Boyle's law. A graph of this shape (a hyperbola) represents an *inverse proportion*.

When two quantities are in inverse proportion, their product is a constant. So *the product of a pressure and its corresponding volume is always a constant.* In equation form,

$$pV = a \text{ constant}$$

In all cases, except under very high pressures, or very low temperatures, or both,

$$pV = p'V'$$

and

$$V' = V \frac{p}{p'}$$

Here p is the original pressure, V is the original volume; p' represents the new pressure, and V' the new volume. See the Sample Problem below.

Boyle's law describes the behavior of an ideal gas. It applies to real gases with a fairly high degree of accuracy, but it does not apply to gases under such high pressure that the molecules are close enough together to attract each other. Under this condition the gas is almost at the point at which it will condense into a liquid.

Sample Problem

We measure 500. cm³ of a gas at a pressure of 750. mm of mercury. What volume will this gas occupy if the pressure is increased to 800. mm?

Solution

$$V' = V \frac{p}{p'}$$

$$V' = 500. \text{ cm}^3 \times \frac{750. \text{ mm}}{800. \text{ mm}}$$

$$V' = 469 \text{ cm}^3$$

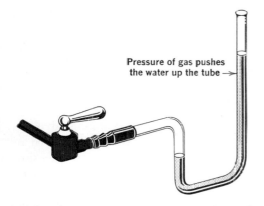

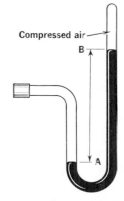

Fig. 8-42. An open manometer may be used to measure gas pressure.

Fig. 8-43. A closed manometer is used to measure high pressure.

36. Variation of gas density with pressure. There is no change in the mass of a gas when its volume is changed by a difference in the pressure exerted upon it. Since an increase in pressure produces a decrease in the volume of a gas, it must also increase the density of the gas. *The density of a gas varies directly with the pressure exerted on it.*

$$\frac{D}{D'} = \frac{p}{p'}$$

A liter of air has a mass of 1.29 g at a pressure of one atmosphere. A liter container can hold four times 1.29 g, or 5.16 g, of air under a pressure of four atmospheres, because the air is four times as dense. See the Sample Problem below.

37. Measuring gas pressure. We buy gas for cooking and heating purposes at a certain price per 1000. ft³. The density of a gas varies with the pressure exerted upon it. Consequently it makes considerable difference whether the gas is measured at a low pressure or at a high pressure.

Suppose we put enough water into a bent tube, like that shown in Fig. 8-42, so that the water is about 4 in. high in each arm. When we attach the tube to a

Sample Problem

A certain gas has a density of 1.50 g/liter at a pressure of 760. mm. What will be its density if the pressure is decreased to 730. mm?

Solution

$$\frac{D}{D'} = \frac{p}{p'}$$

$$D' = D\frac{p'}{p}$$

$$D' = 1.50 \text{ g/liter} \times \frac{730. \text{ mm}}{760. \text{ mm}}$$

$$D' = 1.44 \text{ g/liter}$$

gas valve, we find that the water rises a few inches higher in the open arm when the gas valve is opened. The difference in height enables us to measure the amount by which the gas pressure exceeds the atmospheric pressure. Mercury may also be used in this type of manometer. For high pressures, a closed manometer like that shown in Fig. 8-43 may be used.

A spring gauge is often used to check the pressure of air in automobile tires. Most gauges show a reading of zero at normal atmospheric pressure; the actual pressure, or the *absolute pressure*, equals the *gauge pressure* plus 14.7 lb/in.²

Compressed air is used to transmit pressure, according to Pascal's principle, in a variety of applications. In tires and air-cushion springs, compressed air acts as an elastic cushion to absorb shock. Air brakes on locomotives contribute greatly to the safety of railroad transportation. In diving bells and diving suits, compressed air is used to force water out; caissons used in underwater construction operate on a similar principle. Compressed air tools, such as riveting hammers, pneumatic drills for breaking up concrete or asphalt pavement, and sandblasting equipment, are widely used.

QUESTIONS

A 1. (*a*) Approximately how many diameters apart are gas molecules at room temperature? (*b*) What is their speed? (*c*) How many collisions do they undergo per second?
2. In terms of the kinetic theory, explain why gases (*a*) expand; (*b*) exert pressure; (*c*) diffuse.
3. (*a*) What is an *ideal gas?* (*b*) Why do real gases within the usual experimental ranges of temperature and pressure conform to the behavior of an ideal gas?
4. (*a*) Why are volume units more convenient than mass units for measuring quantities of gases? (*b*) When gases are measured in volume units, what additional information must be given?
5. What is the meaning of S.T.P.?
6. What standard is commonly used for determining the specific gravity of gases?
7. Why do we not feel the pressure exerted by the atmosphere?
8. In what way did Pascal confirm Torricelli's belief that the pressure of the atmosphere supports the column of mercury in a closed glass tube?
9. (*a*) What are the advantages of a mercurial barometer? (*b*) What are its disadvantages?
10. Why is mercury considered to be a more satisfactory liquid to use in a barometer than water?
11. (*a*) What are the advantages of an aneroid barometer? (*b*) What are its disadvantages?
12. What is meant by the *lifting force* of a gas?
13. State Boyle's law.
14. How does the density of a gas vary with the pressure exerted on it?

15. Explain the terms *absolute pressure* and *gauge pressure*.

B 16. What would happen if the gas introduced into the large beaker of the apparatus shown in Fig. 8-31 were (*a*) helium; (*b*) argon?
17. Describe an experiment which shows that air exerts pressure.
18. Suppose you opened a bottle of soft drink and inserted in the mouth of the bottle a tight-fitting stopper through which a glass tube had been passed. When you attempted to drink through the glass tube, would you be able to obtain any soft drink? Explain your answer.
19. Describe an experiment by which the density of the air may be determined.
20. Why is it difficult to calculate the pressure due to any considerable depth of a gas?
21. Does the diameter of a barometer tube have any effect on the height of the mercury column?
22. Does the specific gravity of a liquid have any effect on the height over which it may be siphoned?
23. What will determine the height to which a balloon rises?
24. Why is the product of the pressure on a given mass of gas and its corresponding volume a constant?
25. (*a*) What are the dimensions of the Boyle's law constant? (*b*) What physical quantity has such dimensions?

PROBLEMS

A **1.** What is the density of air in kg/m³ at S.T.P.?

2. A physics laboratory is 45 ft long and 22 ft wide, with a 12-ft ceiling. What is the weight, in pounds, of the air in this laboratory at S.T.P.?

3. The density of carbon dioxide gas at S.T.P. is 1.250 g/l. Calculate its specific gravity, air standard.

4. The specific gravity, air standard, of neon gas at S.T.P. is 0.696. What is the weight of 5.0 ft³ of this gas?

5. If the barometer stands at 740. mm, what is the atmospheric pressure in g/cm²?

6. If the average pressure is 15 lb/in.², calculate the total force on the six faces of an evacuated can 8.0 in. long, 5.0 in. wide, and 12.0 in. high.

7. What is the lifting force of 15 liters of helium?

8. How much greater is the lifting force of 1000. ft³ of hydrogen than that of the same volume of helium?

9. Some nitrogen gas occupies 2.0 liters at 735 mm pressure. What volume would this gas occupy at standard pressure?

10. A quantity of air occupies 30.0 ft³ at 22.5 lb/in.² pressure. What volume would the air occupy at 15.0 lb/in.² pressure?

11. A certain gas occupies 600. ml at 740. mm pressure. What volume does the gas occupy at 800. mm pressure?

12. A cylinder for compressed gas has a volume of 2.0 ft³. What volume of oxygen at 14.7 lb/in.² can be put in the cylinder under a pressure of 100. lb/in.²?

B **13.** Calculate the combined pressure in g/cm² of the air and water on an object immersed in 30. m of water at the bottom of a lake. The barometer reading is 735 mm.

14. If a mercury barometer is sunk 15 ft below the surface of a lake where the air pressure is 29.3 in. of mercury, what is the barometer reading?

15. What must be the volume in m³ of a balloon filled with helium if the balloon is to carry a gross load of 3500 kg?

16. If the total weight of a balloon is 2.5 × 10³ lb, what volume of helium, in ft³, is required to lift it?

17. What is the density of methane in g/liter at 0° C if it is under a pressure of 2.5 atmospheres?

18. What is the mass of 500. ml of chlorine at 0° C and 770. mm pressure?

19. What is the density of the air in a tire in oz/ft³ if it is inflated to a gauge pressure of 28 lb?

20. What is the weight of the air in a tire which has a volume of 800. in.³ if the tire is inflated to 23 lb gauge pressure?

4 FLUIDS IN MOTION

38. Common properties of liquids and gases. So far we have considered liquids and gases as separate states of matter. We have learned, however, that Pascal's principle and Archimedes' principle do apply to both liquids and gases. Now we are ready to learn about some other properties which liquids and gases have in common. The term *fluid* may be applied to both liquids and gases, and since the behavior of moving liquids is similar to the behavior of moving gases, we treat them together as fluids in motion.

39. Streamline flow. The motion of fluids is very complex. If you watch the waves along the shore of an ocean or a large lake, you will soon realize how complicated their movement is. The unpredictable nature of tornadoes shows that the movement of gases is complex, too. We shall limit our discussion of the motion of fluids to a few examples which can be explained in simplified terms.

Suppose we have a tube whose diameter varies as shown in Fig. 8-44. We find that the motion of water flowing through the tube is smooth and even. Water molecules which enter the tube at *A*, *B*, or *C* follow the paths shown by the dotted lines. Since the volume of water passing any cross-sectional area of the tube is the same in any given length of time, the water must flow more rapidly through the narrow portion of the tube than through the wide portion. *This smooth flow of a fluid through a tube is called* **streamline flow.** If the velocity of the fluid becomes too great, or if changes in the diameter or direction of the tube are too abrupt, the fluid does not flow smoothly. The flow then is said to be *turbulent.*

40. Bernoulli's principle. Water is moving with streamline flow through the tube shown in Fig. 8-45. Because the diameter of the center portion is less than that at either end, the water flows faster through the narrow part of the tube. The vertical tubes act as pressure gauges, filling with liquid until the pressure due to the weight of the liquid in the tube equals that of the moving liquid. These gauges show that the pressure is higher where the velocity of the fluid is lower; where the velocity of the fluid is higher, the pressure it exerts is lower. This is the principle of the *Venturi* (ven-*too*-ree) *meter.* This device enables us to calculate the velocity of a fluid in the horizontal tube from the difference in pressure in the vertical tubes.

The explanation for the variation in pressure exerted by a moving fluid when its velocity is changed was given by Daniel Bernoulli (ber-*noo*-lee) (1700–1782). He found that *for the horizontal flow of a fluid through a tube, the sum of the pressure and the kinetic energy per unit volume of the fluid is a constant.*

$$p + \frac{K.E.}{V} = k$$

This statement usually is called ***Bernoulli's principle.***

Fig. 8-44. Streamline flow of water through a tube.

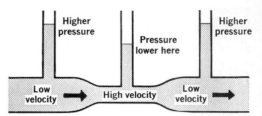

Fig. 8-45. As the water flows more rapidly through the narrow portion of the tube, the pressure is lowered.

The kinetic energy of a moving fluid is directly proportional to the square of its velocity. Bernoulli's principle states, however, that the sum of the pressure and the kinetic energy per unit volume is a constant. Since the velocity of a moving fluid increases, its kinetic energy increases, and consequently, the pressure it exerts must correspondingly decrease. This explains the results we observed in the Venturi meter.

Bernoulli's principle has several important applications. The air passage through an automobile carburetor is partially constricted at the point where the gasoline is mixed with the air. This increases the velocity of the air, lowers its pressure, and permits more rapid evaporation of the gasoline.

A spinning baseball follows a curved path. As shown in Fig. 8-46, the ball, spinning in a counterclockwise direction, drags the adjacent air around with it. At the top of the ball, this air current is moving with the air current set up by the forward motion of the ball; at the bottom, it is moving against this current. The air at the top moves faster, and the pressure is reduced; the air below moves more slowly, and the pressure is increased. Thus, the ball is forced to follow a curved path as shown.

A moving airplane wing experiences an upward force because of the motion of the air over it. Figure 8-47 shows a cross section of an airplane wing with air flowing around it from left to right. The lower

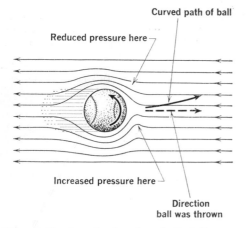

Fig. 8-46. A spinning baseball follows a curved path because its motion makes the air pressure less on one side than on the other.

surface of the wing is at a slight angle to the direction of the moving air. Thus air flowing across the lower surface is deflected slightly by the force the wing exerts on it, but the air exerts an equal and opposite force on the wing. The upward component of this force provides about 15 percent of the force required to lift an airplane. The rest of the force needed to lift an airplane is produced by the movement of the air across the upper surface of the wings, because an airplane wing is shaped like one-half of a Venturi tube. The air moving across the upper surface must travel faster than the air moving beneath, and consequently, the air moving [over] the top surface of the wing exerts less [pressure] than that moving beneath it. [This difference] in pressure provides most [of the force] which causes an air[plane to rise. The vertical] component of the [upward force is called] lift. The [horizontal force which]

airplane engines is the equilibrant of the drag.

41. Fluid friction and viscosity. Friction opposes the movement of fluid molecules over one another in a flowing liquid or gas. *This internal friction of a fluid is viscosity.* Liquids, of course, are much more viscous than gases. Because of viscosity, a force must be exerted to cause one layer of a fluid to slide over another, or to cause one surface to slide over another if there is a layer of fluid between them.

If a fluid moves around a spherical solid with streamline flow, or a spherical solid moves through a fluid at rest, experiments show that the force of fluid friction is directly proportional to the relative velocity of the fluid and the sphere. Thus, the greater the velocity of the sphere with respect to the fluid, the greater the force of friction. We have seen (Chapter 4, Section 10) that the fluid friction of the air limits the terminal velocity of freely falling bodies.

The viscosity of a liquid decreases as the temperature rises, for the cohesive force between the molecules of a liquid determines its viscosity. With increasing temperature, the kinetic energy of the molecules increases, and the cohesive forces between them decrease; therefore the viscosity decreases. For this reason lubricating oils should be selected

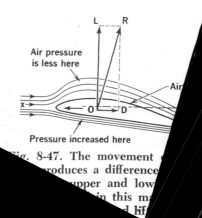

Fig. 8-47. The movement [of air] produces a difference [in pressure on the] upper and lower [surfaces and in this ma]

basis of their viscosity over the range of operating temperatures of a machine.

The viscosity of a gas, however, increases as the temperature increases. There is a different molecular action involved here; the diffusion of gas molecules from one moving gas layer to another determines the viscosity. Since gaseous diffusion is more rapid at higher temperatures due to increased molecular velocity, the viscosity of a gas becomes greater as the temperature rises.

QUESTIONS

A 1. Name three physical principles which apply to both liquids and gases.

2. What is the smooth flow of a fluid called?

3. What causes turbulent flow in a fluid?

4. (a) How does the pressure exerted by a smoothly flowing fluid vary with its rate of flow? (b) What is a practical application of this phenomenon?

5. What is viscosity?

How does fluid friction vary with the city of the body moving through the fluid?

hat design characteristic of an airplane s responsible for the major lift force ing moves through the air?

B 8. What is the purpose of the narrow air passage at the point where the gasoline is mixed with air in a carburetor?

9. Explain why a spinning baseball travels in a slightly curved path.

10. (a) Into what two components may the resultant force of the air moving over an airplane wing be resolved? (b) Which component is useful? (c) Which component acts as a retarding force?

11. (a) How does the viscosity of a liquid vary with the temperature? (b) How does the viscosity of a gas vary with the temperature? (c) Explain any difference which exists.

nary

kinetic theory helps explain the properties of matter in terms of the ween molecules and the energy they possess; it assumes that matter is of continually moving molecules which obey Newton's laws of relative magnitudes of molecular forces and molecular kinetic mine the physical state of a substance. The ratio of the density o that of a standard is called specific gravity.

properties of solids which depend on molecular forces or re diffusion, cohesion, adhesion, tensile strength, ductility, ticity.

liquids which depend on molecular forces, m of molecules include diffusion, cohesi sure and total force, capillarity, uoyant force.

sure, and diffu are meas vo

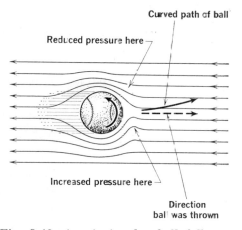

Fig. 8-46. A spinning baseball follows a curved path because its motion makes the air pressure less on one side than on the other.

surface of the wing is at a slight angle to the direction of the moving air. Thus air flowing across the lower surface is deflected slightly by the force the wing exerts on it, but the air exerts an equal and opposite force on the wing. The upward component of this force provides about 15 percent of the force required to lift an airplane. The rest of the force needed to lift an airplane is produced by the movement of the air across the upper surface of the wings, because an airplane wing is shaped like one-half of a Venturi tube. The air moving across the upper surface must travel faster than the air moving beneath, and consequently, the air moving over the top surface of the wing exerts less pressure than that moving beneath it. This difference in pressure provides most of the lifting force which causes an airplane to rise. *The vertical component of the forces on an airplane wing is called* lift. *The horizontal component of these forces, which tends to retard the movement of the airplane through the air, is called* **drag**. As an airplane flies at constant velocity, the forces on its wings must be in equilibrium. The force of gravity is the equilibrant of the lift, while the thrust force produced by the

airplane engines is the equilibrant of the drag.

41. Fluid friction and viscosity. Friction opposes the movement of fluid molecules over one another in a flowing liquid or gas. *This internal friction of a fluid is* viscosity. Liquids, of course, are much more viscous than gases. Because of viscosity, a force must be exerted to cause one layer of a fluid to slide over another, or to cause one surface to slide over another if there is a layer of fluid between them.

If a fluid moves around a spherical solid with streamline flow, or a spherical solid moves through a fluid at rest, experiments show that the force of fluid friction is directly proportional to the relative velocity of the fluid and the sphere. Thus, the greater the velocity of the sphere with respect to the fluid, the greater the force of friction. We have seen (Chapter 4, Section 10) that the fluid friction of the air limits the terminal velocity of freely falling bodies.

The viscosity of a liquid decreases as the temperature rises, for the cohesive force between the molecules of a liquid determines its viscosity. With increasing temperature, the kinetic energy of the molecules increases, and the cohesive forces between them decrease; therefore, the viscosity decreases. For this reason, lubricating oils should be selected on the

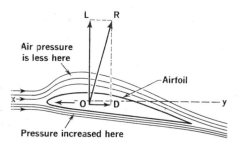

Fig. 8-47. The movement of air over the wing produces a difference in pressure between the upper and lower surfaces. The force produced in this manner may be resolved into an upward lift force and a horizontal drag force.

basis of their viscosity over the range of operating temperatures of a machine.

The viscosity of a gas, however, increases as the temperature increases. There is a different molecular action involved here; the diffusion of gas molecules from one moving gas layer to another determines the viscosity. Since gaseous diffusion is more rapid at higher temperatures due to increased molecular velocity, the viscosity of a gas becomes greater as the temperature rises.

QUESTIONS

A 1. Name three physical principles which apply to both liquids and gases.
2. What is the smooth flow of a fluid called?
3. What causes turbulent flow in a fluid?
4. (*a*) How does the pressure exerted by a smoothly flowing fluid vary with its rate of flow? (*b*) What is a practical application of this phenomenon?
5. What is viscosity?
6. How does fluid friction vary with the velocity of the body moving through the fluid?
7. What design characteristic of an airplane wing is responsible for the major lift force as the wing moves through the air?

B 8. What is the purpose of the narrow air passage at the point where the gasoline is mixed with air in a carburetor?
9. Explain why a spinning baseball travels in a slightly curved path.
10. (*a*) Into what two components may the resultant force of the air moving over an airplane wing be resolved? (*b*) Which component is useful? (*c*) Which component acts as a retarding force?
11. (*a*) How does the viscosity of a liquid vary with the temperature? (*b*) How does the viscosity of a gas vary with the temperature? (*c*) Explain any difference which exists.

ummary

The kinetic theory helps explain the properties of matter in terms of the forces between molecules and the energy they possess; it assumes that matter is composed of continually moving molecules which obey Newton's laws of motion. The relative magnitudes of molecular forces and molecular kinetic energies determine the physical state of a substance. The ratio of the density of a substance to that of a standard is called specific gravity.

Some of the properties of solids which depend on molecular forces or molecular motion are diffusion, cohesion, adhesion, tensile strength, ductility, malleability, and elasticity.

The properties of liquids which depend on molecular forces, molecular motion, or the weight of molecules include diffusion, cohesion, adhesion, surface tension, liquid pressure and total force, capillarity, pressure transmission, and the exertion of a buoyant force.

Gases expand, exert pressure, and diffuse. Like liquids, gases exert a buoyant force. Gases usually are measured in volume units at stipulated temperatures and pressures. The volume of a dry gas varies inversely with the pressure exerted on it, provided the temperature remains constant.

The smooth flow of a fluid through a tube is called streamline flow. Bernoulli's principle states that for the horizontal flow of a fluid through a tube, the sum of the pressure and the kinetic energy per unit volume of the fluid is a constant. The internal friction of a fluid is viscosity.

TERMS TO DEFINE ——————————————————

adhesion	forces between molecules	pressure
amorphous	gauge pressure	pycnometer
Archimedes' principle	Hooke's law	specific gravity
atmospheric pressure	hydraulic press	standard pressure
barometer	hydrometer	standard temperature
Bernoulli's principle	ideal gas	strain
Boyle's law	kinetic theory	streamline flow
buoyant force	lift	stress
capillarity	lifting force	surface tension
cohesion	malleability	tensile strength
crystalline	manometer	theory
diffusion	mass density	total force
drag	meniscus	turbulent flow
ductility	nature of a gas	Van der Waals forces
elastic limit	nature of a liquid	Venturi meter
elastic modulus	nature of a solid	viscosity
elasticity	Pascal's principle	weight density

RESEARCH ON YOUR OWN

1. Repeat the experiment shown in Fig. 8-6, using rubber bands in place of the steel spring. Compare the elasticity of the rubber with that of the steel.
2. Fill a glass to the top with water. Estimate how many pennies you can put in the glass before the water overflows. Were you over or under in your estimate? Why? Repeat the experiment until you can guess when one or two more pennies will cause an overflow. Now add one small drop of a liquid detergent to the middle of the water surface. Account for what happens. Next, add the detergent to the water before starting to add pennies, and account for any difference in the number that cause an overflow.
3. Try to float a cork stopper in the middle of a tumbler of water. Explain the result. Can you suggest a coating for the stopper that would affect your result? What is the effect when detergent is added to the water?
4. Obtain and clean thoroughly two glass cover plates about 4 in. by 4 in. Tie the plates together and then insert a thin wood splint between them at one edge. Put one edge of the plates in water so that the splint is perpendicular to the water. If the plates are clean you will see a fairly smooth curve of water film between the plates. Can you write the equation for the curve?
5. Plan several ways to illustrate Bernouilli's principle and demonstrate them in class.
6. Obtain two small open containers that will fit within a piece of glass tubing that is 1 or 2 in. in diameter and 3 or 4 ft long. Fill one container with HCl and the other with NH_4OH. Insert the containers in the glass tube at opposite ends and close the tube with rubber stoppers. Let the tube stand until a white ring shows somewhere near the middle. Measure its distance from each container. Can you find a mathematical relationship to explain the results?
7. Fit a hot-water bottle with a tight-fitting one-hole stopper. Into the stopper insert the short end of a length of glass tubing bent at right angles about 4 in. from one end. Put enough water in the bottle to cause the water to rise in the tubing when the bottle lies flat on a table. Estimate how far a book placed on the bottle will cause the water to rise. Check your estimate. Try more than one book. Does the water rise proportionally?
8. Make a working model of a hydraulic press or a hydraulic lift. Demonstrate it and explain the principle of operation.

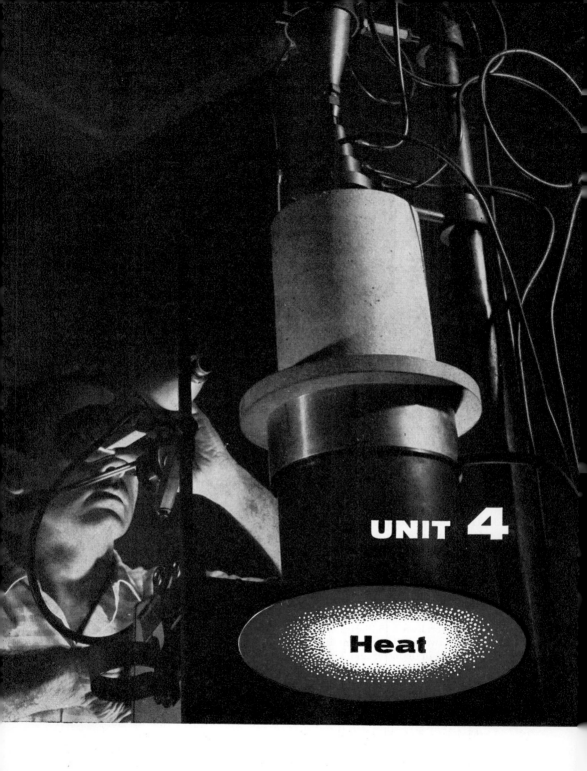

UNIT 4

Heat

CHAPTER 9

THERMAL EXPANSION

1. The nature of heat. Until about the middle of the nineteenth century, heat was thought to be an invisible, weightless fluid called *caloric*. Supposedly, when a substance like wood or coal was burned, large quantities of caloric were produced. Furthermore, it was held, this caloric could be transferred to other materials, and as a result they were warmed. When a hot substance cooled off, it was said to have lost caloric.

About 1800, Count Rumford (1753–1814), a British-American military expert and scientist, was watching the boring of a cannon. In order to keep the boring tools cool, the barrel of the cannon was kept filled with water. This water boiled away as the boring tools cut into the metal, but it also boiled away when the tools became so blunt that they were no longer cutting. Rumford concluded that apparently limitless heat could be obtained in this way from friction alone. This meant that the heat produced could not be some kind of a substance, but must be related to the motion of the tool in the bore of the cannon. About 40 years later, James Prescott Joule, after many careful experiments, showed that a given amount of mechanical energy always produces the same amount of heat. Thus the experiments of Rumford and Joule showed that mechanical energy and heat are equivalent, and *heat must be a form of energy.*

VOCABULARY

Absolute zero of temperature. The lowest possible temperature, attained when a body has given up all the thermal energy it can.

Coefficient of linear expansion. The change in unit length of a solid when its temperature is changed one degree.

Coefficient of volume expansion. The change in unit volume of a solid when its temperature is changed one degree.

Heat. Thermal energy which is being taken up by a body, given up by a body, or being transferred from one body to another.

Temperature. The measure of the ability of a body to give up heat to, or absorb heat from, other bodies.

Thermal energy. The potential and kinetic energy of the particles of a body which can be evolved as heat.

Fig. 9-1. The six most important sources of heat. Can you identify each?

2. The sources of heat energy. Since heat is a form of energy, most of our sources of heat are examples of conversion of other forms of energy into heat. The most important sources are

1. The sun. Directly or indirectly, nearly all our heat may be traced to the nuclear fusion reactions occurring in the sun. Heat from the sun makes it possible for plants to grow. Animals require these same plants for food. On a hot, sultry summer day it may seem that we are getting a large portion of the sun's heat. It has been estimated, however, that the earth as a whole receives only one two-billionth of all the heat given off by the sun.

2. The earth's interior. The molten lava from volcanoes and the boiling water which issues from geysers are both evidence that the interior of the earth is much hotter than its surface.

3. Chemical action. We use fuels such as coal, oil, gas, and wood as our main sources of artificial heat. Heat is produced when these fuels enter into chemical action with oxygen. In our bodies the oxygen we breathe unites chemically with the food we eat, supplying us with enough heat to maintain a body temperature of about 98.6° F.

4. Mechanical energy. We have already seen from the experiments of Rumford and Joule that mechanical energy can be converted into heat. Work that is used to overcome friction appears as heat.

5. Electric energy. Heat is produced from electric energy by the resistance of electric conductors to the passage of electric current. An electric iron and a toaster are heated this way.

6. Nuclear energy. This promises to be an important source of large amounts of energy. We have already learned how nuclear energy is converted into heat in a nuclear reactor.

Fig. 9-2. The water in the teakettle and in the cup is at the same temperature, but that in the teakettle can give out more heat.

3. The difference between heat and temperature. We know from experience that heat and temperature are related. They are not the same, however. A burning match has a much higher temperature than a steam radiator, but the heat given out by the match is not enough to warm a room. Suppose we have a teakettle that is full of boiling water. If we pour some of the water into a cup, the temperature of the water in the cup will be the same as that in the kettle. However, we could melt more ice with the water in the kettle than we could with the water in the cup

because the water in the kettle can give out more heat. Ten pounds of water at 80° F will melt more ice than one pound of water at 100° F. The ten pounds of water can evolve more heat, but the one pound of water is at a higher temperature. From these observations we learn that it is possible for a body to have a high temperature and give out little heat; to have a high temperature and give out a great amount of heat; to have a low temperature and give out little heat; or to have a low temperature and give out a large quantity of heat.

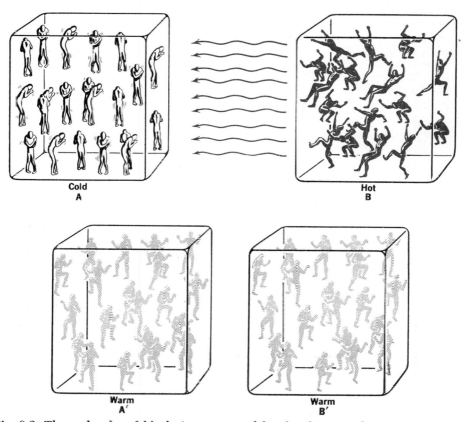

Cold
A

Hot
B

Warm
A'

Warm
B'

Fig. 9-3. The molecules of block A, represented by the shivering figures, possess little thermal energy. Block A therefore has a low temperature—it is cold. The molecules of block B, represented by the jumping figures, possess a great amount of thermal energy. Block B therefore has a high temperature—it is hot. Since block B is at the higher temperature, it can transfer some of its thermal energy in the form of heat to block A until the molecules of both blocks have an equal amount of thermal energy—their temperatures are the same. See blocks A' and B'.

When a body is hot, it has more *thermal energy* than when it is cold. We do not know the exact relationship between thermal energy and the structure of matter, but we do know that *the **thermal energy** of a body is the potential and kinetic energy of its particles that can be evolved as heat.*

What we call temperature is simply the "hotness" or "coldness" of an object. The quantity of thermal energy possessed by a particular body determines its temperature. The same quantity of thermal energy possessed by different bodies, however, does not give each the same temperature. The relationship between temperature and thermal energy is different for different materials. When a body takes up thermal energy, its temperature ordinarily

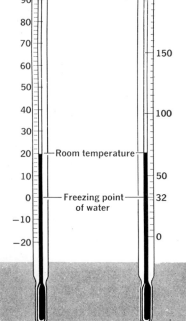

Centigrade   Fahrenheit

Fig. 9-4. Comparison of Centigrade and Fahrenheit thermometers.

rises. If the body gives up thermal energy, its temperature ordinarily goes down. The absorption or emission of thermal energy can also produce a change in the physical state of a body without a change in temperature. *Thermal energy which is being taken up by a body, being given up by a body, or being transferred from one body to another is **heat**. The **temperature** of a body is a measure of its ability to give up heat to, or absorb heat from, other bodies.* See Fig. 9-3.

4. Temperature scales. In order to establish a scale for measuring temperature, two fixed temperatures and the scale difference between them must be defined. The two fixed temperatures used with common temperature scales are (*1*) the freezing temperature of water, called the *ice point;* and (*2*) the boiling temperature of water under a pressure of exactly 760 mm of mercury, called the *steam point.* Several types of temperature scales have been devised; we shall study only two, the *Centigrade* and the *Fahrenheit scales.*

1. Centigrade scale. This scale, devised by a Swedish astronomer, Anders Celsius (*sel*-see-us) (1701–1744), is the one commonly used in many foreign countries. Officially, it is called the Celsius scale, but this name has not been generally accepted in the United States. The Centigrade scale is used for scientific work in the United States. On this scale, the ice point is *0*, and the steam point is *100*. The interval between these fixed temperatures is divided into one hundred equal parts, called *degrees*, °. The degrees between the fixed temperatures are thus numbered from zero *degrees Centigrade*, 0° C, to one hundred *degrees Centigrade*, 100° C. From one degree to the next is a temperature interval of one *Centigrade degree*, 1 C°; 1 C° is $\frac{1}{100}$ of the temperature interval between the ice point and the steam point. Temperatures below 0° C and above 100° C are measured by extending the scale in 1 C° intervals. Temperatures below 0° C have negative values.

2. Fahrenheit scale. This scale, devised in 1714 by Gabriel Daniel Fahrenheit (1686–1736), is used in the United States for weather observations and for most general purposes. On the Fahrenheit scale the ice point is 32°, and the steam point is 212°. The interval between these two fixed points on the Fahrenheit scale is divided into 180°. Thus, one *Fahrenheit degree*, 1 F°, is $\frac{1}{180}$ of the temperature difference between the ice point and the steam point. Temperatures below 32° F and above 212° F are measured by extending the scale in 1 F° intervals. Temperatures below 0° F have negative values.

5. Converting a temperature reading on one scale to the equivalent temperature on the other scale. Just as we sometimes find it necessary to change meters into yards, and inches into centimeters, we may need to change a Fahrenheit temperature reading to the corresponding Centigrade reading, or vice versa. To do this, we must first recognize that 0° C and 32° F are the same temperature, and that 100.° C and 212° F are also the same temperature. Between the ice point and the steam point on the Centigrade scale, there are 100.° Between the same points on the Fahrenheit scale, there are 180.° Consequently 100. C° equal 180. F°.

The temperature difference between any Centigrade temperature, T_C, and the ice point, 0° C, is $T_C - 0°$. The temperature difference between any Fahrenheit temperature, T_F, and the ice point, 32° F, is $T_F - 32°$. Now, if T_C and T_F are the same temperatures,

$$\frac{T_C - 0°}{T_F - 32°} = \frac{100.°}{180.°}$$

because the ratio of the number of Centigrade degrees in a temperature interval to the number of Fahrenheit degrees in the same interval equals the ratio of the number of Centigrade degrees between the fixed temperatures to the number of Fahr-

enheit degrees between the fixed temperatures. Solving in turn for T_C and T_F,

$$T_C = \tfrac{5}{9}(T_F - 32°)$$

and $$T_F = \tfrac{9}{5}T_C + 32°$$

See the Sample Problems on page 222.

6. The expansion of solids. With few exceptions, *solids expand when heated and contract when cooled.* They not only increase in length, but also increase in width and thickness.

Solids expand when their temperature is raised because the increase in thermal energy increases the amplitude of vibration of the atoms and molecules composing the solid. As a result, the atoms and molecules move to equilibrium positions slightly further apart than before, and the solid expands in all directions.

The expansion of solids can be measured experimentally. A metal rod is put into an apparatus equipped with a precise measuring device, and the rod is heated. If the temperature of an aluminum rod 1.0 m long is raised 1.0 C°, the increase in length is 2.3×10^{-5} m. An iron rod of the same length, substituted for the aluminum rod, expands only 1.1×10^{-5} m when its temperature is raised 1.0 C°. Different materials of the same length expand different amounts for the same increase in temperature. *The change in unit length of a solid when its temperature is changed one degree is called its coefficient of linear expansion.* See Fig. 9-5. While the coefficient of linear expansion of most solids varies with temperature, the change is slight and we shall neglect it in our work.

From the experiment, we learned that 1.0 m of aluminum expands 2.3×10^{-5} m when its temperature is raised 1.0 C°. The coefficient of linear expansion of aluminum is therefore $2.3 \times 10^{-5}/$C°. Likewise the coefficient of linear expansion of iron is $1.1 \times 10^{-5}/$C°. Since the coefficient of linear expansion is defined as *the change in unit length*, its value does not depend upon

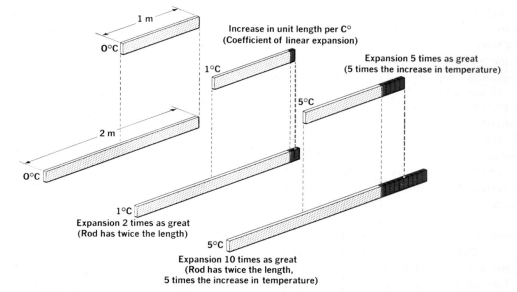

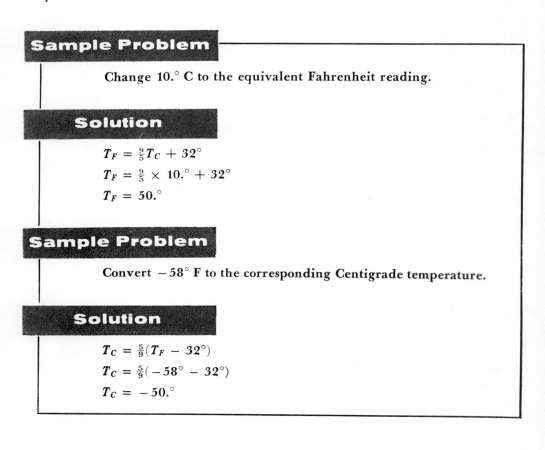

Fig. 9-5. The increase in unit length of a solid when it is heated one degree is the co-efficient of linear expansion. The total increase in the length of a solid when it is heated equals the product of its length, its change in temperature, and its coefficient of linear expansion.

Sample Problem

Change 10.° C to the equivalent Fahrenheit reading.

Solution

$$T_F = \tfrac{9}{5}T_C + 32°$$
$$T_F = \tfrac{9}{5} \times 10.° + 32°$$
$$T_F = 50.°$$

Sample Problem

Convert $-58°$ F to the corresponding Centigrade temperature.

Solution

$$T_C = \tfrac{5}{9}(T_F - 32°)$$
$$T_C = \tfrac{5}{9}(-58° - 32°)$$
$$T_C = -50.°$$

any particular length unit. Its value, however, does depend upon the size of the degree used to measure the temperature change. Table 9, Appendix B, gives the value of the coefficient of linear expansion of several solids per Centigrade degree. The coefficient of expansion per *Fahrenheit degree* will be just $\frac{5}{9}$ as much.

So far, we have been discussing 1.0-m lengths of aluminum and iron, and a rise in temperature of only 1.0 C°. If the temperature of 10.0 m of aluminum rod is raised 1.0 C°, the expansion is 10. times as much as the expansion of the 1.0-m length: 10. $\times$ 2.3 $\times$ 10^{-5} m = 2.3 $\times$ 10^{-4} m. If the temperature of this 10.0 m of aluminum is raised 10.0 C°, the increase is 10. times as great as for 1.0 C°: 10. $\times$ 2.3 $\times$ 10^{-4} m = 2.3 $\times$ 10^{-3} m. We conclude from these observations that *the change in the length of a solid equals the product of its original length, its change in temperature, and its coefficient of linear expansion.*

This may be given by the formula

$$\Delta l = \alpha \, l(T - T_0)$$

where Δl (delta *l*) is the increase in length, α (alpha) is the coefficient of linear expansion, *l* is the original length, *T* is the final temperature, and T_0 is the original temperature. See the Sample Problem below.

In most practical situations, we are interested in the amount of linear expansion of solids. We must remember however, that when solids are heated, they do not just increase in length—they increase in all dimensions. The *coefficient of area expansion,* or the increase in unit area per degree, is approximately *twice* the coefficient of linear expansion. The **coefficient of volume expansion,** or *the increase in unit volume when a solid is heated one degree,* is approximately *three times* the coefficient of linear expansion.

The expansion of solids is taken into account in the design and construction of any object that must undergo temperature changes. When a contractor lays a concrete road, he provides space between the sections to allow for expansion. Steel rails for railroads are often laid with small spaces between the ends of the rails for the same reason. Bridges are also built so that the parts can expand and contract without distorting the entire structure.

Suitable allowance must be made not only for changes in size due to expansion and contraction, but also for the different rates of expansion and contraction of different materials. For a tight seal, the wires that lead into the filament of an incandescent lamp must have the same coefficient of expansion as the glass from

Sample Problem

An iron rod is 60. cm long at 0° C. How much will it expand when heated to 80.° C?

Solution

From Table 9, Appendix B, the coefficient of linear expansion of iron is 1.1 $\times$ 10^{-5}/C°.
$\Delta l = \alpha l(T - T_0)$
$\Delta l = 1.1 \times 10^{-5}/C° \times 60.$ cm (80.° C − 0° C)
$\Delta l = 5.3 \times 10^{-2}$ cm

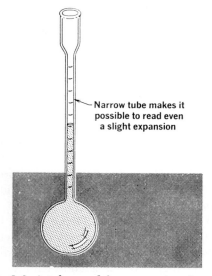

Fig. 9-6. A tube used for measuring the volume expansion of liquids.

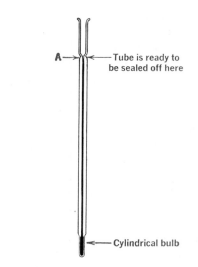

Fig. 9-7. One step in the manufacture of a mercurial thermometer.

which the lamp is made. The principle of the expansion of solids is also applied in metallic thermometers, thermostats, and the compensated balance wheels of watches.

7. The expansion of liquids. If the gasoline tank of an automobile is filled on a cool morning and the car is then parked in the sun, some of the gasoline may overflow the tank. Heat causes the gasoline to expand. Here again the increased thermal energy of the molecules and their resultant increase in amplitude of vibration causes them to move away from each other slightly. The principle of expansion of liquids has many useful applications. Thermometers contain either mercury or alcohol, because these liquids expand uniformly as the temperature rises.

Since liquids do not have a definite shape but take the shape of their container, we are concerned only with their volume expansion. An apparatus like that shown

Sample Problem

A quantity of petroleum occupies 100. liters at 0° C. What will be the increase in volume of the petroleum when its temperature is raised to 30.° C?

Solution

From Table 10, Appendix B, we learn that the coefficient of volume expansion, β, for petroleum is $9.6 \times 10^{-4}/C°$.
$$\Delta V = \beta V(T - T_0)$$
$$\Delta V = 9.6 \times 10^{-4}/C° \times 100. \text{ liters } (30.° C - 0° C)$$
$$\Delta V = 2.9 \text{ liters}$$

in Fig. 9-6 may be used to measure the volume expansion of a liquid.

We find that liquids expand more than solids. Consequently they have higher coefficients of volume expansion. The coefficients of volume expansion for some common liquids are given in Table 10, Appendix B. See the Sample Problem opposite.

8. The mercury thermometer. When mercury is heated, the increased thermal energy of the mercury atoms causes an expansion of the mercury *which is proportional to the temperature increase.* Since mercury is a liquid over a wide and useful range of temperature and its coefficient of volume expansion is nearly constant, it

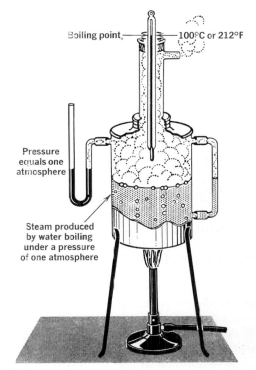

Boiling point.———— 100°C or 212°F

Pressure equals one atmosphere

Steam produced by water boiling under a pressure of one atmosphere

Fig. 9-9. Checking the steam point, 100° C, on a thermometer.

is a very satisfactory liquid to use in a thermometer.

In the construction of a mercury thermometer, a cylindrical, thin glass bulb is sealed to one end of a thick-walled capillary tube. See Fig. 9-7. The bulb and part of the stem are then filled with mercury. The bulb next is heated until the mercury expands and fills the tube, and the tube is then sealed off at *A*. Because the air has been expelled from the tube, the mercury can expand or contract freely as the temperature changes.

9. Graduating a thermometer. The bulb and lower portion of the stem of a thermometer, as constructed by the method described in Section 8, are first packed in a funnel containing melting ice. See Fig. 9-8. Melting ice produces the same temperature as freezing water, and is more convenient. The lowest point to which the mercury falls is marked as the ice point.

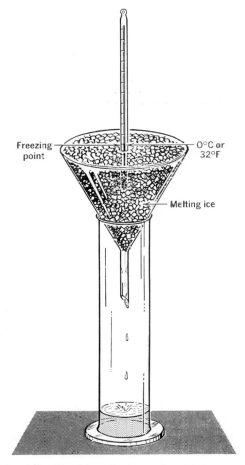

Freezing point ———— 0°C or 32°F

——— Melting ice

Fig. 9-8. Checking the ice point, 0° C, on a thermometer.

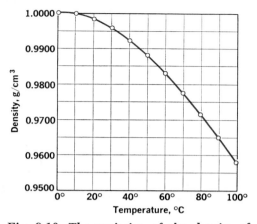

Fig. 9-10. The variation of the density of water with temperature. The density of water is greatest at 4° C.

Next, in order to determine the steam point, the thermometer is suspended in steam from boiling water. See Fig. 9-9. Since the boiling point of water varies with atmospheric pressure, the apparatus must be adjusted so that the water is boiling under a pressure of exactly 760 mm of mercury. The highest point to which the mercury rises is marked as the steam point.

When the two fixed points have been marked on the thermometer stem, the distance between them is divided into 100 parts for a Centigrade thermometer, or 180 parts for a Fahrenheit thermometer. Graduations of the proper size, suitably numbered, are then marked in their proper location on the stem of the thermometer.

10. The abnormal expansion of water. Suppose we fill an expansion bulb, like that shown in Fig. 9-6, with water at 0° C. As we warm the bulb and water, the water gradually *contracts* until a temperature of 4° C is reached. As we raise the temperature of the water above 4° C, the water *expands*. Because the volume of water decreases as the temperature is raised from 0° C to 4° C, the mass density of the water increases. (The mass of the water is constant.) Above 4° C, the volume of water increases as the temperature is raised.

Therefore, water has its maximum mass density, 1.0000 g/cm², at 4° C. The mass density of water at various temperatures is given in Table 11, Appendix B. The variation of the density of water with the temperature is shown in the graph, Fig. 9-10.

This unusual variation of the density of water with the temperature may be explained as follows. When ice melts to water at 0° C, the water still contains groups of molecules bonded in the very open crystal structure of ice. These flow over one another and give the water fluidity. As the temperature of water is raised from 0° C to 4° C, these open crystal structure remnants begin to collapse, and the molecules move closer together. The amplitude of vibration of the molecules also increases during the 0° C to 4° C interval, but the effect of the collapsing crystal structure predominates, and the density increases. Above 4° C the effect of increasing amplitude of molecular vibration overcomes the effect of collapsing crystal structure, and water expands.

11. The expansion of gases. The expansion of gases when heated is due to increased kinetic energy of the molecules of the gas because their thermal energy has been increased.

Different solids and liquids have varying coefficients of expansion, but *all gases have approximately the same coefficient of expansion*. Also, *the coefficient of expansion of gases is nearly constant at all temperatures*, except for those near the liquefying temperature of the gas. The coefficient of volume expansion for gases is $\frac{1}{273}$ of the volume at 0° C, $3.660 \times 10^{-3}/C°$. This is about 20 times the volume expansion of mercury, and almost 60 times that of aluminum. The reason all gases have approximately the same coefficient of expansion is that they all consist of widely separated molecules that are, in effect, independent particles. Gas molecules are separated by distances much greater than their molecular diameters, and consequently, the forces acting between them are negligible. For this reason, except at temperatures and pressures near those at which they liquefy, all gases have similar properties.

If a gas is confined so that it cannot expand when it is heated, it exerts a greater pressure. Suppose the tires on an automobile are inflated to 25 lb/in.² gauge pressure when the temperature is 32° F. If the temperature rises to 68° F, the pressure in the tires will probably increase to 27 lb/in.² When the thermal energy of a gas is increased, the velocity of the molecules becomes greater. They bombard the inner walls of the tire more vigorously. This increases the pressure exerted by the gas.

12. Measuring the coefficient of expansion of a gas. In 1787, Jacques Charles (1746–1823), a Frenchman, performed some important gas experiments which proved that all gases expand the same amount when heated one degree if the pressure is kept constant.

In order to determine the rate at which gases expand, we may use a capillary tube sealed at one end, as shown in Fig. 9-11. A certain mass of air is trapped in this capillary tube by a globule of mercury. First, we measure the length of the air column when the tube is immersed in a mixture of ice and water. Next, we measure the length of the air column when the tube is surrounded by steam. Comparing these two readings, we find that the air column increases by $\frac{100}{273}$ of its original length when heated from 0° C to 100° C. For each degree of temperature change, the expansion is $\frac{1}{273}$ of the volume at 0° C. When gases other than air are used, similar results are obtained.

13. The lowest possible temperature. We know that materials possess thermal energy. When the amount of thermal energy is increased by the addition of heat to a material, its temperature rises

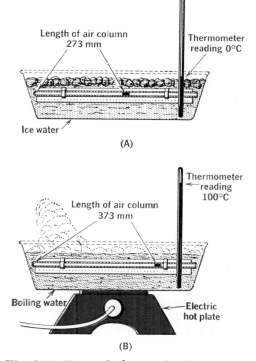

Fig. 9-11. For each degree rise in temperature a gas expands $\frac{1}{273}$ of its volume at 0° C.

or it undergoes a change of state. When the amount of thermal energy is decreased because heat is transferred from the material, its temperature drops or it undergoes a change of state. *When a material gives up all the thermal energy it can,* its temperature can go no lower. The material is as cold as it can get: *it is at the **absolute zero of temperature.*** On the ordinary temperature scales, *absolute zero is* −273.16° C *or* −459.69° F. Scientists have been able to reach temperatures that lie within a few thousandths of a degree of absolute zero.

14. The Kelvin scale. This temperature scale was devised by Lord Kelvin (Sir William Thomson, 1824–1907). The zero point on this temperature scale is taken as absolute zero. The degrees, however, are the same size as Centigrade degrees. For comparison, here are a few temperatures on both the Centigrade and Kelvin scales:

$$
\begin{array}{rcl}
-273°\ C &=& 0°\ K \\
0°\ C &=& 273°\ K \\
100°\ C &=& 373°\ K
\end{array}
$$

From this table we see that a Kelvin temperature is 273 degrees higher than the corresponding Centigrade temperature. *To change from Centigrade scale to Kelvin scale, add 273 degrees to the Centigrade reading.* In equation form,

$$T_K = T_C + 273°$$

where T_K is Kelvin temperature and T_C is Centigrade temperature.

15. Charles' law. The table below gives the volume occupied by a certain mass of an ideal gas at various Centigrade and Kelvin temperatures.

Volume	Centigrade	Kelvin
373 cm³	100°	373°
323 cm³	50°	323°
273 cm³	0°	273°
223 cm³	−50°	223°
173 cm³	−100°	173°

From the table we see that the volume of an ideal gas varies directly with the Kelvin

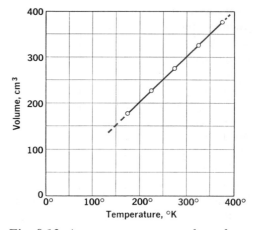

Fig. 9-12. At constant pressure, the volume of a dry gas varies directly with the Kelvin temperature.

temperature. **Charles' law** is: *if the pressure is constant, the volume of a dry gas is directly proportional to the Kelvin temperature.* In equation form,

$$\frac{V}{T_K} = \frac{V'}{T_K'}$$

where V is the original volume, T_K the original Kelvin temperature, V' the new volume, and T_K' the new Kelvin temperature.

We may plot the Kelvin temperatures

Sample Problem

At 20.° C, a gas occupies 500. cm³. What will be the volume of this gas at 70.° C?

Solution

$$20.°\ C = 293°\ K;\ 70.°\ C = 343°\ K$$

$$\frac{V}{T_K} = \frac{V'}{T_K'}$$

$$V' = \frac{V T_K'}{T_K}$$

$$V' = \frac{500.\ cm^3 \times 343°\ K}{293°\ K}$$

$$V' = 585\ cm^3$$

and gas volumes given in the table to show Charles' law graphically. The resulting curve is shown in Fig. 9-12. This straight-line relationship between Kelvin temperatures and volumes shows that they are directly proportional. See the Sample Problem on the opposite page.

Charles' law, like Boyle's law, applies strictly to an ideal gas. However, since the behavior of a real gas is similar to that of an ideal gas except near its condensation conditions, Charles' law can be used with reasonable exactness for real gases.

16. Combining Charles' and Boyle's laws. It frequently happens that temperature and pressure conditions affecting gases both change. In order to find the new volume that a gas will occupy in such a case, we combine the effects of Boyle's law and Charles' law. This may be done in separate steps by first correcting the original volume to the new pressure conditions and then correcting this volume for the temperature change. Usually, however, these two steps are carried out simultaneously.

We can derive a formula which combines Boyle's law and Charles' law. At constant temperature T_{K1}, a certain mass of gas occupying volume V_1 is subject to a change in pressure from p_1 to p_2. The new volume V_2, from Boyle's law, is

$$V_2 = \frac{p_1 V_1}{p_2} \qquad \text{(Equation 1)}$$

Now if V_2 is subject to an increase in temperature from T_{K1} to T_{K2} at constant pressure p_2, the new volume V_3, from Charles' law, is

$$V_3 = \frac{V_2 T_{K2}}{T_{K1}} \qquad \text{(Equation 2)}$$

Substituting the value of V_2 in Equation 1 in Equation 2

$$V_3 = \frac{p_1 V_1 T_{K2}}{p_2 T_{K1}}$$

and, rearranging terms,

$$\frac{p_1 V_1}{T_{K1}} = \frac{p_2 V_3}{T_{K2}}$$

But V_3 is the volume at pressure p_2 and temperature T_{K2}, so

$$\frac{pV}{T_K} = \frac{p'V'}{T_E'}$$

where p, V, and T_K are original pressure, volume, and Kelvin temperature and p', V', and T_K' are new pressure, volume, and Kelvin temperature. See the Sample Problem below.

Sample Problem

We have 500. cm³ of gas at 20.° C and 750. mm pressure. What volume will the gas occupy at 30.° C and 760. mm pressure?

Solution

$20.° \text{C} = 293° \text{K}; \; 30.° \text{C} = 303° \text{K}$

$$\frac{pV}{T_K} = \frac{p'V'}{T_K'}$$

$$V' = \frac{pVT_K'}{p'T_K}$$

$$V' = \frac{750. \text{ mm} \times 500. \text{ cm}^3 \times 303° \text{ K}}{760. \text{ mm} \times 293° \text{ K}}$$

$$V' = 510. \text{ cm}^3$$

ummary

Heat is a form of energy. The thermal energy of a body is the potential and kinetic energy of its particles which can be evolved as heat. Heat is thermal energy which is being taken up by a body, being given up by a body, or being transferred from one body to another. The temperature of a body is a measure of its ability to give up heat to, or absorb heat from, other bodies. Temperature may be measured on the Centigrade, Fahrenheit, or Kelvin scale. The lowest possible temperature, attained when a body has given up all the thermal energy it can, is absolute zero.

The change in unit length of a solid when its temperature is changed one degree is its coefficient of linear expansion. The expansion of most liquids is proportional to their temperature increase, but the expansion of water is abnormal. Gases expand uniformly except at pressures and temperatures near those at which they liquefy. Charles' law states that, if the pressure is constant, the volume of a dry gas is directly proportional to the Kelvin temperature. The gas laws apply strictly only to an ideal gas. However, since the behavior of a real gas is similar to that of an ideal gas except near its condensation conditions, the gas laws can be used with reasonable exactness with a real gas.

TERMS TO DEFINE

absolute zero
calorie
Centigrade scale
coefficient of area
   expansion
coefficient of linear
   expansion

coefficient of volume
   expansion
expansion of gases
expansion of liquids
expansion of water
Fahrenheit scale
heat

ice point
Kelvin scale
sources of heat energy
steam point
temperature
thermal energy
thermometer

QUESTIONS

A **1.** (*a*) What are the usual sources from which we obtain heat? (*b*) Give a specific example to illustrate each source you name.
2. Compare the amount of thermal energy possessed by each of the following: (*a*) a soldering iron and a needle, both at 150.° C.; (*b*) a 4-section radiator and a 10-section radiator; (*c*) a teakettle of boiling water and a cup of boiling water; (*d*) 20. kg of ice at −10.° C and 10. kg of ice at −10.° C; (*e*) a liter of liquid air and a milliliter of liquid air, both at −189° C.
3. How do heat and temperature differ?
4. The temperature of the melting point of ice and the temperature of the boiling point of water are called "fixed points" in calibrating a thermometer. Why?

5. How does the coefficient of volume expansion for mercury compare with the coefficient of volume expansion for glass?
6. Why is mercury used in making thermometers?
7. What is the coefficient of linear expansion?
8. What provision is made to allow for the expansion of (*a*) concrete highways; (*b*) bridges; (*c*) piston rings?
9. A hole 1.00 cm in diameter is drilled through a piece of steel at 20.° C. What happens to the diameter of the hole as the steel is heated to 100.° C?
10. Do you get more gasoline for your money in the winter or in the summer, providing it sells for the same price per gallon during both seasons?

11. A platinum wire may be easily sealed into a glass tube. A copper wire, however, does not form a tight seal with glass. Explain.

12. Why does the pressure of a confined gas increase as its temperature is raised?

13. (a) What is the Centigrade temperature at absolute zero? (b) What would the thermal energy content of a body be at absolute zero?

14. How does the Centigrade scale compare with the Kelvin scale?

B 15. What reasoning led Rumford to believe that heat could be produced from mechanical energy?

16. How does the thermal energy a body possesses determine its temperature?

17. If you examine several similar laboratory thermometers, you may find that the distance between 0° C and 100° C is not exactly the same on all of them. Why is there such a difference when they are all the same make and model?

18. Does the coefficient of linear expansion depend on the unit of length used?

19. How does the coefficient of linear expansion per Centigrade degree of a substance compare with its coefficient of linear expansion per Fahrenheit degree?

20. Why do solids expand when their temperature is raised?

21. (a) Why does water contract as its temperature is raised from 0° C to 4° C? (b) Why does it expand when heated above 4° C?

22. Why are the coefficients of volume expansion very nearly the same for all of the various gases?

23. Why does the measurement of the expansion of a liquid contained in a bulb or tube fail to give a true value for the expansion of the liquid?

24. A brass disk fits a hole in a steel plate snugly at 20.° C. In order to make the disk drop out of the plate, should the disk and plate combination be heated or cooled?

PROBLEMS

A 1. The temperature in a classroom is 75° F. What is the Centigrade reading?

2. Acetone, a colorless liquid used as a solvent, boils at 56.5° C. What is this temperature on the Fahrenheit scale?

3. The temperature in the stratosphere is about −80.° F. Convert this to the corresponding temperature on the Centigrade scale.

4. Liquid nitrogen boils at −196° C. What is the reading on the Fahrenheit scale?

5. During a summer thunderstorm the temperature dropped 15 F°. What was the drop in C°?

6. If water is cooled from 50.° C to 10.° C, what is the temperature change in F°?

7. The boiling point of liquid oxygen is −183° C. What is this temperature in ° K?

8. What will be the boiling point of helium on the Centigrade scale if its boiling point is 4.1° K?

9. A piece of copper pipe is 5.0 m long at 20.° C. If it is heated to 70.° C, what is the increase in its length?

10. A rod of silver is 100. cm long at 0° C. What is its increase in length when heated to 100.° C?

11. The steel cables on a bridge are 1500.00 m long on a day when the temperature is 30.° C. What is their length when the temperature drops to 10.° C?

12. The diameter of a hole drilled through a piece of brass is 1.500 cm when the temperature is 20.° C. What is the diameter of the hole when the brass is heated to 150.° C?

13. What is the increase in volume of 15.0 liters of ethyl alcohol when it is heated from 15.0° C to 25.0° C?

14. A quantity of carbon tetrachloride occupies a volume of 500.00 ml at 20.0° C. What is the volume of this carbon tetrachloride at 45.0° C?

15. Some oxygen occupies a volume of 5.00 liters at 27° C. If the pressure is unchanged, what volume does the gas occupy at 77° C?

16. A certain gas occupies a volume of 250. ml at 37° C. What is its volume at 67° C if the pressure is not changed?

B 17. The stem of a thermometer is marked off in 150 equal scale divisions. When the bulb of this thermometer is placed in melting ice, the mercury stands at 30.; and when the bulb is suspended in the steam from water boiling at standard pressure, the mercury stands at 80. To what Centigrade temperature does a reading of 125 on this thermometer correspond?

18. At what temperature is the reading the same on the Centigrade and Fahrenheit scales?

19. The spaces between 39-ft steel rails are 0.30 in. at 0° F. If the rails close up at 90.° F, what is the coefficient of linear expansion per Fahrenheit degree?

20. Mercury has a specific gravity of 13.546 at 20.0° C. Find its specific gravity at 100.° C.

21. What is the volume at S.T.P. of 350. ml of hydrogen measured at 27° C and 740. mm pressure?

22. A quantity of nitrogen occupies 2.00×10^3 liters at S.T.P. What is its volume at 20.° C and 735 mm pressure?

23. What volume of air at a pressure of 15 lb/in.² and a temperature of 70.° F can be pumped into an "empty" 25-ft³ tank to raise the gauge pressure to 125 lb/in.² if at the same time the temperature of the gas is raised to 110.° F?

24. A new refrigerator is being installed in a room which contains dry air at a temperature of 80.0° F and a barometric pressure of 30.0 in. of mercury. During installation the door of the refrigerator stands open. When the refrigerating mechanism is turned on, the door is immediately closed. What is the difference in the pressures inside and outside the refrigerator when the temperature inside the refrigerator drops to 40.0° F?

RESEARCH ON YOUR OWN

1. Construct an apparatus to use in finding the coefficient of volume expansion of a liquid. Fill with water a piece of glass tubing about 50 cm long. Run the water into a burette and compute the volume of the tube per millimeter of length. Cut off about 10 cm of the tubing and insert the tube in a one-hole stopper to fit into a test tube. If your school owns an apparatus for finding the coefficient of volume expansion, find this coefficient over a series of 10-degree ranges for alcohol from as cold a temperature as you can obtain to the boiling point. Is the coefficient the same in each 10-degree range?

2. Obtain an old thermostat with a bimetallic strip. Use the strip and contacts as a switch to control a flashlight lamp in series with a flashlight battery. Try to adjust this so that it is sensitive to the heat from a match.

3. Mount a length of chromel or nichrome wire (#22 or #24) horizontally between two supports so that it is drawn taut. Connect the ends of the wire with the terminals of a model train transformer, and adjust the voltage until the wire turns red hot. Can you observe the wire expand? Does it seem to expand uniformly?

4. Study the history of the caloric theory of heat. Draw some conclusions about how scientific theories change as new discoveries are made.

5. It can be easily shown mathematically that the Centigrade and Fahrenheit readings are the same at −40°. Find the points at which the Fahrenheit temperature is twice, three times, four times, and one half the Centigrade readings. Prepare a graph of your results.

6. Construct working models of thermometers using solids, liquids, and gases. Compare the useful ranges of your instruments. Try to calibrate (graduate) your instruments.

CHAPTER 10

CHANGE OF STATE

1 HEAT UNITS—SPECIFIC HEAT

1. The measurement of heat. We stated in Chapter 9, Section 8, that the expansion of mercury in the capillary tube of a thermometer provides a convenient and accurate method of measuring temperature. The measurement of heat is not so simple, for there is no instrument that will tell us directly the amount of thermal energy a body can give out or absorb. Therefore, *we measure quantities of heat by the effects which they produce.* For example, the amount of heat given out when a fuel burns may be measured by the tempera-ture change its burning produces in a known quantity of water. If one sample of coal warms 1000. g of water 1.0 C°, and another sample warms 1000. g of water 2.0 C°, then twice as much heat is given out by the second sample.

2. Heat units. Water serves as a standard substance for defining heat units in both metric and English systems.

1. Metric system—MKS units. *The quantity of heat needed to raise the temperature of one kilogram of water one Centigrade degree is one **kilocalorie** (kcal). If the temperature*

VOCABULARY

Boiling. Rapid vaporization which disturbs a liquid and which occurs when the vapor pressure of the liquid equals the pressure on its surface.

Equilibrium vapor pressure. The pressure exerted by water vapor molecules in equilibrium with liquid water.

Fusion. The change of state from a solid to a liquid.

Heat capacity. The quantity of heat needed to raise the temperature of a body one degree.

Heat of fusion. The amount of heat needed to melt a unit mass or weight of a substance at its normal melting point.

Heat of vaporization. The heat required to vaporize a unit mass or weight of liquid at its normal boiling point.

Specific heat. The ratio of the heat capacity of a body to its mass or weight.

Vaporization. The production of a vapor or gas from matter in another physical state.

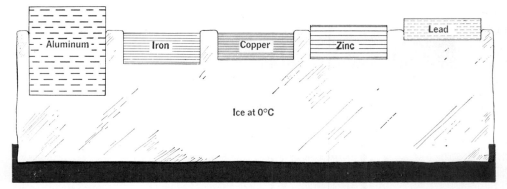

Fig. 10-1. Because metals have different heat capacities, these blocks, all of equal mass and heated to the same temperature, melt the ice to different depths.

of 1 kg of water drops 1 C°, the water gives out 1 kcal of heat. To warm 1.0 kg of water 10. C°, 10. kcal are required, a quantity of energy which could also warm 10. kg of water 1.0 C°. The kilocalorie is the "Calorie" which biologists and dieticians use in measuring the fuel value of foods. While it is possible to use MKS units in heat measurements, physicists have used CGS units more commonly, and we shall follow this custom.

2. Metric system—CGS units. *The quantity of heat needed to raise the temperature of one gram of water one Centigrade degree is one* **calorie** (cal).

3. English system—FPS units. *The quantity of heat needed to raise the temperature of one pound of water one Fahrenheit degree is one* **British thermal unit** (Btu).

Observe that a unit *mass* of water is used for defining metric system heat units and a unit *weight* of water is used for defining the English system heat unit. Since these heat units are energy units, they may be related to each other as well as to the energy units which we studied in mechanics. *One Btu equals 252 cal.* The relation between calories and joules, and between British thermal units and foot-pounds, will be given in Chapter 11.

3. Heat capacity. Blocks of five different metals, aluminum, iron, copper, zinc, and lead, are shown in Fig. 10-1. They all have

the same mass and the same cross-sectional area, but because these metals have different densities, the pieces have different heights. We first place all of them in a pan of boiling water and leave them for a long enough time to heat them to the same temperature. Then we transfer them to a block of ice. The diagram shows the relative depths to which they melt the ice. We see that the aluminum block melts the most ice, iron follows as a poor second, copper and zinc are tied for third, and lead melts the least ice. This experiment shows that different materials absorb or give out different amounts of heat, even though the materials have the same mass and undergo the same temperature change. Similarly, different amounts of heat are absorbed by blocks of the same material if their mass is different and their temperature change the same, if their mass is the same and their temperature change is different, or if they have different masses and undergo different temperature changes. Such bodies differ in *heat capacity*. Those with a high heat capacity warm more slowly because they must absorb a greater quantity of heat; they cool more slowly, too, because they must give out more heat. *The* **heat capacity** *of a body is the quantity of heat needed to raise its temperature 1°.*

$$\text{heat capacity} = Q/\Delta T$$

where Q is the quantity of heat needed to produce a change in the temperature of the body, ΔT. The units for heat capacity will therefore be cal/C° or Btu/F°.

4. Specific heat. The heat capacity of a body does not tell us very much about the thermal properties of the material of which the body is made. For example, the heat capacity of 100. g of copper differs from that of 100. g of aluminum, but the heat capacity of 100. g of aluminum also differs from that of 200. g of aluminum. In order to obtain a quantity which is characteristic of copper or aluminum, we must compare the heat capacities of equal masses or of equal weights.

*The specific heat capacity, or **specific heat,** of a material is the ratio of its heat capacity to its mass or weight.* (You recall from the study of specific gravity that the term "specific" implies a ratio.) If Q represents the quantity of heat needed to produce a temperature change, ΔT, in an amount of material, m, the specific heat, c, is given by

$$c = \frac{Q/\Delta T}{m}$$

which, on being simplified, yields

$$c = \frac{Q}{m\Delta T}$$

Since 1 calorie raises the temperature of 1 g of water 1 C°, the specific heat of water in CGS units is 1 cal/gC°. Using English system units, the specific heat of water is 1 Btu/lbF°. Because of the way in which the calorie and the Btu are defined, the specific heat of water is *numerically* 1.00 in both the metric and the English systems. The specific heats of other substances are likewise *numerically* equal in the two systems of measurement. In the metric system specific heat is measured in cal/gC°, while in the English system it is measured in Btu/lbF°. From Table 12, Appendix B, we learn that the specific heat of most substances is less than that of water.

5. The quantity of heat needed to raise the temperature of materials. Let us solve for Q the equation for specific heat we derived in Section 4:

$$Q = mc\Delta T$$

Thus the quantity of heat needed to produce a certain temperature change in a body equals the product of the amount of material, its specific heat, and its temperature change. If m is given in g, c in cal/gC°, and ΔT in C°, Q is expressed in cal; when m is in lb, c in Btu/lbF°, and ΔT in F°, Q is expressed in Btu. See the Sample Problem below.

Sample Problem

How many calories are needed to raise the temperature of 300. g of aluminum 50.0 C°?

Solution

From Table 12, Appendix B, we find the specfiic heat of aluminum is 0.214 cal/gC°.
$Q = mc\Delta T$
$Q = 300.$ g $\times$ 0.214 cal/gC° $\times$ 50.0 C°
$Q = 3.21 \times 10^3$ cal

6. The method of mixtures. If water is too hot for washing, you may cool it quickly by adding some cold water. As the two mix, the temperature of the hot water is lowered, but the temperature of the added cold water is raised. The final temperature of the mixture lies between the original temperatures of the hot and cold water. Each time we bring into contact or mix two substances of unequal temperature, the warmer one loses heat and the cooler one gains heat until they both finally reach the same temperature. Heat is a form of energy; no heat energy is lost when substances of unequal temperatures are mixed. *The heat given off by hot objects equals the heat received by cold objects. This is the **law of heat exchange**.* The total number of heat units given off by warmer substances equals the total number of heat units received by cooler substances.

$$Q_{lost} = Q_{gained}$$

This important relationship can be used in a variety of ways, some of which will be described in later sections of this chapter.

The Sample Problem on the opposite page illustrates how this relationship is used in calculating the final temperature of a mixture. See Fig. 10-2.

7. The measurement of specific heat. The method of mixtures and the law of heat exchange can be used to determine the specific heat of a solid. The hot solid of unknown specific heat, but of known mass and temperature, is "mixed" with water of known mass and temperature in a calorimeter (usually a metal cup) of known mass and temperature. The final temperature of the mixture is measured. Thus, all of the data for the law of heat exchange equation are known except the specific heat of the solid, which may then be readily calculated as shown in the Sample Problem on page 238. An essential

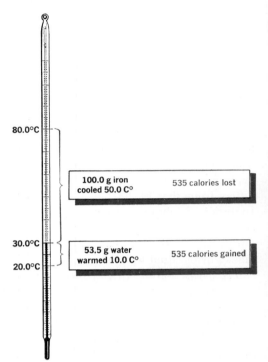

Fig. 10-2. When 100.0 g of iron at 80.0° C is added to 53.5 g of water at 20.0° C, the final temperature of the mixture is 30.0° C. The number of calories lost by the iron equals the number of calories gained by the water.

step in a laboratory specific heat determination is shown in Fig. 10-3.

The method illustrated by the Sample Problem is a general one. In all problems involving heat exchange and specific heat, the substances which lose heat and those which gain heat must first be identified. The heat loss or gain for each substance is then expressed in terms of mass or weight, specific heat, and temperature change. The sum of the individual heat losses equals the sum of the individual heat gains. The resulting equation is solved algebraically to isolate the required quantity on the left of the equals sign. The actual values may then be substituted for the various quantities in this equation and the unit computation and the numerical computation carried out in sequence.

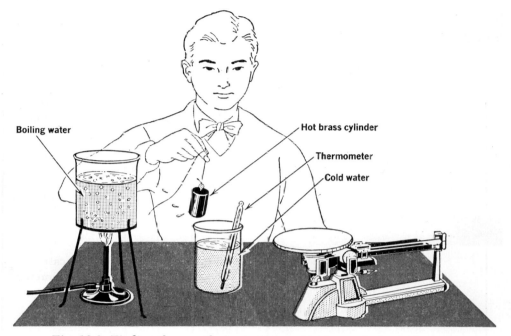

Fig. 10-3. Finding the specific heat of brass by the method of mixtures.

Sample Problem

In a laboratory experiment, 100.0 g of iron at 80.0° C was added to 53.5 g of water at 20.0° C. What is the final temperature of the mixture?

Solution

From Table 12, Appendix B, we learn that the specific heat of iron is 0.107 cal/gC°, and the specific heat of water is 1.00 cal/gC°. Using T_m as the final temperature of the mixture, the heat lost by the iron is

$$Q_i = m_i c_i \Delta T_i = m_i c_i (T_i - T_m)$$

and the heat gained by the water is

$$Q_w = m_w c_w \Delta T_w = m_w c_w (T_m - T_w)$$

These expressions are equal.

$$m_i c_i (T_i - T_m) = m_w c_w (T_m - T_w)$$

Solving for T_m,

$$T_m = \frac{m_i c_i T_i + m_w c_w T_w}{m_i c_i + m_w c_w}$$

$$T_m = \frac{100.0 \text{ g} \times 0.107 \text{ cal/gC}° \times 80.0° \text{ C} + 53.5 \text{ g} \times 1.00 \text{ cal/gC}° \times 20.0° \text{ C}}{100.0 \text{ g} \times 0.107 \text{ cal/gC}° + 53.5 \text{ g} \times 1.00 \text{ cal/gC}°}$$

$$T_m = 30.0° \text{ C}$$

Sample Problem

Given the following data:

Mass of calorimeter	110. g
Specific heat of calorimeter	0.10 cal/gC°
Mass of water	405 g
Mass of brass	202 g
Initial temperature of water	20.0° C
Initial temperature of brass	100.0° C
Final temperature of water, calorimeter, and brass	23.5° C

Calculate the specific heat of brass.

Solution

First identify the bodies losing and gaining heat. In this case the lump of brass lost heat, while both the water and the calorimeter gained heat.

Heat lost = heat gained

Heat lost by brass = heat gained by calorimeter
+ heat gained by water

$$Q_b = Q_c + Q_w$$
$$m_b c_b \Delta T_b = m_c c_c \Delta T_c + m_w c_w \Delta T_w$$

Since we are to calculate the specific heat of brass, we solve this expression for c_b.

$$c_b = \frac{m_c c_c \Delta T_c + m_w c_w \Delta T_w}{m_b \Delta T_b}$$

Substituting the given data,

$$m_c c_c \Delta T_c = 110. \text{ g} \times 0.10 \text{ cal/gC°} \times (23.5° \text{ C} - 20.0° \text{ C})$$
$$m_w c_w \Delta T_w = 405 \text{ g} \times 1.00 \text{ cal/gC°} \times (23.5° \text{ C} - 20.0° \text{ C})$$
$$m_b \Delta T_b = 202 \text{ g} (100.0° \text{ C} - 23.5° \text{ C})$$

Solving,

$c_b = 0.093$ cal/gC°, the specific heat of brass

QUESTIONS

A 1. How are quantities of heat measured?
2. What is (a) a kilocalorie; (b) a calorie; (c) a British thermal unit?
3. What is the heat capacity of a body?
4. (a) Give a word definition for specific heat. (b) What is the formula which defines specific heat?
5. How do the specific heats of most common substances compare with the specific heat of water?
6. How is the amount of heat required to produce a given temperature change in a substance calculated?
7. What is the law of heat exchange?
8. What data are required for the determination of specific heat by the method of mixtures?

B 9. (a) What type of unit serves as the unit quantity of matter for defining the kilocalorie and calorie? (b) For defining the Btu?
10. Why are specific heats numerically equal in the English system and metric system?

PROBLEMS

A 1. A cube of iron weighs 4.00 lb. How many Btu will be needed to raise its temperature from 70.° F to 500.° F?

2. How many calories will be needed to change the temperature of 500. g of water from 20.° C to 100.° C?

3. An aluminum cylinder is heated to 300.° F. If the cylinder weighs 3.0 lb, how many Btu are given out as the cylinder cools to 50.° F?

4. How much heat is given out when 85 g of lead cool from 200.° C to 10.° C?

5. If 10.0 g of water at 0.0° C is mixed with 20.0 g of water at 30.0° C, what is the final temperature of the mixture?

6. What is the final temperature of a mixture of 0.300 lb of water at 70.0° F in a 0.100 lb brass calorimeter, and 0.400 lb of silver at 210.0° F?

7. An aluminum calorimeter has a mass of 60.0 g. Its temperature is 25.0° C. What is the final temperature attained when 75.0 g of water at 95.0° C is poured into it?

8. A piece of tin weighing 0.50 lb and having a temperature of 210.° F is dropped into 0.20 lb of water at a temperature of 50.° F. If the final temperature of the mixture is 68° F, what is the specific heat of the tin?

B 9. A block of metal has a mass of 1000. g. It is heated to 300.° C and then placed in 100.0 g of water at 0.0° C in a calorimeter. The mass of the calorimeter is 50.0 g; its specific heat is 0.200. If the final temperature is 70.0° C, calculate the specific heat of the metal.

10. A block of brass, mass 500.0 g, temperature 100.0° C, is placed in 300.0 g of water, temperature 20.0° C, in an aluminum calorimeter, mass 75.0 g. If the final temperature is 30.0° C, what is the value of the specific heat of the brass?

11. A lump of copper has a mass of 95.3 g and a specific heat of 0.092. It is heated to 90.5° C and then placed in 75.2 g of turpentine, temperature 20.5° C. The temperature of the mixture, after stirring, is 35.5° C. Determine the specific heat of this sample of turpentine.

12. A metal cylinder, mass 450. g, temperature 100.° C, is dropped into a 150.-g iron calorimeter, specific heat 0.100, which contains 300. g of water at 21.5° C. If the resulting temperature of the mixture is 30.5° C, what is the value of the specific heat of the metal cylinder?

2 FUSION

8. The fusion process. As a solid absorbs heat, its temperature usually rises. Upon reaching a certain temperature, the solid melts and becomes a liquid. *This change of state from a solid to a liquid is called fusion.* (Do not confuse this term with nuclear fusion described in Chapter 7.) Fusion is the scientific term for what is commonly called melting, or liquefaction. The temperature at which this change occurs is called the *melting point.* Pure *crystalline* solids generally have a definite melting point, and different solids have different melting points.

When a substance changes from a liquid to a solid, it is said to freeze. The physicist calls this change of state *solidification,* and the temperature at which solidification occurs is known as the *freezing point.* For pure crystalline substances, the melting point and the freezing point are the same temperature.

Solids like paraffin have no definite melting point; when they are heated, they soften gradually. The temperature at which *noncrystalline solids* first soften and that at which they flow freely are often rather widely separated.

Heat must be supplied to a body undergoing fusion. This heat increases the kinetic energy of the particles of the solid, enabling them to overcome the forces that hold them in fixed positions, and giving them the freedom of motion characteristic of the particles of a liquid. Since the bond forces in crystalline solids have a fixed

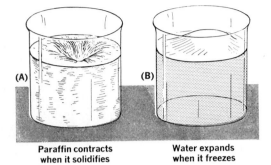

Paraffin contracts
when it solidifies

Water expands
when it freezes

Fig. 10-4. (A) Most substances are like paraffin and contract when they solidify. (B) Water is one of a few substances which expand on solidification.

strength, a definite amount of energy is required to overcome them. This energy is acquired by the particles of the crystal when they reach a certain temperature; thus crystalline solids have a definite melting point. When the liquid formed by melting a crystalline solid cools to a certain temperature, the energy of the liquid particles is reduced to such an extent that the forces between them draw them into fixed positions in a crystal; thus a liquid which forms a crystalline solid freezes at a definite temperature.

The particles of noncrystalline solids are commonly held by Van der Waals forces and by the physical entanglement of long-chain molecules. The bonding combination is not of such definite strength that the bonds are broken when the particles acquire a fixed amount of energy. The energy required to overcome these bonds varies with the extent of the bonding and entanglement of each molecule. Consequently, as they are heated, such substances soften at a lower temperature than that at which they flow freely. Similarly, as they are cooled, the molecules become bonded at various kinetic energies and the liquid does not solidify at a definite temperature.

9. Volume changes during solidification. The separation of particles of a substance is different in the solid and liquid

states, because of the difference in the energy of the particles. If we pour melted paraffin into a glass vessel and let it harden, the center becomes indented, or depressed, as shown in Fig. 10-4(A); the paraffin contracts as it solidifies. All but a very few substances behave in this manner, for the particles of most substances are closer in the solid than in the liquid state.

Water is the most important exception to the rule that a substance contracts when it changes from a liquid to a solid. The level of the water in the sections of an ice cube tray is uniform when the tray is placed in the freezing compartment, but when the ice cubes are formed, each one has a slightly raised spot in the center. See Fig. 10-4(B). The volume occupied by ice is about 1.1 times that occupied by the water from which it was formed. The force of expansion when water freezes is enormous.

If water did not expand slightly as it is cooled below 4° C and expand much more as it freezes, the ice which forms on the surface of a lake would immediately sink to the bottom. During the cold winter months, ice would continue to form until the lake was frozen solid; then in the summer months only a few feet of ice at the top of the lake would melt. However, because of the unusual properties of ice and water, no ice forms at the surface of a lake until all the water in it is cooled to 4° C. Then as the surface is cooled further and freezes at 0° C, the ice remains on the surface.

The graph in Fig. 10-5 shows, from right to left, the contraction of a given mass of water as it is cooled to 4° C, the expansion from 4° C to 0° C, the sharp expansion on freezing, and the slight contraction as ice is cooled below 0° C.

Bismuth and antimony are two metals which expand rather than contract when they solidify. Antimony is used as a component of type metal because it expands

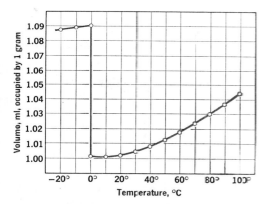

Fig. 10-5. A graph showing the variation in the volume of one gram of ice as it is warmed from −20° C to 0° C, melted to water, and further warmed from 0° C to 100° C. The point of maximum density is 4° C.

when the molten metal is poured into a mold, producing type that is sharp and clear-cut.

Substances like ice, bismuth, and antimony have very open crystal structures in which the particles are more widely separated, on the average, than they are in the liquid state. Thus the solid occupies a larger volume than the liquid.

10. The effect of pressure on the freezing point. In substances that contract when they freeze, like the paraffin in Fig. 10-4(A), the molecules of the solid are closer together than the molecules of the liquid. If additional pressure is exerted, such a liquid can be made to solidify at a higher temperature than its normal freezing point under atmospheric pressure. An increase in pressure raises the freezing temperature of most substances. Some of the rocks in the interior of the earth are probably hot enough to melt at normal pressure, but they remain solid because of the tremendous pressure. If the pressure is released, as when a volcano erupts, the rocks melt, forming lava.

An increase in pressure has the opposite effect on the freezing point of a substance like water, which expands as it freezes.

In such a substance the molecules are farther apart in the solid than they are in the liquid. An increase in pressure makes formation of the solid more difficult, so that the freezing point is lowered if the pressure is raised.

We may illustrate this by suspending two brass weights by means of a strong wire over the surface of a large cake of ice, as shown in Fig. 10-6. The pressure of the wire on the ice lowers the melting point of the ice immediately below the wire. This part of the ice melts, and the molecules of water are forced upward around the wire. When they reach a spot above the wire, the pressure returns to normal, and the water molecules freeze again. In this way, the wire may cut its way through the cake of ice, and yet leave the ice completely solid. This melting under pressure and freezing again after the pressure is released is called *regelation* (ree-jeh-*lay*-shun).

An increase in pressure produces only a slight effect on the melting point of ice. At two atmospheres pressure, the melting point of ice is lowered only to −0.0075° C. When the pressure of ice skate blades on

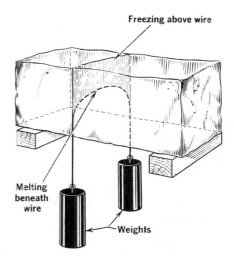

Fig. 10-6. Melting under pressure and freezing again after the pressure is released is called regelation.

ice is sufficient to melt it at its existing temperature, the blades slide along with very little friction on a thin layer of water, and the ice is said to be "fast." However, if the ice is so cold that the pressure of the skate blade on it cannot melt it, the blades are retarded by the higher friction of steel on ice, and skating is more difficult. Sharpening the skates increases the pressure. (Why?)

11. The effect of dissolved materials on the freezing point. The freezing point of a liquid is lowered when another substance is dissolved in it. The extent of the lowering depends on the nature of the liquid and of the dissolved substance, as well as on the relative amounts of each. The greater the amount of the substance dissolved in a fixed amount of liquid, the lower the freezing point of the solution. We apply this principle when we use rock salt to melt the ice on roads and sidewalks and when we add antifreeze to the water in an automobile cooling system. The dissolved substance interferes with crystal formation as the liquid cools. Thus the kinetic energy of the liquid particles must be reduced to a level below that at which they normally go into a crystal pattern, before crystals form.

12. The heat of fusion of ice. The addition of heat to a solid at its melting point produces a change of physical state instead of a rise in temperature. Thus, the addition of heat to ice at $0°$ C causes it to change into water at $0°$ C. Since this added heat produces a change of state instead of an increase in temperature, it is sometimes called *latent* (hidden) *heat.*

The amount of heat needed to melt a unit mass (or weight) of a substance at its normal melting point is called its **heat of fusion.** The symbol for heat of fusion is L_f. Thus L_f for ice in CGS units is approximately 80. cal/g at $0°$ C, meaning that 80. cal of heat must be added to 1.0 g of ice at $0°$ C to convert it into water at $0°$ C. In FPS units, L_f for ice is 144 Btu/lb at $32°$ F. The heat

of fusion of some other substances is given in Table 12, Appendix B.

The method of mixtures can be used to determine the heat of fusion of a solid. Suppose we wish to determine experimentally the heat of fusion of ice. Since hot water melts ice, we find the mass of ice at a known temperature that can be melted by a known mass of water at a known temperature. The Sample Problem on page 243 illustrates the calculations involved.

13. Water gives up heat when it freezes. The heat added to ice to make it melt increases the thermal energy of its molecules and changes it into water. This same amount of heat is given out when water freezes because this is a reversible energy change. Each gram of water at $0°$ C that forms ice at $0°$ C gives off 80. cal. When the atoms and molecules of water return to their fixed positions in ice, they give up, in the form of heat, the energy which enabled them to slide over one another. The reversible energy change between 1.0 g of ice and 1.0 g of water at $0°$ C is shown in Fig. 10-7. To change the ice to water, 80. cal must be added; to change the water to ice, 80. cal must be taken away.

★ If pure water is very carefully cooled without being disturbed, it may reach temperatures as low as $-40°$ C without freezing. Water that is cooled below the normal freezing point is said to be *supercooled.* If a piece of ice or a speck of dust is added to such water, freezing takes place rapidly and the temperature rises to $0°$ C, the normal freezing point. The formation of ice takes place readily at $0°$ C if there is some dust or other foreign matter on which the first crystals of ice can condense. Supercooling occurs when no such foreign matter is present.

14. Producing low temperatures in the laboratory. In order to demonstrate the expansion of water on freezing, or the solidification of mercury, we must be able to produce low temperatures conveniently.

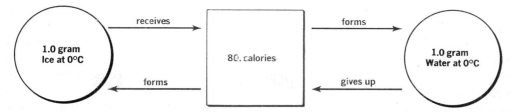

Fig. 10-7. The reversible energy change between 1 g of ice and 1 g of water at 0° C.

A salt-ice mixture may be used to freeze water. When salt is put on ice, it dissolves in the surface moisture; this process absorbs heat. Moreover, a solution of salt in water has a lower freezing point than pure water; a saturated salt solution freezes at −21° C. Since a salt solution has a lower melting point than water, salt added to ice makes the ice melt rapidly. Both the more rapid melting of the ice and the dissolving of the salt absorb heat.

Temperatures as low as −78.5° C may be obtained from a mixture of solid carbon dioxide (Dry Ice) and a liquid such as acetone or ether. If this mixture is made in an unstoppered vacuum bottle, it does not absorb heat too rapidly from its surroundings.

Sample Problem

A calorimeter has a mass of 100.0 g and a specific heat of 0.0900 cal/gC°. It contains 400.0 g of water at 40.0° C. When 91.0 g of ice at 0° C is added and completely melted, the temperature of the water is 18.2° C. What is the heat of fusion of ice?

Solution

Heat lost = heat gained
Heat lost by water + heat lost by calorimeter = heat gained by ice on melting + heat gained by resulting water

$$m_w c_w \Delta T_w + m_c c_c \Delta T_c = m_i L_f + m_{w'} c_{w'} \Delta T_{w'}$$

But

$\Delta T_w = \Delta T_c$ and $m_{w'} = m_i$, so

$$L_f = \frac{(m_w c_w + m_c c_c)\Delta T_w}{m_i} - c_{w'}\Delta T_{w'}$$

Substituting the given data,

$m_w c_w = 400.0 \text{ g} \times 1.00 \text{ cal/gC}°$
$m_c c_c = 100.0 \text{ g} \times 0.0900 \text{ cal/gC}°$
$\Delta T_w = (40.0° \text{ C} - 18.2° \text{ C})$
$m_i = 91.0 \text{ g}$
$c_{w'}\Delta T_{w'} = 1.00 \text{ cal/gC}° \times (18.2° \text{ C} - 0° \text{ C})$

Solving,

$L_f = 79.8 \text{ cal/g}$, heat of fusion of ice

15. Industry uses low temperatures. Many new low temperature processes are being used by various industries. The frozen food industry provides a wide variety of meats, fish, poultry, fruits, and vegetables, preserved from decay. Blood plasma is prepared for storage by freezing. Temperatures between 32° F and −40° F are used in these freezing processes.

Solid carbon dioxide is widely used for storing ice cream. Liquid carbon dioxide is used as a cooling agent in certain grinding operations. Soft manufactured parts, such as those made of rubber, may be smoothed by being hardened at −100° F and then tumbled in revolving containers.

Special hard steels are produced by rolling at temperatures well below zero; liquid air is used as the cooling agent. Metal parts may be shrink-fitted if one part is cooled in liquid air or liquid nitrogen and then is placed in position within the other part. As the cooled part warms up, it expands and fits tightly.

Temperatures near that of liquid helium, −452° F, offer interesting industrial possibilities, for matter sometimes behaves in unexpected fashion at this very low temperature. Some metals, such as tin and lead, that are poor electric conductors at room temperature become superconductors when cooled in liquid helium. Helium itself, when cooled below −455° F, exhibits properties different from those commonly observed in solids, liquids, or gases. Helium in this state creeps up the sides of its containing vessel and also becomes a good conductor of heat.

The branch of physics which is concerned with such low temperature phenomena is called *cryogenics*. The low temperatures required for this study are usually attained by using liquid helium, although magnetic techniques produce lower temperatures. Low temperatures may be measured far more precisely than higher ones. Changes in the electric resistance of fine gold or platinum wires with temperature permit detection of temperature differences of 0.0001 K°.

QUESTIONS

A **1.** (a) Which change of state is called fusion? (b) What name is given to the temperature at which fusion occurs? (c) What is solidification? (d) What name is given to the temperature at which solidification occurs?
2. Why is the density of most substances greater in the solid state than in the liquid state?
3. Why is the density of water greater than that of ice?
4. What is the meaning of the term *regelation?*
5. What is meant by *latent heat?*
6. (a) What is *heat of fusion?* (b) What is the value for the heat of fusion of ice?
7. What is *supercooling?*
8. Describe two convenient methods of producing low temperatures in a high school physics laboratory.

B **9.** Why do crystalline solids have a definite melting point, while noncrystalline solids do not?

10. The air above the ice of a pond is −10° C. What is the probable temperature of (a) the upper surface of the ice; (b) the lower surface; (c) the water just beneath the surface; (d) the water at the bottom of the pond?
11. (a) What is the effect of increased pressure on the freezing point of substances which contract as they freeze? (b) What is the effect of increased pressure on the freezing point of substances which expand as they freeze?
12. What effect will a drop in temperature from 25° F to 0° F probably have on the coefficient of sliding friction between the runners of a sled and the snow?
13. Why does a dissolved material lower the freezing point of a liquid?
14. What data are necessary to determine the heat of fusion of ice by the method of mixtures?
15. Why does it often happen that the temperature of the air slowly rises during a prolonged snowfall?
16. What unusual properties do some materials exhibit at very low temperatures?

PROBLEMS

A 1. A 50.-lb block of ice melts completely to water at 32° F. How many Btu are required to produce this change of state?

2. How many calories will be absorbed by 1.50 kg of ice at 0° C as it melts?

3. To what temperature must a 5.00-lb iron ball be heated in order that it may completely melt 2.5 lb of ice at 32° F?

4. A 500.-g aluminum block is heated to 350.° C. How many grams of ice at 0° C does the aluminum block melt on cooling?

5. A copper calorimeter has a weight of 0.10 lb. It contains 0.20 lb of water at 70.° F. How many ounces of ice at 32° F must be added to reduce the temperature of the mixture to 40.° F?

6. To what temperature must a 500.0-g brass weight be heated in order to convert 60.0 g of ice at −20.0° C to water at 20.0° C?

B 7. What is the final temperature reached by a mixture of 50.0 g of ice at 0.0° C and 50.0 g of water at 80.0° C?

8. What is the final temperature attained when 300. g of ice at 0.0° C, 500. g of ice water at 0.0° C, and 1200. g of water at 100.0° C are mixed?

9. A calorimeter, specific heat 0.100, has a mass of 200.0 g. It contains 300.0 g of water at 40.0° C. If 50.0 g of ice at 0.0° C is dropped into the water and stirred, the final temperature of the mixture when all the ice has melted is 23.8° C. Calculate a value for the heat of fusion of ice.

10. A block of silver, mass 500.0 g, temperature 100.0° C, is placed in a calorimeter with 300.0 g of water, temperature 30.0° C. The mass of the calorimeter is 50.0 g and its specific heat is 0.100. A block of ice, mass 50.0 g, temperature −10.0° C, is then also placed in the calorimeter. Calculate the final temperature.

11. What is the final temperature attained when 2.00 lb of ice at 0.0° F is dropped into 7.50 lb of water at 200.0° F in a calorimeter weighing 3.00 lb which has a specific heat of 0.210?

3 VAPORIZATION

16. The nature of vaporization. If you place some ether in a shallow dish, you notice in a short time that the quantity of liquid decreases, while the odor of ether becomes quite strong near the dish. Apparently molecules of ether in the liquid state become molecules of ether vapor and mix with the molecules of the gases in the air surrounding the dish. Similarly, though much more slowly, a piece of camphor left out in the air becomes smaller and smaller and eventually disappears, while its characteristic odor is noticed in the air near it. In this case, molecules of camphor in the solid state become molecules of camphor vapor and mix with the gases in the surrounding air. These are two examples of *vaporization,* which is *the production of a vapor or gas from matter in another physical state.* See Fig. 10-8.

17. Evaporation and sublimation. The particles of all liquids and solids have an average kinetic energy that depends on the temperature of the liquid or solid. However, because of random collisions or vibratory motion, some particles have energies higher than average and others have energies lower than average. When a particle on the surface of a liquid or solid acquires enough energy to overcome the forces that hold it to the substance, it escapes and becomes a particle in the vapor state. When this vaporization process occurs from liquids, it is known as *evaporation;* when it occurs from solids, it is called *sublimation.* Sublimation is a direct change of physical state from solid to vapor in which the substance does not pass through the liquid state.

Since the rate at which evaporation or sublimation occurs depends on the energy of the particles undergoing the change,

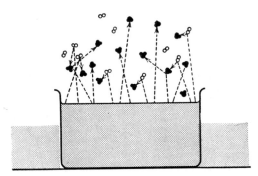

Fig. 10-8. Water molecules escape at the surface of the liquid. Some rebound into the surface after colliding with molecules of gases in the air or with water vapor molecules.

and their energy depends upon their temperature, evaporation and sublimation occur more rapidly at higher temperatures and more slowly at lower temperatures.

18. Equilibrium vapor pressure. The tendency of liquids to evaporate and of solids to sublime is determined by a property called *equilibrium vapor pressure.* A bell jar placed over a container of water is shown in Fig. 10-9. There are as many molecules of the gases of the air within the bell jar as are in an equal volume of air outside it. The pressure exerted by the gas molecules on the inside walls of the bell jar is the same as the pressure such molecules exert on the outside walls. In other words, the pressure of the gas in the bell jar is one atmosphere.

When a molecule at the surface of the water within the bell jar acquires sufficient kinetic energy to overcome the forces of attraction holding it in the liquid, it escapes and becomes a water vapor molecule. As this happens, some of the water evaporates, and water vapor molecules mix with the gas molecules in the bell jar. As soon as water vapor molecules enter the air above the water, they collide with gas molecules, the walls of the bell jar, the outside surface of the container of water, and the surface on which the bell jar rests. They may also touch the water

surface, be held by it, and become molecules of liquid again. The conversion of molecules of vapor to molecules of liquid is called *condensation.* Eventually the rate of evaporation equals the rate of condensation, and a condition of equilibrium results. At equilibrium, evaporation and condensation do not cease. Because these processes occur at the same rate, however, the number of water vapor molecules in the air in the bell jar remains constant.

The collision of water vapor molecules against the walls of the bell jar increases the pressure on it beyond that exerted by the gases of the air. *This added pressure exerted by the water vapor molecules in equilibrium with liquid water is the* **equilibrium vapor pressure.**

If we raise the temperature of the water, its molecules more readily acquire the kinetic energy needed to escape from the water surface, and the water evaporates more rapidly. More water vapor molecules become mixed with the gas molecules before the rate of condensation once again equals the rate of evaporation. Thus, when the water temperature is raised, the water vapor molecules exert a greater pressure

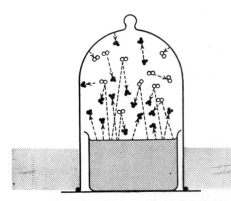

Fig. 10-9. When the number of water molecules evaporating from the liquid equals the number of water vapor molecules returning to the liquid, the pressure exerted by the water vapor molecules against the walls of the bell jar is the equilibrium vapor pressure.

against the walls of the bell jar, and the equilibrium vapor pressure is greater. Of course, if we lower the temperature, the equilibrium vapor pressure decreases.

The equilibrium vapor pressure of a liquid is a characteristic of the liquid which depends only on the temperature. Table 13, Appendix B, gives the equilibrium vapor pressure of water at various temperatures. The vapor pressure curve for water is graphed in Fig. 10-10. Other liquids show similar vapor pressure curves.

Solids, like liquids, exert a vapor pressure. The equilibrium vapor pressure of ice at 0° C equals about 4.5 mm of mercury. The vapor pressure of solids is much less than that of liquids, since they sublime more slowly, or practically not at all, at normal temperatures.

19. Boiling. When you heat a pan of water, bubbles of water vapor first form on the bottom and sides of the container. At these spots the water is sufficiently hot for its vapor pressure to equal the combined pressure of the atmosphere and the liquid pressure of the water, and the liquid water changes to bubbles of vapor. As these bubbles rise into the cooler layers of water above them, they collapse as the vapor condenses back into liquid. When the entire quantity of water is so hot that its vapor pressure equals the pressure on the liquid surface, bubbles of vapor reach the surface freely. Vaporization then occurs at such a rapid rate throughout the entire quantity of water, that the water becomes agitated. *This rapid vaporization which disturbs the liquid, and which occurs when the vapor pressure of the liquid equals the pressure on its surface, is called* **boiling.** If the pressure on the liquid surface is one atmosphere, the temperature at which boiling occurs is called the *normal boiling point.* If the pressure on the liquid surface is greater than one atmosphere, boiling occurs at a higher temperature than the normal boiling point; if the pressure on the liquid

surface is less than one atmosphere, boiling occurs at a lower temperature than the normal boiling point.

Since the vapor pressure of water at 100.° C is 760. mm of mercury, or one atmosphere pressure, this is the *normal boiling point* of water. If we reduce the air pressure to 525.8 mm of mercury, water boils at 90.° C, because at this temperature the vapor pressure of water is 525.8 mm of mercury. In order to make water boil at 50.° C, the pressure must be reduced to 92.5 mm. If we increase the pressure to 787.5 mm of mercury, water will not boil until its temperature reaches 101° C.

Strong-walled pressure cookers, in which water is boiled at pressures up to about 2 atmospheres and temperatures up to about 120° C, are useful for rapid cooking of foods. Vacuum pans, in which water is boiled at room temperature or slightly

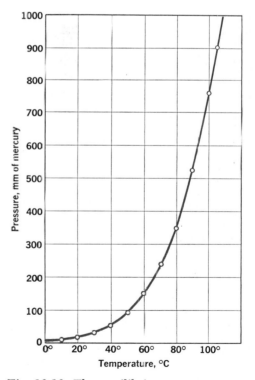

Fig. 10-10. The equilibrium vapor pressure of water increases rapidly as the temperature is raised.

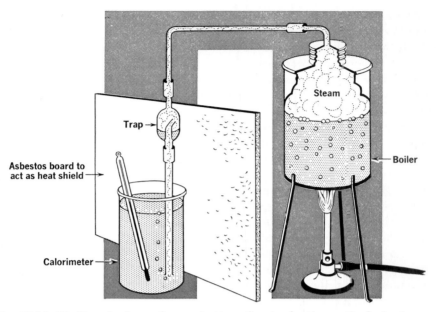

Fig. 10-11. Finding the heat of vaporization of water by the method of mixtures.

above, are used in the production of sugar crystals, concentrated fruit juices, and evaporated and powdered milk.

Water, or any other liquid that is boiling rapidly, does not get hotter than water that is simmering. While a liquid is boiling away, the boiling temperature remains constant until all the liquid has vaporized.

Solids or gases dissolved in a liquid change the boiling temperature of the liquid. For example, salt water boils at a higher temperature than pure water. In general, solids dissolved in liquids raise the boiling temperature, while gases dissolved in liquids usually lower the boiling temperature.

If we mix ethyl alcohol with water and boil the mixture, we find that its boiling temperature is not the same as the boiling point of either liquid by itself. Alcohol boils at 78° C and water at 100.° C; the boiling temperature of the mixture is between 78° and 100° and depends on the proportions of alcohol and water in the mixture. When two or more liquids having different boiling points are mixed, the mixture usually has a boiling temperature different from that of any of the liquids used.

A liquid can be separated from a non-vaporizing solid by *distillation*. Distillation includes evaporation followed by condensation of the vapors in a separate vessel. Two liquids which have different boiling points may be separated by *fractional distillation*. The mixture of liquids is boiled and separated into several fractions collected at different boiling temperatures. These fractions are then redistilled one at a time, and a new set of fractions obtained. By repeating the process several times, a rather complete separation may be made.

20. The heat of vaporization of water. Suppose a liter of water having a temperature of 0° C is placed on a stove. During the time the water is heating from 0° C to 100.° C, each gram of water absorbs 100. cal. If heat is supplied to the water at a constant rate, the water takes more than five times as long to boil away as it did to heat from 0° C to 100.° C. Each gram of water absorbs more than 500 calories as it changes into steam. Since the temperature of the boiling water does not change, and the steam has the same temperature as the boiling water, this is another example of latent heat. *The heat required to vaporize a unit mass (weight) of liquid at its normal boiling point is called its* **heat of vaporization.** The symbol for heat of vaporization is L_v.

The latent heat required for vaporization gives the particles of liquid sufficient kinetic energy to overcome the forces binding them to the liquid, and enables them to separate from one another and move among the molecules of the gases surrounding the liquid. Since the energy required to bring about these changes varies with the temperature, the latent heat of vaporization varies with the temperature. In CGS units, L_v for water is about 540. cal/g at 100.° C. In FPS units L_v for water is 970. Btu/lb at 212° F. For water boiling under reduced pressure at a lower temperature the heat of vaporization is somewhat higher; at boiling temperatures above the normal boiling point, the heat of vaporization is less.

21. Measuring heat of vaporization. We use the method of mixtures to determine the heat of vaporization of water. As shown in Fig. 10-11, a known mass of steam is passed into a known mass of cold water at a known temperature and the increase in temperature is measured. We make sure

Sample Problem

Given the following data:

Mass of calorimeter	120.0 g
Specific heat of calorimeter	0.100 cal/gC°
Mass of water	402.0 g
Mass of steam	23.5 g
Initial temperature of cold water	6.0° C
Temperature of steam	100.0° C
Final temperature of water	40.0° C

Calculate the heat of vaporization of water.

Solution

Heat lost = heat gained
Heat lost by steam in condensing + heat lost by resulting water
= heat gained by calorimeter + heat gained by water
$$m_s L_t + m_{w'} c_{w'} \Delta T_{w'} = m_c c_c \Delta T_c + m_w c_w \Delta T_w$$
But $m_s = m_{w'}$ and $\Delta T_c = \Delta T_w$, so
$$L_v = \frac{(m_c c_c + m_w c_w) \Delta T_w}{m_s} - c_{w'} \Delta T_{w'}$$
Substituting the given data,
$$m_c c_c + m_w c_w = 120.0 \text{ g} \times 0.100 \text{ cal/gC°} + 402.0 \text{ g} \times 1.00 \text{ cal/gC°}$$
$$\Delta T_w = 40.0° \text{ C} - 6.0° \text{ C}$$
$$m_s = 23.5 \text{ g}$$
$$c_{w'} \Delta T_{w'} = 1.00 \text{ cal/gC°} (100.0° \text{ C} - 40.0° \text{ C})$$
Solving,
$$L_v = 540. \text{ cal/g, heat of vaporization of water}$$

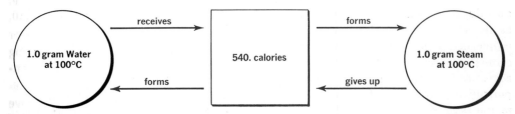

Fig. 10-12. It takes 540. calories to change 1 g of water at 100° C into steam. Steam at 100.° C sets free this much heat in condensing to water.

that only steam enters the water in the calorimeter by using a trap which catches any condensed water from the steam generator. The calculations for this method are given in the Sample Problem which appears on page 249.

22. Steam gives out heat as it condenses. Heat is absorbed during vaporization. This increase in the thermal energy of the atoms and molecules of a liquid enables them to break away from the body of the liquid and become molecules of

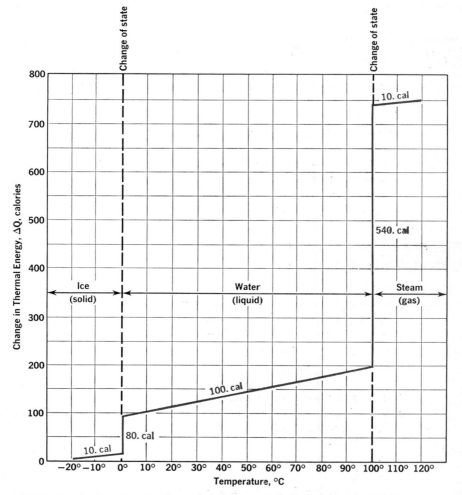

Fig. 10-13. Graph showing the heat absorbed as 1.0 g of ice at −20.° C is converted into steam at 120.° C.

vapor. When the vapor condenses into a liquid, this thermal energy is given out in the form of heat. This reversible thermal energy change, shown in graphic form in Fig. 10-12, is used in a steam heating system. The heat of vaporization is added to the water in the boiler, changing the water into steam. The steam passes into the radiators, where it gives up its heat of vaporization and condenses to a liquid.

Even though steam and boiling water are at the same temperature, steam can produce a more severe burn, because steam at 100.° C has absorbed 540. more calories per gram than water has at 100.° C. When such steam condenses, 540. cal/g is given out. Then the water which is formed gives out the same amount of heat that water at 100.° C does as it cools.

23. Summary of the effects of heat on water. We have stated several effects which the addition or loss of heat produces in water. All of these are summarized in Fig. 10-13, which shows what happens from the time heat is added to ice at −20.° C until it becomes steam at 120.° C. Since the specific heat of ice is 0.5, 1.0 g of ice absorbs 10. cal in being warmed to 0° C. As this ice melts, there is *no temperature change* while 80. cal of heat is being absorbed. As heating continues, the next 100. cal increases the temperature to 100.° C. As the water boils, 540. cal of heat converts the water into steam at 100.° C; during this change of state, there is *no temperature change*. If the steam is maintained under one atmosphere pressure, its specific heat is about 0.5, and to heat the steam to 120° C, 10. cal is needed. Thus 740. cal is required to change 1.0 g of ice at −20.° C into 1.0 g of steam at 120.° C. Similarly 740. cal would be evolved if 1.0 g of steam at 120.° C were changed into 1.0 g of ice at −20.° C.

24. The liquefaction of gases. So far we have discussed only the vaporization and condensation of water, but there are other substances whose evaporation and

liquefaction should be mentioned. Some of these substances are liquids, but many of them are gases at ordinary temperatures. Michael Faraday, an English scientist (1791–1867), conducted an important series of experiments on liquefying gases, using a thick-walled tube of the type shown in Fig. 10-14. In one experiment he filled the tube with chlorine gas, packed one end of the tube in a freezing mixture of salt and ice, and heated the other end of the tube. The heated gas expanded, increasing the pressure exerted on the gas in the cold end. By the combined effect of increasing the pressure and cooling the gas, Faraday condensed the chlorine to a liquid. Using this method, he succeeded in liquefying such gases as ammonia and carbon dioxide; but he could not liquefy oxygen, hydrogen, and nitrogen.

Actually Faraday's freezing mixture was not cold enough to liquefy these gases no matter what pressure was exerted upon them. Oxygen must be cooled to −119° C, nitrogen to −147° C, and hydrogen to −240° C before they will liquefy at any pressure. The temperature to which any gas must be cooled before it can be liquefied by pressure is called its *critical temperature*, and the pressure needed to liquefy a gas at this temperature is called its *critical pressure*. All known gases have now been liquefied. They are greatly compressed, cooled, and then allowed to expand so

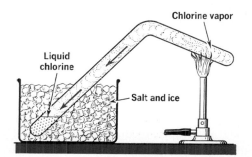

Fig. 10-14. The type of apparatus used by Faraday in his experiments on liquefying gases.

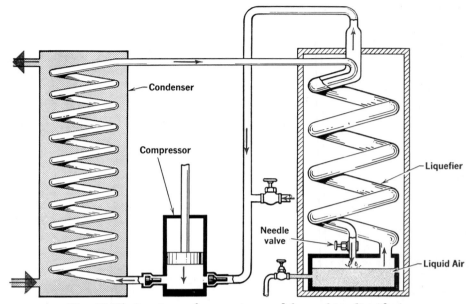

Fig. 10-15. One type of apparatus used for making liquid air.

that they are cooled further. Gases with very low boiling points may be condensed by successive compressions and coolings.

25. The production of liquid air. In the type of apparatus illustrated in Fig. 10-15, the air is first compressed. The hot, compressed air is then cooled as it goes through the coils of the condenser. Next the compressed air passes to the liquefier, and as it escapes through the needle valve, it expands rapidly. This expansion lowers its temperature. The expanded air now returns to the compressor through the outer concentric coil. On its way it cools the air in the inner coil. The process of continual compression of the air, absorption of the heat of compression, and expansion of the air results in lower and lower air temperatures. Finally, some of the air reaches its critical temperature and changes into a liquid.

Liquid air under atmospheric pressure boils at temperatures between −183° C and −196° C, depending upon the amount of nitrogen present. Liquid hydrogen boils at −253° C, while liquid helium boils at −269° C. Liquefied gases such as these must be transported in large double-walled insulated bottles.

26. All liquids absorb heat when they evaporate. The human body uses evaporation to help control its temperature. When it becomes too warm, noticeable amounts of water are given off through the skin. This water evaporates, and since the heat of vaporization comes from the skin, the body is cooled. If you sit in a breeze where perspiration may evaporate more rapidly, you cool off faster. When it is humid, you may have difficulty keeping cool because perspiration does not evaporate readily under such conditions.

The cooling effect of an alcohol rub or of ether poured on your hand is the result of rapid evaporation of these liquids. Since the heat of vaporization comes from your body, the liquids feel cold on your skin.

Liquefied gases behave in a similar fashion. Gases which may be liquefied easily by pressure alone at room temperature are important refrigerants. These gases are compressed and then cooled to room temperature; in this process they give off heat and condense to liquids. Then they are allowed to expand and evaporate; for this process they must gain heat from their surroundings. By recycling the gas through this process, the gas transports heat from one location to another. In prac- tice, the heat required for evaporation and expansion is absorbed from the freezing compartment of the refrigerator. This heat is given up to the air of the room as it cools the gas in the condenser coils.

QUESTIONS

A 1. (a) What is vaporization? (b) Distinguish between evaporation and sublimation. (c) Define condensation.

2. (a) What is equilibrium vapor pressure? (b) On what does the equilibrium vapor pressure of a substance depend?

3. Distinguish between evaporation and boiling.

4. (a) For what purposes are pressure cookers used? (b) For what purposes are vacuum pans used?

5. (a) Explain the process of distillation. (b) Explain the process of fractional distillation.

6. (a) What is heat of vaporization? (b) What is the magnitude of the heat of vaporization of water?

7. Why does steam at 100.° C produce a more severe burn than water at 100.° C?

8. Why does an easily vaporized liquid, such as acetone or ether, feel cool to the skin?

9. (a) Explain how Faraday succeeded in liquefying chlorine. (b) Explain why he failed to liquefy nitrogen in the same apparatus.

10. How is liquid air produced?

B 11. Describe what happens to the molecules of a liquid as it evaporates.

12. How does the equilibrium vapor pressure of a substance vary with the temperature?

13. (a) Why does the boiling temperature of a liquid depend on the pressure exerted on its surface? (b) How does the boiling temperature of a liquid vary with the pressure exerted on its surface?

14. How is fractional distillation used in separating the different materials found in petroleum?

15. What data are required in order to determine the heat of vaporization of water by the method of mixtures?

16. Why does the latent heat of vaporization vary with the boiling temperature?

PROBLEMS

A 1. How many Btu are required to vaporize 50.0 lb of water at 212° F?

2. How many calories are given off by 50.0 g of steam at 100.° C when it condenses?

3. Calculate the number of Btu evolved when 10.0 lb of steam at 212° F is condensed, cooled, and changed into ice at a temperature of 32° F.

4. How many grams of mercury may be vaporized at its boiling point, 356.58° C, by the addition of 1.00×10^3 calories?

5. What is the final temperature attained by the addition of 0.025 lb of steam at 212° F to 1.50 lb of water at 75° F in an aluminum calorimeter weighing 0.40 lb?

6. A calorimeter contains 400. g of water at 20.0° C. How many grams of steam at 100.0° C are needed to raise the temperature of the water and calorimeter to 80.0° C? The calorimeter has a mass of 100. g; its specific heat is 0.100.

B 7. In an experiment to determine the heat of vaporization of water, 15.0 g of steam at 100.0° C is added to 150.0 g of water at 20.0° in a calorimeter. The mass of the calorimeter is 75.0 g; its specific heat is 0.100. The equilibrium temperature of the mixture is 73.9° C. What is the heat of vaporization of water?

8. A mixture of ice and water, mass 200.0 g, is in a 100.0-g calorimeter, specific heat .0200. When 40.0 g of steam is added to the mixture, the temperature is raised to 60.0° C. Determine how many grams of ice were originally in the calorimeter.

9. An aluminum cylinder, mass 50.0 g, is placed in a 100.0-g brass calorimeter with 250.0 g of water at 20.0° C. What equilibrium temperature is reached after the addition of 25.0 g of steam at 120.0° C?

10. A copper ball weighing 10.0 lb is removed from a furnace and dropped into 3.00 lb of water, temperature 72.0° F. After the water stops boiling, the combined weight of the ball and water is 12.0 lb. What was the furnace temperature?

ummary

Quantities of heat are measured by the effects they produce, using calories or British thermal units as heat units. The heat capacity of a body is the quantity of heat needed to raise its temperature one degree, while its specific heat is the ratio of its heat capacity to its mass (or weight) The heat given off by hot objects equals the heat received by cold objects.

The change of state from a solid to a liquid is called fusion. The amount of heat needed to bring about this change in a unit mass (or weight) of a substance at its normal melting point is the heat of fusion

The production of a vapor or gas from matter in another physical state is vaporization. The pressure exerted by water vapor molecules in equilibrium with liquid water is the equilibrium vapor pressure. Boiling occurs when the vapor pressure of a liquid equals the pressure on its surface. The heat required to vaporize a unit mass (or weight) of liquid at its normal boiling point is the heat of vaporization.

The temperature to which any gas must be cooled before it can be liquefied by pressure is called its critical temperature, and the pressure needed to liquefy a gas at this temperature is called its critical pressure.

TERMS TO DEFINE

boiling	fractional distillation	melting point
British thermal unit	freezing point	method of mixtures
calorie	fusion	normal boiling point
condensation	heat capacity	regelation
critical pressure	heat of fusion	solidification
critical temperature	heat of vaporization	specific heat
distillation	kilocalorie	sublimation
equilibrium vapor pressure	latent heat	supercooling
evaporation	law of heat exchange	vaporization

RESEARCH ON YOUR OWN

1. Devise and conduct quantitative experiments to show the effects of dissolved substances on the freezing and boiling points of water. Graph your results.
2. Using Dry Ice or a mixture of Dry Ice and alcohol demonstrate some effects of low temperatures on different forms of matter.
3. Conduct an experiment showing the relationship of the relative humidity of the air to the rate at which water evaporates. Graph your results and explain them in terms of vapor pressure.
4. Melt some moth balls or acetamide in a large test tube. (It is best to do this in a water bath.) The tube should be half to two-thirds full. Mount the bulb of a thermometer as near to the center of the liquid as you can. Without touching or jarring the apparatus, read and record the temperature of the cooling material at one-minute intervals. Make a graph of your results and explain it in terms of energy transfer.

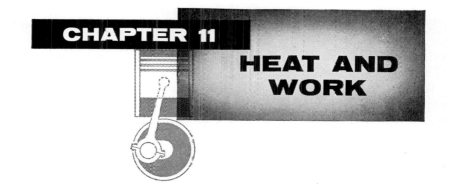

CHAPTER 11

HEAT AND WORK

1. The relationship between heat and work. About 1800 Count Rumford discovered that work done in overcoming friction produces heat. About 40 years later Joule found that a definite amount of mechanical energy could always be transformed into the same amount of heat. These discoveries showed that heat was another form of energy, and could therefore be related to work.

The study of the quantitative relationships between heat and other forms of energy is called **thermodynamics.** In this chapter we shall be concerned with the relation of heat to mechanical energy. The experiments of Count Rumford, Joule, and others led to the *first law of thermodynamics: When heat is converted to another form of energy, or when other forms of energy are converted to heat, there is no loss of energy.*

Joule used an apparatus similar to that shown in Fig. 11-1 to find the relation between heat and work. The weights are permitted to fall through a measured distance, turning the shaft and paddles. The paddling warms the water by friction. Thus all the work put into this machine is transformed to heat.

The weight multiplied by the distance it falls gives the amount of work done in the course of the experiment. The weight of water multiplied by its temperature changes during the experiment gives the number of units of heat produced by the work. The average of many experiments shows that, using FPS system units, *778 ft-lb of work is equivalent to one Btu of heat.* In metric system units, *4.19 joules or 4.19×10^7 ergs of work equals one calorie.*

2. Methods of converting heat into work. This conversion of work to heat is reversible; that is, we can also change heat to work. *One British thermal unit of heat can do 778 ft-lb of work. One calorie can do 4.19 joules or 4.19×10^7 ergs of work.* See Fig. 11-2. This reversible equivalence of work

VOCABULARY

Adiabatic process. A process which occurs without the addition or withdrawal of heat from the surroundings.

Isothermal process. A process which occurs without a change in temperature.

Mechanical equivalent of heat. The conversion factor which relates heat units to work units.

Thermodynamics. The study of the quantitative relationships between heat and other forms of energy.

and heat may be expressed as

$$W = JQ$$

where W is work, Q is heat, and J is the necessary conversion factor called the **mechanical equivalent of heat.** Values of J commonly used are 4.19 joules/cal, 4.19×10^7 ergs/cal, and 778 ft-lb/Btu.

There are several methods by which heat may be converted to useful work.

1. *In our bodies.* A thick slice of bread, if completely oxidized, would furnish 10^2 kcal, or 10^5 cal of heat, enough energy to perform 4.19×10^5 joules of work. If the heat energy from a slice of bread were all converted to muscular energy, it would enable a 125-lb boy to climb a hill nearly 2500 ft high. Experiments have shown, however, that only about 25 percent of the heat energy in our food is so converted.

2. *By means of steam.* Steam is generated when heat causes water to boil. The heat may come from burning wood, coal, or oil, and since the steam is generated by the burning of fuel outside the engine, steam engines and steam turbines are

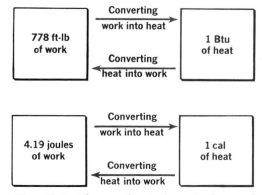

Fig. 11-2. The mechanical equivalents of heat.

external combustion engines. When water is converted to steam under normal atmospheric pressure it expands about 1700 times. In a boiler, however, the steam is confined and exerts considerable pressure in all directions. Steam pressure may do work by exerting its force against the piston of a steam engine, or against the blades of a steam turbine. In either case, the heat of the burning fuel is transformed to work through the use of steam.

3. *By means of burning gases.* When we convert heat to work by means of burning gases, we eliminate the need for a boiler. The pressure built up by burning compressed gases may convert heat to work by exerting a force to move a piston or turn the blades of a turbine. Since the burning of the fuel occurs within the cylinder or turbine chambers, such engines are called *internal combustion engines.*

3. Isothermal and adiabatic processes. The common ways of converting heat to work use the expansion of hot compressed gases. Before explaining the theory of heat engines we must first discuss two types of thermal processes, isothermal and adiabatic.

Isothermal processes are those which occur without a change in temperature. The isothermal expansion and compression of ideal gases occurs in accordance with Boyle's law. If the volume of an ideal gas

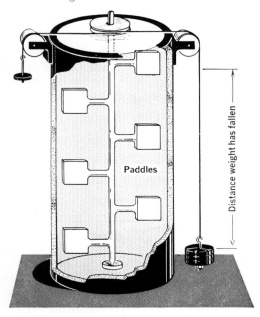

Fig. 11-1. A simplified form of the apparatus Joule used to determine the mechanical equivalent of heat.

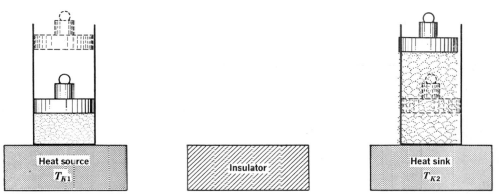

Fig. 11-3. A diagram of an ideal gas engine which operates on a Carnot cycle.

increases at constant temperature, its pressure decreases. Similarly, if the volume of an ideal gas decreases at constant temperature, its pressure increases. Since the thermal energy of an ideal gas is determined by its temperature, there can be no change in the thermal energy of an ideal gas during isothermal processes. However, work is done by a gas during expansion. Some work is done on the gas molecules, increasing their potential energy by moving them farther apart; other work is done against external pressure since the volume occupied by the gas becomes greater. The heat equivalent of the work done isothermally *by* an ideal gas during expansion must be absorbed from its surroundings. In a similar manner, work must be done *on* an ideal gas during isothermal compression and the equivalent amount of heat must be evolved to the surroundings.

Adiabatic processes are those which occur *without the addition or withdrawal of heat from the surroundings.* During an adiabatic expansion of an ideal gas, work is done just as it is during an isothermal expansion. Now, however, the equivalent amount of heat is not withdrawn from the surroundings, but is obtained at the expense of the thermal energy of the gas. Thus during adiabatic expansion not only the pressure, but also the temperature of the ideal gas

is lowered. Similarly, when work is done on a gas as it is adiabatically compressed, the heat equivalent of the work is not lost to the surroundings, but increases the thermal energy of the gas. As a consequence, during adiabatic compression both the pressure of the gas and its temperature increase.

4. The Carnot cycle. Sadi Carnot (1796–1832), a French engineer, was the first to develop the theory of heat engines in a quantitative fashion. He proposed an ideal heat engine which might operate through a cycle of reversible isothermal and adiabatic steps. (Although it is not possible to construct any real engine which operates on this cycle, we can imagine such an engine and learn much from it.)

Let us suppose that this ideal engine, shown in Fig. 11-3, consists of a cylinder containing a piston on which a load has been placed. The cylinder contains an ideal gas at pressure p_1, volume V_1, and Kelvin temperature T_{K1} (point K, Fig. 11-4). The cylinder is placed in contact with a heat source also at temperature T_{K1}. The ideal gas absorbs a quantity of heat Q_1 from this source and expands isothermally to conditions p_2, V_2, and T_{K1} (point L, Fig. 11-4). The volume V_2 is, of course, greater than V_1, while p_2 is less than p_1.

During this isothermal expansion the

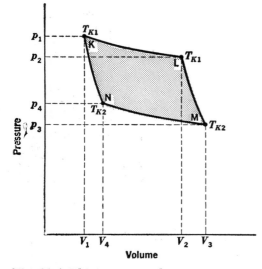

Fig. 11-4. This pressure-volume-temperature graph shows the conditions within an ideal gas engine operating on a Carnot cycle.

gas did work by raising the loaded piston. We have stated (Chapter 5, Section 2) that

$$W = Fs \qquad \text{(Equation 1)}$$

In this case F is the average pressure of the gas, $\bar{p}_{1,2}$, multiplied by the cross-sectional area of the piston, A, or

$$F = \bar{p}_{1,2}A \qquad \text{(Equation 2)}$$

The distance the piston moves, s, is the difference in volume of the gas, $V_2 - V_1$, divided by the cross-sectional area of the cylinder, A, or

$$s = \frac{V_2 - V_1}{A} \qquad \text{(Equation 3)}$$

Substituting the expressions for F and s in Equations 2 and 3 in Equation 1, and using W_{KL} to represent the work done by the gas during the change of conditions from K to L, Fig. 11-4,

$$W_{KL} = \bar{p}_{1,2}A \times \frac{V_2 - V_1}{A}$$

and simplifying

$$W_{KL} = \bar{p}_{1,2}(V_2 - V_1)$$

In Fig. 11-4, W_{KL} is represented graphically by the area KLV_2V_1.

If the cylinder is now removed from the heat source and placed on an insulator, the gas will expand adiabatically to the new conditions p_3, V_3, and T_{K2} (point M, Fig. 11-4). Note that $p_3 < p_2$; $V_3 > V_2$; and $T_{K2} < T_{K1}$. Still more work, W_{LM}, is done on the loaded piston during this expansion. By the reasoning we used earlier, we see that W_{LM} is represented graphically in Fig. 11-4 by the area LMV_3V_2.

Next the cylinder is placed in contact with a heat "sink" (a heat receiver) at temperature T_{K2}. The gas in the cylinder is compressed isothermally to conditions p_4, V_4, T_{K2} (point N, Fig. 11-4) and in doing so gives up to the sink an amount of heat Q_2. Work is done on the gas during this compression. This work, W_{MN}, is represented graphically by the area NMV_3V_4 in Fig. 11-4. Finally, the gas is removed from the heat sink to the insulator and further compressed adiabatically until it returns to the original conditions p_1, V_1, and T_{K1} (point K, Fig. 11-4). Still more work is done on the gas during this further compression. This work, W_{NK}, is represented in Fig. 11-4 by the area KNV_4V_1.

From Fig. 11-4, we see that the total work done *by* the ideal gas is the sum of W_{KL} and W_{LM}, which is represented graphically by the area $KLMV_3V_1$. The work done *on* the ideal gas is the sum of W_{MN} and W_{NK}, which is represented graphically by the area $KNMV_3V_1$. The difference is the W_{output} of the ideal engine, and is represented by the area $KLMN$.

Since the ideal gas was returned at the end of the cycle to its original conditions, it suffered no permanent loss or gain of energy. The source of energy for the W_{output} must be the difference between the heat absorbed from the hot source, Q_1, and that given up to the cold sink, Q_2. So,

$$W_{\text{output}} = Q_1 - Q_2$$

We have stated (Chapter 5, Section 13) that

$$\text{efficiency} = \frac{W_{\text{output}}}{W_{\text{input}}} \times 100\%$$

And since Q_1 was the energy (work) input, and $Q_2 - Q_1$ was the energy (work) output,

$$\text{efficiency} = \frac{Q_1 - Q_2}{Q_1} \times 100\%$$

Furthermore, since the mass of the ideal gas was constant, $Q \propto T_K$ and

$$\text{efficiency} = \frac{T_{K1} - T_{K2}}{T_{K1}} \times 100\%$$

This expression gives the efficiency of Carnot's ideal engine, the theoretically highest efficiency of any real heat engine operating between Kelvin temperatures T_{K1} and T_{K2}. Naturally such an efficiency is greater than that of any real heat engine. This relationship shows that the efficiency of a heat engine is increased when $T_{K1} - T_{K2}$, the range of operating temperatures, is made as great as possible. See the Sample Problem below.

5. The second law of thermodynamics. The study of the operation of the Carnot cycle and its graphic representation in Fig. 11-4 show that work may be obtained by the transfer of thermal energy from a heat source at high temperature to a heat sink at low temperature. It also follows that transfer of thermal energy from a low temperature heat source to a high temperature sink requires work. This

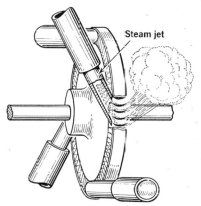

Fig. 11-5. The force of the steam against the cupped blades causes them to move.

latter type of thermal energy transfer takes place in refrigerators and air conditioners. These observations are summarized by the *second law of thermodynamics: It is impossible for an engine to transfer heat from one body to another at a higher temperature unless work is done on the engine.*

6. The steam turbine. Steam turbines are used for ship propulsion and for driving generators in electric power plants. The principle of the steam turbine is illustrated in Fig. 11-5. Steam at a high temperature and high pressure is directed through nozzles against a set of cupped blades attached to a turbine wheel. The

Sample Problem

What is the theoretically highest efficiency of a steam engine which has a steam input temperature of 200.° C and a steam exhaust temperature of 100.° C?

Solution

200.° C = 473° K; 100.° C = 373° K.

$$\text{Efficiency} = \frac{T_{K1} - T_{K2}}{T_{K1}} \times 100\%$$

$$\text{Efficiency} = \frac{473° \text{ K} - 373° \text{ K}}{473° \text{ K}} \times 100\%$$

$$\text{Efficiency} = 21.2\%$$

sidewise component of the force of the steam against the blades causes the turbine wheel and the shaft on which it is mounted to rotate. The shaft may be connected through large reduction gears to the propeller shafts of a ship or may be directly attached to an electric generator.

A large steam turbine consists of two main parts: a rotor and a stator. The rotor consists of a long shaft on which are mounted wheels containing a large number of blades. These are set much like the blades of a windmill, as shown in Fig. 11-7. The stator, in which the rotor is mounted, contains a large number of fixed nozzles. The steam enters near one end of the turbine and strikes the first set of movable blades. After passing through this set, the steam is redirected by a set of fixed nozzles to strike a second set of movable blades

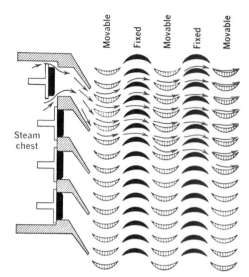

Fig. 11-7. In a steam turbine, steam strikes a set of movable blades, exerts force against them and is deflected, is redeflected by a set of fixed blades against a second set of movable blades, and so on.

Fig. 11-6. The rotor of a large steam-turbine generator placed in the lower half of the stator for testing during assembly. Notice the many blade wheels of varying diameters. (General Motors Corp.)

and give up more of its energy. Again its direction is changed by fixed nozzles. The process continues as the steam passes each set of blades. The diameters of both the rotor and the stator are made larger near the outlet end to allow expansion of the steam. The pitch and size of the blades vary throughout the length of the turbine so that the expansive force of the steam is most efficiently used.

In a modern turbine, steam may enter at a pressure of 2000 lb/in.^{2} or more, and at a temperature of about 1000° F. On its way through the turbine—a distance of 15–20 ft which it travels in 0.03 sec—the steam passes through about 20 blade wheels and the same number of nozzles, pushes against 5000 or more blades, and drops in temperature to about 70° F. It expands to about 1000 times its original volume. A condenser converts the spent steam into water so rapidly that the pressure at the cool end of a turbine is less than one atmosphere. This helps draw steam through the turbine more rapidly. The water is returned to the boiler to be reheated to steam and continue its steam-water cycle through the boiler, turbine, and condenser.

The steam input temperature is made as high as possible by the burning of coal or fuel oil with a forced draft of air in high pressure boilers which are almost white hot. The steam exhaust temperature is made as low as possible by the use of cold condenser water. This great difference in temperature increases the efficiency of the steam turbine, as explained in Section 4.

Several factors in the design of a steam turbine contribute to its efficiency. The large number of turbine wheels and blades transforms all of the heat energy of the steam possible into mechanical energy. The size, shape, and angle of the blades are such that as the steam pressure through the turbine decreases, the total force on each turbine wheel remains constant. The blades are made of alloys which withstand the high steam pressure, operate at

the dull red heat to which the first blades are raised by the incoming steam, withstand the sand blasting effect of the rain from the exhausted steam, and hold together at speeds of rotation which produce centrifugal reactions of over 10^5 pounds.

7. The gas turbine. This newer type of heat engine was originally developed for use in airplanes. Today the gas turbine is being used in locomotives, large trucks, small ships, and in small power plants and pumping stations.

The principle of the gas turbine is remarkably simple. A large volume of air is continually drawn into a compressor, where its pressure is increased. This compressed air then flows into the combustion chamber, where the fuel—natural gas, gasoline, fuel oil, or powdered coal—is injected and burns with a continuous hot flame. Only part of the compressed air is needed for complete combustion of the fuel. From the combustion chamber the hot

Fig. 11-8. Schematic diagram of a steam turbine generating station. Trace the flow of water or steam through the boiler, superheater, turbine, and condenser. (Steelways)

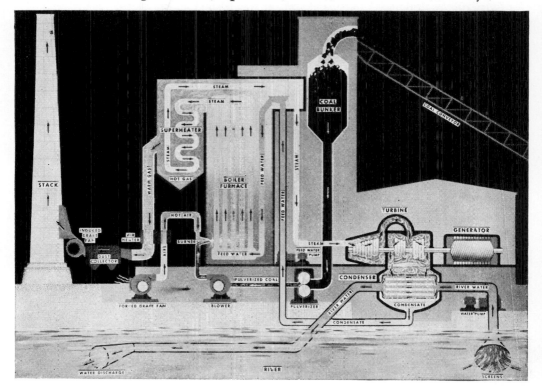

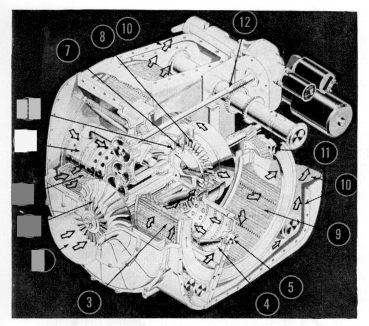

Fig. 11-9. Cut-away diagram of the gas turbine engine which powers the Firebird III experimental automobile. (General Motors Corp.)

combustion gases and heated air expand and rush at tremendous speed, first through a turbine and then through the exhaust nozzle.

Some of the energy imparted to the turbine is used to drive the compressor. The remaining energy may be taken from the turbine-compressor shaft and used to turn a propeller (as in a turboprop airplane engine) or to run an electric generator, a pipeline pump, or other machine.

The gas turbine has the advantages of compactness, a larger power-to-weight ratio, and wide flexibility of use. The higher the temperature at which it operates, the greater is its efficiency. In attempting to raise the operating temperature, engineers have encountered problems in developing heat-resistant materials and in finding methods for cooling the turbine blades. Special alloys and combinations of metals with ceramic materials show promise in overcoming these difficulties.

An experimental automobile, the Firebird III, is powered by the gas turbine engine shown in the cut-away diagram, Fig. 11-9. Air is admitted through the inlet (1) and is compressed and consequently heated by the centrifugal compressor (2) to over three atmospheres pressure. The temperature of the compressed air is further raised by exhaust heat in revolving heat exchangers (3) and then enters the combustion chambers (4) where fuel for combustion is added through the nozzles (5). The hot combustion gases strike the turbine blades (6), driving the turbines (7) and (8). The hot exhaust is cooled as it passes through the revolving heat exchangers (9), and then out the ports (10). Turbine (7) is connected by a set of reduction gears (12) to the engine equipment drive shaft. Turbine (8) is connected by a single reduction gear (11) to the power output shaft. Such a gas turbine engine has several advantages over a conventional gas piston engine. It has a higher power-to-weight ratio, can use low-grade fuel, has no radiator or cooling system, and runs free of the vibration which is characteristic of reciprocating engines.

8. The turbojet—an air-dependent jet engine. The long shaft through the center is the only moving part in a turbojet engine. Attached to the front end of this shaft is the compressor; the turbine is attached at the other end. The compressor draws air into the front of the engine and

Fig. 11-10. In this installation gas turbines are used to drive electric generators. These units each produce 16,000 kilowatts of power. (General Electric Co.)

compresses it as the air moves straight through the compressor chamber. Fuel, usually kerosene, is injected into the air stream just behind the compressor. Here it burns very rapidly at high temperature, producing a tremendous pressure. The hot, high-pressure gases pass through the turbine which drives the compressor, and the terrific unbalanced forward force exerted by the gases as they rush out through the exhaust pushes the engine forward at great speed. Modern jet engines like the one shown in Fig. 11-11 produce up to 25,000 horsepower and 10,000 lb of thrust.

9. The ramjet—the simplest jet engine. A ramjet such as that shown in Fig. 11-12 is very simple in design since it has no moving parts. Like the turbojet, it requires air for fuel combustion and must operate in the earth's atmosphere. The motion of the engine forces air at increased pressure into the combustion chamber. There, fuel is added and burns just as in the turbojet engine. The hot combustion

gases and heated air rushing out the exhaust produce the unbalanced forward force which moves the engine.

Since a ramjet depends on its speed to compress the air necessary for combustion, it must have a high speed to operate efficiently. Consequently an airplane powered by a ramjet engine must be boosted to the proper speed for ramjet operation by some other type of power plant. Ramjets operate efficiently at speeds of 1800 to 2000 mi/hr.

10. The rocket—an air-independent jet engine. A rocket operates on the same principle as a jet engine. However, a rocket carries both fuel and the oxidizer needed to burn it, while a jet engine carries only fuel, and uses oxygen from the air as the oxidizer. Thus a rocket may go beyond the earth's atmosphere. Rockets can travel better in outer space than through air, because there is no friction.

Since a rocket, like the other devices we have been studying, is a heat engine, it converts the heat energy of fuel into work.

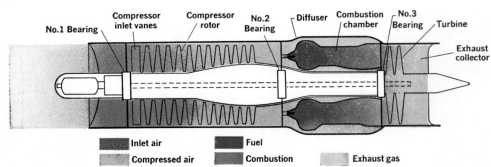

Fig. 11-11. Cutaway diagram of the J-57 turbojet engine similar to those which power some of the new commercial jet airplanes.

However, since a rocket's range of operation is so much greater, and refueling is impossible, the amount of work obtained from a given quantity of fuel is of much greater importance.

The magnitude of the thrust of a reaction motor depends on the exhaust velocity of the gases. The factors which influence exhaust velocity most markedly are the temperature of the gas as it leaves the combustion chamber and the average weight of its molecules. The higher the temperature, the greater the exhaust velocity. Rockets propelled by chemical fuels have combustion temperatures of about 5000° F. The maximum possible combustion temperature using such fuels is 8000° F.

The velocity of the exhaust gases can also

be increased if they have a lower average molecular weight. The average molecular weight of the gases in the exhaust of present chemically powered rockets is about 19 amu. It appears likely that the use of newer types of chemical fuels will reduce this to about 9 amu. The highest exhaust velocity attainable with present chemical fuels is about 13,000 ft/sec. This velocity is just slightly more than that of the rockets which put the first satellites into orbit around the sun.

If man is to send rockets further into outer space, more powerful fuels must be developed. Scientists are now working on nuclear-powered rockets which they hope will overcome the fuel problem. The simplest such rocket might contain a compact nuclear reactor which would heat

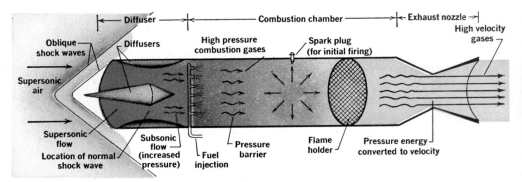

Fig. 11-12. A supersonic ram-jet engine. Ram-air pressure makes its operation possible; the faster it goes the more efficient it is. Color key is the same as that in Fig. 11-11.

SUMMER COOLING   WINTER HEATING

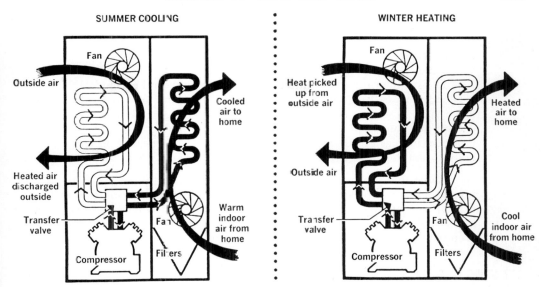

Fig. 11-13. The heat pump can be used to cool a home in summer and heat it in winter. In summer the refrigerant evaporates in the piping, absorbing heat from the air circulating inside the home. In winter the refrigerant cools after being compressed, giving out heat to the air circulating inside the home.

liquid hydrogen. The hydrogen, pumped at a pressure of about 1000 lb/in.² between the heating elements of the reactor, would be raised to the maximum temperature the structural materials of the reactor could stand, and would then flow through the exhaust nozzle. At an operating temperature of 4000° F. the hydrogen would have an exhaust velocity of 25,000 ft/sec, nearly double that possible with a chemically powered rocket. Some of the problems in designing such a rocket are the size and weight of the reactor, the high operating temperature required, the transfer of heat efficiently from the reactor to the hydrogen, and the increased "weight" due to the high acceleration.

11. The heat pump. A heat pump is a device like a refrigerator, in which work is done in order to transfer heat from a low temperature source to a higher temperature sink. It can be used for heating in winter or cooling in summer.

The working fluid in a heat pump is a vapor which may be easily condensed to a liquid when pressure is applied. The liquid, under pressure, gives up the heat developed during compression to the higher temperature sink. The liquid is then released into a low pressure zone where it quickly evaporates, taking its heat of vaporization from the low temperature source of heat. The vapor is then recompressed and the cycle repeated. Work must be done on the vapor in order for the heat pump to transfer heat from a low temperature source to a higher temperature sink.

In the winter, a house to be heated by a heat pump is made the high temperature sink. The outside air, water in a well, or buried pipes serve as the low temperature source. In the summer, these conditions are reversed, the house acts as the low temperature source, and the outside air or earth as the high temperature sink.

Refrigerators and home freezers are other forms of heat pumps. In these devices the freezing compartment acts as the low temperature source of heat, and the air of the room in which the refrigerator is located absorbs the heat energy.

Summary

The study of the quantitative relationships between heat and other forms of energy is called thermodynamics. The first law of thermodynamics: when heat is converted to another form of energy, or when other forms of energy are converted to heat, there is no loss of energy. The second law of thermodynamics: it is impossible for an engine to transfer heat from one body to another at a higher temperature unless work is done on the engine.

Isothermal processes are those which occur without a change in temperature. Adiabatic processes are those which occur without the addition or withdrawal of heat from the surroundings. The Carnot cycle consists of reversible isothermal and adiabatic steps; its study provides an expression for the theoretically highest efficiency of any real heat engine.

TERMS TO DEFINE

adiabatic process
Carnot cycle
external combustion engine
first law of thermodynamics
heat pump

heat sink
heat source
internal combustion engine
isothermal process
mechanical equivalent of heat

refrigerator
rocket
second law of thermodynamics
thermodynamics
turbine
turbojet

QUESTIONS

A 1. What is thermodynamics?
2. What is the statement of (a) the first law of thermodynamics; (b) the second law of thermodynamics?
3. What are the metric system and English system values for the mechanical equivalent of heat?
4. Distinguish between an external combustion engine and an internal combustion engine.
5. What is (a) an isothermal process; (b) an adiabatic process?
6. What is the purpose of (a) a heat source; (b) a heat sink?
7. On what does the efficiency of Carnot's ideal engine depend?
8. Heat naturally flows from a body at a higher temperature to one at a lower temperature and may be used to do work in the process. How may we cause heat to flow from a body at a lower temperature to one at a higher temperature?
9. List several applications of a gas turbine.
10. What are the differences between a turbojet and a rocket?

B 11. Describe Joule's method for determining the mechanical equivalent of heat.
12. What percentage of the heat energy of food is converted into muscular energy?
13. What physical law governs the isothermal expansion and compression of an ideal gas?
14. What physical laws govern the adiabatic expansion and compression of an ideal gas?
15. (a) What is the source of the heat equivalent of the work done by an ideal gas during isothermal expansion? (b) What happens to the heat equivalent of the work done on an ideal gas during isothermal compression?
16. (a) What is the source of the heat equivalent of the work done by an ideal gas during adiabatic expansion? (b) What happens to the heat equivalent of the work done on an ideal gas during adiabatic compression?
17. (a) What temperature conditions affect the efficiency of a steam turbine? (b) How are they adjusted to insure maximum efficiency?
18. Compare the use of a heat pump for house heating and cooling with its use in a refrigerator or air-conditioning unit.

PROBLEMS

A **1.** How many foot-pounds of work are required to produce 500. Btu?

2. How many joules of work can be obtained from 1.00×10^4 cal?

3. A sample of coal furnishes 1.20×10^4 Btu/lb. How many foot-pounds of work can be obtained from the complete combustion of 1.00 ton of this coal?

4. Gasoline liberates 1.15×10^4 cal/g when it is burned. How many joules of work can be obtained by burning 1.00 liter of gasoline? The specific gravity of gasoline is 0.700.

5. The water going over Niagara Falls drops 167 ft. How much warmer is the water at the bottom of the falls than it is at the top?

6. How many Btu/hr are needed to generate 1.00 hp?

B **7.** The over-all efficiency of a boiler and steam turbine is 20.0%. If 50.0 lb of coal is burned each hour in the boiler, what is the horsepower developed? The coal has a heating value of 1.00×10^4 Btu/lb.

8. The natural gas burned in a gas turbine has a heating value of 1.00×10^5 cal/g. If 2.00 g of gas is burned in the turbine each second, and the efficiency of the turbine is 25.0%, what is the output in kilowatts?

9. A gasoline engine develops 200. hp with an efficiency of 25.0%. If gasoline has a heat of combustion of 1.20×10^5 Btu/gal, how many gallons are consumed per hour?

10. What must be the velocity in m/sec of a snowball at 0° C, if the snowball is completely melted by its impact against a wall?

11. What is the theoretical efficiency of a steam turbine which has a steam input temperature of 1000.° F and a steam output temperature of 70.° F?

12. The following data were obtained by the use of an apparatus like that shown in Fig. 11-1: falling mass, 2.50×10^3 g; distance fallen, 150. cm; number of falls, 25; temperature rise of water and calorimeter, 0.31 C°; mass of water, 700. g; mass of copper calorimeter, 150. g. Calculate a value for the mechanical equivalent of heat.

RESEARCH ON YOUR OWN

1. Put a small piece of iron or lead on a heat-insulating surface (such as stone or concrete) and pound it vigorously with a hammer for a minute or two. Lower it quickly into some water in an insulated container such as a Thermos bottle. Record the water temperature before putting the metal into the container and again after five minutes. Explain any change in temperature and calculate the amount of work done in pounding the metal. Drive a large nail into a thick block of wood. Pull the nail quickly from the block with a claw hammer and immediately put the nail into water in an insulated container, following the same procedure as with the piece of metal above. Explain any change in temperature and calculate the work done in pulling the nail from the block.

2. In a reference book, find a description of Hiero's engine. Make a working model and demonstrate its operation.

3. Devise an experiment to determine the mechanical equivalent of heat, using a cardboard mailing tube, corks to fit it, lead shot, and a thermometer.

4. Prepare a chart comparing the structure of a piston engine, a turbine engine, and a rocket engine. Discuss their basic similarities and differences.

5. Report on the relative advantages and disadvantages of liquid fuels and solid fuels for rocket engines.

UNIT 5

Sound

CHAPTER 12

WAVE MOTION AND SOUND

1 WAVE MOTION

1. Energy transfer by waves. You already know that energy may be transferred by the motion of particles or large masses of material. Electricity is conducted along a wire by the motion of electrons. Heat is conducted from the bowl of a spoon to the handle by the motion of the atoms and molecules of the metal. Winds and tides illustrate the transfer of energy by the motion of fluids.

Wave motion is a second means by which energy is transferred. All of the energy from the sun is transferred to the earth by waves. Radio waves are an important method of energy transfer which provides almost instantaneous communication. Sound waves are still another method by which energy may be transferred. While there are several types of waves, each having certain characteristic properties, all waves have some common properties which we shall study first.

VOCABULARY

Beat. An outburst of sound followed by an interval of comparative silence.

Doppler effect. The variation of the pitch heard from a moving source of sound.

Intensity. The rate at which sound energy flows through a unit area.

Interference. The superimposing of one wave on another.

Longitudinal wave. A wave in which the particles of the medium vibrate to and fro along the path which the wave travels through the medium.

Loudness. The effect of the intensity of sound waves on the ears.

Pitch. The effect of the frequency of sound waves on the ears.

Resonance. The inducing of vibrations of a natural rate in matter by a vibrating source having the same or a simple multiple frequency.

Sound. The series of disturbances in matter which the ear interprets as sound. Also, similar disturbances in matter that are above and below the normal range of human hearing.

Transverse wave. A wave in which the particles of the medium vibrate at right angles to the path along which the wave travels through the medium.

Wave. A disturbance that moves through a medium.

2. The characteristics of a wave. If a stone is dropped into a quiet pool of water, the water where the stone enters is disturbed. The disturbance, however, is not limited to one spot, but sets up waves which travel through the water to all parts of the pool. The particles disturbed by the entrance of the stone disturb particles adjacent to them, and these, in turn, disturb other particles adjacent to them, and so on to the edge of the pool. As the disturbance moves through the water, it does not move any individual particle very far from its equilibrium position. After the disturbance passes, the particles return to their equilibrium positions. *A wave is a disturbance that moves through a medium.*

Since a particle wave is the result of the interaction of particles of a medium, such waves will only travel through a medium which is elastic. If the particles of a medium have no effect on each other, a particle wave cannot pass through it.

Two main classes of waves may be distinguished by the motion of the particles transmitting the wave; these are *transverse waves* and *longitudinal waves.*

3. Transverse waves. We may illustrate transverse waves by means of a long spiral spring stretched between two supports several meters apart. Plucking this spring at right angles to its length sets up a wave which travels from one end of the spring to the other and is reflected back again. See Fig. 12-1(*A*). *A wave,* such as this one, *in which the particles vibrate at right angles to the path along which the wave travels, is called a* **transverse wave.**

Water waves set up by a stone in a quiet pool are transverse waves, because as the wave advances, the water rises and falls. There is no net forward movement of the water itself, except when the waves tumble onto the shore. Transverse waves can be set up in elastic media in which the particles are close enough together to exert relatively large forces on one another.

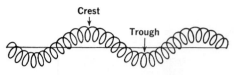

(A) Transverse waves in a spring

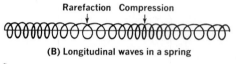

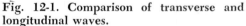

(B) Longitudinal waves in a spring

Fig. 12-1. Comparison of transverse and longitudinal waves.

4. Longitudinal waves. We may use the same stretched spring we used in Section 3 to illustrate longitudinal waves. Compressing several turns of the spring near one end and releasing them quickly sets up a compression that travels to the opposite end of the spring and returns by reflection. Now the particles of the spring do not vibrate at right angles to the direction of wave motion, as was the case with transverse waves; instead, *they vibrate to and fro along the path which the wave travels,* producing **longitudinal waves.** See Fig. 12-1(*B*). An example of a longitudinal wave is a sound wave. Longitudinal waves can be set up in elastic media in which the particles are rather widely separated.

5. Characteristics of waves. All waves have several common characteristics. A wave has a finite *speed;* that is, it travels a given distance in unit time. Wave speed may be quite slow, like that of water waves; it may be moderately fast, like that of sound waves, which travel with speeds of the order of 10^2 and 10^3 m/sec; or it may be the fastest possible speed, that of light or radio waves, 3×10^8 m/sec. Wave speed depends primarily on the type of wave and on the medium through which it is passing.

As a wave travels through a medium, the particles of the medium vibrate about their equilibrium positions in identical fashion; however, the particles are in

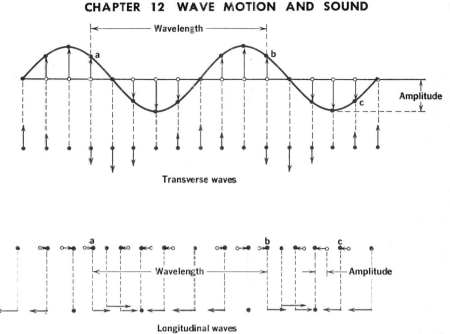

Fig. 12-2. Characteristics of transverse and longitudinal waves. The black circles show the equilibrium positions of the particles of the medium. The red dots show their displaced positions. The black arrows indicate the displacement of the particles from their equilibrium positions. The red arrows are the velocity vectors for the particles above them.

corresponding positions of their vibratory motion at different times. The position and motion of a particle indicate the *phase* of the wave. Particles which have the same displacement and are moving in the same direction are said to be in phase. Particles *a* and *b* in both waves of Fig. 12-2 are in phase. Those with opposite displacement and moving in the opposite direction (particles *b* and *c*) are in opposite phase.

The *frequency* of a wave, represented by *f*, is the number of such waves passing a given point in unit time. The *period* of a wave is the time T required for a single wave to pass a given point. Of course T is the reciprocal of *f*, so

$$f = \frac{1}{T}$$

The *wavelength* is the distance between any particle in a wave and the particle in the next wave which is in phase with it.

The distance between particles *a* and *b*, Fig. 12-2, is a wavelength, representing one complete cycle of vibration. Wavelength is represented by the Greek letter λ (lambda). If a wave has a wavelength λ and a frequency *f*, its speed, *v*, is given by the equation

$$v = f\lambda$$

This is a very important equation which is true for all types of waves.

The maximum displacement of the vibrating particles of the medium is the *amplitude* of the wave motion; it is determined by the energy of the wave.

6. Common properties of waves. Waves travel through a uniform medium in a straight line. We use this property of sound waves and light waves to locate the position of an object. When a wave reaches the boundary of the transmitting medium, it is *reflected*. Familiar examples are the reflection of water waves from the edge of a pool, the echoing of sound waves from walls, and the reflection of light waves by a mirror.

Waves also pass from one medium to another. Difference of density between the two media results in a change of wave speed; if the wave enters the second medium at any angle other than the perpendicular, the direction of the wave is also changed. The direction of the wave is also changed when a wave travels through a nonuniform medium. This phenomenon is called *refraction;* the bending of light rays by lenses is a familiar illustration.

When two waves travel through a medium, each moves as though the other were not present. However, the vibratory motion of the particles of the medium is the resultant of the motions imparted by the two waves. If the disturbances of the two wave motions arrive in phase, the resultant disturbance is a maximum; if the disturbances arrive in opposite phase, the resultant disturbance is a minimum. This phenomenon is called **interference.** At points where the waves arrive in phase the interference is said to be *constructive.* At points where the waves arrive in opposite phase, the interference is said to be *destructive.*

Waves bend around obstacles in their path. Water waves wash around the supports of a pier and sound waves travel from one room of a house to another. This property of waves is called *diffraction.*

These properties are common to all types of waves. They help us determine whether or not a phenomenon involves wave motion.

2 SOUND

7. The nature of sound. An age-old riddle asks: If a tree falls in a forest where there are no ears to hear it, is sound produced? To answer this question, we must define sound. In the *physiological* sense of the term, there are three requirements for sound: (*1*) a source of sound; (*2*) a medium for transmitting the sound; and (*3*) an ear to receive the sound. In the *physical* sense, **sound** is *the series of disturbances in matter which an ear interprets as sound. The term sound also applies to similar disturbances in matter which are above and below the normal range of human hearing.* So you see the answer to the riddle depends on the definition used. In this book "sound" will be used in its physical sense.

8. The production of sound. Suppose we take a very thin strip of wood, or a piece of steel like a hacksaw blade, and clamp one end in a vise. When we strike this clamped material sharply, the free end vibrates to and fro, as shown in Fig.

12-3. If the wood or steel vibrates rapidly, it produces a humming sound that can be heard. This and other experiments, such as the bowing or plucking of a violin string and the striking of a tuning fork, show that *sounds are produced by vibrating matter.*

When the steel strip of Fig. 12-3 is

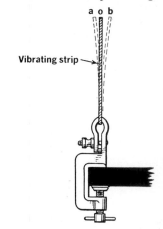

Fig. 12-3. Sounds are produced by vibrating matter.

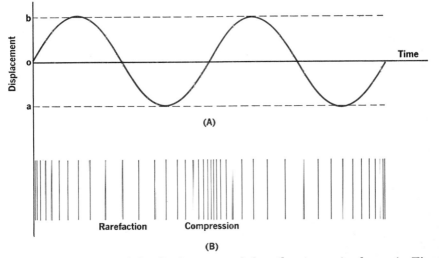

Fig. 12-4. (A) Variation of the displacement of the vibrating strip shown in Fig. 12-3 with time. (B) Corresponding longitudinal sound waves produced at the right of the vibrating strip.

vibrating, its motion approximates simple harmonic motion. A graph of its displacement with time produces the sine wave shown at (A) Fig. 12-4. As the vibrating steel strip is moving from a to b, it does work on the gas molecules to the right by compressing them; the strip thus transfers energy to the molecules in the direction in which the compression occurs. At the same time, the gas molecules to the left of the strip expand into the space left behind the strip as it moves, and become rarefied; this removes energy from the molecules to the left of the strip. The combined effect of the simultaneous *compression* and *rarefaction* transfers energy to the molecules from left to right in the direction of vibration of the strip.

As the strip moves in the reverse direction, from b to a, it does work on the gas molecules to the left of it and transfers energy to them; the gas molecules to the right of the strip now lose energy. The combined effect of this simultaneous compression and rarefaction transfers energy to the molecules from right to left. Thus the energy transfer alternates in direction just as the motion of the strip does.

If we consider just the series of compressions and rarefactions produced to the right of the strip, we see that the maximum compression occurs as the strip moves through its equilibrium position o in its vibration from a to b. See (B) Fig. 12-4. The maximum rarefaction occurs as the strip moves through its equilibrium position o in its reverse vibration from b to a. Of course, a corresponding series of rarefactions and compressions is being produced simultaneously to the left of the strip. The vibration of the steel strip thus generates longitudinal trains of waves in which the vibrating gas molecules move back and forth along the path in which the waves are traveling, receiving energy from adjacent molecules nearer the source and passing it on to adjacent molecules farther from the source. *Sound waves are longitudinal waves.*

Variations in the work done in setting the steel strip in vibration alter the amplitude of its vibration but not the frequency. The greater the energy of the strip, the greater is the amplitude of its vibrations and the amplitude of the resulting longitudinal waves.

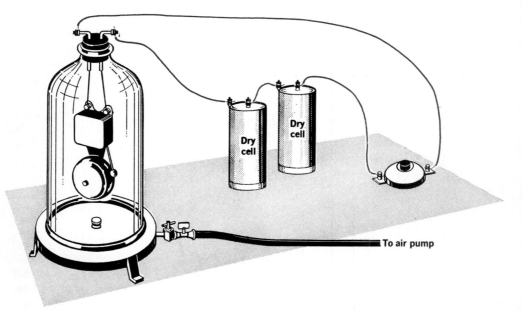

To air pump

Fig. 12-5. As air is pumped from the bell jar, the sound of the bell becomes fainter. A material medium is needed for the transmission of sound.

9. The transmission of sound. Most sounds come to us through the air, the air acting as the *transmitting medium*. At ordinary altitudes, we usually have no difficulty hearing one another. However, the air on a mountain is less dense than in a valley and therefore does not transmit sound as readily. As we might expect, dense gases are better transmitters of sound than rarefied gases, because the molecules are closer and can transmit the kinetic energy of the sound wave to one another more efficiently.

The following experiment shows how the density of air affects the transmission of sound. An electric bell under a bell jar, as shown in Fig. 12-5, is connected to some batteries so that it rings. While it is ringing, air is pumped out of the bell jar; as the air becomes less and less dense, the sound becomes fainter and fainter. When air is allowed to re-enter, the sound becomes louder. This suggests that if all the air could be pumped from the bell jar, no sound would be heard. *Sound does not travel through a vacuum, but it does travel*

through air. Sound is transmitted only when there is a material medium for its transmission.

A person listening under water can hear quite plainly the sound of rocks struck together in the water nearby, or an outboard motor at some distance. *Liquids are better transmitters of sound than gases* because they are more elastic and transmit the sound wave energy more readily.

Sometimes a loose faucet washer vibrates when water is drawn from the water pipe. The sound of this vibration can usually be heard in all parts of the house, because it is carried by the water pipes. A train can be heard from a great distance by the sound which comes through the rails. In general, because of their higher elasticity, *solids are better transmitters of sound than either liquids or gases.*

10. The speed of sound. During a thunderstorm you may see a distant lightning flash and several seconds later hear the accompanying thunder. The timer at the finish line during a track meet sees the smoke from the starter's gun before he hears the report. Over short distances, light travels practically instantaneously. Therefore, the time which elapses between seeing a lightning flash and hearing the thunder, or between seeing the smoke of the gun and hearing the report, must be the time required for the sound to travel from its source to your ears.

The speed of sound in air is about 331.5 m/sec at 0° C. As the temperature of the air rises, the speed of sound increases at the rate of about 0.6 m/sec/C°. Using English system units, the speed of sound is 1087 ft/sec at 32° F, and the rate of increase is about 1.1 ft/sec/F°.

The speed of sound in water is about four times that in air; in water at 19° C (66° F) sound travels 1461 m/sec or 4794 ft/sec. In some solids, the speed of sound is even greater; in a steel rod, for example, sound may travel 5000. m/sec, or 16,410 ft/sec—about 15 times as fast as in air. The speed of sound in liquids and solids is not appreciably affected by changes in temperature. (See Table 14, Appendix B.)

11. The ear as a receiver of sound. The human ear is shown in Fig. 12-6. The outer ear collects sound waves and conducts them through the ear canal to the eardrum, which is the thin membrane separating the outer ear from the middle ear. The small bones of the middle ear are connected to the eardrum. Sound waves do work on the eardrum and cause it and the small bones of the middle ear to vibrate. The bones act as levers which transmit these vibrations as force variations to the oval window, a membrane which separates the middle ear from the inner ear. Vibration of the oval window produces pressure changes in the inner ear. Since the area of the eardrum is greater than the area of the oval window, and the bones of the middle ear act to multiply force, the pressure changes transmitted to the inner ear are multiplied between 30 and 60 times.

The auditory structure of the inner ear is a small coiled tube filled with liquid.

In this small tube there are about 30,000 nerve endings, which are acted upon by pressure changes in the fluid. Certain nerve endings are affected only by low frequency vibrations, while others are affected only by higher frequency vibrations. When the pressure changes in the fluid stimulate these auditory nerves, they carry to the brain nerve impulses which are there interpreted as sound.

12. The properties of sounds. A nearby clap of thunder is loud; a whisper is soft and low. A cricket has a shrill, high chirp; a bulldog has a deep growl. Each of these sounds has characteristics we associate with that sound and no other. Sounds differ from each other in several fundamental properties. In this chapter we shall discuss two physical properties of sound waves: *intensity* and *frequency*. The effects of these two properties on the ear are called *loudness* and *pitch*. Another property of sound waves, *quality*, will be discussed in Chapter 13.

13. Intensity and loudness. *The intensity of a sound is the rate at which the sound energy flows through a unit area.* Intensity thus has the dimension of power/area. The amplitude of a sound wave of given frequency and wavelength is a measure of its energy.

Sound waves are given off in all directions from a vibrating body. If they travel through a uniform medium, they spread out in a spherical pattern. Thus the area of the expanding wave front is directly proportional to the square of its distance from the source. Since the total power of the wave is constant, the intensity of the wave diminishes as it moves away from the source. The sound waves produced by a whistle are only one-fourth as intense at a distance of one mile as they are at a distance of half a mile from the source. The intensity of a sound wave in a uniform medium is inversely proportional to the square of its distance from the source of the sound.

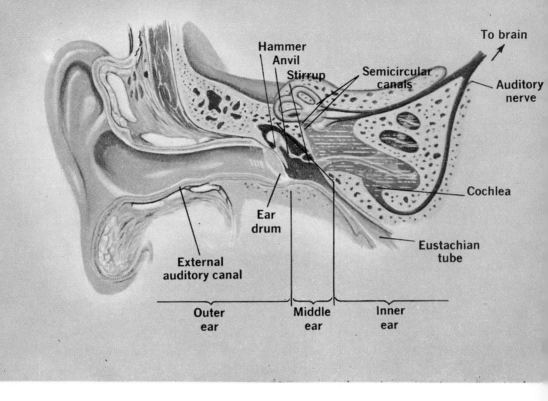

Fig. 12-6. The structure of a human ear.

The **loudness** of a sound depends on the effect of the intensity of the sound waves on the ears. In general, sound waves of higher intensity are louder. The ear is not equally sensitive to sounds of all frequencies. Consequently, a high frequency sound may not seem as loud as one of lower frequency having the same intensity.

An increase in the intensity of a sound of fixed frequency, while the observer remains at a fixed distance from its source, causes the sound to seem louder to him. However, the relation between intensity and loudness is not one of direct proportion, but is more nearly logarithmic. A sound must be 10 times more intense before it becomes twice as loud; it must be 100 times as intense before it becomes three times as loud. The degree of loudness is difficult to measure accurately, since it depends on the judgment of a listener and not on any purely physical measurement.

14. The measurement of intensity level. Intensity is measured with acoustical apparatus and does not depend on the hearing sense of an observer. The intensity of the average faintest audible sound, called the *threshold of hearing*, is 10^{-16} watts/cm². In measuring the intensity level of a sound wave, the intensity of the unknown sound is compared with the intensity of this faintest sound. The *intensity level* of a sound wave is given by the equation,

$$\beta = 10 \log \frac{I}{I_0}$$

where β (Greek letter beta) is the intensity level in decibels of a sound of intensity I, measured in watts/cm². I_0 is the intensity of the threshold of hearing, 10^{-16} watts/cm². The decibel is named for Alexander Graham Bell (1847–1922), the inventor of the telephone.

The intensity levels of a number of familiar noises are given on page 277.

Type of Sound	Decibels
Threshold of hearing	0
Whisper	10–20
Quiet office	20–40
Automobile	40–50
Conversation	60
Heavy street traffic	70–80
Elevated trains, riveters	90–100
Thunder	110
Threshold of pain	120

15. Pitch depends on frequency. A siren disk, like that in Fig. 12-7, will demonstrate how the frequency of a sound determines its pitch. A stream of air directed against a row of holes is cut off, as the disk rotates rapidly, by the metal between the holes. A steady pitch is heard if the holes are evenly spaced and the rotation of the disk is constant; the pitch rises as the disk's rotation is accelerated, it falls if the disk's rotation is decelerated. If the air stream is directed at the 24-, the 30-, the 36-, and the 48-hole rows successively (while the disk rotates steadily), the notes *do*, *mi*, *sol*, and *do'* are produced; doubling the number of holes causes a rise in pitch of an octave. *The* **pitch** *of a sound depends on the frequency, or number of cycles per second, which the ear receives.*

16. The Doppler effect. At some time, probably, you have stood at a railroad crossing waiting for a train to pass. As you listened to the steady warning horn of the Diesel locomotive coming toward you, you noticed that the pitch of the horn dropped abruptly as the locomotive passed. *This variation of the pitch heard from a moving source of sound is called the* **Doppler** **effect.** The pitch of the horn changes, even though the frequency of the sound which the horn produces is constant.

If the train is not moving as the horn is sounded, the listener receives the same number of vibrations per second that the horn produces, and he hears a sound of steady pitch. When the horn is sounded as the train approaches, the number of

Fig. 12-7. The pitch of a sound depends on the frequency of the sound waves received by the ear.

vibrations per second reaching the listener is greater than the frequency of the sound produced. *The motion of the source of sound toward the listener* causes him to receive the vibrations at a faster rate than they are produced. Each vibration travels at the same speed, but each successive vibration has a shorter distance to travel. Thus, they arrive more frequently than they are sent out, and the pitch heard is correspondingly higher than the frequency of the sound produced.

When the horn is sounded as the train recedes, each successive vibration has farther to travel to the listener. The vibrations do not arrive as frequently as they are sent out, and the sound heard as the train goes away is of lower pitch.

★ It is possible to observe the Doppler effect when the source of sound is stationary and the listener moves toward it or away from it. The motion of the medium transmitting the sound also affects the frequency received by the listener. The relationship between the frequency of a source of sound and the frequency of the sound received by a listener when the source, the transmitting medium, and the listener are moving in the same or opposite directions along the same path is given by

$$\frac{f_L}{f_S} = \frac{v + v_M - v_L}{v + v_M - v_S}$$

in which f_L is the frequency observed by the listener, f_S is the frequency produced by the source, v is the velocity of sound in the transmitting medium, v_M is the velocity of the transmitting medium, v_L is the velocity of the listener, and v_S is the velocity of the source. In using this formula, the source must be to the left of the listener with velocities toward the right considered positive, and those toward the left considered negative. The sign of v is always positive.

17. The range of audible frequencies. When we wave our hands we produce compressions and rarefactions in the air, just as any vibrating object does. However, we do not produce audible sounds because the frequency of such vibrations is too low to affect our auditory nerves. Most persons cannot hear a sound whose frequency is below 20 cycles/sec. This frequency is the *lower limit of audibility* for most people.

There is also an *upper limit of audibility* because some vibrations are so rapid that the ear does not respond to them. The upper limit of the audio range for most people is about 20,000 cycles/sec. There is considerable variation in the ability of individuals to hear sounds of high or low frequency.

18. Inaudible sounds. In the past few years scientists have been actively studying the properties of sound waves having frequencies both below and above the audio range. Vibrations below 20 cycles/sec are in the *infrasonic range*. These sound waves have been used with some success in drill-

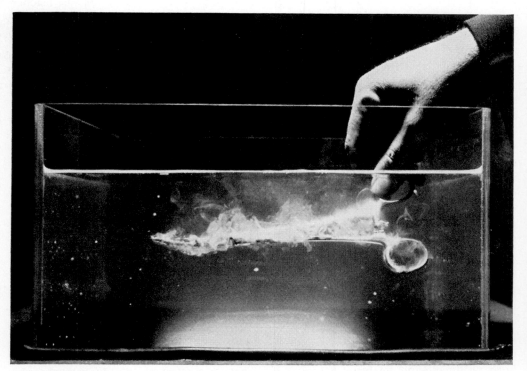

Fig. 12-8. Surgical forceps being cleaned in a transparent model of an ultrasonic washing machine. The sound waves form and collapse tiny bubbles on the surface of the forceps that loosen the dirt. (Acoustica Associates, Inc.)

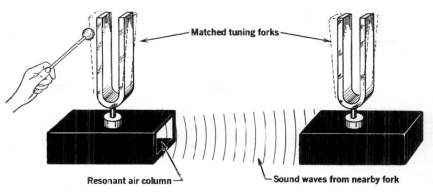

Fig. 12-9. Resonance between two matched tuning forks.

ing deep oil wells, because the low-frequency vibrations break up hard rock much more easily than the conventional rotary drill bits.

Sound waves above the audio range, beginning at about 20,000 cycles/sec, are in the *ultrasonic range*. The simplest application of these waves is a dog whistle. We cannot hear the sound it makes, but a dog can because his ears are sensitive to sounds of higher frequency. Today these ultrasonic waves are used to control automatic garage doors, and literally to shake the dirt out of your clothing. They are also used to detect flaws in metal castings or automobile tires, and tenderize frozen foods by breaking up tough fibers without changing the taste, color, or shape. Ultrasonic waves are also used in new kinds of nerve surgery, and in the production of almost permanent emulsions of heretofore immiscible materials.

Ultrasonic waves are produced by applying a high frequency alternating voltage to opposite faces of a quartz crystal. This causes the crystal to vibrate mechanically. Frequencies as high as 10 billion cycles/sec have been attained.

19. Forced vibrations. When we strike a tuning fork with a rubber hammer we cause it to vibrate. The vibration of a tuning fork is at a natural frequency which depends upon the fork's length, its thickness, and the material of which it is made.

When we strike a key on a piano, we set strings in vibration at a natural frequency, too; the only external forces which affect this natural rate of vibration are friction and gravitation. Suppose we set a tuning fork in vibration and then press its stem against the top of a table. The tone we hear becomes louder when the fork is in contact with the table because the fork *forces* the table top to vibrate with the same frequency. It does this even though the natural vibration rate of the table top is undoubtedly different from that of the fork. When the tuning fork is vibrating, a varying force transmitted through the stem causes the table top to vibrate with the same frequency. Since the table has a much larger vibrating area than the tuning fork, these *forced vibrations* produce a more intense sound.

A violin string stretched tightly between two clamps does not produce a very intense sound as it vibrates. When the same string is stretched across the bridge of a violin, however, the thin wood of the violin is forced to vibrate in response to the vibrations of the string; the intensity of the sound is increased by the forced vibrations of the violin. The sounding board of a piano acts in the same way to intensify the sound produced by the vibrations of its strings.

20. Resonance or sympathetic vibration. The two tuning forks shown in Fig.

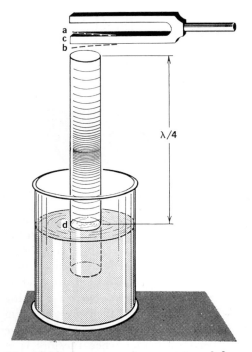

Fig. 12-10. A compression must travel down the tube during one-fourth cycle of the tuning fork and back during one-fourth cycle of the tuning fork to reinforce the sound.

12-9 have the same frequency. They are mounted on individual boxes (each with one end open) to increase the intensity of the sound through forced vibrations. Let us place these forks some distance apart, with the open ends of the boxes toward each other. Now let us set one fork in vibration, and after it has vibrated several seconds, touch its prongs to stop them. We now find that the other fork is vibrating weakly. The compressions and rarefactions of the sound waves produced in the air by the first tuning fork act on the second fork in a regular fashion, causing it to vibrate. Such action is called *resonance* or *sympathetic vibration.* A person who sings near a piano causes the strings which produce similar frequencies to vibrate. **Resonance** *occurs when the natural vibration rates of two objects are the same. It also occurs when the vibration rate of one of them is a multiple of the source.* Changing the

frequency of one of the mounted tuning forks by adding a weight to one of its prongs alters the conditions of the experiment and no resonance is evident; both forks must have the same frequency in order to produce sympathetic vibration.

21. Resonance in tubes. Let us hold a vibrating tuning fork over a cylinder as shown in Fig. 12-10. As we gradually add water to the tube, we find that there is a certain water level at which the sound is loudest. The sound wave reflected by the water surface meets the direct wave produced by the tuning fork exactly in phase. This causes the air column in the cylinder to vibrate sympathetically, or to resonate with the tuning fork, producing a more intense sound. During resonance, a compression of the reflected wave unites with a compression of the direct wave and a rarefaction of the reflected wave unites with a rarefaction of the direct wave. This uniting of two waves in phase amplifies the sound, just as the piling of the crest of one water wave upon the crest of another makes the resulting wave higher. When the tube is adjusted so that it reinforces sound waves, it acts as a *resonator.*

In Fig. 12-10, as the prong of the tuning fork goes down from c to b, the compression it forms travels from c to d in air. This compression is reflected and reaches c just as the prong returns to c. As the prong continues to move upward to a, it produces a compression. This compression, however, is formed from air already somewhat compressed by the simultaneous passing of the reflected wave. The result is a much higher degree of compression than the prong of the fork alone could produce. While the prong of the fork has been moving from c to a, a rarefaction was formed *beneath it,* and this rarefaction has traveled to d. There it is reflected and reaches c just as the prong returns to c. As the prong once again moves down from c to b, a rarefaction is formed *above it.* This rarefaction is being produced in air already rarefied by the reflected wave, and the combined rarefaction is greater than what the fork prong alone could produce. These more intense compressions and rarefactions formed above the prongs of the tuning fork produce sound waves of higher energy which are therefore louder.

The cycle of the tuning fork prong which produces one sound wave is from c to b to c to a and back to c again. We have seen that the sound wave in the tube travels the distance from c to d while the prong of the fork moves from c to b. When the fork is making one-fourth of a cycle, the sound wave travels the length of the tube; while the fork makes a cycle, the sound wave can travel a distance four times the length of the tube. This distance, or four times the length of the tube, is therefore the length of one sound wave. Conversely, the length of the tube is one-fourth the wavelength of the sound. *A closed tube produces the best possible resonance when its length is one-fourth that of the sound wave which it reinforces.* (Actually it is slightly less than one-fourth of a wavelength, because a correction must be made for the diameter of the tube.) Expressed as a formula:

$$\lambda = 4(l + 0.4d)$$

in which λ is the wavelength, l is the length of a closed tube, and d is the diameter of the tube.

When a vibrating fork is held over an *open* tube, resonance is also produced. Experiments show that such a tube produces the *best resonance when its length is about one-half* the wavelength of the sound it reinforces. The formula is

$$\lambda = 2(l + 0.8d)$$

in which λ is the wave length, l is the length of the open tube, and d is the diameter of the tube.

22. Sound wave interference. If you drop two pebbles simultaneously into a smooth pool, each produces its own set of

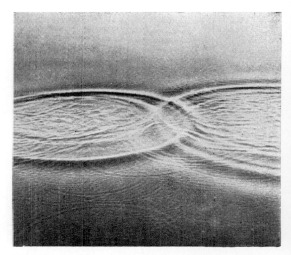

Fig. 12-11. Wave patterns formed by water when two pebbles are dropped into a still pool. Notice the effects of constructive and destructive interference.

ripples. Where two crests, one from each set, cross each other, the water is piled up higher than in either crest alone; where two troughs cross each other, an even deeper trough is formed; if a crest crosses a trough, the water level is hardly disturbed. A similar thing happens to sound waves; the experiment with resonance in tubes shows that the meeting in phase of two sound waves produces a louder sound. If two sound waves meet out of phase they should cancel each other; either a much quieter sound or no sound at all should be produced. This does happen in the "dead spots" in a large room or auditorium; here, however, because of the number of echoes, there usually is not complete silence.

When one sound wave is superimposed on another, we have interference of sound. If, as in the resonating tube, the reflected wave is added to the effect of the direct wave, we have constructive interference. When two waves tend to cancel each other's effects, the interference is destructive.

23. Beats. Let us imagine that there are two sound waves traveling in the same direction through air, or through some other medium. One of these waves, 1.20 m long, is represented by the graph (*A*) in

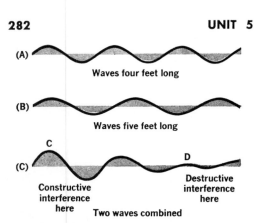

(A)

Waves four feet long

(B)

Waves five feet long

C

(C)

D

Constructive interference here   **Destructive interference here**

Two waves combined

Fig. 12-12. Constructive and destructive interference of waves.

Fig. 12-12. The other wave is 1.50 m long. Its graph is (B). At some places the two waves are in almost the same phase, while in other places they are in almost the opposite phase. The straight line represents the mid-point of the wave motion in each case.

A composite curve, Fig. 12-12(C), is plotted by using the resultants of all the

crests and troughs of the two sets of waves. At point C, the crests which represent sound condensations meet and the *sound is intensified;* at point D, a condensation coincides with a rarefaction, and the *sound is diminished*, perhaps resulting in silence. When two tuning forks of unequal frequency are sounded at the same time, the sound is alternately louder and softer; the rapidly fluctuating constructive and destructive interference that was noted in Fig. 12-12(C) occurs. *This outburst of sound followed by an interval of comparative silence is called a **beat.*** The number of beats produced per second is equal to the difference between the frequencies of the two vibrating bodies. For example, if tuning forks having frequencies of 256 and 260 cycles/sec are sounded simultaneously, 4 beats/sec will be heard. If the frequencies of the forks were 256 and 252 cycles/sec, 4 beats/sec would occur again.

ummary

Energy may be transferred by a wave, which is a disturbance which moves through a medium. A wave in which the particles vibrate at right angles to the path along which the wave travels is a transverse wave; a wave in which the particles vibrate to and fro along the path which the wave travels is a longitudinal wave. Waves have common characteristics such as speed, phase, frequency, period, wavelength, and amplitude. Common properties of waves include reflection—turning back at the boundary of the transmitting medium, refraction—changing direction on passing from one medium to another of different density, interference—combining the disturbances of two wave motions, and diffraction—bending of a wave around obstacles in its path.

Sound is the series of disturbances in matter which an ear interprets as sound; it also applies to similar disturbances which are above and below the normal range of human hearing. Sounds are produced by vibrating matter, and require an elastic material medium for transmission. The intensity of a sound is the rate at which the sound energy flows through a unit area. The effect of the intensity of sound waves on the ears is loudness. The pitch of a sound depends on the frequency of the sound which the ear receives.

The variation of the pitch heard from a moving source of sound is called the Doppler effect. Resonance occurs when the natural vibration rates of two objects are the same or when the vibration rate of one of them is a multiple of the source. When one sound wave is superimposed on another, interference of sound results.

TERMS TO DEFINE

amplitude	intensity level	sound
beat	longitudinal wave	speed of a wave
compression	loudness	speed of sound
constructive interference	lower limit of audibility	sympathetic vibrations
crest	period	threshold of hearing
cycle	phase	transmitting medium
destructive interference	pitch	for sound
diffraction	production of sound	transverse wave
Doppler effect	rarefaction	trough
forced vibrations	reflection	ultrasonic range
frequency	refraction	upper limit of audibility
infrasonic range	resonance	wave
intensity	resonator	wavelength

QUESTIONS

A   1. In what ways may energy be transferred?

2. What is a wave?

3. (a) Distinguish between transverse and longitudinal waves. (b) Give an example of each.

4. For wave motion, define (a) speed; (b) phase; (c) frequency; (d) period; (e) wavelength; (f) amplitude.

5. How is the speed of a wave related to its frequency and wavelength?

6. List the common properties of waves and give an illustration of each.

7. What is the difference between the physiological and physical definitions of sound?

8. How are sounds produced?

9. Why is sound not transmitted through a vacuum?

10. (a) What is the speed of sound in air at the ice point in both the metric and English systems of measurement? (b) What is the rate of increase of speed with rise in temperature in both systems?

11. Distinguish between intensity and loudness.

12. Distinguish between frequency and pitch.

13. The engineer of a Diesel locomotive sounds the horn as his train approaches you. How does the pitch you hear compare with the pitch he hears?

14. (a) What is the range of audio frequencies? (b) What name is applied to sound vibrations below the audio range? (c) What name is applied to sound vibrations above the audio range?

15. Why does a tuning fork sound louder when its stem is pressed against a table top?

16. What conditions are necessary to produce resonance?

17. To produce the best resonance, how must the length of a closed tube compare with the wavelength of the sound?

18. To produce the best resonance, how must the length of an open tube compare with the wavelength of the sound?

19. In sound waves, what is (a) constructive interference; (b) destructive interference? (c) What are beats?

B   20. (a) What is a particle wave? (b) What type of medium is required for the passage of a particle wave?

21. What difference is there in the media required for the passage of transverse and longitudinal waves?

22. Describe how a vibrating hacksaw blade sets up longitudinal waves in the air surrounding it, and thereby transfers its energy to the surrounding air.

23. (a) How does variation in the work done in setting a hacksaw blade in vibration affect the sound produced by the blade? (b) How does variation in the length of the vibrating portion of the hacksaw blade affect the sound?

24. (a) Why is sound better transmitted through solids than through liquids and gases? (b) Why is sound better transmitted through liquids than through gases?

25. Using Fig. 12-6, describe how the human ear receives sound waves and transforms them into nerve impulses which are sent to the brain.

26. Why is the intensity level of sound measured on a logarithmic scale?

PROBLEMS

A **1.** (*a*) What is the speed of sound in ft/sec at 72° F? (*b*) How many seconds are required for sound to travel 1.00 mi at this speed?

2. What time is required for sound to travel 5.00 km if the temperature is 10.0° C?

3. A tuning fork has a frequency of 256 cycles/sec. What is the wavelength, in feet, of the sound produced when the temperature is 82° F?

4. What is the wavelength, in meters, of the sound produced by a tuning fork which has a frequency of 320. cycles/sec? The temperature is 15° C.

5. At 52° F a tuning fork produces resonance when held over a closed tube 12.0 in. long and 1.0 in. in diameter. What is the frequency of the fork?

6. What is the frequency of a tuning fork which resonates with an open tube 25.0 cm long and 2.0 cm diameter when the temperature is 20.° C?

7. What is the length of an open tube 1.5 in. in diameter which produces resonance with a tuning fork which has a frequency of 128 cycles/sec? The temperature is 68° F.

8. A tuning fork which vibrates at the rate of 384 cycles/sec produces resonance with a closed tube 20.0 cm long and 4.0 cm in diameter. What is the speed of sound?

9. A tuning fork has a frequency of 440. cycles/sec. If another tuning fork of slightly lower pitch is sounded at the same time, 5 beats/sec are heard. What is the frequency of the second tuning fork?

10. How many beats/sec will be heard when a string with a frequency of 288 cycles/sec is plucked simultaneously with another string which has a frequency of 320. cycles/sec?

B **11.** The echo of a ship's fog horn, reflected from an iceberg, is heard 5.0 sec after being sounded. The temperature is −10.° C. How many meters away is the iceberg? (Remember that the sound must travel to the iceberg and back to the ship during the 5.0 sec interval.)

12. A man drops a stone into a mine shaft 250. m deep. The temperature is 5.0° C. How many seconds pass before he hears the stone strike the bottom?

13. A rifle shot is fired in a valley with parallel walls. The echo from one wall is heard in 2.0 sec and the echo from the other wall is heard 2.0 sec later. The temperature is 20.° C. How many kilometers wide is the valley?

14. A man throws a stone over a cliff and hears it strike the rocks at the bottom after 8.00 sec. The temperature is 25° C. How many meters high is the cliff?

15. A Diesel locomotive approaches a crossing at 60.0 mi/hr. The horn has a frequency of 288 cycles/sec, the temperature is 60.° F, and the wind is blowing in the direction the locomotive is moving at 10.0 mi/hr. What is the frequency of the sound heard by the watchman at the crossing?

16. What is the drop in frequency of the sound a listener hears as a train, with its horn sounding, passes at 90.0 mi/hr? The frequency of the horn is 320. cycles/sec, the temperature is 85° F, and the wind is blowing in the direction opposite to that in which the train is traveling, at 5.0 mi/hr.

17. What is the intensity level in decibels of a sound which has an intensity of 10^{-11} watt/cm²?

18. What is the intensity in watt/cm² of a sound which has an intensity level of 30. decibels?

RESEARCH ON YOUR OWN

1. Look up pictures of ripple tanks. Design one of your own and make it. Use the tank to show the phenomena of reflection, interference, and diffraction of waves. Can you measure the wavelength and frequency?

2. If you have access to an oscilloscope, you can show the beats between two tuning forks. Connect the output terminals of an amplifier to the oscilloscope while the forks are in front of a microphone.

3. Look up Kundt's experiment for measuring the speed of sound in a metal. Try to extend the experiment to find the speed of sound in carbon dioxide by filling the tube with this gas.

4. Obtain one of the "twirling bird" whistles. How does it illustrate the Doppler effect?

CHAPTER 13
SOUND AND MUSIC

1. The difference between musical tones and noise. In Chapter 12, Section 15, we described the use of a siren disk to show that the pitch of a sound depends on its frequency. When a stream of air is directed toward each of the regularly spaced rows of holes while the disk is being rotated at constant speed, the sounds produced are pleasant and of steady pitch. These are *musical tones*. The strings of a violin produce musical tones when bowed or plucked. *Musical tones are sounds produced by matter which vibrates in regular fashion.*

On most laboratory siren disks, the row of holes closest to the center is irregularly spaced. A stream of air directed against this row of holes makes an unpleasant, jarring sound. *Sound waves produced by irregular vibrations in matter are called **noise.** When you strike a desk with a ruler, scrape your feet across the floor, or drop a drinking glass, you produce irregular vibrations; the resulting sounds are noise.

2. The diatonic scale. A stream of air directed *successively* against the four rows of regularly spaced holes of a siren disk produces sounds corresponding to the notes *do, mi, sol, do'* of a musical scale. If air flows through the first three of these rows of holes *simultaneously*, sounding *do, mi,* and *sol* together, the combination is a *major chord,* or *major triad.* As these three rows have 24, 30, and 36 holes respectively,

VOCABULARY

Chromatic scale. A diatonic scale with five added half tones.
Diatonic scale. A musical scale built up of three major chords.
Fundamental. The lowest pitch produced by a musical tone source.
Harmonics. The fundamental and the tones whose frequencies are whole number multiples of the fundamental.
Major chord. The combination of three tones whose vibration ratios are 4, 5, and 6.
Musical tone. A sound produced by matter which vibrates in regular fashion.
Noise. Sound produced by irregular vibrations in matter.
Quality. The property of sound waves which depends on the number of harmonics present and on their prominence.
Tempered scale. A musical scale with twelve equal frequency ratio intervals between the successive notes of an octave.

DIATONIC SCALE									
Syllable	do	re	mi	fa	sol	la	ti	do	re
Letter	C	D	E	F	G	A	B	C'	D'
Frequency (cycles/sec)	256	288	320	341	384	426	480	512	576
Relative frequency	24	27	30	32	36	40	45	48	54
Chord (tonic)	4		5		6				
Chord (dominant)					4		5		6
Chord (subdominant)				4		5		6	

24, 30, and 36 are the relative frequencies of the musical tones. Dividing these frequencies by 6 results in the simpler ratios of 4, 5, and 6. *Any three tones whose vibration ratios are 4, 5, and 6 produce a* **major chord** *when sounded together.* The major **diatonic** (dy-uh-*ton*-ik) **scale** *is built up of three major chords.* You can see how this is done by studying the table of frequencies above.

Physicists use 256 cycles/sec as the frequency of middle C. The table above shows the frequencies of tones that would be produced by the white keys of a piano tuned to this frequency, in a little more than an octave above middle C. The frequencies for C, E, and G have ratios of 4, 5, and 6, forming a major chord. Another major chord is formed by the notes G, B, and D', and a third by the notes F, A, and C'.

The note C', which is one octave above middle C, has a frequency just twice that of C. Any tone having a frequency twice that of another is an octave higher; doubling the frequency raises the pitch one octave. The table shows that the frequency of D is $\frac{288}{256}$, or $\frac{9}{8}$, times that of C. The frequency of E is $\frac{320}{256}$, or $\frac{5}{4}$ that of C. F is $\frac{341}{256}$, or $\frac{4}{3}$; G is $\frac{384}{256}$, or $\frac{3}{2}$; A is $\frac{426}{256}$, or $\frac{5}{3}$; and B is $\frac{480}{256}$, or $\frac{15}{8}$. C' is $\frac{512}{256}$, or $\frac{2}{1}$. See Fig. 13-1.

In the next octave, D' is $\frac{576}{512}$, or $\frac{9}{8}$, times the frequency of C'. In the same way we can find the frequency of any note in this octave by multiplying the frequency of C' by the ratios we found in the first octave. For example, the frequency of E' is $\frac{5}{4} \times 512$ cycles/sec, or 640 cycles/sec. This frequency is also double the frequency of E, 320 cycles/sec, since E' is an octave higher than E.

★ **3. The chromatic scale.** Suppose we construct a scale using D, with a frequency of 288 cycles/sec, as the first note. To find the frequencies of the notes in this scale, we multiply 288 cycles/sec in turn by $\frac{9}{8}$, $\frac{5}{4}$, $\frac{4}{3}$, $\frac{3}{2}$, $\frac{5}{3}$, $\frac{15}{8}$, and 2. The table on the opposite page shows how the D scale compares with the C scale.

In some cases the frequencies of notes on the two scales are equal, while others vary so slightly that the difference is not very noticeable to the ear. However, in the frequencies of F and C' there is considerable variation. The difference is so great that two new notes, F♯ (F sharp) and C♯, are used by a musician when he plays in the key of D.

How does the frequency of F♯ compare with that of F? Simplifying their frequency ratio, $\frac{360}{341}$, gives approximately $\frac{25}{24}$; the vibration rate of F♯ is thus about $\frac{25}{24}$ that of F. The note F♯ is said to be a half tone higher than F. If a note in the *chromatic scale* is to be lowered a half tone or flatted, the frequency of the flatted tone is $\frac{24}{25}$ of the original tone.

Building up a series of scales using each of the notes in the C scale as the first note requires at least five new notes, or tones,

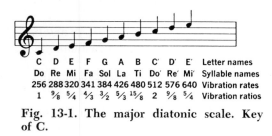

C	D	E	F	G	A	B	C'	D'	E'	Letter names
Do	Re	Mi	Fa	Sol	La	Ti	Do'	Re'	Mi'	Syllable names
256	288	320	341	384	426	480	512	576	640	Vibration rates
1	$\frac{9}{8}$	$\frac{5}{4}$	$\frac{4}{3}$	$\frac{3}{2}$	$\frac{5}{3}$	$\frac{15}{8}$	2	$\frac{9}{8}$	$\frac{5}{4}$	Vibration ratios

Fig. 13-1. The major diatonic scale. Key of C.

	C	D	E	F	G	A	B	C′	D′
Key of C	256	288	320	341	384	426	480	512	576
Key of D		288	324	360	384	432	480	540	576

in each octave to take care of serious variations in frequency between the scales. In
other words, *a chromatic scale is a diatonic
scale with five half tones added.*

★ **4. The tempered scale.** In building
up a chromatic scale we found that there
are five serious variations in frequency
between the notes we need and those provided in a diatonic scale. Further comparison of the calculated frequencies shows
many cases where there is a difference of
about 4 to 6 cycles/sec. It must also be
recognized that in the chromatic scale
there is a difference in frequency between
C♯ and D♭ (D flat): C♯ = $\frac{25}{24} \times 256$
cycles/sec = 266 cycles/sec; D♭ = $\frac{24}{25} \times 288$
cycles/sec = 276 cycles/sec. Building all
the possible scales, using C, C♯, D♭, D,
D♯, E♭, E, and so on, as first tones, requires so many different frequencies that
an octave would have about 70 notes. It
would be highly impractical, if not impossible, to play a piano or an organ having
70 keys in each octave.

The scale commonly used for tuning
and playing musical instruments is a compromise scale, one in which there is a constant ratio of frequencies between successive notes. This scale comprises approximations of the eight notes from C to C′ and
the five additional notes that were found
absolutely necessary in the chromatic
scale. This gives a *tempered scale with
twelve intervals between the successive notes.*
Since the frequency of C′ must be twice
that of C, the ratio between the frequencies
of successive notes is the twelfth root of 2;
$\sqrt[12]{2} = 1.05946$. Thus the frequency of any
note in the tempered scale can be obtained
by multiplying the frequency of the preceding note by 1.05946. This equally
tempered scale is used in playing most
musical instruments. In playing certain

stringed instruments, however, the player
controls very precisely the pitch of each
string, and a skillful violinist, for example,
may use the true intervals of the diatonic
scale. A comparison of the two scales is
given in Fig. 13-2.

**5. Physicists' pitch differs from musi-
cians' pitch.** The middle C tuning forks
used in physics laboratories have a frequency of 256 cycles/sec. We used this
basic frequency for our illustrations in calculating the frequencies for the tones in
the diatonic, chromatic, and tempered
scales. When C has a frequency of 256
cycles/sec, the frequency of A above
middle C is 427 cycles/sec.

The American Federation of Musicians
has adopted 440 cycles/sec as the frequency of A, and the actual scales used by
musicians are built around this frequency.

CHROMATIC SCALE		TEMPERED SCALE	
C	256	C	256
C♯	266.6	C♯ or D♭	271.2
D♭	276.5		
D	288	D	287.3
D♯	300	D♯ or E♭	304.4
E♭	307.2		
E	320	E	322.5
F	341.3	F	341.7
F♯	355.5	F♯ or G♭	362
G♭	368.6		
G	384	G	383.6
G♯	400	G♯ or A♭	406.4
A♭	409.5		
A	426.6	A	430.5
A♯	444.4	A♯ or B♭	456.1
B♭	460.8		
B	480	B	483.3
C′	512	C′	512

**Fig. 13-2. The chromatic scale compared
with the tempered scale. Key of C.**

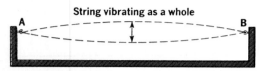

Fig. 13-3. A string vibrating as a whole sounds its fundamental.

The National Bureau of Standards regularly broadcasts a musical tone of 440 cycles/sec on a shortwave radio frequency of 5000 kilocycles. Comparing a C tuning fork from the physics laboratory with the middle C note on a properly tuned piano will show the tuning fork to have a lower pitch.

6. Harmony and discord. Some pairs of keys struck on the piano produce pleasing tone combinations; these tones produce *harmony*. Such a combination might be the notes C and E. However, if two adjacent white keys, like C and D, are struck, the sound is not so pleasant; these tones are *discordant*. The two combinations of tones produce different reactions.

We stated earlier that beats are heard when two sounds of different frequency are produced simultaneously, and that the number of beats per second is equal to the difference in frequency. When C and E are sounded together, 64 beats/sec result. These beats are close enough together to be undetectable to the ear; the sound is harmonious. When C and D are struck at the same time, there are 32 beats/sec; this number of beats has an unpleasant effect and produces considerable discord.

In general, two tones which produce between 10 and 50 beats/sec are discordant.

7. Fundamental tones. Let us stretch a piece of piano wire about a meter in length between two clamps, drawing it tight enough to vibrate when plucked. If plucked in the middle, the wire vibrates *as a whole*, like that shown in Fig. 13-3. When an *entire wire or string vibrates back and forth as a single unit*, it produces its lowest pitch, a pitch called its *fundamental tone*, or **fundamental**.

Physicists have elaborated on this simple apparatus of a wire stretched between two clamps, to make it into the *sonometer* shown in Fig. 13-4. This consists of two or more wires or strings stretched over a sounding board, which intensifies the sounds produced by the wires. Since the strings may vary in diameter, tension, length, or material, the instrument is useful for testing the frequency of strings and for showing how they vibrate.

8. Harmonics. A wire or string may vibrate as an entire unit, but may also vibrate in other ways. Let us divide the length of a sonometer string into eight equal parts and place V-shaped paper riders at positions 1, 2, 3, 4, and 5, as in Fig. 13-5, top. If a bridge is placed under the string at *A*, and the string is bowed at *B*, the paper riders at positions 1, 3, and 5 are thrown off. Those at 2 and 4 are not disturbed. Evidently the string is not vibrating as a whole, or all the riders would be thrown off. Actually, the string is vibrating in four equal parts, or seg-

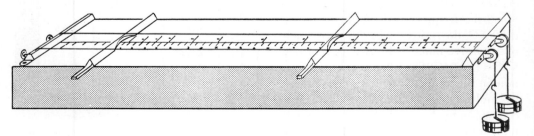

Fig. 13-4. The sonometer is used to study the laws of strings.

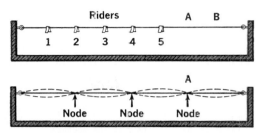

Fig. 13-5. Top: The paper riders show that a string vibrates in segments. Bottom: The vibration pattern of the string. Notice the loops and nodes.

ments, as in Fig. 13-5, bottom. The places between the segments where there is no vibration are called *nodes*. Riders 1, 3, and 5 are at the midpoints of the vibrating segments, or *loops*, and are thrown off. Riders 2 and 4 are at the nodes. The string vibrates in this fashion because the first node was created at *A*, causing nodes to be formed at the other two positions.

When a string is plucked or bowed near one end, it may vibrate in several segments.

In the experiment just described, the vibrating segment is one-fourth the length of the string. As will be shown in Section 10 of this chapter, the pitch of this segment is two octaves above the fundamental, so its frequency is four times that of the fundamental. If the string vibrates in only two segments, a tone one octave above the fundamental is heard. Its frequency is twice that of the fundamental. *The fundamental and the tones whose frequencies are whole number multiples of the fundamental are called* **harmonics.** *The fundamental is the first harmonic,* the tone whose frequency is twice that of the fundamental is the *second harmonic,* the tone whose frequency is three times that of the fundamental is the *third harmonic,* and so on.

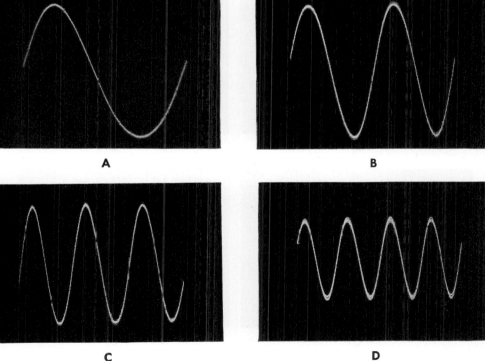

Fig. 13-6. Oscillograms of (*A*) a fundamental, (*B*) the second harmonic, (*C*) the third harmonic, and (*D*) the fourth harmonic. (Hugh Lineback)

**String vibrating as a whole and
in segments at the same time**

Fig. 13-7. Harmonics in addition to the fundamental are produced when a string vibrates in two or more segments.

Let us tune a string so that when it vibrates as a whole it produces C, 256 cycles/sec, as its fundamental; an oscillogram of such a fundamental is shown in Fig. 13-6(A). If the string vibrates in two segments, the second harmonic of C, with a frequency of 2×256 cycles/sec, or 512 cycles/sec, is heard; this is C', an octave above C. See Fig. 13-6(B). The third harmonic of C, heard when the string vibrates in three segments, has a frequency of 3×256 cycles/sec, or 768 cycles/sec; this

is G'. See Fig. 13-6(C). The fourth harmonic is produced when the string vibrates in four segments at a frequency of 4×256 cycles/sec, or 1024 cycles/sec; the note is C''. See Fig. 13-6(D). The fifth harmonic of C is E'', whose frequency is 5×256 cycles/sec, or 1280 cycles/sec.

9. The quality of sound. It is not difficult to pick out the sounds produced by different instruments in an orchestra, even though they may be producing the same tone with equal intensity. The difference is a property of sound called *quality*.

If the string of a sonometer is touched *very lightly* in the middle while it is bowed, it can be made to vibrate in two segments and as a whole at the same time. See Fig. 13-7. The fundamental is audible, but added to it is the sound of the second harmonic. The combination is richer and

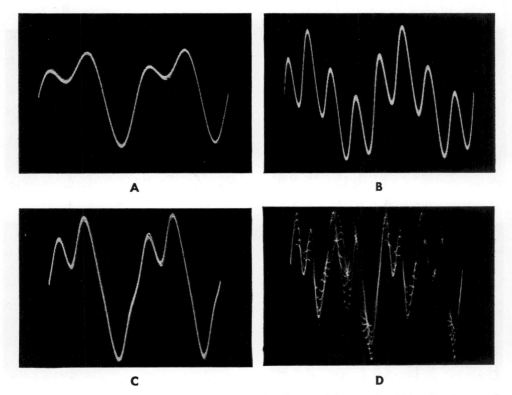

A

B

C

D

Fig. 13-8. Oscillograms of (A) a fundamental and second harmonic, (B) a fundamental and fourth harmonic, (C) the sound of a French horn, and (D) the sound of a trumpet. (Hugh Lineback)

fuller; the quality of the sound has been improved by the addition of the second harmonic to the fundamental. See Fig. 13-8(*A*). *The quality of a sound depends on the number of harmonics present and on their prominence.* When stringed instruments are played, they are bowed, plucked, or struck near one end instead of in the middle. This tends to produce other harmonics which blend with the fundamental and give a richer sound. See Fig. 13-8(*B*).

The quality of the tones produced by orchestral instruments varies greatly. For example, the tone produced by a French horn consists almost entirely of the fundamental and the second harmonic. You can readily see this by comparing Figs. 13-8(*A*) and 13-8(*C*). The tonal quality of an instrument like the trumpet, however, is due to the great intensity of its high-frequency harmonics. See Fig. 13-8(*D*).

10. Variation in frequency of strings. *The frequency of a string varies with its length, diameter, tension, and density.* The strings of a piano produce tones with a wide range of frequencies. If we examine these strings we find great differences among them. The strings that produce the low frequency tones are long, thick, and loose, while the strings that produce the high-frequency tones are short, thin, and tight. One string produces a loud enough tone for the low notes, but three strings are needed to produce high notes of comparable loudness.

Use of a sonometer has made clear several facts about conditions affecting the frequency of vibrating strings. These are often called the *laws of strings.*

1. Law of lengths. When a musician wishes to raise the pitch produced by a stringed instrument, he may shorten the vibrating length of the string. A violinist shortens the vibrating length of the A string about 2.5 cm when he wishes to produce the note B. *The frequency of a string is inversely proportional to its length, if its diameter, density, and tension are constant.*

$$\frac{f}{f'} = \frac{l'}{l}$$

Here f and f' are the frequencies corresponding to the lengths l and l'. See the Sample Problem below.

Sample Problem

If the **D** string of a violin is 30.0 cm long, how much must it be shortened to produce the note **E**?

Solution

The frequency of D is 288 cycles/sec; that of E is 320. cycles/sec.

$$\frac{f}{f'} = \frac{l'}{l}$$

$$l' = \frac{fl}{f'}$$

$$l' = \frac{288 \text{ cycles/sec} \times 30.0 \text{ cm}}{320. \text{ cycles/sec}}$$

$$l' = 27.0 \text{ cm}$$

30.0 cm − 27.0 cm = 3.0 cm, the amount by which the string must be shortened

2. Law of diameters. In a piano, the strings which produce the higher frequencies have smaller diameters. This is also true of other stringed instruments like the cello and the harp. A string with a diameter of 0.1 cm will vibrate twice as fast as a similar string 0.2 cm in diameter. *The frequency of a string is inversely proportional to its diameter, if its length, density, and tension are constant.*

$$\frac{f}{f'} = \frac{d'}{d}$$

Here f and f' are the frequencies corresponding to the diameters d and d'.

3. Law of tensions. When a violin is tuned, the strings are tightened to increase their frequency, or loosened to decrease it. Experiments have proved that *the frequency of a string is directly proportional to the square root of the tension on the string, if all the other factors are constant.*

$$\frac{f}{f'} = \frac{\sqrt{F}}{\sqrt{F'}}$$

Here f and f' are the frequencies corresponding to the tensions F and F'. See the Sample Problem below.

4. Law of densities. The denser a string is, the slower it vibrates. The strings which produce the low frequency tones of a piano are thick; the lowest strings are even wound with copper wire to make them vibrate more slowly. *The frequency of a string is inversely proportional to the square root of its density, if other factors are constant.*

$$\frac{f}{f'} = \frac{\sqrt{D'}}{\sqrt{D}}$$

Here f and f' are the frequencies corresponding to the densities D and D'.

11. Stringed instruments. Many musical instruments use vibrating strings to produce sounds. The basic part of a symphony orchestra is the string section, composed of violins, violas, cellos, and string basses. The piano, harp, guitar, and ukulele are other stringed instruments. Their vibrating strings do not produce very intense sounds, but each instrument has a sounding board to intensify the sound. Strings for such instruments are made from a variety of materials, and in many lengths and thicknesses. They are mounted across the sounding board and tuned to proper pitch by adjusting the tension. In many

Sample Problem

A string stretched with a force of 50.0 nt produces the note C. What force must be applied to this string to make it produce the note C′?

Solution

The frequency of C is 256 cycles/sec; that of C′ is 512 cycles/sec.

$$\frac{f}{f'} = \frac{\sqrt{F}}{\sqrt{F'}}$$

$$F' = \frac{f'^2 F}{f^2}$$

$$F' = \frac{(512 \text{ cycles/sec})^2 \times 50.0 \text{ nt}}{(256 \text{ cycles/sec})^2}$$

$$F' = 200. \text{ nt}$$

Closed pipe   Open pipe

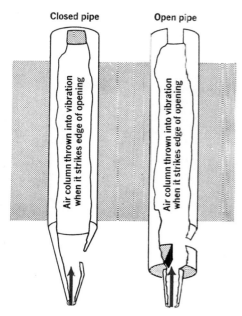

Fig. 13-9. A vibrating air column in an organ pipe produces sound.

stringed instruments the pitch produced by a single string must be varied as the instrument is played. The vibrating length of a string is shortened when the string is held at some point by the player's finger.

12. Organ pipes. The air blown into an organ pipe is usually directed against one edge of an opening in the pipe, causing the air within the pipe to vibrate. See Fig. 13-9. The wavelength of these vibrations, and consequently their frequency, is determined by the length of the pipe, as we learned from our study of resonance in tubes. *A closed organ pipe produces a sound whose wavelength is four times the length of the pipe.* A closed pipe one foot long will produce a sound wave four feet long. *An open pipe produces a sound wave which has a wavelength twice the length of the pipe. An open pipe produces a tone an octave higher than a closed pipe of the same length.*

In a set of organ pipes for the notes of an octave, the length of the pipes must be inversely proportional to the vibration ratios given in Section 2 because sounds of higher frequency have shorter wave-

lengths. The lengths of the pipes used to sound the eight notes of one octave must have the following ratios: $1, \frac{8}{9}, \frac{4}{5}, \frac{3}{4}, \frac{2}{3}, \frac{3}{5}, \frac{8}{15},$ and $\frac{1}{2}$. *The frequency of the tone produced by a pipe varies inversely with its length.*

13. The tones produced by pipes. When a pipe is blown gently, its fundamental is usually the only tone produced, but harder blowing may add other harmonics to this fundamental. If the pipe is closed, there will always be a node at the closed end, and a loop at the other end. In addition to the fundamental, the only harmonics possible with closed pipes are therefore those whose frequencies are *odd* multiples of the fundamental. Thus, the first three harmonics sounded by a closed C organ pipe are C, G', and E'', its first, third, and fifth harmonics.

In open pipes there is a node in the middle and a loop at each end. With these pipes the entire series of harmonics is possible. The first three harmonics sounded by an open C organ pipe are C, C', and G', its first, second, and third harmonics.

When a hole is bored in a pipe, the effect is almost the same as cutting the pipe off at that point, since a loop is produced at the opening. Wind instruments of nearly all kinds have several holes so that the length of the vibrating air column may be varied to produce sounds of varying pitch. The opening of such holes is controlled by the fingers directly, or by keys or valves.

14. Wind instruments. A vibrating air jet is the source of the sound in many wind instruments. The air jet may be produced by a vibrating reed, as in the harmonica, accordion, clarinet, and saxophone. The pitch of a harmonica or accordion is altered by setting different reeds vibrating; these instruments have a separate reed for each tone they produce. The pitch of a clarinet or saxophone depends primarily on the length of the vibrating air column within the instrument.

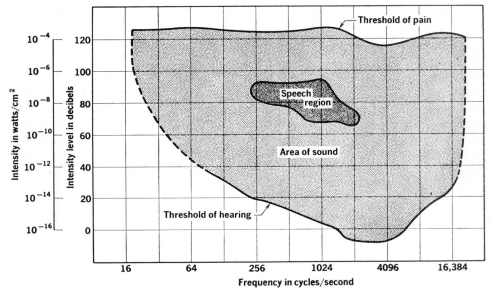

Fig. 13-10. The range of audibility of the human ear.

In the flute, fife, and piccolo the vibrating air jet is produced in the same manner as in the organ pipe, a stream of air being directed against the edge of an opening near one end of the instrument. The pitch is regulated by the length of the vibrating air column and by the method of blowing.

In the trumpet, trombone, and other types of horns, the lips of the player vibrate. The frequency of the sound produced depends upon the speed of vibration of the player's lips and upon the length of the instrument tube. The latter may be controlled by valves, or, as in the case of the trombone, by a slide.

15. Vibrating membranes. In some musical instruments, such as the tambourine, bass drum, and kettle drum, the vibrating part is a membrane. The human voice is also produced by the vibration of membranes. The vocal cords are really two folds of muscular membrane stretched across the larynx. Their tension is controlled by muscular contraction, changes in tension producing changes in the pitch of the voice. When we speak, we alter or modulate the sounds produced by the vocal

cords by using our tongue, palate, teeth, and lips to form the various vowel and consonant sounds. The quality of the voice depends on the harmonics which are made prominent by resonance in the air passages of the respiratory organs.

16. The sensitivity of the human ear. The graph in Fig. 13-10 shows the characteristics sound waves must have in order to be heard. Since the graph is a composite of the results obtained by testing many persons, the hearing characteristics of individuals may vary somewhat from those shown.

The lower curve, the *threshold of hearing,* indicates the minimum intensity level at which sound waves of various frequencies can be heard. Observe that the lowest intensity which will produce audible sound is for frequencies between 2000 and 4000 cycles/sec. The ear is most sensitive in this frequency range. At the lower and higher limits of audibility the intensities of sound waves must be higher.

The upper curve, the threshold of pain, indicates the upper intensity level for audible sounds. Sounds which are more intense produce the sensation of pain rather than hearing.

The graph shows the frequency limits for the audio range to be between 20 and 20,000 cycles/sec. The intensity limits in the region of maximum sensitivity are between 0 and 120 decibels, corresponding to intensities of from 10^{-16} watt/cm² to 10^{-4} watt/cm².

17. Graphic representation of sound waves. The frequency of the sound waves produced by a tuning fork may be measured in a high school physics laboratory by means of a *vibrograph*. This is essentially a tuning fork with a stylus attached to one prong. The stylus traces the vibrations of the fork on a piece of glass coated with whiting.

The *cathode-ray oscilloscope* shows on a screen a visual pattern of sound waves which a microphone has transformed into electric impulses.

ummary

A musical tone is the sound produced by matter which vibrates in regular fashion, while noise is the sound produced by matter which vibrates in irregular fashion.

A major chord consists of tones whose frequencies are in the ratio of 4, 5, and 6. The major diatonic scale is built up of three major chords; the chromatic scale has five additional half tones. The tempered scale has twelve equal frequency ratio intervals between the successive notes in an octave.

The lowest tone produced by a musical tone source is the fundamental. The fundamental and the tones whose frequencies are whole number multiples of the fundamental are called harmonics. The quality of a sound depends on the number of harmonics present and on their prominence.

The frequency of a vibrating string is inversely proportional to its length, its diameter, and the square root of its density; it is directly proportional to the square root of the tension.

A closed organ pipe produces a fundamental whose wavelength is four times the length of the pipe and harmonics which are odd multiples of the fundamental. An open organ pipe produces a fundamental which has a wavelength twice the length of the pipe and the entire series of harmonics.

The threshold of hearing is the minimum intensity level for hearing sound waves of various frequencies. The threshold of pain is the upper intensity level for audible sounds. The frequency limits for the audio range are 20 to 20,000 cycles/sec; the intensity level limits are 0 to 120 decibels.

TERMS TO DEFINE

chromatic scale	law of diameters	noise
diatonic scale	law of lengths	octave
discord	law of tensions	quality
fundamental	loop	sonometer
harmonics	major chord	tempered scale
harmony	musical tone	threshold of hearing
law of densities	node	threshold of pain

QUESTIONS

A **1.** How do the vibrations of a source which produces a musical tone differ from the vibrations of a source which produces noise?

2. What is a major chord?

3. How is the major diatonic scale built up from major chords?

4. How do the frequencies of notes an octave apart compare?

5. Why does the tone of middle C on a tuned piano not correspond with the tone of a C tuning fork used in a physics laboratory?

6. Explain how beats cause two notes which are struck simultaneously to sound harmonious or discordant.

7. (*a*) What is a fundamental? (*b*) How is a plucked string vibrating when it produces the fundamental?

8. What is (*a*) the first harmonic of C; (*b*) the second harmonic; (*c*) the third harmonic? (*d*) How do their frequencies compare?

9. Which law of strings is used (*a*) in tuning a violin; (*b*) in playing the instrument?

10. Define (*a*) audio frequency range; (*b*) threshold of hearing; (*c*) threshold of pain.

B **11.** By what fractions must the frequency of an initial tone be multiplied to give the frequencies of the tones comprising an octave of a diatonic scale?

12. Why is it easy for us to distinguish between the note A on a piano and the note A as sounded on a trombone?

13. How do the strings on a piano illustrate all of the laws of strings?

14. What is the function of the thin, wooden bridge between the strings and the sounding board of a cello?

15. Some of the pipes of a pipe organ are made of wood and some are of metal. Why?

16. How is the vibrating air column produced in a clarinet, in a trombone, and in a flute?

★ **17.** How is the chromatic scale constructed?

★ **18.** (*a*) How was the tempered scale devised? (*b*) In what way is it a compromise scale?

PROBLEMS

A **1.** What is the wavelength of the tone produced by an open organ pipe 4.0 ft long?

2. If a closed organ pipe 2.0 m long is played, what is the wavelength of the tone produced?

3. What is the length in feet of a closed organ pipe which produces the note A, 440. cycles/sec, when the temperature is 72° F?

4. What must be the length in meters of an open organ pipe if it is to produce a tone with a frequency of 1760 cycles/sec at 25° C?

5. If the A string on a violin is 10.0 in. long, by how much must it be shortened to produce C'? Assume that the violin is tuned to the physical scale in which A = 426 cycles/sec.

6. Compare the frequency of one string 25 cm long and 0.50 mm in diameter with that of another string 100. cm long and 0.25 mm in diameter. The strings are of the same material and are subject to the same tension.

7. When a string is stretched by a force of 16 lb, it sounds the note C. By how much force must the string be stretched to yield the note E? Use the frequencies of the physical scale.

8. What is the frequency of C' on the scale where A = 440. cycles/sec?

9. A closed organ pipe sounds the note E, 320. cycles/sec. (*a*) What are the frequencies of the first three harmonics produced by this

pipe? (*b*) To what notes on the scale do they correspond?

10. An open organ pipe sounds the note G_1, 192 cycles/sec. (*a*) What are the frequencies of the first three harmonics produced by this pipe? (*b*) To what notes on the scale do they correspond?

B **11.** When a string 0.500 m long is stretched with a force of 2.50×10^2 nt, its frequency is 440. cycles/sec. If the string is shortened to 0.400 m and the stretching force is increased to 5.00×10^2 nt, what is the new frequency?

12. If a string is 0.350 m long and under a tension of 3.25×10^2 nt, it gives *do* on a certain scale. (*a*) How much must the string be shortened to produce *re*? (*b*) If the length is not changed, by how much must the tension be increased in order to produce *re*?

13. Calculate the frequency, and the wavelength in meters, of the lowest note on the piano, A_4, a little more than three octaves below middle C, when the temperature is 20.° C. A = 440. cycles/sec.

14. Calculate the frequency, and the wavelength in meters, of the highest note on the piano, C'''', when the temperature is 20.° C; A = 440. cycles/sec.

RESEARCH ON YOUR OWN

1. Make an instrument that will produce a diatonic scale, using test tubes filled with varying amounts of water. Take the note produced by the tube that contains no water as *do* and build up the successive notes of the octave by ear. Measure the lengths of the air columns and compare your ratios with those given in Section 2 of this chapter.

2. Connect the output terminals of an amplifier to an oscilloscope. In front of the microphone, sound two tuning forks whose frequencies are harmonious. Contrast the effect with the pattern produced by two discordant tones.

3. Look up the singing flame experiment in a reference on sound and music. Devise an apparatus to illustrate the experiment and demonstrate it.

4. Obtain two mailing tubes such that one just slips inside the other. Listen at one end of the combination while you change the total length of the tube. A hallway before school starts is a good location for this experiment. Explain your results.

5. Make two simple pendulums of equal length. Suspend the pendulums by means of paper clips at the top from a strong horizontal string which is stretched tightly. Start one pendulum in motion and observe the results. Explain. Try changing the distance between the pendulums and the tautness of the string as you repeat the experiment. Place a third pendulum of different length on the string and observe the result of the experiment. Take one of the equal-length pendulums off. Is the result the same as that obtained with equal-length pendulums? Try to predict the result if one of the equal-length pendulum bobs is decidedly heavier than the other. Test your prediction.

6. Test your school auditorium to find "dead spots" for certain frequencies. Explain why you do not find such dead spots for all frequencies.

7. Study several types of musical instruments commonly used in bands and orchestras. For each instrument, determine how vibrations are produced, how the pitch is altered, and what range of frequencies the instrument can produce.

8. Prepare a report on the construction and operation of a pipe organ or an electric organ.

UNIT 6

Light

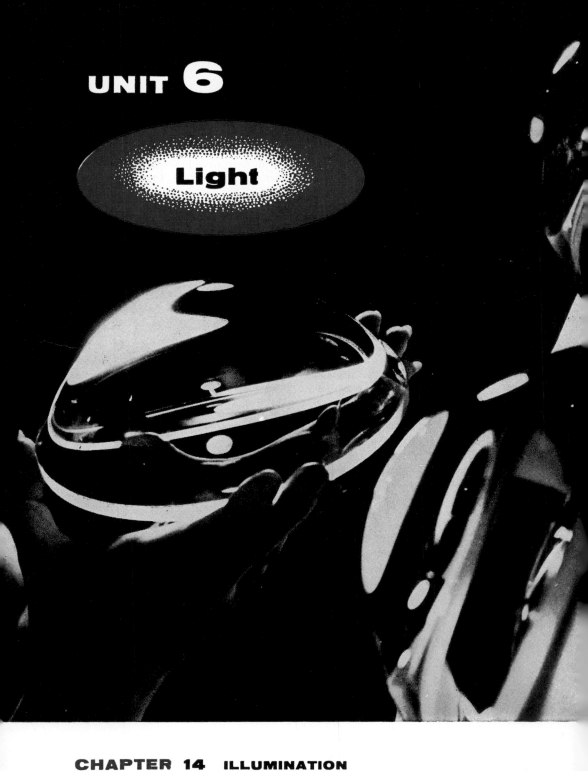

CHAPTER 14
ILLUMINATION

1 THE NATURE OF LIGHT

1. Particles vs. waves. Until the early part of this century, the nature of light was explained by conflicting theories. Sir Isaac Newton believed that light consists of tiny particles of matter emitted from a source and propagated outward in straight lines, or *rays*. This theory as supported by Newton was called the corpuscular theory of light. Christian Huygens (1629–1695), a Dutch mathematician, physicist, and astronomer, proposed that light consists of trains of waves having wave fronts perpendicular to the paths of the light rays. He considered the rays to be merely lines of direction of waves propagated outward from a light source.

The properties of waves in general have been discussed in Chapter 12, Section 6.

VOCABULARY

Candle. The unit of intensity of a light source.

Illumination. The density of luminous flux on a surface.

Light. The aspect of radiant energy of which an observer is aware through the visual sense.

Lumen. The unit of illumination on a surface.

Luminous flux. The part of the total energy radiated per unit of time from a luminous source which is capable of producing the sensation of sight.

Photoelectrons. Electrons emitted from a light-sensitive material when it is illuminated.

Photometry. The science of measuring light.

Photon. A quantum of light energy.

Quantum. An elemental unit of energy.

Quantum theory. A unifying theory applicable to the divergent phenomena of light which assumes that the transfer of energy between light and matter occurs only in discrete quantities proportional to the frequency of the energy transferred.

Wave mechanics. An extension of the quantum theory in which wave characteristics of particles are considered on the basis of their mass-energy equivalency.

Fig. 14-1. Christian Huygens explained his wave theory of light to Louis XIV of France in 1678. (Bausch & Lomb Optical Co.)

Fig. 14-2. The characteristics of waves can be studied by means of a ripple tank. (Kingston Scientific Co.)

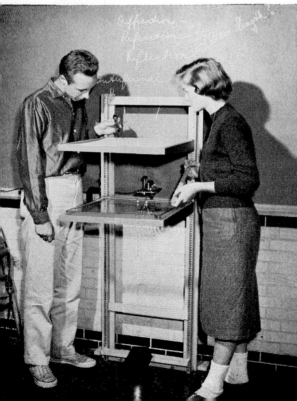

They may be summarized as follows:

1. *Rectilinear propagation* within a uniform medium.
2. *Reflection* at the surface, or boundary, of a medium.
3. *Refraction*, or bending, where a change in speed is experienced.
4. *Interference* where two waves are superimposed.
5. *Diffraction*, or bending around corners, where waves pass the edges of obstacles.

These characteristics are easily recognized in sound and water waves. However, particle behavior is similar in that a particle moves in a straight line when the net force acting on it is zero; a particle in motion rebounds from a surface; and a change in the velocity of a particle may produce a change of direction. (Reflection and refraction are discussed in Chapters 15 and 16.)

In the seventeenth century, when both Newton and Huygens were living, only rectilinear propagation, reflection, and refraction of light had been observed. Since arguments favoring both Newton's particle theory and Huygens' wave theory were plausible in regard to these characteristics of light, a scientific debate developed among the followers of these two scientists and continued unresolved for over a century.

Early in the nineteenth century the phenomena of interference and diffraction of light were first observed. Since these phenomena imply a wave characteristic and cannot be explained satisfactorily by the behavior of particles, the wave theory of light became firmly established. (Interference and diffraction are discussed in Chapter 17.)

2. The photoelectric effect. At the beginning of the twentieth century it was discovered that light falling on the surface of certain metals causes them to emit electrons, the rate of emission being directly proportional to the intensity of the light striking the metal. This phenomenon is known as the *photoelectric effect*, the emitted electrons are referred to as *photoelectrons*, and the tube containing the light-sensitive material is called a *photoelectric cell*.

The discovery of this proportional relationship jarred the wave theory to its very foundation, for according to the wave theory of light, an increase in intensity should result in an increase in the velocities of the photoelectrons emitted. This is not the case; more electrons are emitted per second, these electrons having the same group of discrete velocities as those emitted at the lower light intensity.

Had Newton perhaps been right all along? Certainly, the particle theory explained the increased rate of electron emission, but it did not explain the discrete velocities of the photoelectrons. Both classical theories were, in themselves, inadequate. The discovery of the photoelectric effect, following the discovery of interference and diffraction, created a dilemma. Was there no theory to explain these widely divergent phenomena?

3. The quantum theory. Max Planck (1858–1947), a German physicist, arrived at the conclusion that electrons were capable of acquiring energy from a radiation only in discrete amounts proportional

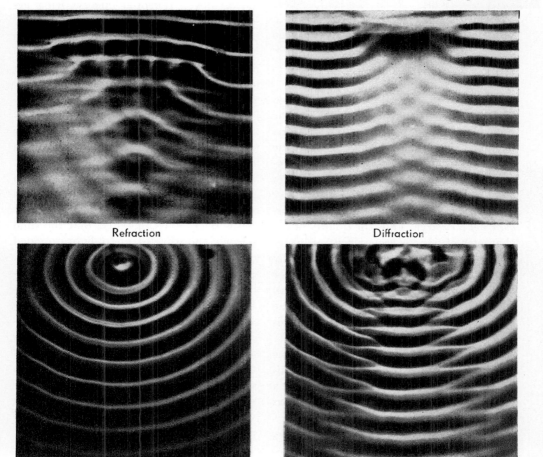

Refraction

Diffraction

Radial waves

Interference

Fig. 14-3. Some wave characteristics as shown by water waves in a ripple tank. (Kingston Scientific Co.)

Fig. 14-4. Max Planck, a German physicist, developed the initial assumptions on which the quantum theory is based. (Bettmann Archive)

to the frequency. In 1905, Einstein used Planck's new concept to explain the photoelectric effect, the combined efforts of these two scientists representing the beginning of the *quantum theory*. The **quantum theory** assumes that the transfer of energy between light and matter occurs only in discrete quantities, or quanta, proportional to the frequency of the energy. Thus the quality of the character of light is recognized; propagation from one point to another occurs by wave transfer of energy; absorption or emission of light energy occurs at quantum levels proportional to the frequency of the energy. A quantum of light energy is called a *photon*.

The quantity of energy contained in one photon (quantum) is determined by multiplying the frequency of radiation f by a proportionality constant h, known as *Planck's constant*.

$$W = hf$$

When f is given in vibrations per second and h is in joule-seconds ($h = 6.624 \times 10^{-34}$ joule-sec), the energy W in a photon is

expressed in joules. All interchanges of light energy occur as multiples of this quantum of energy.

In 1913, Niels Bohr devised a model of an atom in its simplest form (see Chapter 6, Section 9) to which he applied Planck's quantum theory. Bohr assumed that electrons could move about the nucleus only in certain orbits or *discrete energy levels*, the energy level closest to the nucleus being the lowest. As long as an electron remained at one energy level no energy change could occur; that is, energy could be neither radiated nor acquired. He concluded that as the atom absorbs a definite amount of energy an electron is moved out to a higher energy level, potential energy being acquired in the process. As the "excited" atom reverts to its stable state, the electron falls back to a lower energy level, radiating energy in quantum units, the number depending on the magnitude of the energy change.

Bohr's atom model provided no information about the actual emission of light energy when an electron passes from a higher to a lower energy level; however, his concept of energy levels provided a great stimulus for theoretical studies in this field. About 1925 the French physicist Louis de Broglie suggested that the dual particle and wave nature of light provided evidence of the wave nature of all particles. Accepting Einstein's idea of the equivalence between mass and energy, he postulated that *in every mechanical system, waves are associated with mass particles*. In its present form, this theory is known as *wave mechanics*. Just as the ordinary laws of mechanics are essential to any explanation of the behavior of bodies of large dimensions, *wave mechanics* is necessary in dealing with masses of atomic and subatomic dimensions.

A photon has energy which is the product of Planck's constant and the frequency at which it is radiated.

$$E = hf$$

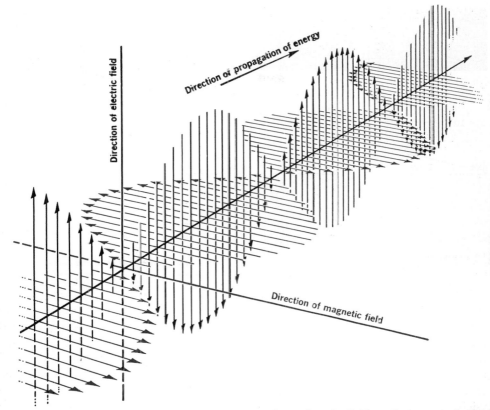

Fig. 14-5. An electromagnetic wave consists of an electric field and a magnetic field at right angles to each other. Both are perpendicular to the direction in which the wave advances. (From *College Physics*, 4th Ed., by Saunders and Kirkpatrick, Holt, 1953)

From Einstein's equation for mass-energy equivalency,

$$E = mc^2$$

the photon may be assigned a mass:

$$mc^2 = hf$$

$$m = \frac{hf}{c^2}$$

where c is the velocity of light. Since

$$c = f\lambda$$

by substitution,

$$\lambda = \frac{h}{mc}$$

Thus, the wavelength of a photon may be expressed in terms of its mass. Similarly, a wavelength for any particle, having any velocity v, may be expressed in terms of its mass:

$$\lambda = \frac{h}{mv}$$

There is abundant evidence today of the wave nature of subatomic particles. Accelerated electrons have been found to behave in a manner similar to X rays. The electron microscope is an application of electron waves. The development of the quantum theory and the system of wave mechanics has provided physicists with their most powerful means of studying the properties of matter.

4. The electromagnetic spectrum. Hot objects transfer heat by radiation, and if the temperature is high enough, they radiate light as well as heat. If a light source is cut off from an observer, its

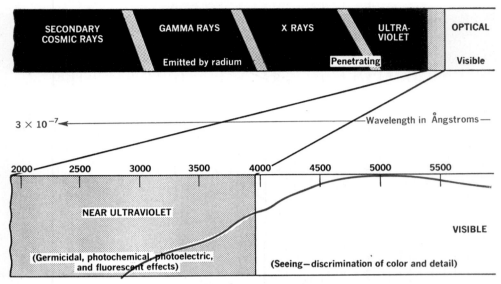

Fig. 14-6. The electromagnetic spectrum.

heating effect is cut off at the same time. For this reason, a cloud which obscures the sun cuts off some of the sun's heat as well.

James Clerk Maxwell (1831–1879), a Scot and the first great mathematical physicist after Newton, set out to determine the properties of a medium which would transmit the energies of heat, light, and electric action. By 1865 he had developed a series of mathematical equations from which he predicted that all three are propagated in free space at the speed of light as *electromagnetic disturbances*. This unification, the *electromagnetic theory*, brought into common focus the various phenomena of radiation. Maxwell determined that the energy of electromagnetic waves is equally divided between an electric field and a magnetic field, each being perpendicular to the other and both perpendicular to the direction in which the waves are propagated. See Fig. 14-5.

By 1885 experimental confirmation of the electromagnetic theory had been achieved by the German physicist, Heinrich Rudolph Hertz (1857–1894), who showed that light waves and electrically generated waves are of the same nature.

Of course, many of their properties are quite different because of the very marked differences in wavelength.

Electromagnetic energy can be detected and measured by physical means only when it is intercepted by matter and changed into thermal, electric, mechanical, or chemical energy. Today, the electromagnetic spectrum is known to consist of a tremendous range of radiation frequencies extending from about 10 to more than 10^{25} cycles per second. Since all electromagnetic radiations travel in free space with a velocity of 3×10^8 meters per second, the range of wavelengths is from about 3×10^7 meters at the low-frequency end to less than 3×10^{-17} meters at the high-frequency end. In *Ångström* units (Å), the units commonly used to express the wavelengths of electromagnetic radiations, the range is from 3×10^{17} Å to 3×10^{-7} Å. One Ångström unit equals 10^{-10} m. In millimicrons (one micron = 10^{-6} meter) the range of wavelengths extends from 3×10^{16} mμ to 3×10^{-8} mμ.

The electromagnetic spectrum may be divided into eight major regions depending on the general character of the radiations. These are (1) electric waves; (2) radio

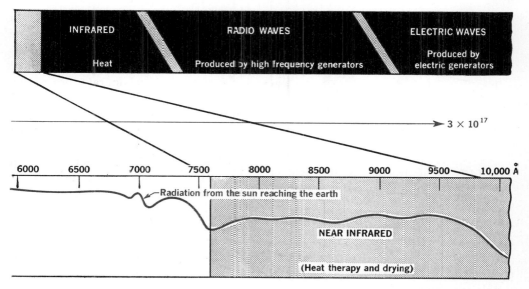

waves; (3) infrared; (4) optical; (5) ultra-violet; (6) X rays; (7) gamma rays; and (8) secondary cosmic rays. See Fig. 14-6.

The optical spectrum includes those radiations, commonly called light, that are capable of visual detection. They range from 7600 Å to 4000 Å. Accordingly, **light** *may be defined as the aspect of radiant energy of which a human observer is aware through the visual sense.* The optical spectrum extends into the near infrared and into the near ultraviolet. These radiations, although our eyes cannot see them, can be detected by means of photographic film.

5. Sources of light. There are two general sources of light.

1. Natural. Nearly all the natural light we receive comes from the sun; moonlight is really sunlight reflected to us from the surface of the moon. Distant stars furnish us with an extremely small amount of light.

2. Artificial. There are several ways of producing artificial light. Materials may be heated until they glow, or become incandescent, as in the case of the filament of an electric lamp. Molecules of a gas at reduced pressure may be bombarded with electrons to produce the light we see in a neon sign. Visible light from fluorescent tubes or panels results from the action of ultra-violet radiations on phosphors with which the glass is coated. The light of a firefly is produced by complex chemical reactions.

6. Luminous and illuminated objects. When a platinum wire is heated, it emits radiations of shorter and shorter wavelength as its temperature rises, finally becoming incandescent. It is now a *luminous body,* visible primarily because of the light it emits. *An object which gives off light because of the energy of its oscillating particles is said to be luminous.* The sun and the stars are luminous bodies.

Just as radiant heat may be reflected, light waves may be reflected from the surfaces of bodies. Mirrors reflect most of the light they intercept from some other source. *A body that is seen because of the light reflected from it is said to be illuminated.* The moon is illuminated, for it acts as a mirror reflecting radiant energy from the sun.

7. Reflection, absorption, and transmission of light. Some of the light waves reaching the surface of a substance are

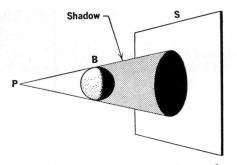

Fig. 14-7. An obstruction in the path of light from a point source casts a shadow of uniform density.

reflected, some are *transmitted*, and others are *absorbed* by the substance.

1. Reflection. Smooth water makes a fairly good mirror, as does glass. Highly polished metals are also good reflectors of light.

2. Absorption. Any dark-colored object absorbs light, but a black one absorbs nearly all the light it receives. When the rays of the sun strike a body of water vertically, most of the rays are either absorbed or transmitted, whereas most of the rays are reflected when they strike the water at an oblique angle. For this reason you can look at the image of the sun in the water without discomfort when the sun is directly overhead, but not when the sun is near the horizon.

3. Transmission. Air, glass, and water transmit light readily and are said to be *transparent*. Other substances transmit light but scatter or diffuse it so that objects seen through them cannot be identified; these are *translucent* substances, typical examples being frosted electric lamps and parchment lampshades. *Opaque* substances do not transmit light at all.

8. Rays, beams, and pencils of light. From a luminous point-source, light waves travel outward in all directions. If the medium through which they pass is of the same nature throughout, light waves travel in straight lines, a property of light that is useful in aiming a rifle. A single line of light coming from a luminous point is called a *ray;* several parallel rays form a

beam of light. Light coming from the sun is in rays so nearly parallel that it may be considered as a beam. When several rays of light come from a point, they are called a *diverging pencil*, while rays proceeding toward a point form a *converging pencil*. When the sun's rays pass through a "burning glass," they converge at a point called a *focus*.

9. The cause of shadows. Since an opaque object absorbs light, it produces a shadow in the space behind it. When the source of light is a point, as in Fig. 14-7, an opaque ball, *B*, cuts off all the rays which strike it, and produces a shadow of uniform darkness on screen *S*. If the light comes from a source larger than a point, the shadow varies in intensity as shown in Fig. 14-8. The part from which all the rays of light are excluded is called the *umbra;* the lighter part of the shadow is the *penumbra*, where the luminous source is not entirely hidden from an observer, but some of its rays are cut off.

10. The speed of light. The velocity of light is one of the most important constants used in physics and the determination of the speed of light in traveling from point to point represents one of the most precise measurements achieved by man. Before 1675, light propagation was generally considered to be instantaneous, although Galileo had suggested that a finite time was required for it to travel through space.

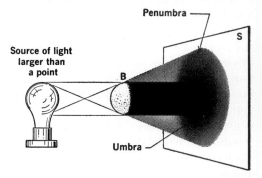

Fig. 14-8. An obstruction in the path of light from a source larger than a point casts a shadow of varying intensity.

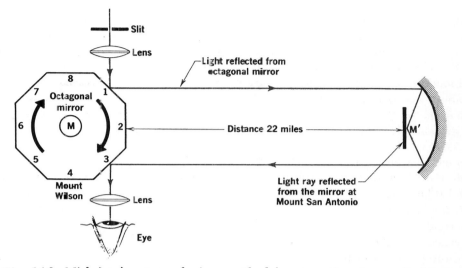

Fig. 14-9. Michelson's octagonal-mirror method for measuring the speed of light.

In that year a Danish astronomer, Olaus Römer, determined the speed of light to be about 186,000 miles per second. He had been puzzled by a variation from his calculations of the time of eclipse of one of Jupiter's moons as seen from different positions in the earth's orbit about the sun. Römer concluded that the variation was due to differences in the distance which the light traveled to reach the earth.

Very precise modern measurements of the speed of light are made using laboratory methods. The most notable experiments were performed by Albert A. Michelson (1852–1931), a professor of physics at the University of Chicago, who measured the speed of light in air and in a vacuum with extraordinary precision.

1. The speed of light in air. Professor Michelson measured the speed of light over the accurately determined distance between Mt. Wilson and Mt. San Antonio, California. His method is illustrated, in principle, by Fig. 14-9. The light source, octagonal mirror, and telescope were located on Mt. Wilson and the concave mirror and plane mirror were located on Mt. San Antonio, approximately 22 miles away. The octagonal mirror, M, could be

rotated rapidly under controlled conditions and was timed very accurately.

With mirror M stationary, a pencil of light from the slit opening was reflected by M_1 to the distant mirror M', from which it was returned to M_3. The image of the slit in the mirror at the M_3 position could be observed accurately through the telescope. The octagonal mirror was then set in motion and the speed of rotation brought up to the value which moved M_2 into the position formerly occupied by M_3 during the time required for the light to travel from M_1 to Mt. San Antonio and return. The slit image was again seen in the telescope precisely as it was when the octagon was stationary. The light traveled twice the optical path of approximately 22 miles in one-eighth of the time of one revolution of the octagonal mirror. Thus,

$$c = \frac{2MM'}{t}$$

where MM' is the optical path, t is the time of one-eighth revolution of the octagon, and c is the velocity of light in air.

Michelson's investigation of the speed of light in air required several years to complete and extremely high accuracy was attained in making the necessary observations. The optical path was measured by the U.S. Coast and Geodetic Survey and found to be 35,385.5 meters, accurate to about one part in seven million. The rate of the revolving mirror was measured by stroboscopic comparison with an electric signal of standard frequency. The average of a large number of determinations yielded a speed of light in air of 299,700 km/sec.

2. The speed of light in a vacuum. Michelson conducted similar experiments using an evacuated tube one mile long to eliminate the problems of haze and variations in air density. In these investigations he determined the speed of light to be 299,790 km/sec, which he believed to be accurate to within 1 km/sec.

Modern laboratory methods of measuring the speed of light are considered to be more accurate than Michelson's and require very complex apparatus. In some experiments, electromagnetic waves much longer than light waves have been used. Good agreement was found between their speed and that of visible light, as was to be expected according to the electromagnetic theory.

As Michelson's figures show, the velocity of light in a vacuum is very slightly higher than that in air; the velocity in a vacuum generally accepted as most accurate is

$$c = 2.997928 \times 10^{10} \text{ cm/sec}$$

Useful approximations in close agreement with this precise velocity are 300,000 km/sec and 186,000 mi/sec. These common values for the speed of light may be used in all ordinary computations with negligible error.

2 PHOTOMETRY

11. The measurement of light. The science of measuring light is called *photometry*. Three quantities are generally measured in practical photometry: the *luminous intensity* of the source, the *luminous flux* or light flow from a source, and the *illumination* on a surface.

1. Luminous intensity. Most of the terms used in photometry are based on the intensity of a luminous source, the common unit of luminous intensity being the *candle*. Originally the light from an actual candle was used as a standard, but this was not very satisfactory because the exact luminous intensity of a candle is not easy to reproduce. *The* **candle** *is defined as the intensity of the light emitted through an opening $\frac{1}{60}$ of a square centimeter in area from a hollow enclosure maintained at the temperature of solidification of platinum, about 1773° C.* In practice it is convenient to use incandescent lamps which have been rated by comparison with the standard.

Incandescent lamps used for interior lighting generally have an intensity ranging from a few candles to several hundred candles. A 40-watt lamp has an intensity of about 35 candles; a 100-watt lamp gives about 130 candles, while a 40-watt fluorescent lamp has an intensity of about 200 candles. The intensity of any lamp depends on the direction from which it is measured; the average candlepower in all directions in space (spherical candlepower) is often given.

2. Luminous flux. Not all of the energy radiated from a luminous source is capable of producing a visual sensation. For example, over 70 percent of the energy radiated by a 100-watt incandescent lamp is in the infrared region and 10 percent is visible light. **Luminous flux** *is that part of the total energy radiated per unit of time from a luminous source which is capable of producing the sensation of sight.* The unit of luminous flux is the *lumen.*

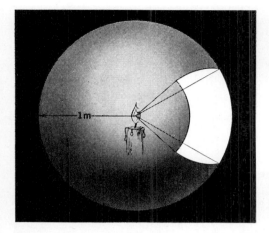

Fig. 14-10. A 1-candlepower source radiates luminous flux at the rate of 4π lumens.

Suppose a 1-candlepower source is placed at the center of a hollow sphere having a radius of 1 meter as illustrated in Fig. 14-10. The luminous source is presumed to radiate light equally in all directions and to have such small dimensions that it may be termed a "point source." The area of the surface of a sphere of radius r is equal to $4\pi r^2$. Since the radius of the unit sphere being considered is 1

meter, the surface area is $4\pi \times (1\text{ m})^2$. One lumen of flux is radiated by the 1-candlepower source to each square meter of the inside surface of the sphere. *The lumen is equal to the luminous flux on a unit surface all points of which are at unit distance from a point source of one candle.* Observe that the lumen is not a measure of a total quantity of luminous energy but a rate at which luminous energy is being emitted, transmitted, or received.

Since there are 4π unit areas in the surface of a sphere the total luminous flux emitted by a source is 4π times the luminous intensity of the source. Thus a luminous source having an intensity of 1 candle emits light at the rate of 12.57 lumens. In fact, light sources are usually rated in terms of the total flux emitted, 12.57 lumens being the equivalent of 1 candle. The 40-watt incandescent lamp mentioned earlier is rated at about 450 lumens and the 40-watt fluorescent lamp at about 2600 lumens.

3. Illumination. In Fig. 14-10 it is evident that as the intensity of the source is increased, the luminous flux transmitted to each unit area of surface and the flux on

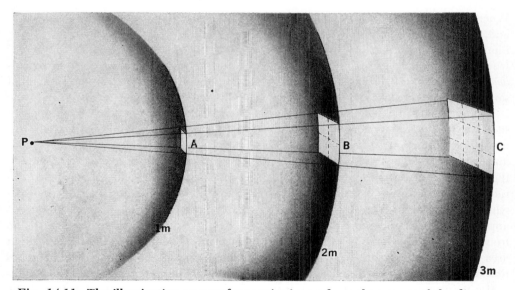

Fig. 14-11. The illumination on a surface varies inversely as the square of the distance from the luminous source.

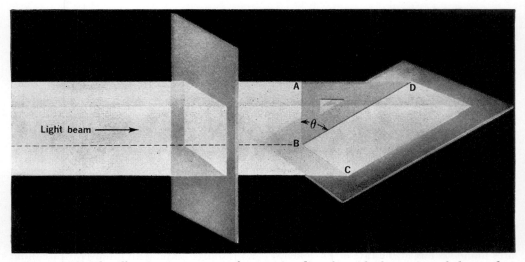

Fig. 14-12. The illumination on a surface varies directly with the cosine of the angle between the luminous flux and the normal to the surface.

each unit area are similarly increased. The *illumination* on the surface is said to be increased. **Illumination** *is the density of the luminous flux on a surface.* When the surface is uniformly illuminated, it is the quotient of the flux on the surface divided by the area of the surface and is expressed as the luminous flux per unit area.

$$E = \frac{F}{A}$$

Where F is the luminous flux in lumens and A is the area in square meters, the illumination E is in *lumens per square meter;* where A is in square feet, E is expressed in *lumens per square foot.* (This latter expression is sometimes called the *foot-candle.*)

Suppose the radius of the unit sphere shown in Fig. 14-10 is increased to 2 meters. The surface area is $4\pi(2 \text{ m})^2$, or approximately 50 m², and is *four* times the area of the unit sphere. Similarly, a radius of 3 meters gives an area of $4\pi(3 \text{ m})^2$ which is nine times the unit area. It is apparent that, as the radius or distance from the luminous source is increased, the area illuminated is increased in proportion to the *square* of the distances.

If a point source of constant intensity is located at the center of the sphere, *the level*

of illumination decreases as the square of the distance from the source. See Fig. 14-11. If the intensity of the source is doubled, of course the luminous flux transmitted to the surface is doubled, and the level of illumination is doubled. Thus the illumination E on a surface perpendicular to the luminous flux falling on it is dependent on the intensity I of the source and its distance s from the source according to the following relation:

$$E = \frac{I}{s^2}$$

The inverse square law is used to calculate the illumination from an individual point source on planes *perpendicular* to the beam. In practice, if the dimensions of the source are negligible compared with its distance from the surface, it is considered as a point source. For large sources, such as long fluorescent tubes, *at short distances*, the illumination varies approximately inversely as the distance.

When a surface is tilted so that it is no longer perpendicular to the beam of light illuminating it, the luminous flux spreads over a greater area and the level of illumination is reduced. In Fig. 14-12 the perpendicular surface *ABC* illuminated by the beam is square, having an area equal to $AB \times BC$. As the surface is tilted away from the source the illuminated area becomes rectangular, the width remaining the same and the length increasing to BD. In the right triangle ABD

$$BD = \frac{AB}{\cos \theta}$$

where θ equals the angle between the surface and the perpendicular with respect to the beam. (It is quite evident that θ also represents the angle which the light beam makes with the perpendicular to the illuminated surface.)

As θ reaches $60°$, $\cos \theta$ equals 0.5 and the length BD becomes twice the length AB. Thus the area is doubled and, since the same flux is spread over twice the area, the illumination is reduced to half the original level. In the general case,

$$E = \frac{I \cos \theta}{s^2}$$

The illumination on a surface varies inversely with the square of the distance from the luminous source and directly with the cosine of the angle between the luminous flux and the normal to the surface. A surface that is perpendicular to the luminous flux falling on it is simply a special case of the general expression for illumination in which the angle θ becomes zero and $\cos \theta = 1$. See the Sample Problem below.

12. The need for varying amounts of illumination. The illumination from direct sunlight on a clear day is about 10,000 lumens/ft². Lighting engineers suggest that at least 30 lumens/ft² are actually needed for reading ordinary print, 50 lumens/ft² for reading fine print, and 200 lumens/ft² for sewing on dark-colored fabrics.

To provide 30 lumens/ft² illumination

Sample Problem

(a) What illumination is provided on the surface of a table located 4.00 m directly below a 1630-lumen lamp? (b) What is the illumination on the surface when the table is moved 3.00 m to one side of its original position?

Solution

(a) $I = \dfrac{1630 \text{ lumens}}{12.57 \text{ lumens/candle}} = 128 \text{ candles}$

$E = \dfrac{I}{s^2}$

$E = \dfrac{128 \text{ candles}}{(4.00 \text{ m})^2} = 8.00 \text{ lumens/m}^2$

(b) $s = \sqrt{(4.00 \text{ m})^2 + (3.00 \text{ m})^2} = 5.00 \text{ m}$

$\cos \theta = \dfrac{4.00 \text{ m}}{5.00 \text{ m}} = 0.800$

$E = \dfrac{I \cos \theta}{s^2}$

$E = \dfrac{128 \text{ candles} \times 0.800}{(5.00 \text{ m})^2} = 4.08 \text{ lumens/m}^2$

Fig. 14-13. Adequate lighting provides general illumination in addition to the proper illumination of the working area. (General Electric Co.)

for reading, if we neglect reflection, we may use a 100-watt lamp with an intensity of about 130 candles, and sit slightly farther than 2 feet from the lamp. However, walls and ceilings greatly affect the amount of light reflected to our reading matter; lampshades likewise direct much light, that would otherwise be wasted, into more useful directions. As a result, it is possible to get adequate illumination with lower candlepower lamps or at greater distances.

13. Measuring the intensity of a light source. The candlepower of any light source can be measured by comparing its intensity with that of a standard light source, using an instrument called a *photometer*.

1. Bunsen photometer. The Bunsen photometer is sometimes called the grease-spot

photometer. If a piece of paper with a grease spot in the center is held toward the window, the grease spot will appear lighter than the rest of the paper because it transmits more light. On the other hand, because it is a poorer reflector of light than the paper, the grease spot will appear darker than the paper when held away from the window and seen by reflected light. A laboratory model of the Bunsen photometer, consisting of such a piece of paper placed on a meter stick between a standard lamp and the lamp of unknown candle power, is shown in Fig. 14-14. The paper is moved back and forth along the meter stick until it is equally illuminated on both sides; when the paper is in this position, the intensities of the two light sources, in candles, are directly proportional to the squares of their distance from the paper.

$$\frac{I_1}{I_2} = \frac{s_1^2}{s_2^2}$$

where I_1 and I_2 are the intensities of the two sources, and s_1 and s_2 are their respective distances from the paper. See the Sample Problem on the opposite page.

2. Joly photometer. The Joly photometer generally gives more satisfactory results than the grease-spot photometer does. It

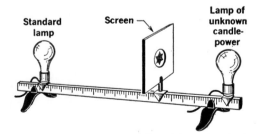

Standard lamp   Screen   Lamp of unknown candle-power

Fig. 14-14. The Bunsen, or grease-spot, photometer.

Fig. 14-15. A modern spherical photometer. These instruments vary from 1 in. to 120 in. in diameter. (General Electric Co.)

Sample Problem

A lamp with an intensity of 20. candles is used as a standard on a Bunsen photometer. The grease-spot screen is equally illuminated when it is 20. cm from the standard lamp and 80. cm from the lamp of unknown intensity. What is the intensity of the unknown lamp?

Solution

The unknown lamp must have the greater intensity. It provides the same illumination at 80. cm that the standard lamp provides at 20. cm.

$$\frac{I_1}{I_2} = \frac{s_1^2}{s_2^2}$$

$$I_1 = I_2 \frac{s_1^2}{s_2^2}$$

$$I_1 = 20.\text{ candles} \times \frac{(80.\text{ cm})^2}{(20.\text{ cm})^2}$$

$$I_1 = 320 \text{ candles, the intensity of the unknown lamp}$$

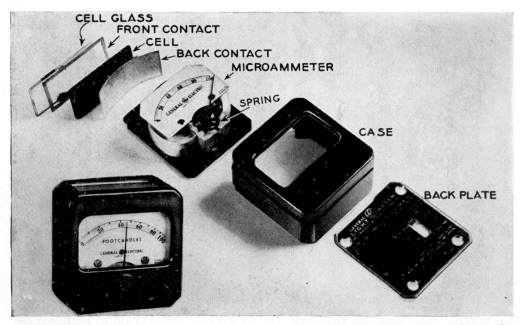

Fig. 14-16. An exploded view of a light meter. A light-sensitive cell consists of a steel plate with a selenium coating. The copper front contact is connected to the negative side of the microammeter which registers the current generated when light strikes the cell. (General Electric Co.)

consists of two blocks of paraffin separated by a thin sheet of metal. The light from either side is transmitted by the paraffin, but is stopped by the metal. By looking at the edges of the blocks of paraffin it is easy to adjust the photometer so that both sides are equally illuminated. Then distances to the lamps are measured and calculations made in the same manner as with the Bunsen photometer.

3. Spherical photometer. This accurate photometer is used commercially; the lamp being tested is placed in the center of a large sphere which is painted white on the inside. The luminous flux is gathered by a photocell which is located inside the sphere but shielded from direct view of the lamp. The light on this cell is equal to that received by any other similar portion of the sphere interior, due to cross-reflections, and is therefore proportional to the total light emitted by the source under test. A meter outside the sphere is connected to the cell and is calibrated to read the mean spherical candlepower or lumens directly.

14. Measuring the amount of illumination. When planning lighting installations or when taking photographs, it is necessary to know the amount of illumination available. The instruments used for these purposes are photoelectric cells called "light meters" or "exposure meters." The light-sensitive cell transforms light energy striking it into electric energy, the amount of illumination and the electric current produced being proportional within the range of the instrument. Consequently, a light meter can be calibrated directly in lumens/ft² or foot-candles, although most of them have an arbitrary scale. A typical light meter is shown in Fig. 14–16.

Exposure meters fall into two classes, incident-light meters which measure the light falling on a cell held in the scene so as to face the camera, and reflected-light meters which measure light reflected from the scene towards the camera.

ummary

The duality of the character of light is recognized in the quantum theory. The electromagnetic spectrum includes the radiations recognized as light.

An object is luminous if it is visible because of the light it emits; it is illuminated if it is visible because of the light it reflects. An object may reflect, absorb, or transmit the light which it receives. The illumination on a surface is directly proportional to the product of the intensity of the luminous source and the cosine of the angle between the luminous flux and the normal of the surface and is inversely proportional to the square of the distance from the luminous source.

Photometry deals with the measurement of light. Three quantities generally measured are luminous intensity, luminous flux, and illumination. Intensity is measured in candles, luminous flux is measured in lumens, and illumination is measured in lumens per square foot or lumens per square meter. The Bunsen, Joly, and spherical photometers measure the intensity of light sources.

TERMS TO DEFINE

absorption	light	photoelectron
artificial sources of light	light meter	quantum
beam	light waves	ray
Bunsen photometer	lumen	reflection
candle (unit)	luminous	shadow
electromagnetic spectrum	luminous flux	speed of light
focus	micron	spherical photometer
illuminated	natural sources of light	translucent
illumination	octagonal mirror	transmission
intensity	opaque	transparent
Joly photometer	penumbra	umbra

QUESTIONS

A 1. How do scientists explain the nature of light?

2. Arrange the following in order of increasing wavelength: visible light; infrared radiations; ultraviolet radiations; X rays; radio waves; cosmic rays.

3. Compare visible light and sound in each of the following categories: (a) origin; (b) transmitting media; (c) wavelength; (d) type of wave; (e) speed.

4. (a) What is our most important source of natural light? (b) What are our common sources of artificial light?

5. Distinguish between luminous and illuminated objects.

6. Define and illustrate the following terms: (a) transparent; (b) translucent; (c) opaque.

7. What are the quantities generally measured in practical photometry?

8. (a) Define luminous flux. (b) In what unit is it measured?

B 9. (a) In what unit do we measure the intensity of a light source? (b) How is this unit defined?

10. (a) In what unit do we measure illumination? (b) How is this unit defined?

11. Why is it important to have a moderate level of illumination in a room in addition to the light concentrated on your work?

12. How does an atom of a substance radiate energy according to the quantum theory?

13. By using Fig. 14-9, explain how Michelson determined the speed of light in air.

PROBLEMS

Note: Assume lamps to be point sources.

A **1.** The distance from the earth to the sun is approximately 9.3×10^7 miles. What time, in minutes, is required for light from the sun to reach the earth?

2. What is the illumination on the page of a book 3.00 ft directly below a source whose intensity is 100. candles?

3. It is recommended that the illumination be 50 lumens per square foot for newspaper reading. How far from the paper should a 200-candle source be placed to provide this illumination? (Assume the paper to be perpendicular to the luminous flux reaching it.)

4. What is the maximum illumination 5.0 ft from a lamp whose intensity is 150 candles?

5. The amount of illumination thrown on a screen by two sources of light is the same when the distances from the lamps to the screen are 3.0 m and 2.0 m respectively. If the intensity of the first lamp is 20. candles, what is the intensity of the second lamp?

6. A lamp, intensity 16.0 candles, is placed at the 0.0-cm mark on a meter stick. A lamp of unknown intensity is placed at the 100.0-cm mark. If a Bunsen photometer is equally illuminated when placed at the 60.0-cm mark, what is the intensity of the unknown lamp?

7. Two lamps, 30. candles and 20. candles respectively, are placed at opposite ends of a meter stick. Where must the screen of a photometer be placed so that both sides are equally illuminated?

8. The illumination on a screen located 3 ft from a source of light is 4 times as much as that on a second screen which is illuminated by the same source. The intensity of the source is 25 candles. How far is the second screen from the source?

B **9.** The intensity of a fluorescent lamp is 60.0 candles. At what distance does it provide an illumination of 10.0 lumens per square foot on a table located directly beneath it?

10. How far away is the nearest star if it takes 4.3 years for the light from the star to reach the earth?

11. A standard 40.0-candle lamp is placed at one end of a meter stick. A lamp of unknown intensity is placed at the other end. If the two sides of a photometer are equally illuminated when it is placed 70.0 cm from the standard lamp, what is the intensity of the unknown?

12. A 100-watt lamp placed at one end of a meter stick and a 10-candle source placed at the other end equally illuminate a photometer which is 75 cm from the 100-watt lamp. How many candles per watt does the lamp supply?

13. How many revolutions per second did Dr. Michelson's octagonal mirror make if light traveled 44.0 miles while the mirror made one-eighth of a revolution?

14. What is the range of frequencies of visible light?

● **15.** A surface 75 cm from a luminous source of 150 candles has a level of illumination of 0.025 lumen/cm². At what angle is it tilted?

RESEARCH ON YOUR OWN

1. Report on the early attempts of Galileo and Roemer to measure the speed of light.
2. Try to produce a shadow that shows only an umbra with no penumbra. It is best to try this experiment after dark.
3. Devise and perform an experiment to show the effects of various types of light filters on the transmission of light energy.
4. Place a foot-candle meter one foot in front of an extinguished electric lamp. Read the meter and then turn on the lamp. By subtraction, record the additional foot-candles of illumination. Repeat with the lamp at distances of two and three feet from the meter. Does the illumination vary inversely as the distance? If not, why not? If possible, repeat the experiment after dark.
5. Measure intensities of various sources of light by means of a light meter and by counting the speed of rotation of the vanes in a Crookes radiometer. Graph your results and explain any substantial differences between the results obtained by use of these different instruments.

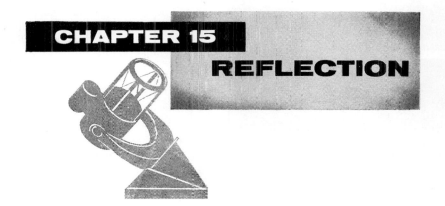

CHAPTER 15

REFLECTION

1. The reflection of light. One of the usual means of controlling light is to cause it to be reflected from a surface. *Reflection is the turning back of light waves from the boundary of a medium.* Part of the light traveling through air and arriving at a boundary such as a glass surface is reflected. The remaining light enters the glass and is partially absorbed and partially transmitted, as illustrated in Fig. 15-1. The amount of light an object reflects depends on the kind of material the object is made of, the smoothness of its surface, and the angle at which the light strikes its surface.

The ratio of the light reflected from a surface to the light falling on it is called *reflectance* and is commonly expressed in percentage. Materials differ widely in their reflectance characteristics and in the extent to which the reflected rays are scattered. See Fig. 15-2. The material of highest reflectance is magnesium carbonate, a white chalky substance, which reflects about 98 percent of the incident light with practically complete scattering. The reflectance of vaporized silver is about 95 percent, with negligible scattering. Certain black plastic surfaces may have reflectances of 5 percent or less.

VOCABULARY

Angle of incidence. The angle between the incident ray and the normal drawn to the point of incidence.

Angle of reflection. The angle between the reflected ray and the normal drawn to the point of incidence.

Normal. A line drawn perpendicular to a line or plane.

Principal focus. A point to which rays parallel to the principal axis converge, or from which they diverge, after reflection.

Real image. An image which is formed by actual rays of light.

Reflectance. The ratio of the light reflected from a surface to the light falling on it, expressed in percentage.

Spherical aberration. The failure of parallel rays to meet at a single point after reflection.

Virtual image. An image which only appears to the eye to be formed by rays of light.

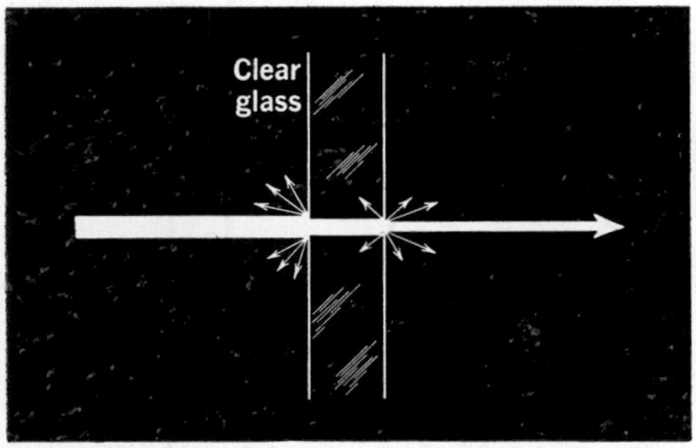

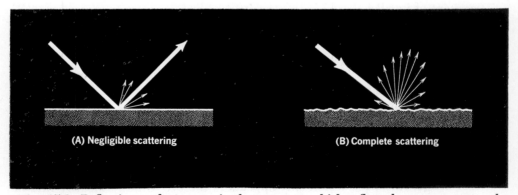

Fig. 15-1. The transmission of light through a glass plate.

2. The laws of reflection. The reflection of light is similar to the reflection of sound or to the rebound of an elastic ball. The line *MN* in Fig. 15-3(*A*) represents the reflecting surface; *AD* is a ray of light incident upon the reflector at *D*; *DB* is the path of the reflected ray. The line *CD* is drawn perpendicular to the reflecting surface at the point of incidence and is called a *normal*. In Fig. 15-3(*B*), the normal is drawn perpendicular to the tangent to the curved reflecting surface at the point of incidence. *Angle ADC, the* **angle of incidence** (*i*), *is the angle between the incident ray and the normal drawn to the point of incidence. Angle BDC, the* **angle of reflection** (*r*), *is the angle between the reflected ray and the normal drawn to the point of incidence.*

The relationships between an incident ray of light and the reflected ray, and be- tween the angles they form with the nor- mal, are easily determined in the labora- tory. These may be summarized in the form of two *laws of reflection* as follows:

1. The incident ray, the reflected ray, and the normal to the reflecting surface lie in the same plane.

2. The angle of incidence is equal to the angle of reflection.

These laws hold for all forms of wave motion.

3. Regular reflection. The reflection of sunlight by a mirror produces a blinding glare, for the sun's rays are practically parallel and have the same angle of inci- dence; they are therefore practically paral- lel when reflected from a plane mirror. Such reflection, in which scattering of the reflected rays is negligible, is called *regu- lar* reflection. Polished, or *specular*, surfaces cause regular reflection and the image of the luminous source is sharply defined. The nature of regular reflection is shown in Fig. 15-4.

Regular reflection from highly polished surfaces provides for relatively accurate control of light rays. Searchlights, beacons, and automobile spotlights use concentrated light sources of high intensity and highly polished regular reflectors to redirect the beam in the desired direction.

4. Diffused reflection. In Fig. 15-5 we see what happens to a beam of light that

(A) Negligible scattering   **(B) Complete scattering**

Fig. 15-2. Reflecting surfaces vary in the extent to which reflected rays are scattered.

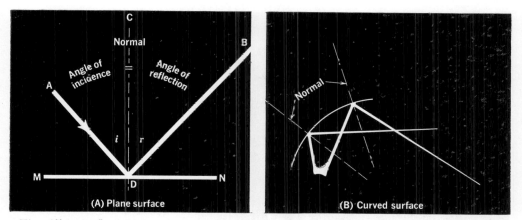

Fig. 15-3. Reflection from plane and curved surfaces. Which law of reflection is not clearly illustrated here?

is incident on an irregular surface; *the laws of reflection hold true for each particular ray of light,* but the normals to the surface are not parallel, and the light is reflected in many different directions. Such scattering, or *diffusion,* of light is extremely important. If the sun's rays were not diffused by rough surfaces and by dust particles in the air, the corners of a room and the space under shade trees would be in almost total darkness and the glare would be dazzling in sunlit areas.

5. Increasing the diffusion of light. In order to avoid glare we often increase the diffusion of light by reflection or transmission.

(1) By reflection. Newspapers are printed on very inexpensive paper which, because of its rough unglazed surface, diffuses the incident light and makes the small print easily read. However, the quality of reproduction of the illustrations in newspapers is generally poor. Drawings or halftones are clearest when printed on full-gloss paper, but printed words are very difficult to read on such paper because of the glare from the smooth surface. As a compromise, textbooks and magazines which use many illustrations are usually printed on semi-gloss paper. Unglazed wall paper and "flat" paints are commonly used in decorating living rooms and bedrooms because they produce diffused reflection, yielding "softer" light.

(2) By transmission. Practically all electric lamps are now frosted on the inside to promote diffusion and prevent glare. Some are designed for use in unshaded fixtures, and are shaped and colored so that their direct rays do not produce glare.

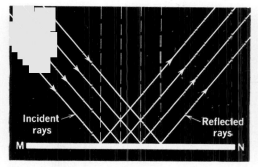

Fig. 15-4. Regular reflection of light from a specular surface.

Fig. 15-5. Irregular reflection promotes the diffusion of light.

Fig. 15-6. Draperies and lampshade of Fiberglas help to diffuse light and reduce glare. (Owens-Corning Fiberglas Corp.)

Lampshades of cloth and semitransparent paper soften the light by increasing diffusion; glass blocks and roughened plate glass are similarly used in windows to admit light and yet prevent glare.

6. Mirrors as reflectors. *Any highly polished surface which can be used to form images by the regular reflection of light may be called a* **mirror.** The most frequently used mirrors are those consisting of *plane* pieces of plate glass, silvered on one surface so that they reflect a large amount of light. The reflectance of a plane silvered mirror may be as high as 85 percent.

Curved mirrors, whose surfaces are sec-

tions of spheres, are commonly used for special purposes. The laws of reflection hold for spherical mirrors; however, the size and position of the images formed are quite different from those of images formed by plane mirrors. When the outer surface of a spherical mirror is the reflecting surface, the mirror is *convex*, which means curved outward toward the observer. When the inner surface of a spherical mirror forms the reflecting surface, the mirror is *concave*, or curved inward away from the observer.

7. Two kinds of images. Rays of light are sometimes reflected from a curved

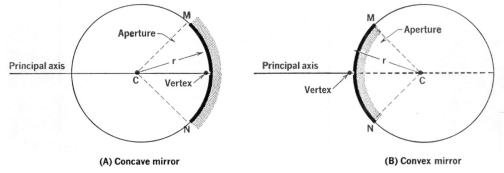

(A) Concave mirror   (B) Convex mirror

Fig. 15-7. Plane diagrams of spherical mirrors.

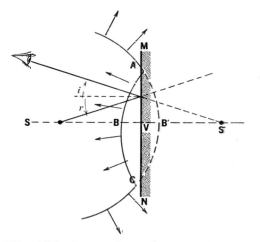

Fig. 15-8. A wave-front diagram of reflection of light from a point source by a plane mirror.

cannot be projected on a screen. Virtual images are always erect; they, too, may be enlarged or reduced in size.

In Fig. 15-8, light traveling outward from a point source in spherical wave fronts is reflected from a plane mirror. At the instant that points A and C on the wave front reach the mirror, point B has been reflected back towards the source at S, having traveled the distance VB. The reflected wave front ABC has a center of curvature S' whose apparent distance behind the mirror VS' is equal to the distance of the source in front of the mirror VS. The reflected wave front approaches an observer at O as though its source were S', S' being the virtual image of the source S.

8. Images formed through small openings. An excellent image of a candle flame can be formed on a white screen in a darkened room by letting the rays from the candle pass through a small opening as shown in Fig. 15-9. Since light travels in straight lines, a ray of light from A, the tip of the candle, will pass through the opening to form an image of the tip of the flame at A'. From D a ray of light will fall upon the screen at D'. Rays from B form an image at B'. If the opening is very small, the image will be sharp and well-defined, although not very bright. When the size of the opening is increased, the image becomes brighter, but less distinct. The pinhole camera is an application of this method of forming images.

mirror so that they meet in front of the mirror to form an image of the object from which the light comes. Such a picture or visual counterpart of the object may be projected on a screen. *An image of this kind, which is formed by actual rays of light, is called a* **real image.** Real images are always inverted and may be either larger or smaller than the object.

When you look at yourself in a plane mirror, the rays of light appear to come from behind the mirror, although you know that the rays producing the image actually are reflected from the surface of the mirror. *An image of this kind, which only appears to the eye to be formed by rays of light, is called a* **virtual image.** Such an image

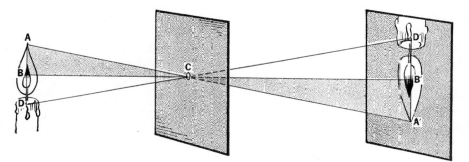

Fig. 15-9. Small apertures may be used to form images. Is this image real or virtual?

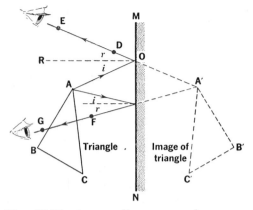

Fig. 15-10. A ray diagram used to construct an image formed by a plane mirror.

In Fig. 15-9, the triangles ABC and $A'B'C$ are similar. Therefore, $AB : A'B' = BC : B'C$. The distance AB equals one-half the height of the object, and $A'B'$ equals one-half the height of the image. The line BC is the distance of the object from the opening, and $B'C$ equals the distance of the image from the opening. Therefore, the relative sizes of the object and image are proportional to their relative distances from the opening. Increasing the distance of the object from the opening reduces the size of the image; moving the screen farther from the opening increases the size of the image.

9. Images formed by plane mirrors. The image formed by a plane mirror is neither enlarged nor reduced, but is always virtual, erect, and apparently as far behind the mirror as the object is in front of it. Because the image is formed on the extension of the normal behind the mirror, it will be reversed, the right side appearing as the left side and the left side appearing as the right.

The ray diagram of Fig. 15-10 shows an experimental method for constructing the image of an object as formed by a plane mirror. The triangle ABC drawn on paper is used as the object in front of a small mirror, MN. A pin is placed at each vertex of the triangle. On the mirror image

of the pin, pairs of sight lines are drawn. From the intersection of each pair of sight lines, when produced behind the mirror, the apparent location of the virtual image of the triangle is determined. Thus ED and GF are the sight lines drawn to locate the image of vertex A at A' with the object pin at A. The images of B and C are located in similar fashion at B' and C'. In each instance *the image is found to be as far behind the mirror as the object is in front*, and when the image points $A'B'C'$ are joined, it becomes evident that *the image is the same size as the object and reversed left and right*.

This method of constructing images verifies the laws of reflection of light. The light ray AO is reflected at point O and is sighted at E. By erecting a normal to the mirror at O, the angle AOE is bisected and the angle of reflection EOR is equal to the angle of incidence AOR. The incident ray AO, the reflected ray OE, and the normal OR all lie in the same plane.

10. Multiple reflection. Sound waves bound and rebound between parallel cliffs or walls and produce multiple echoes. In a similar fashion, light waves reflect back and forth between parallel mirrors, or mirrors set at an acute angle, and form multiple images, the image formed in one mirror acting as the object which forms an image in the next mirror. Because some

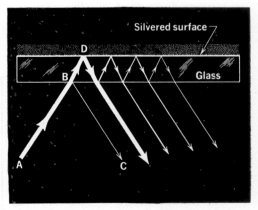

Fig. 15-11. Multiple reflections result from the use of a back-silvered mirror.

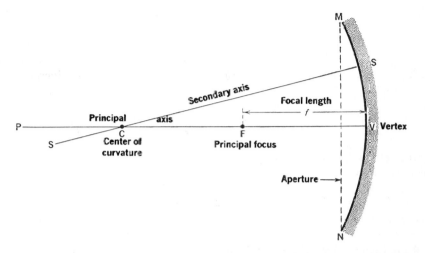

Fig. 15-12. A plane diagram for defining terms used with curved mirrors.

light energy is absorbed and some is scattered at each mirror, the succeeding images become fainter. A thick plate-glass mirror produces multiple reflection, as shown in Fig. 15-11, some light being reflected each time a boundary is encountered.

11. Curved-mirror terminology. Before we can discuss how images are formed by curved mirrors, several terms used in connection with them must be defined. As an aid to understanding of these terms, we shall use Fig. 15-12, in which MN represents a spherical mirror in two dimensions.

(1) The *center of curvature*, C, is the center of the sphere of which the mirror forms a part.

(2) The *aperture* is the angular portion,

MCN, of the sphere that is included by the mirror. Generally, only a few degrees of the total surface of the sphere are used as the reflecting surface.

(3) The *vertex*, V, is the center of the mirror itself.

(4) The *principal axis* is the line PV drawn through the center of curvature and the vertex.

(5) A *secondary axis* is any other line drawn through the center of curvature, SS' for example.

(6) The *normal* to the surface of a concave mirror is the radius drawn from the point of incidence. (The radius is perpendicular to the tangent to the surface drawn through the point of incidence.) In

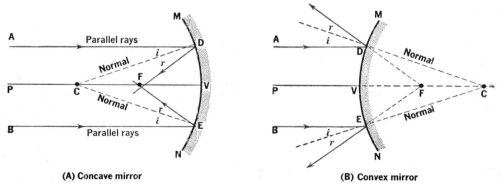

(A) Concave mirror   (B) Convex mirror

Fig. 15-13. Locating the principal focus of spherical mirrors.

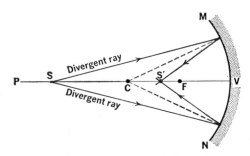

Fig. 15-14. The reflection of diverging rays by a concave mirror.

a convex mirror, the normal is the radius produced; that is, extended beyond the mirror.

12. Rays focused by spherical mirrors. In Fig. 15-13(A) the rays AD and BE, traveling parallel to the principal axis, are shown incident on a concave spherical mirror at points D and E respectively. The normals CD and CE are drawn to the points of incidence and, by the second law of reflection, the reflected rays converge on the principal axis at F. *The point on the principal axis to which rays parallel to the principal axis converge (or from which they diverge) is known as the **principal focus**.* Since the incident rays converge on being reflected, concave mirrors are known as *converging* mirrors. The distance FV becomes the *focal length* of the mirror. For spherical mirrors of small aperture, the focal length is one-half the radius of curvature.

Parallel rays incident on the convex surface of a spherical mirror are shown in Fig. 15-13(B). The normals CD and CE, produced beyond the mirror surface, show the reflected rays to be divergent, traveling along the lines FD and FE produced, F being the principal focus of the mirror. Rays parallel to the principal axis appear to diverge from the principal focus of a convex mirror. Since incident rays diverge on being reflected, convex mirrors are known as *diverging* mirrors.

Diverging rays coming from a point S on the principal axis will be brought to a focus on the principal axis of a concave mirror, but at some point S′ beyond the principal focus, as shown in Fig. 15-14. Points S and S′ are known as *conjugate foci.* Thus rays coming from S′ will be focused at S. Converging rays are also focused by concave mirrors, as shown by Fig. 15-15, the point of focus being on the principal axis between the vertex and the principal focus. In every instance, the direction of a reflected ray is determined by the laws of reflection.

13. Constructing the image of a point in a spherical mirror. In Fig. 15-16, the image of point S formed by a concave mirror is to be located. First the principal axis PV is drawn through C. Because light is given off in all directions from point S, *any two lines* may be drawn from S to represent rays of light incident on the mirror. The point of intersection of the

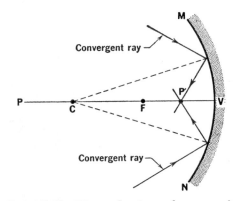

Fig. 15-15. The reflection of converging rays by a concave mirror.

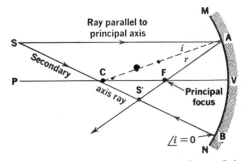

Fig. 15-16. Locating an image formed by a concave mirror.

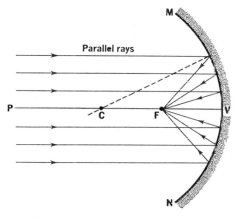

Fig. 15-17. The image formed by a concave mirror when rays parallel to the principal axis are reflected.

reflected rays locates the image of point S at S'.

The construction is greatly simplified if two rays are selected for which the directions of the reflected rays are already known. One of these, *a ray traveling parallel to the principal axis*, is known to be reflected through the principal focus. The other, *a ray traveling along a secondary axis*, is known to be reflected back along itself, the angle

of incidence being zero. These rays are shown as SA and SB respectively, their reflected paths intersecting at S' to form the image of S.

14. Images formed by concave mirrors. We may construct the image formed by a concave mirror by locating the images of enough different points. If, for example, the object is an arrow, the entire image can be located by finding the positions of the image of the head and the image of the tail of the arrow. The formation of images with concave mirrors may be grouped conveniently in six cases.

Case 1. Object at an infinite distance. An object at an infinite distance from the mirror would provide only parallel rays which, if parallel to the principal axis, would be reflected through the principal focus, as shown in Fig. 15-17. We therefore conclude that *the image formed by a concave mirror when an object is at an infinite distance is a point at the principal focus.* The sun's rays reaching the earth are essentially parallel and provide a simple method of determining the focal length of a concave mirror.

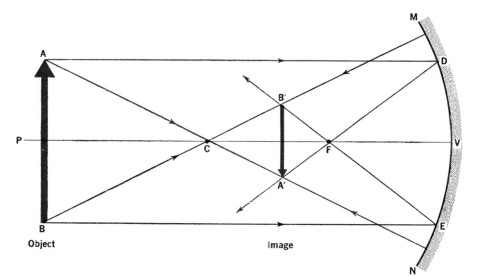

Fig. 15-18. When the object is a finite distance beyond the center of curvature of a concave mirror, the image formed is real, inverted, reduced and located between the center of curvature and the principal focus.

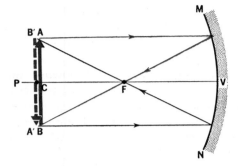

Fig. 15-19. When the object is at the center of curvature of a concave mirror, the image formed is real, inverted, the same size as the object, and located at the center of curvature.

Case 2. Object at a finite distance beyond the center of curvature. In Fig. 15-18, the image of the object *AB* can be located using the method illustrated in Section 13. The secondary axis ray *AE* and the parallel ray *AD* are drawn, *AE* being reflected back along itself and *AD* through the principal focus to locate the image *A′*. The image of *B* is located at *B′* in similar fashion. *The image in this case is real, inverted, smaller than the object, and located between the center of curvature and the principal focus.* The nearer the object approaches

the center of curvature, the larger the image becomes and the nearer it approaches *C*.

Case 3. Object at the center of curvature. When the object is at the center of curvature, as shown in Fig. 15-19, the image of *A* is formed at *A′*, a point coincident with *B*. The image of *B* is at *B′*, a point coincident with *A*. (The secondary axes cannot be shown in this case unless the aperture of the mirror is 180°.) *When the object is at the center of curvature, the image is real, inverted, the same size as the object, and located at the center of curvature.*

Case 4. Object between the center of curvature and principal focus. This case is the converse of Case 2 and is shown in Fig. 15-20. *The image is real, inverted, larger than the object, and located beyond the center of curvature.* The nearer the object approaches the principal focus, the larger the image becomes and the farther it is beyond *C*.

Case 5. Object at principal focus. This case is the converse of Case 1, all reflected rays originating from any point on the object being parallel. See Fig. 15-21. When the object is at the principal focus, no image is formed. If the object is a point source, all rays reflected are mutually parallel.

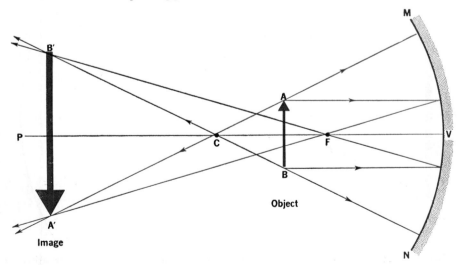

Fig. 15-20. When the object is between *C* and *F* of a concave mirror, the image formed is real, inverted, enlarged, and located beyond the center of curvature.

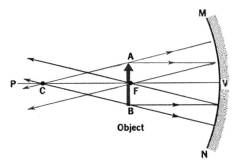

Fig. 15-21. When the object is at the principal focus of a concave mirror, the reflected rays from each point are parallel and no image is formed.

Case 6. Object between principal focus and mirror. The reflected rays from any point on the object which leave the mirror are divergent; they can never meet to form a real image. They appear to meet behind the mirror, however, to form a virtual image as shown in Fig. 15-22. In this case, *the image is virtual, erect, enlarged, and located behind the mirror.*

15. Images formed by convex mirrors. When we look into a convex mirror of the type sometimes used as an outside rearview mirror, we see a small, erect image of reduced size. The diagram shown in Fig. 15-23 may be used to show how such an image is formed. The line *AB* represents the object. The secondary axes and the normals to the points of incidence of the parallel rays are *radii produced.* The parallel rays are reflected from the surface of the mirror and made divergent. When produced behind the mirror, they *appear* to meet at the principal focus, the image being formed where the reflected parallel ray produced and secondary-axis ray produced intersect. In a convex mirror, *all images are virtual, erect, smaller than the object, and located behind the mirror between the vertex and the principal focus.* The size of the image is increased by bringing the object closer to the mirror, but it can never become as large as the object itself.

16. Uses of curved mirrors. Curved mirrors are used in amusement parks to form fantastic images. The convex rearview mirror sometimes used by automobile and truck drivers gives a wide field of vision.

Concave mirrors are used to reflect light and to form images. Cases 1 and 3 may be used to find the focal length and the radius of curvature of concave mirrors. Cases 2 and 4 are used to form images on a screen, Case 2 giving a bright image of reduced size and Case 4 giving an enlarged image.

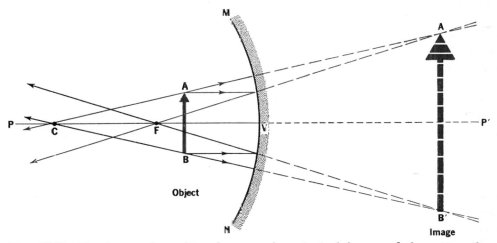

Fig. 15-22. The image of an object between the principal focus and the vertex of a concave mirror is virtual, erect, enlarged, and located behind the mirror.

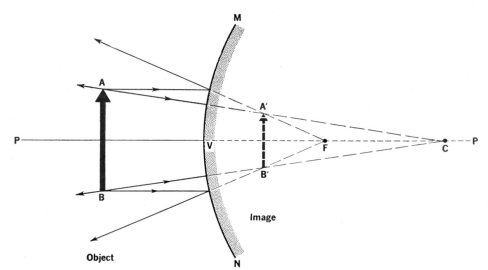

Fig. 15-23. The only image formed by a convex mirror is virtual, erect, reduced, and located behind the mirror.

When an enlarged image is formed, the illumination on the screen is always reduced. The concave shaving mirror is an application of Case 6.

17. The reflecting telescope. The largest telescopes in the world are reflecting telescopes using large concave mirrors to collect and focus light rays. Because it is easier to make a large mirror than a lens of the same size, a reflecting telescope can be made much larger than a refracting (lens) telescope.

Since the objects being viewed with a reflecting telescope are at a finite distance beyond the center of curvature of the mirror, Case 2 applies. The image produced is real, inverted, and located near the principal focus of the mirror. This real image is reflected out of the path of the rays of light incident on the mirror so that it can be viewed or photographed from a position outside the telescope. The inversion of the image is unimportant, since reflecting telescopes are commonly used for viewing celestial bodies in outer space.

18. Spherical aberration. If the aperture of a spherical mirror is large, the parallel rays of light striking the mirror near its edge are not reflected through the principal focus, but are focused at a point nearer the mirror as shown in Fig. 15-24. Only those parallel rays which are incident on the mirror near its vertex are reflected to the principal focus. This imperfection in spherical mirrors with large apertures is known as *spherical aberration*, and results in the formation of distorted images.

There are several ways in which spherical aberration may be reduced. *First*, the

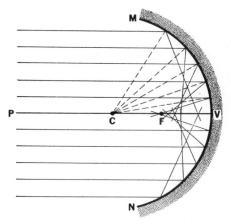

Fig. 15-24. Spherical aberration.

Fig. 15-25. A reflecting telescope is being used here to track a guided missile during flight for photographic purposes. (Steelways Magazine)

aperture of the mirror may be made less than approximately 12°, at which the distortion of the image is negligible. *Second*, with a mirror of larger aperture to collect more light rays, a ring-shaped diaphragm of some opaque material may be used to cut off those reflected rays near the edge which cause distortion. *Third*, the mirror surface may be made parabolic instead of spherical. A parabolic mirror, shown in Fig. 15-26, brings all parallel rays to a focus at one point and reflects those originating at the focus as parallel rays. Automobile headlights are generally fitted with parabolic reflectors. Large reflecting telescopes also use parabolic reflectors to collect and focus the light rays from distant objects.

19. The relative sizes of the object and image. In Section 8 we stated that the relative sizes of the object and the image formed through a small opening depend

on their respective distances from the opening. Similarly, the sizes of the object and the image formed by a curved mirror depend upon their relative distances from the center of curvature. It is possible to show that for mirrors of small aperture the relative sizes of the object and image depend on their respective distances from the mirror.

$$\frac{S_o}{S_i} = \frac{D_o}{D_i}$$

where S_o and S_i are the sizes of the object and image respectively, and D_o and D_i are the distance of the object and image from the mirror.

20. The mirror formula. A simple relationship exists between the distance of an object, the distance of its image, and the focal length of a curved mirror. This relationship, known as the *mirror formula*, is easily derived by considering the diagram of Fig. 15-27 in which a real image of the object AB is formed by a concave mirror.

In similar triangles $A'B'F$ and MVF

$$\frac{A'B'}{MV} = \frac{B'F}{VF}$$

Taking $MV = AB$, $VF = f$, and $B'F = D_i - f$, we have

$$\frac{A'B'}{AB} = \frac{D_i - f}{f} = \frac{D_i}{f} - 1$$

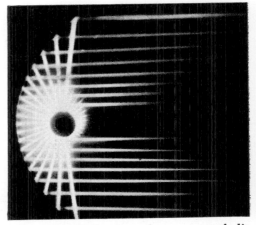

Fig. 15-26. Reflections from a parabolic mirror. (General Electric Co.)

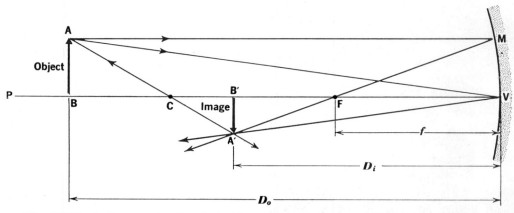

Fig. 15-27. A diagram for the derivation of the mirror formula for curved mirrors.

In similar triangles ABV and $A'B'V$,

$$\frac{A'B'}{AB} = \frac{B'V}{BV}$$

Taking $BV = D_o$ and $B'V = D_i$,

$$\frac{A'B'}{AB} = \frac{D_i}{D_o}$$

Therefore,

$$\frac{D_i}{D_o} = \frac{D_i}{f} - 1$$

Dividing by D_i,

$$\frac{1}{D_o} = \frac{1}{f} - \frac{1}{D_i}$$

Or,

$$\frac{1}{D_o} + \frac{1}{D_i} = \frac{1}{f}$$

where D_o represents the object distance from the mirror, D_i the image distance, and f the focal length of the mirror.

The mirror formula is applicable to all cases of concave and convex mirrors. When an object is located less than one focal length in front of a concave mirror, the image is virtual and lies behind the mirror and the image distance D_i is a *negative* quantity. In the case of convex mirrors, the radius of curvature is negative and the image is always virtual. Therefore, both the focal length f and the image distance D_i are negative quantities. See the Sample Problem below.

Sample Problem

An object located 20. cm in front of a convex mirror forms an image 10. cm behind the mirror. What is the focal length of the mirror?

Solution

$$\frac{1}{D_o} + \frac{1}{D_i} = \frac{1}{f}$$

Solving for f:

$$f = \frac{D_o D_i}{D_o + D_i} = \frac{20.\ \text{cm} \times (-10.\ \text{cm})}{20.\ \text{cm} + (-10.\ \text{cm})}$$

$$f = -20.\ \text{cm}$$

ummary

The amount of light reflected from an object depends upon the kind of material it is made of, the smoothness of its surface, and the angle at which the light strikes its surface. The angle of reflection equals the angle of incidence. These angles both lie in the same plane.

Images are real or virtual. A real image is inverted and can be projected on a screen. Virtual images are erect and cannot be projected on a screen. Images formed by plane mirrors are erect, virtual, the same size as the object, and as far behind the mirror as the object is in front.

A focus is a point where rays of light meet or from which rays of light diverge. Rays parallel to the principal axis of a concave mirror are reflected to a point on the principal axis, midway between the center of curvature and the vertex. This point is the principal focus; its distance from the vertex is the focal length and is equal to half the radius of curvature.

The sizes of the object and image are related to their distances from the mirror and are related to the focal length of the mirror.

TERMS TO DEFINE

angle of incidence	incident ray	real focus
angle of reflection	laws of reflection	real image
aperture	luminous body	reflected ray
boundary of a medium	mirror	reflection
center of curvature	multiple reflection	regular reflection
concave mirror	normal	secondary axis
conjugate foci	parabolic reflector	spherical aberration
convex mirror	plane mirror	vertex
diffused reflection	principal axis	virtual focus
focal length	principal focus	virtual image

QUESTIONS

A 1. What three factors determine the amount of light an object will reflect?

2. What are the two laws of reflection?

3. When you look in a plane mirror, do you see yourself as others see you? Why?

4. Illustrate the following by diagram as they are related to curved mirrors: center of curvature; vertex; principal axis.

5. What type of mirror produces real images?

6. In what three ways may spherical aberration in mirrors be reduced?

B 7. Suppose we paint on a mirror with white paint the word "paint." When the mirror is placed in a beam of sunlight, the reflection of the sunlight on a smooth wall consists of a bright area in which the letters of the word "paint" appear dark. Explain.

8. What kind of trick mirror produces (a) a short, fattened image; (b) a tall, thin image?

9. What kinds of mirrors could be used and where should the object be placed to produce (a) an enlarged real image; (b) a small real image; (c) a real image the same size as the object; (d) an enlarged virtual image; (e) a small virtual image?

10. (a) Construct a ray diagram to show the formation of an image by a concave mirror when the object is at a finite distance beyond

the center of curvature. (*b*) Describe fully the image that is formed.

11. (*a*) Construct a ray diagram to show the formation of an image by a concave mirror when the object is between the principal focus

and the center of curvature. (*b*) Describe fully the image that is formed.

12. (*a*) Construct a ray diagram to show the formation of an image by a convex mirror. (*b*) Describe fully the image that is formed.

PROBLEMS

A **1.** A concave mirror has a focal length of 10 cm. What is its radius of curvature?

2. If the radius of curvature of a curved mirror is 8 in., what is its focal length?

3. While you are looking at the image of your feet in a plane vertical mirror, you see a scratch in the glass of the mirror. How far is the scratch from the floor? Assume that you are 5 ft 8 in. tall.

4. A boy 5.0 ft tall stands 20. ft from the opening of a small pinhole camera. If the camera is 6.0 in. deep, how large is the boy's image?

5. The light from a distant star is collected by a concave mirror. If the radius of curvature of the mirror is 5.0 ft, how far from the mirror is the image formed?

6. An object is placed 25.0 cm from a concave mirror whose focal length is 5.00 cm. Where is the image located?

7. An object 10. in. high is located 36 in. from a concave mirror, focal length 6.0 in. (*a*) Where is the image located? (*b*) How large is it?

8. An object placed 21.0 in. from a spherical concave mirror gives a real image 14.0 in. from the mirror. (*a*) What is the radius of curvature of the mirror? (*b*) If the image is 12.0 in. tall, what is the height of the object?

B **9.** An object and its image in a concave mirror are the same size when the object is 15 in. from the mirror. What is the focal length of the mirror?

10. An object is placed 5.0 cm from a concave mirror whose focal length is 15 cm. (*a*) Where is the image located? (*b*) If the object is 2.0 cm high, what is the size of the image?

● **11.** A man 6.0 ft tall stands in front of a mirror. (*a*) What is the smallest vertical mirror that will allow him to see his full image? (*b*) If the mirror makes an angle of 30° from the vertical toward him, what is the minimum length that will enable him to see his full image assuming his line of vision is not depressed below the horizontal?

● **12.** An object 5.00 cm tall stands at the 0.0-cm mark on a meter stick. (*a*) If a convex mirror having a focal length of 25.0 cm is placed at the 50.0-cm mark, where is the image formed? (*b*) How tall is the image?

● **13.** The image of the moon is formed by a concave mirror whose radius of curvature is 4.00 meters at a time when the distance to the moon is 221,000 mi. What is the diameter of the image, the diameter of the moon being approximately 2160 mi?

RESEARCH ON YOUR OWN

1. Locate the image of an object placed in front of two plane mirrors at right angles to each other. Try the mirrors at angles other than 90°. Locate the images of objects placed in front of three mirrors arranged like those used in clothing stores.

2. Manufactured range finders are usually made with prisms. Design, make, and calibrate a range finder made with two plane mirrors.

3. Prove geometrically that if the reflecting surfaces of two plane mirrors make an angle of exactly 45° with each other, any light ray that is reflected first off one mirror and then off the other will always cross its original path (or the projection of its original path) at a right angle.

4. Construct and demonstrate a simple periscope, using two small plane mirrors as the reflecting surfaces.

5. Prove geometrically that the minimum length of a plane mirror necessary to reflect a head-to-foot image of a person is just half the person's height.

6. Report on the use of mirrors in the construction of solar furnaces.

CHAPTER 16
REFRACTION

1 REFRACTION OF LIGHT

1. The nature of refraction. A person aiming a rifle at a target relies on the fact that light travels in straight lines. It does so, however, only if the transmitting medium has a uniform *optical density: a property of a transparent material which is a measure of the speed of light through the material.* Light travels in straight lines only when the medium in which it travels is of the same optical density throughout.

When light traveling in air is incident on the surface of a body of water, some of the light is reflected at the boundary between the air and water and some is absorbed by the water. However, because

water is transparent, most of the light is transmitted through it. Since water has a higher optical density than air, the speed of the light is reduced as it enters the water. This change in speed is shown in the wave-front diagram of Fig. 16-1.

A ray of light that enters the surface of the water at an *oblique* angle (less than 90° to the surface) experiences an abrupt change of direction due to the change in speed. The reason for this change in direction with a change in speed may be illustrated by redrawing the wave-front diagram of Fig. 16-1, making the angle of the incident ray oblique, as in Fig. 16-2. In

VOCABULARY

Angle of refraction. The angle between the refracted ray and the normal drawn to the point of refraction.

Converging lens. A lens that is thicker in the middle than it is at the edge.

Critical angle. That limiting angle of incidence in the denser medium which results in an angle of refraction of 90°.

Diverging lens. A lens that is thicker at the edge than it is in the middle.

Index of refraction. The ratio of the speed of light in a vacuum to its speed in a given substance.

Optical density. A property of a transparent material which is a measure of the speed of light through it.

Refraction. The bending of light rays as they pass obliquely from one medium into another of different optical density.

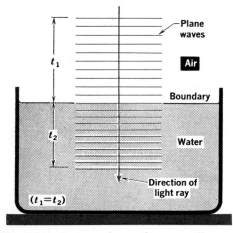

Fig. 16-1. A wave-front diagram illustrating the difference in the speed of light in air and water.

interpreting this diagram, remember that a light ray is the direction the light travels and is perpendicular to the wave front. This bending of a light path is called *refraction*. **Refraction** *is the bending of light rays as they pass obliquely from one medium into another of different optical density.*

Because of refraction a fish appears higher in the water, when viewed from the bank, than it actually is. A stick or teaspoon placed in a tumbler of water appears to be bent or broken at the surface of the water. A coin placed in the bottom of a teacup, out of the line of vision of an observer, will become visible when the cup is filled with water.

2. Refraction and the variation in the speed of light. Suppose MN of Fig. 16-3 represents the surface of a body of water. The line AO represents the path of a ray of light traveling through the air and striking the water at O. Some of the light is reflected along the path OE, but the light entering the water, instead of continuing along OF in a straight line, is bent as it passes from air into water, taking the path OB.

The incident ray AO makes the angle AOC with the normal (angle of incidence). The refracted ray OB makes the angle

DOB with the normal produced. *This angle between the refracted ray and the normal drawn to the point of refraction is called the* **angle of refraction,** r.

In the examples given so far, the light rays have passed from one medium into another of *higher* optical density with a resulting reduction in speed. Whenever a ray enters the denser medium normal to the boundary, no bending occurs; whenever a ray enters the denser medium at an oblique angle, bending does occur and the ray is bent *towards* the normal.

What is the nature of the refraction if the order is reversed so that the light passes obliquely from one medium into another of *lower* optical density? Suppose the light source is at B, in Fig. 16-3, and light rays travel along line BO to the surface at point O, angle BOD being the angle of incidence. Of course, some light is reflected at this boundary; however, the main portion of the beam will be refracted along the line OA on entering the air. The angle of refraction in this case is COA, showing that the light is bent *away* from the normal.

3. The index of refraction. The speed of light in a vacuum, as stated in Chapter 15, is approximately 186,000 miles per

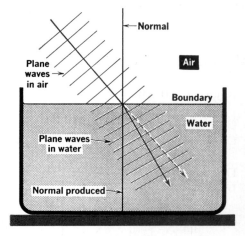

Fig. 16-2. A wave-front diagram illustrating the refraction of light at an air-water boundary.

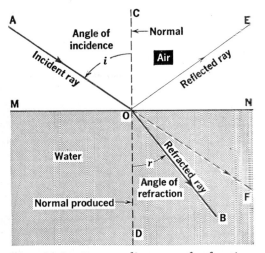

Fig. 16-3. A ray diagram of refraction showing the angle of incidence and the angle of refraction.

second. The speed of light in water is almost 140,000 miles per second, just about three-fourths of that in a vacuum. The speed of light in ordinary glass is about 124,000 miles per second, about two-thirds the speed of light in a vacuum. *The ratio of the speed of light in a vacuum to its speed in another substance is called the* **index of refraction** *for that substance.* For example,

index of refraction (glass) =

$$\frac{\text{speed of light in vacuum}}{\text{speed of light in glass}}$$

The value for glass is $\frac{3}{2}$, or 1.5. Since the speed of light in water is only three-fourths as great as in a vacuum, the index of refraction of water is $\frac{4}{3}$, or 1.33. The index of refraction of a few common substances is given in Table 15, Appendix B. The speed of light in air is only slightly different from the speed of light in a vacuum. Therefore, without much error, we can use the index of refraction for cases where light travels *from air* into another medium.

The fundamental principle of refraction was discovered by Willebrord Snell (1591–1626), a Dutch mathematician and astronomer. He did not publish his discov-

ery, but his work was taught at the University of Leyden where he was a professor of mathematics and physics. René Descartes (1596–1650), a French mathematician, published Snell's conclusions in 1637.

Snell's discoveries about refraction were not stated in terms of the speed of light, which was not determined until 1675. From his observations, however, he defined the index of refraction as the ratio of the sine of the angle of incidence to the sine of the angle of refraction. This mathematical relationship is known as Snell's law. If we let n represent the index of refraction, i the angle of incidence, and r the angle of refraction,

$$n = \frac{\sin i}{\sin r}$$

The sine of an angle is defined in Fig. 16-4. The sines of angles from 0° to 90° are given in Table 3, Appendix B.

In Fig. 16-6, the line AO represents a ray of light traveling through the air and incident upon a glass plate at O. This ray is refracted as it enters the glass along the path OB. To find the index of refraction, a circle is drawn in the plane of the ray about point O and the normal to the surface of the glass at point O is constructed as NN'. The lines AC and DB are drawn perpendicular to NN'.

$$\sin i = \frac{AC}{AO} \quad \text{and} \quad \sin r = \frac{DB}{OB}$$

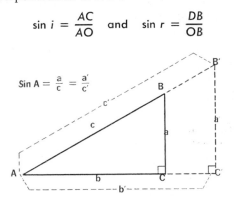

Fig. 16-4. The sine of an angle is the ratio of the length of the side opposite the angle to the length of the hypotenuse.

Fig. 16-5. Willebrord Snell contributed one of the fundamental laws of optics, now known as Snell's law. (Bausch & Lomb Optical Co.)

Since *AO* and *OB* are radii of the same circle, they are equal. Thus,

$$n = \frac{\sin i}{\sin r} = \frac{AC}{DB}$$

4. Importance of the index of refraction. The index of refraction of a pure, transparent substance is a constant quantity which is a definite physical property of the substance. Consequently, the identity of substances can be determined by measuring their index of refraction. An instrument known as a *refractometer* is used to measure the index of refraction of a substance quickly and accurately. For example, butterfat and margarine have different indexes of refraction; one of the first tests made in a food-testing laboratory to determine whether butter has been adulterated with margarine is the measurement of the index of refraction. The exceedingly high index of refraction of a diamond furnishes one of the most positive tests for its identification.

5. The laws of refraction. The facts about refraction of light may be summarized in three *laws of refraction*.

First law. The incident ray, the refracted ray, and the normal to the surface at the point of incidence are all in the same plane.

Second law. The index of refraction for any two media is a constant that is independent of the angle of incidence.

Third law. When a ray of light passes obliquely from a medium of lesser to one of greater optical density, it is bent toward the normal. Conversely, a ray of light passing obliquely from an optically denser medium to a rarer medium is bent from the normal to the surface.

6. Light through a glass plate. If the index of refraction of a transparent substance is known, it is possible to trace the path that a ray of light will take in passing through the substance. In Fig. 16-8, *ABCD* represents a piece of plate glass, the surfaces of which are parallel, and *EO* represents a ray of light incident upon it at point *O*. From *O* as a center two arcs are described having the ratio 3 to 2, the index of refraction of glass being taken as 1.5. The normal *OF* is drawn; then the line *GH* is drawn parallel to *OF*, passing

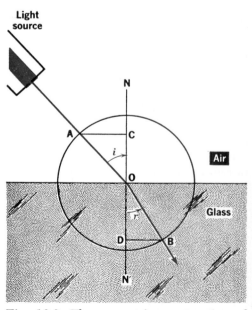

Fig. 16-6. The geometric construction of Snell's law.

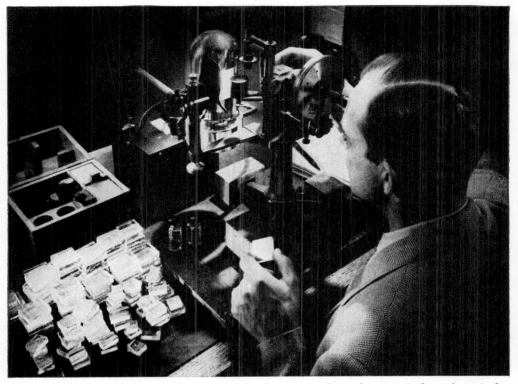

Fig. 16-7. A refractometer being used to determine the refractive index of optical glass. (American Optical Co.)

through the point where the incident ray intersects the *smaller* arc. The line *OP*, which is determined by the points *G* and *O*, marks the path taken by the refracted ray as it travels through the glass.

If the ray were not refracted as it leaves the glass, it would proceed along the line *PK*. To indicate the refraction at *P*, *P* is used as a center and arcs are drawn having the same ratio, 3 to 2, as before. The normal *PL*, and a line, *MN*, parallel to the normal are drawn, the parallel line passing this time through the point where the larger arc is intersected by the refracted ray produced. The points *P* and *M* determine the line which marks the path of the refracted ray as it leaves the glass.

If the ray of light *AO* is incident upon a triangular glass prism, as shown in Fig. 16-9, it is bent toward the normal and travels along the line *OB*. As the light

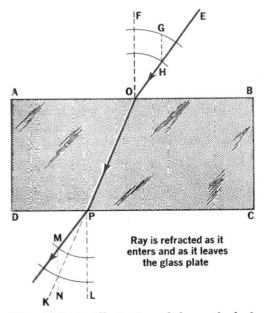

Fig. 16-8. An illustration of the method of tracing a light ray through a glass plate.

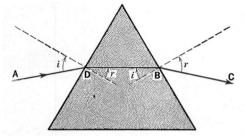

Fig. 16-9. The path of a light ray passing through a prism.

leaves the prism, it is refracted from the normal along the line *BC*.

7. Atmospheric refraction. Because light travels slightly faster in a vacuum than it does through air, light from the sun or the stars, entering the earth's atmosphere obliquely, is refracted. Since the atmosphere gradually increases in density, a ray of light coming from the sun or a star follows a path suggested by the curve shown in Fig. 16-10. There is no abrupt refraction such as that which occurs at the boundary between two media of different optical densities.

Because of atmospheric refraction, we do not see the sun or the stars in their true positions except when they are directly overhead. In the figure, we see the setting sun at *S'*, instead of in its true position at *S*. The refraction of light by the earth's atmosphere makes the sun at this time appear about one diameter higher than it really is. Since the index of refraction from outer

space to air is only 1.00029, the diagram is greatly exaggerated in order to show the bending.

8. Mirages. Sometimes a person driving along a smooth, black-top road on a hot, dry summer day, sees what look like pools of water on the road ahead. However, when he gets to the spot where the pools apparently were, the road is quite dry.

When the road is actually wet, it is the light from the sky reflected from the surface of the road which gives the characteristic impression. On a hot day the layer of air nearest the road has a lower density, and light rays from the sky, obliquely entering this layer of air of lower density, are refracted upward, away from the road. It is this refracted light from the sky that is sometimes seen as an optical illusion, called a *mirage*. The observer cannot distinguish between light reflected from water and light refracted by warm air. As a result, he may think pools of water exist when actually there are none. Other mirages, in the form of inverted images of distant objects, may appear as reflections from the surface of these phantom pools.

9. The critical angle. A ray of light which passes from a medium of higher optical density into one of lower optical density is bent from the normal. Suppose an incident ray of light, *AO*, is traveling from water into air and bends from the perpendicular along the line *OB*, as shown in Fig. 16-12. What happens to this refracted ray, *OB*, as the angle of incidence, *i*, is increased? As the angle of incidence is increased, the angle of refraction

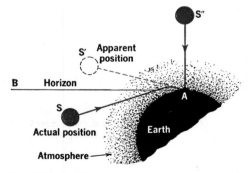

Fig. 16-10. The sun is visible before actual sunrise and after sunset because of atmospheric refraction.

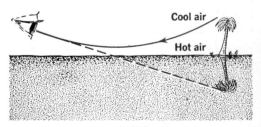

Fig. 16-11. A mirage results from atmospheric refraction in the hot surface air.

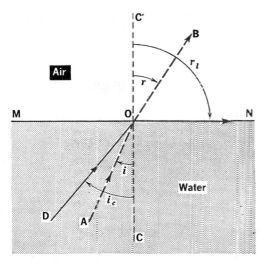

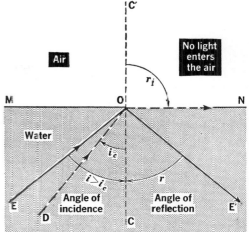

Fig. 16-12. The critical angle i_c is the limiting angle of incidence in the denser medium which results in an angle of refraction of 90°.

Fig. 16-13. Total reflection occurs when the angle of incidence exceeds the critical angle.

increases approaching the limiting value $r_l = 90°$, and the refracted ray emerges from the water along a path approaching closer and closer to the water surface. As the angle of incidence continues to increase, a limiting value is finally reached at which the angle of refraction equals 90° and the refracted ray does not enter the air at all but takes the path ON, along the water surface. *The limiting angle of incidence in the denser medium, resulting in an angle of refraction of 90°, is known as the critical angle,* i_c. The critical angle for water is reached when the incident ray DO makes an angle of 48.5° with the normal; the critical angle for crown glass is 42°, while that of a diamond is only 24°.

In Section 3 we defined the index of refraction of a material as the ratio of the velocity of light in a vacuum (air) to the velocity of light in the material, or as the ratio $\sin i / \sin r$. In Fig. 16-12, the light passes from the denser material to the air, the angle of refraction r being thus related to the velocity of light in air. The index of refraction of the water in this instance is

$$n = \frac{\sin r \text{ (air)}}{\sin i \text{ (water)}}$$

At the critical angle i_c, r is the limiting value r_l which equals 90°, thus,

$$n = \frac{\sin r_l}{\sin i_c} = \frac{\sin 90°}{\sin i_c} = \frac{1}{\sin i_c}$$

Therefore,

$$\sin i_c = \frac{1}{n}$$

where n is the index of refraction of the denser medium relative to air and i_c is the critical angle of this medium.

10. Total reflection. If the angle of incidence of a ray of light passing from water into air is increased beyond the critical angle, no part of the incident ray enters the air; it is totally reflected from the water boundary. In Fig. 16-13, EO represents a ray of light whose angle of incidence exceeds the critical angle, the angle of incidence EOC being greater than the critical angle DOC. The ray of light is reflected back into the water medium along the line OE', a case of simple reflection in which the angle of incidence EOC equals the angle of reflection $E'OC$. Total reflection always occurs when the angle of incidence exceeds the critical angle.

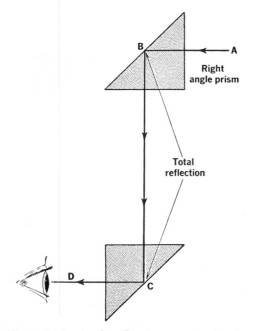

Fig. 16-14. Total reflection occurs in the prisms within a periscope.

Fig. 16-15. The light-piping effect of a rod made of Lucite acrylic resin. The light source is at the bottom right. Observe how brightly the chart is illuminated, while the person holding it is in almost total darkness. (E. I. duPont deNemours Co.)

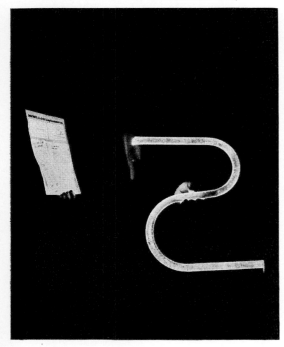

11. Applications of total reflection. A diamond is a very brilliant gem because its index of refraction is high and its critical angle is therefore small. Very little of the light that enters a cut diamond passes through it; most of the light is reflected internally (total reflection), emerging from the top of the diamond.

When a ray of light enters a right-angle glass prism like that shown in Fig. 16-14, it is totally reflected. The periscope of a submarine has two such prisms; the observer at D sees objects along the line AB. The light rays are reflected down the tube by the first prism, and then reflected at right angles by the second prism. Right-angle prisms are used in such instruments as periscopes because they yield total reflection of light, whereas mirrors reflect only about 70 percent of the light they receive.

In high-grade binoculars, right-angle prisms are often used to reinvert an image, making an inverted image erect, two prisms being required for each ocular system. Special types of field telescopes, such as the spotting telescopes used on rifle ranges, have an optical system which includes a pair of right-angle prisms. These prisms enable a real image to be reinverted without the use of an inverting lens in the field telescope. They allow for relatively high magnification with relatively close spacing of objective and eyepiece lenses. Right-angle prisms are also used in reflecting telescopes, range finders, and other optical instruments.

Rods of clear, colorless plastic are sometimes used for transmitting light. Rays of light entering one end of such a rod are totally reflected by the walls of the rod and emerge only from the other end of the rod, even though the rod is curved or bent into an unusual shape. The light-piping effect of Lucite acrylic resin is illustrated in Fig. 16-15. The applications of this light-piping effect of Lucite rods and plates are numerous and varied.

2 REFRACTION BY LENSES

12. Types of lenses. A lens can be made from almost any transparent substance that is bounded by two nonparallel, curved surfaces, or by one plane surface and one curved surface. The curved surfaces may be spherical, parabolic, or cylindrical, although spherical surfaces are the most common. Lenses are nearly always made of glass and are of two kinds.

1. Converging lenses. Some converging lenses are shown in Fig. 16-16; all are thicker in the middle than they are at the edge. The first two lenses in the figure are *flat* lenses; the third is a *meniscus* lens.

A converging lens bends the wave front of light passing through it, the thick portion retarding the light more than the thin portion near the edge. Thus plane waves incident on the surface of a converging lens parallel to the lens axis are refracted and converge at a point *beyond* the lens (the principal focus), as shown in Fig. 16-17.

2. Diverging lenses. Lenses that are thicker at the edge than in the middle are called *diverging* lenses. The double concave

lens and the plano-concave lens of Fig. 16-18 are flat lenses; the convexo-concave lens is a meniscus lens.

A diverging lens bends the wave front of light passing through it, the thick portion near the edge retarding the light more than the thin portion. Plane waves incident on the surface of a diverging lens parallel to the lens axis are refracted and diverge from a point *in front of the lens* (the principal focus), as shown in Fig. 16-19.

13. Ray diagrams. The nature and location of the image formed by a lens is more easily determined by a ray diagram than by a wave-front diagram. Plane waves that approach a lens parallel to the lens axis, as illustrated in Figs. 16-17 and 16-19, may be represented by light rays drawn perpendicular to the lens plane. These parallel rays are refracted as they pass through a converging lens and converge at the *principal focus* of the lens, as in Fig. 16-20. At point D the incident ray is bent towards the normal, and at point E it is bent away from the normal. Because the rays of light actually pass through the principal focus it is called a *real* focus, and real images are formed on the same side of the lens as the real focus.

Parallel rays incident on a diverging lens perpendicular to the lens plane are refracted as they pass through the lens and diverge from the principal focus located

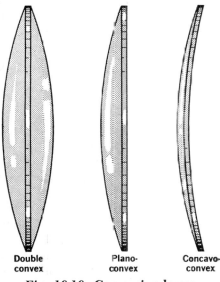

Double convex   Plano-convex   Concavo-convex

Fig. 16-16. Converging lenses.

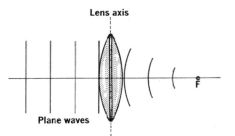

Fig. 16-17. Refraction of plane waves by a converging lens.

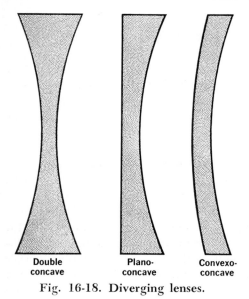

Double concave   Plano- concave   Convexo- concave

Fig. 16-18. Diverging lenses.

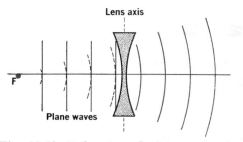

Fig. 16-19. Refraction of plane waves by a diverging lens.

of light *AB*, parallel to the principal axis, is refracted and passes through the *principal focus, F*. The *secondary axes* pass through the *optical center* of a lens, which practically coincides with the *geometrical center* of the lens. The ray *AOA'* travels along the secondary axis drawn from *A*. Rays of light passing through the optical center of a lens are *not appreciably refracted*.

Lenses refract parallel rays so that they meet at the principal focus. However, this focus is not midway between the lens and the center of curvature as we found it to be in spherical mirrors; its position on the principal axis depends on the index of refraction of the lens. With a double convex lens of crown glass, the principal foci and the centers of curvature almost coincide, and the radius of curvature and the focal length are almost equal. The

in front of the lens, as in Fig. 16-21. Because the rays do not actually pass through the principal focus it is called a *virtual focus* and virtual images are formed on the same side of the lens as the virtual focus.

Spherical lenses usually have two *centers of curvature*, the centers of the intersecting spheres which form the lens surfaces. These centers are shown in Fig. 16-22 as points *C* and *C'*. The *principal axis* passes through the centers of curvature. The ray

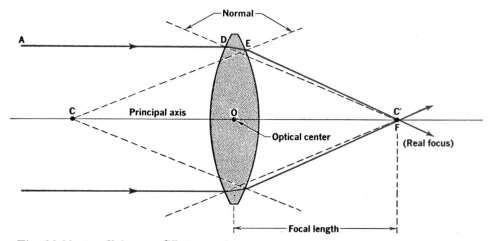

Fig. 16-20. Parallel rays of light are brought to a real focus by a converging lens.

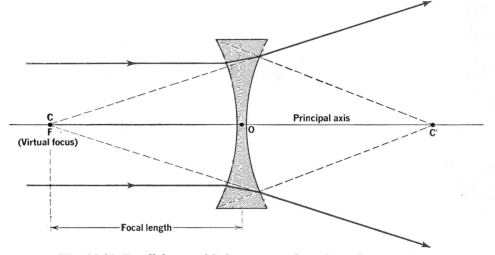

Fig. 16-21. Parallel rays of light are spread out by a diverging lens.

focal length of a lens is the distance between the optical center of the lens and the principal focus. Increasing the index of refraction shortens the focal length; the thicker a lens, the shorter its focal length.

14. Forming images with lenses. To understand how images are formed by lenses, let us refer again to Fig. 16-22. As in the case of curved mirrors, any two rays coming from point *A* on the object are sufficient to locate the image point. For convenience we use two particular rays. One ray, traveling along the secondary axis, is not appreciably refracted as it passes through the optical center of the lens, *O*. The other ray travels toward the lens parallel to the principal axis and this ray, *AB*, is refracted as it enters the lens at *B* and as it leaves the lens at *D*. It passes through the principal focus *F*, intersecting the secondary-axis ray at *A'*, thus locating the image of *A* at *A'*.

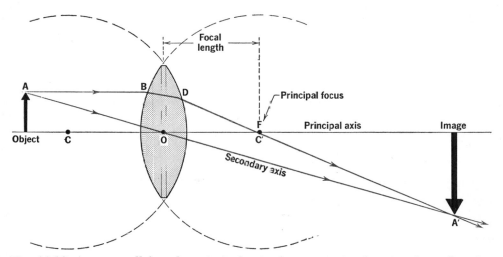

Fig. 16-22. A ray parallel to the principal axis of a converging lens is refracted so that it passes through the principal focus. A ray passing through the optical center is not appreciably refracted.

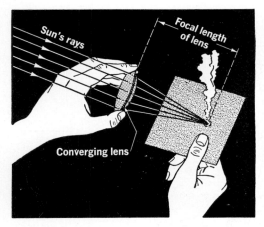

Fig. 16-23. The image formed when parallel rays of light pass through a converging lens is a point at the principal focus.

Lenses and mirrors differ in several ways.

1. Secondary axes pass through the optical center of a lens and not through either of its centers of curvature.

2. The principal focus is apt to be near the center of curvature, depending on the refractive index of the glass from which the lens is made. This often makes the focal length of a double convex lens practically equal to its radius of curvature.

3. Since the image produced by a lens is formed by rays of light which actually pass through the lens, a *real* image is formed on the side of the lens opposite the object. Virtual images formed by lenses appear to be on the same side of the lens as the object.

4. Convex lenses form images in almost the same manner as concave mirrors, while concave lenses are like convex mirrors in the manner in which they form images.

15. Images formed by converging lenses. We shall consider six different cases of image formation.

Case 1. Object at infinite distance. The use of a small burning glass to focus the sun's rays upon a point illustrates this first case. While the sun is not at an infinite distance, it is so far away that its rays reaching the earth are nearly parallel. When an object is at an infinite distance, so that its rays are parallel, *the image formed is a point at the principal focus.* This principle may be used to find the focal length of a lens by focusing the sun's rays on a white screen, as in Fig. 16-23. The distance from the screen to the lens is the focal length of the lens.

Case 2. Object at a finite distance beyond twice the focal length. Case 2 is illustrated in Fig. 16-24, in which secondary axes are drawn from points A and B on the object. The light traveling along these paths passes through the lens unrefracted. Rays parallel to the principal axis are also drawn from A and B. These rays are refracted and pass through the principal focus. They intersect the secondary axes at A' and B' to form the image A'B'. *The image is real, inverted, smaller than the object, and located between F' and 2F' on the opposite side of the lens.* The lenses of the eye, the camera, and the telescope are all applications of this case.

Case 3. Object at a distance equal to twice the focal length. The construction of the image is shown in Fig. 16-25. *The image is real, inverted, the same size as the object, and located at 2F' on the opposite side of the lens.* This principle is used to invert an image

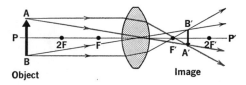

Fig. 16-24. The image formed by a converging lens of an object a finite distance beyond 2F.

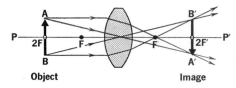

Fig. 16-25. The image formed by a converging lens of an object at 2F is real, inverted, and the same size as the object.

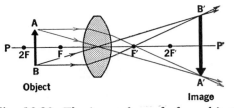

Fig. 16-26. The image formed of an object between F and 2F.

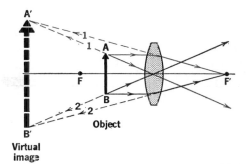

Fig. 16-28. The image formed of an object less than a focal length from the lens.

without changing its size, as in the field telescope.

Case 4. Object at a distance between one and two focal lengths away. This case is the converse of Case 2 and is shown in Fig. 16-26. *The image is real, inverted, enlarged, and located beyond 2F' on the opposite side of the lens.* The compound microscope, slide projector, and motion picture projector are all applications of a lens used in this manner.

Case 5. Object at the principal focus. This case is the converse of Case 1. No image is formed, since the rays of light are parallel as they leave the lens. See Fig. 16-27. A lighthouse and a searchlight are applications of Case 5.

Case 6. Object at a distance less than one focal length away. The construction in Fig. 16-28 shows that the rays are divergent after passing through the lens and cannot form a real image on the opposite side of the lens. These rays appear to converge behind the object to produce *an image that is virtual, erect, enlarged, and located on the same side of the lens as the object.* The simple magnifier and the eyepieces of microscopes and telescopes all make use of this method of forming images.

16. Images formed by diverging lenses. The only kind of image that can be formed by a diverging lens is one that is *virtual, erect, and reduced in size.* Such lenses are used to neutralize the effect of a converging lens, or to reduce, to some extent, their converging effect, as shown in Fig. 16-29.

17. Spherical aberration in lenses. When a camera is used on a bright day, the diaphragm is closed almost entirely to exclude a major portion of the light. Light then passes through only the central part of the camera lens, and the image thus produced is very well-defined. If the day is cloudy, more light must be admitted to expose the film satisfactorily. Under these conditions, the image produced by some lenses may not be so distinct and clearcut. As the diaphragm is opened, some light rays enter the camera through parts of the lens nearer its edge; these light

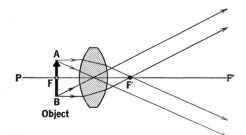

Fig. 16-27. No image is formed when the object is located at the principal focus.

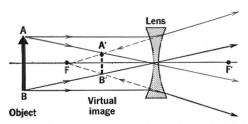

Fig. 16-29. The image of an object formed by a diverging lens.

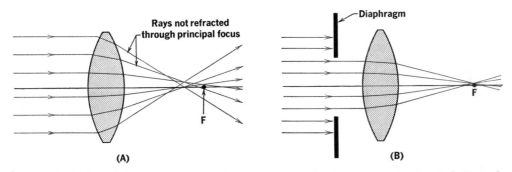

Fig. 16-30. Parallel rays near the edge of a converging lens are not refracted through the principal focus. A diaphragm may be used to prevent these rays from reaching the lens.

rays do not focus at exactly the same point as the rays passing through the center of the lens. This defect of a spherical lens is called *spherical aberration*.

The diaphragm used in optical instruments to avoid spherical aberration of lenses does not actually correct the defect. It merely masks out the rays of light which are not properly refracted.

18. Lens formulas. For lenses, the formula for the relationship of object size to image size and object distance to image distance is the same as that for curved mirrors:

$$\frac{S_o}{S_i} = \frac{D_o}{D_i}$$

The symbols S_o and S_i represent the sizes

of the object and the image, and D_o and D_i represent the respective distances of the object and image from the optical center of the lens.

The formula for curved mirrors used to determine the distances of the object and image in relation to focal length applies also to lenses:

$$\frac{1}{D_o} + \frac{1}{D_i} = \frac{1}{f}$$

where D_o represents the distance of the object from the lens, D_i the distance of the image, and f the focal length. When the image is virtual, D_i is negative. For diverging lenses, both $1/D_i$ and $1/f$ are negative.

★3 LENS APPLICATIONS

19. The structure of the human eye. The eye is a remarkable optical instrument. The several parts of its structure are shown in Fig. 16-31.

1. The white coat, or sclera. This is the hard, tough outer coat of the eyeball, which maintains the shape of the eyeball and protects the eye. The transparent *cornea*, in the front part of the sclera, admits light into the eyeball.

2. The middle coat, or choroid layer. This coat contains a black pigment, whose function is to absorb stray rays of light and to

prevent the blurring of images by reflection from the walls.

3. The inner coat, or retina. This covers only the rear portion of the eyeball. The nerves of the eye spread through the retina, forming a light-sensitive screen to receive images.

4. The crystalline lens. This double convex lens forms a *real image* of objects in the field of vision on the retina.

5. The iris. This is the colored portion of the eye, which serves as a diaphragm to regulate the amount of light entering the

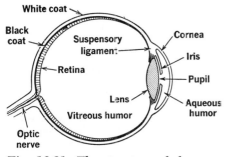

Fig. 16-31. The structure of the eye.

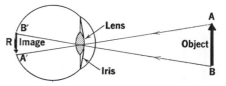

Fig. 16-32. The image formed on the retina by the eye lens is real, inverted, and smaller than the object.

inner eye. The opening in the center of the iris is called the *pupil*. In a dark room the pupil becomes larger to admit more light; in bright sunlight it becomes smaller, reducing the amount of light admitted, thus protecting the retina from damage by exposure to intense light.

The eye is filled with watery and jelly-like materials which aid in the formation of images. The eyelids act as shutters to screen out the light and in general to protect the eye.

20. The formation of images in the eye. Each lens forms an image of objects on the retina which is *real, inverted, and smaller* than the object, as shown in Fig. 16-32. The image is bright and well-defined if the object is not too close to the eye.

Our eye lenses have considerable *power of accommodation* because they are connected to muscles which can change the curvature of the lenses when necessary.

If the muscles increase the convexity of the lenses, the focal length is decreased. If an object is brought close, our lens muscles contract, increasing the convergence of the lenses so as to form a sharp image on each retina. For the average eye, the shortest distance for distinct vision is 25 cm. The lens muscles are completely relaxed when we look at objects more than 20 ft away.

21. Correcting defects of the eye. Within certain limits, a normal eye is self-focusing, since the lens muscles can change the shape of the lens enough to make the image fall upon the retina whether the object is nearby or remote. However, some persons are *nearsighted*, while others are *farsighted*. Those who are **nearsighted** *either have eyeballs that are too long, or lenses that are too convex, so that the image is formed in front of the retina.* Only when the object is brought very close to the eye, so that its rays are diverging when they reach the lens, will such an eye give distinct vision. See Fig. 16-33.

Nearsightedness can be corrected by

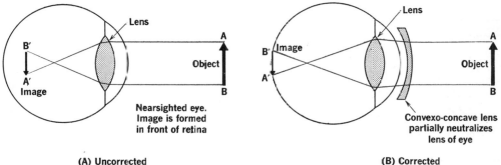

(A) Uncorrected

Nearsighted eye.
Image is formed
in front of retina

(B) Corrected

Convexo-concave lens
partially neutralizes
lens of eye

Fig. 16-33. A diverging lens may be used to correct nearsightedness.

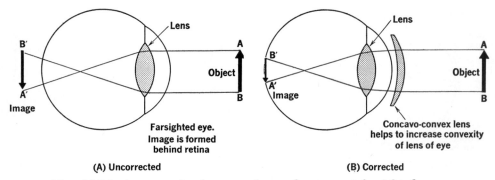

(A) Uncorrected   (B) Corrected

Fig. 16-34. A converging lens may be used to correct farsightedness.

eyeglasses which partially neutralize the abnormal convexity of the lens of the eye. Such eyeglasses have convexo-concave lenses which make the rays of light more divergent before they enter the eye.

If the eyeball is too short, or if the lens is too flat, **farsightedness** *results.* In order for the lens to form the image on the retina, instead of behind it, an object must be held unusually far from the eye. See Fig. 16-34.

Eyeglasses with concavo-convex lenses are prescribed to correct farsightedness. These glasses make the light rays more convergent before they enter the eye, so that the lens of the eye can form the image on the retina. Glasses with double lenses, called bifocals, are sometimes used to enable a person to read with one set of lenses and see more remote objects clearly with the other set.

If the surface of the cornea is not perfectly curved, or if the lens itself is somewhat irregular, all parts of an object are not in clear focus. To a person with this type of eye, the lines of Fig. 16-35 do not all appear equally distinct. *The defect in vision caused by an irregularly curved cornea or lens is known as* **astigmatism.** Glasses which have been specially ground to counteract these irregularities are used to correct for astigmatism. The concavo-convex lenses and convexo-concave lenses used in glasses are meniscus lenses. They provide a wider field of clear vision than flat lenses.

22. Estimating size and distance. We judge the size of an object from the size of the visual angle. In Fig. 16-36 the image of *AB* formed on the retina is larger than the image of *A'B'*. When we know how far away an object is, we can estimate its size, but we need considerable experience

Fig. 16-35. The lines are not all equally distinct if the eye is astigmatic.

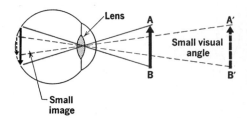

Fig. 16-36. We judge the size of an object from the size of the visual angle.

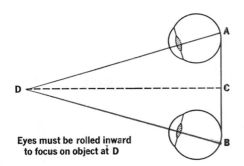

Eyes must be rolled inward
to focus on object at D

Fig. 16-37. We judge the distance of an object by the amount of muscular effort required to focus both eyes on the object.

before we can estimate both size and distance. Our judgment of size depends on our knowledge of the object's distance, while if we know the size of an object, we can estimate its distance.

Our two eyes form images on corresponding parts of their respective retinas, which the brain interprets as a single image. This is *binocular* vision. The position of the eyes allows us to see a little more of the right side of a three-dimensional object with our right eye than with the left, and vice versa. The brain's interpretation of the combined image gives us depth of vision, or perspective.

From Fig. 16-37, it is evident that our eyes roll inward to some extent when we focus both eyes on the point D. A certain amount of muscular effort is used in such a case. The distance between the eyes is the base line from which we learn to estimate the distance CD by the amount of muscular effort needed to roll the eyes inward to the angles CAD and CBD so that both eyes are focused on the object in view.

23. A camera's similarity to the eye. From a comparison of Fig. 16-38 and the diagram of the eye, Fig. 16-31, it is evident that the photographic camera and the eye are similar. The sensitive emulsion on the film or plate corresponds to the retina, and receives the image. The camera lens, or combination of lenses, acts like the crystalline lens of the eye, forming on the film or plate an image that is real, inverted, and smaller than the object. The diaphragm regulates the amount of light which enters the camera just as the iris regulates the amount of light entering the eye through the pupil. The shutter of the camera also excludes light just as the eyelids do. The blackened interior of the camera, like the

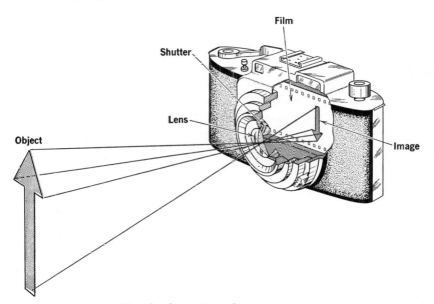

Film

Shutter

Lens

Object

Image

Fig. 16-38. The formation of an image in a camera.

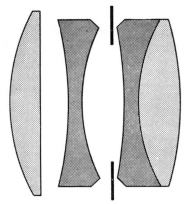

Fig. 16-39. An anastigmatic lens.

Lenses that can be used with a large aperture are said to be *fast* and are used in high-speed photography. The effective aperture of a lens equals the diameter of the camera diaphragm when it is open as wide as possible. The "speed" of a lens depends upon the ratio of its focal length to the effective aperture and is called its *relative aperture*. In an f-4 lens, the focal length is 4 times the effective aperture. Such a lens is 4 times as fast as an f-8 lens, and 16 times as fast as an f-16 lens, the speed ratio being proportional to the squares of the relative apertures.

25. The simple magnifier. A converging lens of short focal length may be used as a simple magnifier. The lens is held slightly nearer the object than one focal length and the eye is placed close to the lens on the opposite side. This is a practical example of Case 6; the image is enlarged, virtual, and erect as shown in Fig. 16-41. Because the object is near the principal focus, the magnification of a simple magnifier is approximately equal to the ratio of the distance for most distinct vision to the focal length of the lens. The equation representing this relationship is

choroid layer, absorbs stray rays of light.

24. Anastigmatic lenses. When ordinary lenses are used with the diaphragm of a camera opened wide, the image on the film is generally sharp and well defined at the center but blurred near the edges because of spherical aberration. Rays of light from horizontal and vertical lines in a plane in the object are not focused in the same plane on the edges of the image. This defect of lenses is known as *lens astigmatism*. By using a combination of lenses of suitable refractive indexes and focal lengths, lens makers produce *anastigmatic* lenses which give good definition over a wide area. See Fig. 16-39.

$$\text{Magnification} = \frac{D_i}{D_o} = \frac{25 \text{ cm}}{f}$$

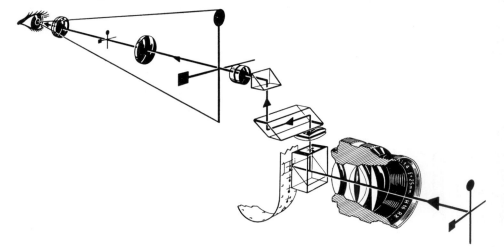

Fig. 16-40. The optical system of a modern movie camera. (Paillard, Inc.)

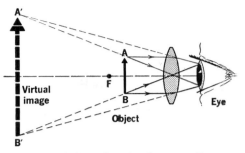

Fig. 16-41. The simple magnifier.

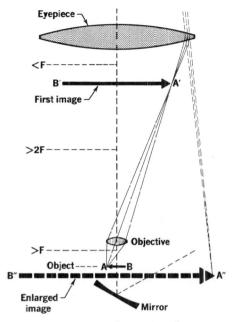

Fig. 16-42. Image formation by a compound microscope.

26. The compound microscope. The compound microscope, probably invented in Holland by Zacharias Janssen about 1590, uses a lens, the *objective*, to form an enlarged image on the principle of Case 4. This image is then magnified by a second lens, called the *eyepiece*, on the principle of Case 6.

In Fig. 16-42 a converging lens is used as the objective, with the object AB placed just beyond its focal length. At $A'B'$, a distance greater than twice the focal length of the objective lens, an enlarged, real, and inverted image is formed. The eyepiece acts as a simple magnifier to enlarge this image.

The magnifying power of the objective is approximately equal to the length of the tube l, divided by the focal length, f_o, of the objective, or l/f_o. The magnifying power of the eyepiece, acting as a simple magnifier, equals $25 \text{ cm}/f_e$. The total magnification equals the product of the two lens magnifications.

$$\text{Total magnification} = \frac{25 \text{ cm} \times l}{f_e \times f_o}$$

See the Sample Problem below.

Sample Problem

The tube of a microscope is 16 cm long. The focal length of the objective is 0.50 cm, and the focal length of the eyepiece is 2.5 cm. What is the magnification of the microscope?

Solution

$$\text{Total magnification} = \frac{25 \text{ cm} \times l}{f_e \times f_o}$$

$$\text{Total magnification} = \frac{25 \text{ cm} \times 16 \text{ cm}}{2.5 \text{ cm} \times 0.50 \text{ cm}}$$

$$\text{Total magnification} = 320$$

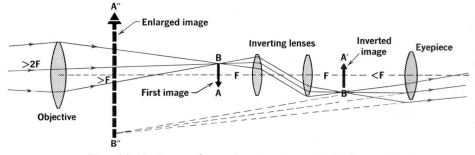

A″
Enlarged image

Inverting lenses

Inverted image

Eyepiece

>2F

B

>F

F

F

A′

<F

First image   **A**

Objective

B′

B″

Fig. 16-43. Image formation in a terrestrial telescope.

27. Refracting telescopes. A *celestial* telescope has two lens combinations. The objective lens is of large diameter so that it will admit large quantities of light. The objects to be viewed in telescopes are always distant more than twice the focal length of the objective lens; as a consequence, the image formed is smaller than the object, but it is exceedingly bright. The eyepiece magnifies the real image produced by the objective lens. The magnifying power is approximately equal to the focal length of the objective, f_o, divided by the focal length of the eyepiece, f_e, or f_o/f_e.

The lenses of a *terrestrial*, or field, telescope form images just as their counterparts do in the refracting astronomical telescope. However, it would be very awkward to see objects inverted and reversed in a field telescope, so another lens system is used to reinvert the real image formed by the objective, making the final image erect, as shown in Fig. 16-43. This additional lens system inverts the image but does not magnify it, being placed exactly its own focal length from the image formed by the objective.

The *prism binocular* is actually a double field telescope, using two sets of totally reflecting prisms to reinvert the final image, rather than a third lens system as in the field telescope. This method of reinverting the first image makes possible a shorter distance between the objective and eyepiece, so that binoculars can be more compact and convenient to carry than field telescopes.

Fig. 16-44. A pair of totally reflecting prisms reinvert the image in binoculars. (Bausch & Lomb Optical Co.)

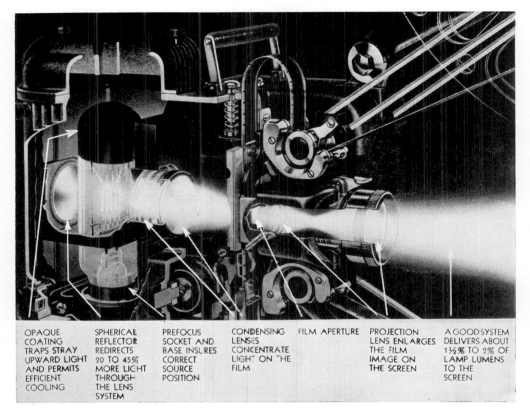

| OPAQUE COATING TRAPS STRAY UPWARD LIGHT AND PERMITS EFFICIENT COOLING | SPHERICAL REFLECTOR REDIRECTS 20 TO 45% MORE LIGHT THROUGH THE LENS SYSTEM | PREFOCUS SOCKET AND BASE INSURES CORRECT SOURCE POSITION | CONDENSING LENSES CONCENTRATE LIGHT ON THE FILM | FILM APERTURE | PROJECTION LENS ENLARGES THE FILM IMAGE ON THE SCREEN | A GOOD SYSTEM DELIVERS ABOUT 1½% TO 2% OF LAMP LUMENS TO THE SCREEN |

Fig. 16-45. The optical system of a motion picture projector.   (General Electric Co.)

28. Image projection. A common optical system used in many projection instruments is shown in Fig. 16-45. Film-strip projectors, slide projectors, and motion picture projectors all produce an image on a screen by the same optical method. The object in all such projection is a brightly illuminated, transparent film or glass slide. A combination of converging lenses acts as the objective lens. The object is placed slightly farther from the lens than one focal length, and the screen on which the image is to be formed is placed at a distance considerably more than twice the focal length of the objective. Because the image is real, inverted, and enlarged, the film or slide must be placed upside down in the projector so that the image appears erect on the screen.

A projection lamp has a highly concentrated filament which is accurately located in the optical system of the projector by the use of a prefocusing base. The filament coils lie in a plane perpendicular to the optical axis of the lens system. The use of a tubular glass envelope allows the spherical reflector and condensing lenses to be located close to the filament in order to intercept the maximum amount of luminous flux.

A 750-watt projection lamp operating at its normal filament temperature of 5300° F dissipates approximately the same amount of energy as a one-horsepower motor. The glass envelope, located only three-quarters of an inch away, has a safe operating temperature of less than 1000° F. Thus, forced ventilating is necessary to prevent the glass from softening. Ordinarily, projection lamps having power ratings above 300 watts require forced ventilation.

Summary

The laws of refraction describe the behavior of light rays which pass obliquely from one medium into another of different optical density. The index of refraction of any transparent material is defined in terms of the speed of light in a vacuum and in the material. Total reflection is explained on the basis of the critical angle of a material and the limiting value of the angle of refraction, this limiting value being 90°.

Converging lenses having convex surfaces form images in a manner similar to that of concave mirrors. Diverging lenses having concave surfaces form images in a manner similar to that of convex mirrors. The general lens formulas are the same as those for curved mirrors.

The eye is an optical device performing the same general functions as a camera. The eye lens forms real, inverted, reduced images on the retina. The camera lens forms similar images on photographic film. Lens functions in such common types of optical equipment as the microscope, the telescope, and the projector can be analyzed by considering each lens separately.

TERMS TO DEFINE

anastigmatic lens
angle of incidence
angle of refraction
astigmatism
atmospheric refraction
binocular vision
center of curvature
converging lens
cornea
critical angle
crystalline lens
diverging lens
erect image

farsightedness
flat lens
focal length
index of refraction
inverted image
laws of refraction
lens
meniscus lens
mirage
nearsightedness
optical center
optical density
power of accommodation

principal axis
principal focus
pupil
real focus
real image
refraction
refractometer
retina
secondary axis
spherical aberration
total reflection
virtual focus
virtual image

QUESTIONS

A 1. Define (a) refraction; (b) angle of refraction; and (c) index of refraction.
2. What property of a transparent substance causes the refraction of light rays which strike it at an oblique angle?
3. What are the three laws of refraction?
4. What is meant by the terms (a) critical angle and (b) total reflection?
5. (a) What causes spherical aberration in lenses? (b) How may it be remedied?
★ 6. Identify and give the function of the following parts of the eye: (a) retina; (b) lens; (c) pupil; (d) iris; (e) eyelid.

★ 7. Is the image formed by the eye (a) real or virtual; (b) erect or inverted; (c) smaller or larger than the object; (d) closer to the lens or farther from the lens than the object; (e) on the same or opposite side of the lens from the object?
★ 8. (a) What type of lens is used to correct nearsightedness? Explain. (b) What type of lens is used to correct farsightedness? Explain.
★ 9. What causes astigmatism?
★ 10. How do our eyes enable us to see three-dimensional images?
★ 11. Compare the functions of the following parts of a camera with the corresponding parts

of the eye: (a) film; (b) diaphragm; (c) shutter; (d) lens; (e) blackened interior.

★ 12. Of which principle of converging lenses is the simple magnifier an application?

★ 13. Explain the lens system and image formation of a compound microscope in terms of the lens principles used.

★ 14. Explain the lens system and image formation of a refracting astronomical telescope in terms of the lens principles used.

★ 15. How does a terrestrial telescope compare with a refracting astronomical telescope?

B 16. What practical use is made of the index of refraction of a substance?

17. When we see a mirage, we usually think that the substance we see is water. Why?

18. You are looking diagonally down at a fish in a pond. To the fish, does your head appear higher or lower than it actually is?

19. Explain why we see the sun before it ac- tually rises above the horizon in the morning, and why we see it after it has dropped below the horizon in the evening.

20. What kinds of lenses could be used and where should the object be placed to produce (a) an enlarged real image; (b) a reduced real image; (c) a real image the same size as the object; (d) an enlarged virtual image; (e) a small virtual image?

21. Which is the better reflector of light, a right-angle prism or a plane silvered mirror? Explain.

★ 22. What is the power of accommodation of the eye?

★ 23. Why do meniscus lenses produce clearer images than flat lenses when used in eyeglasses?

★ 24. When the distance between a projector and the screen is increased, what adjustment must be made in the distance between the film and the objective lens to bring the image back into focus?

PROBLEMS

A 1. The speed of light in chloroform is 123,000 mi/sec. What is the refractive index?

2. What is the speed of light in a diamond whose refractive index is 2.42?

3. A penny at the bottom of a glass cylinder is 30. cm from the eye. If water is poured into the cylinder to a depth of 16 cm, how much closer does the coin appear?

4. A converging lens has a focal length of 20.0 cm. If it is placed 50.0 cm from an object, at what distance from the lens will the image be?

5. If an object is 10 in. from a converging lens of 5-in. focal length, how far from the lens will the image be formed?

6. The focal length of the lens in a box camera is 10.0 cm. The fixed distance between the lens and the film is 11.0 cm. If an object is to be clearly focused on the film, how far must it be from the lens?

7. An object 3.0 in. tall is placed 20. in. from a converging lens. A real image is formed 10. in. from the lens. (a) What is the focal length of the lens? (b) What is the size of the image?

8. An object 30 cm from a converging lens forms a real image 60 cm from the lens. (a) Find the focal length of the lens. (b) What is the size of the image if the object is 5 cm high?

9. The focal length of a camera lens is 2.00 in. How far must the lens be from the film to produce a clear image of an object 10.0 ft away?

10. What is the focal length of the lens in your eye when you read a book 14 in. from your eye? Distance from lens to retina is 0.75 in.

11. What is the focal length of the lens in your eye when you are looking at a person standing 50. ft away? The distance from the lens to the retina is 0.75 in.

★ 12. What is the magnifying power of a simple magnifier whose focal length is 10. cm?

B 13. Make a drawing which shows the path of a ray of light passing from a medium of refractive index 1.33 into a medium of refractive index 1.5. The angle of incidence is 45°.

14. An object 3 cm tall is placed 16 cm from a converging lens with a focal length of 24 cm. (a) Find the location of the image. (b) What is its size?

15. When an object 2.0 in. tall is placed 8.0 in. from a converging lens, an image is produced on the same side of the lens as the object, but 24 in. away from the lens. (a) What is the focal length of the lens? (b) What is the size of the image?

● 16. An optical bench pointer 1.0 cm tall is placed at the 55.0-cm mark on the meter stick. When a diverging lens is placed at the 0.0-cm mark, an image is formed at the 5.0-cm mark. (a) What is the focal length of the lens? (b) What is the size of the image?

● **17.** If the angles of incidence and refraction of a ray of light passing from air into water are 60.0° and 41.0°, what is the index of refraction of the water?

● **18.** Calculate the critical angle for carbon tetrachloride.

★ **19.** The objective lens of a compound microscope has a focal length of 0.500 cm. The eyepiece has a focal length of 2.00 cm. If the lenses are 15.0 cm apart, what is the magnifying power of the microscope?

★ **20.** The dimensions of the picture on a standard lantern slide are 2.5 in. by 3.0 in. This slide is to be projected to form an image 5.0 ft by 6.0 ft at a distance of 30. ft from the objective lens of the projector. (*a*) What is the distance from the slide to the objective lens? (*b*) What focal length objective lens must be used?

★ **21.** The tube of a microscope is 160. mm long. If the focal length of the eyepiece is 30.0 mm and the focal length of the objective is 5.00 mm, find the magnifying power.

22. What is the distance between the objective lens and the eyepiece lens of a terrestrial telescope when viewing an object 1 mile away? The focal length of objective is 5 in., the focal length of inverting lens system is 1 in., and the focal length of eyepiece is 2 in. The two lenses are 2 in. apart.

RESEARCH ON YOUR OWN

1. Drop a penny to the bottom of a hydrometer jar or tall glass cylinder filled with water. Looking straight down at the jar, run your finger down the outside of the jar until it seems to be at the same level as the penny in the jar. Explain the result.
2. Determine by experiment the indices of refraction of different samples of glass and other transparent substances.
3. Experiment with the variously shaped pieces of glass which are part of the equipment of an optical disk, to discover how their surfaces refract rays of light which are incident on them.
4. Using an ordinary reading glass, find the focal length of the lens by the formula that uses the sizes of the object and the image. Then find the focal length when the outer edge of the lens (about half the radius) is covered with an iris. Next find the focal length when the central portion of the lens is covered. Explain any differences in the results.
5. Set up a convex lens of known focal length and locate the object position and the real image position. Then, without moving the object or the lens, insert a concave lens between the object and the lens. Determine the new position of the image. With these data, calculate the focal length of the concave lens.
6. Dissect the eye of a mammal and study its structure to gain a clearer understanding of the functions of the human eye.
7. By a series of charts or models, show how increased knowledge of optical principles brought about the development of the microscope from the first crude instruments to the modern precision microscopes.
8. Convert a compound microscope into a microprojector, using a right-angle prism and a bright source of light.
9. Devise and use an apparatus for taking photomicrographs, using an ordinary camera and a compound microscope.
10. Report on the various methods used to produce motion pictures for the different types of wide-screen projection.

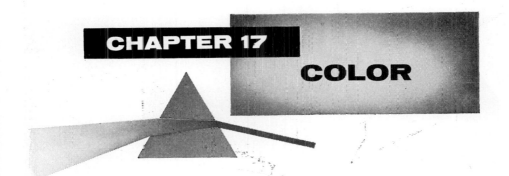

CHAPTER 17

COLOR

1. Dispersion by a prism. Suppose a narrow beam of sunlight falls on a glass prism in a darkened room. If the light which leaves the prism now strikes a white screen, it spreads into a band of colors, in which one shade blends gradually into another. *This band of colors produced when sunlight is dispersed by a prism is called a* **solar spectrum.** The dispersion of sunlight into a band of colors was described by Newton, whose experiments showed that sunlight is composed of six distinct colors: *red, orange, yellow, green, blue,* and *violet. Light consisting of several colors is called* **polychro-** *matic light; light consisting of only one color is called* **monochromatic light.**

The dispersion of light by a prism is shown in Fig. 17-1. It is evident that the angle of refraction for red light is not so great as that for violet light, and that the refraction angles of other colors lie between these two. Thus the index of refraction of a substance is not the same for light of different colors. If we wish to be very precise in measuring the index of refraction of a substance, monochromatic light must be used and the monochrome color must be stated. Some variations in the

VOCABULARY

Absorption spectrum. A continuous spectrum interrupted by dark lines or bands.

Chromatic aberration. The nonfocusing of light of different colors.

Complementary colors. Two colors which combine to form white light.

Diffraction. The spreading of light into a region behind an obstruction.

Emission spectrum. A spectrum formed by the dispersion of light from an incandescent solid, liquid, or gas.

Interference. The mutual effect of two beams of light resulting in a loss of energy in certain areas and a reinforcement of energy in others.

Monochromatic light. Light consisting of only one color.

Polarized light. Light in which vibrations occur in a single plane perpendicular to the ray.

Polychromatic light. Light composed of several colors.

Primary colors. Colors, in terms of which all other colors may be described, or from which all other colors may be evolved by mixtures.

Primary pigments. The complements of the primary colors.

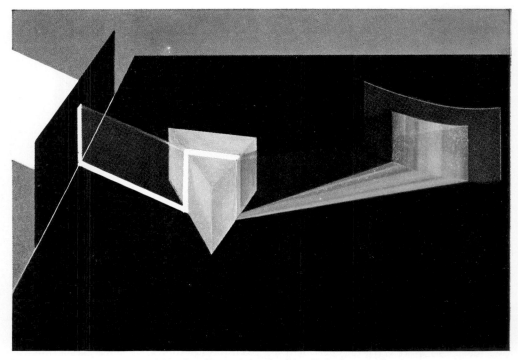

Fig. 17-1. The dispersion of white light by a prism.

Fig. 17-2. A second prism recombines the spectral colors to produce white light.

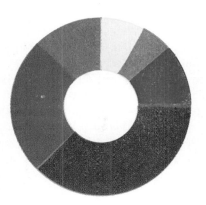

Fig. 17-3. When this disk is rotated rapidly, it appears white. Explain.

index of refraction of glass are given in the table below.

2. The color of light. The color of light is dependent on the frequencies, or wavelengths, of the radiation which reaches the eye, and has much the same relationship to light that pitch has to sound. The energy radiated from a source of polychromatic light is distributed over a range of frequencies that may extend through the entire visible spectrum.

A hot solid radiates an appreciable amount of energy, which increases as the temperature is raised. At relatively low temperatures, the energy is radiated only in the infrared region. As the temperature of the solid is raised, some of the energy is radiated at higher frequencies, ranging into the red portion of the visible spectrum as the body becomes "red hot." At still higher temperatures the body may be "white hot," as the major portion of the

VARIATION OF THE INDEX OF REFRACTION		
Color	Crown Glass	Flint Glass
Red	1.515	1.622
Yellow	1.517	1.627
Blue	1.523	1.639
Violet	1.533	1.663

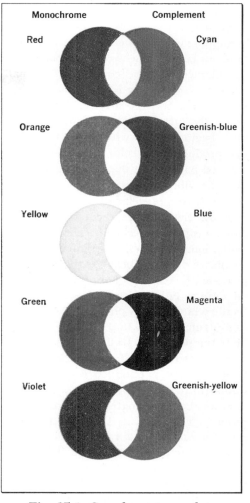

Fig. 17-4. Complementary colors.

Fig. 17-5. The additive mixtures of three beams of light of the primary colors produce their complements and white light.

radiated energy shifts toward the higher frequencies.

Suppose we have a clear-glass, tungsten-filament lamp connected so the current in the filament can be controlled. A small current of electricity in the filament does not change its appearance, but as we gradually increase the current, the filament begins to glow with a dark red color. To produce this color, the electrically charged particles in the atoms of tungsten must be vibrating fast enough to radiate energy with a wavelength of the order of 7000 Å. Even before the lamp filament glows visibly, experiments show that it emits longer waves, the infrared rays, which we detect as heat. As the current is increased further, the lamp filament gives off orange light, then yellow light, and finally white light. A photographer's tungsten-filament flood lamp operates at a very high temperature. If the white light of such a lamp is passed through a prism, a band of colors is obtained which is quite similar to the solar spectrum.

From the wavelengths of various colors given in Fig. 17-1, it is evident that our eyes are sensitive to a range of frequencies equivalent to about one octave. The wavelength of the light at the upper limit of visibility (7000 Å) is about as great as the wavelength of the light at the lower limit of visibility (4000 Å). *Color is a property of light waves which depends entirely on their frequency.*

3. The color of objects. Color is a property of the light waves which reach our eyes. It is not a property of the objects we see, since objects absorb certain wavelengths from the light incident upon them and reflect others. For example, consider a piece of cloth which looks blue in sunlight. When held in the red portion of a solar spectrum in a darkened room, the cloth seems black. A piece of red cloth held in the blue portion of the solar spectrum also appears black. *The color of an opaque object depends upon the kind of light which it is capable of reflecting to the eye.* If an object reflects all the colors it receives, we say it is *white*. We call an object *black* if it absorbs all the light rays that fall upon it. An object is called red if it absorbs all other colors and reflects only red light. A piece of blue cloth appears black in the red portion of the spectrum because there is no blue light there for it to reflect, and it absorbs all other colors. For the same reason, a red cloth appears black in the blue portion of the spectrum. *The color of an opaque object also depends on the color of the light incident upon it.*

Ordinary window glass, which transmits all colors, is said to be colorless. Red glass absorbs all colors but red, which it transmits. The stars of the United States flag would appear red on a black field if viewed through red glass. *The color of transparent objects depends upon the color of the light waves which they transmit.*

4. Combining colors to produce white light. Since polychromatic light can be dispersed into its simple colors, it is reasonable to suppose that we can combine simple colors to form polychromatic light. There are three ways in which this may be done.

1. A prism placed in the path of the solar spectrum formed by another prism will recombine the different colors to produce white light. See Fig. 17-2. Other colors may be compounded in the same manner.

2. A disk which has the spectral colors painted on it, as shown in Fig. 17-3, may be rotated rapidly to produce the effect of combining the colors. The light from one color forms an image which persists on the retina of the eye until each of the other colors in turn has been reflected to the eye. If pure spectral colors are used in the proper proportion, they will blend to produce white light.

3. Wavelengths from the mid-region of the visible spectrum may be combined with wavelengths from the two end regions to produce white light. This method will be treated in Section 6.

5. Complementary colors. Using the prisms shown in Fig. 17-2, instead of permitting all of the colors produced by dispersion from the first prism to enter the second prism, we can cut off the red light from the first prism. The remaining spectral colors combine as they pass through the second prism to produce a blue-green color called *cyan*. Red light and cyan should therefore combine to produce white light; and a rotating color wheel shows this to be true. *Any two colors which combine to form white light are said to be complementary.*

In similar fashion, it can be shown that blue and yellow are complementary colors. White goods acquire a yellow color after continued laundering. Bluing, or a bluish dye added to the laundry detergents, neutralizes the yellow color and makes the wash white. Iron present in sand used for making glass imparts a green color to the glass. Manganese gives glass a *magenta*, or purplish-red color. However, if both these elements are present in the right proportion, the resulting glass will be colorless. The complements of the six simple spectral colors are shown in Fig. 17-4.

6. The primary colors. We have seen that sunlight is composed of six simple colors, sometimes called elementary colors, which cannot be further dispersed, and which combine to produce white light. Two complementary colors also combine to produce white light. However, the complement of an elementary color is not monochromatic, but is a mixture of all of the elementary colors remaining after the given elementary color has been removed.

Experiments with beams of different colored lights have shown that any color or hue can be described in terms of three different colors. Light from one end of the visible spectrum combined with light from the middle region in various proportions will yield all of the color hues in the half of the spectrum that lies in between. Light from the opposite end, when combined with light from the middle region, will also yield all hues in the half of the spectrum that lies in between. Colored light from the two end regions and the middle region can be combined to match all of the hues, when mixed in the proper proportions. The three colors which can be used most successfully in color matching experiments of this sort are *red, green,* and *blue.* Consequently, these have been called the *primary colors.*

Von Nardroff's color apparatus, or other suitable light sources, may be used for a variety of color-matching experiments. A beam of light from a projector is thrown on a screen through three circular openings in the color apparatus. Each opening accommodates a glass slide; by inserting red, blue, and green slides we may project the three primary colors on a white screen. The three beams may be adjusted to overlap, producing additive mixtures of the colored lights as shown in Fig. 17-5. Observe that green and blue lights combine to produce cyan, the complement of red; green and red lights combine to produce yellow, the complement of blue; and red and blue lights combine to produce magenta, the complement of green. Thus, two primary colors combine to produce the complement of the third primary color, and where the three overlap, white light is produced.

7. Mixing pigments. When the complements blue light and yellow light are mixed, white light results by an addition process. If we mix a blue pigment with a yellow pigment, a green mixture results. This is a subtraction process, since each pigment subtracts or absorbs certain colors. For example, the yellow pigment subtracts blue and violet lights and reflects red, yellow, and green. The blue pigment subtracts red light and yellow

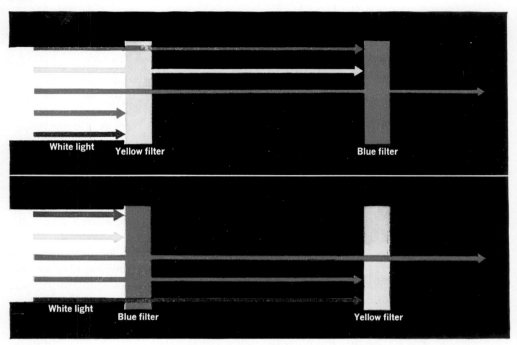

White light | Yellow filter | Blue filter

White light | Blue filter | Yellow filter

Fig. 17-6. Subtraction of light by color filters.

light and reflects green, blue, and violet. Green light is the only color reflected by both pigments; thus the mixture of pigments appears green under white light.

The subtraction process can be demonstrated by the use of color filters which absorb certain wavelengths and transmit others from a single white-light source.

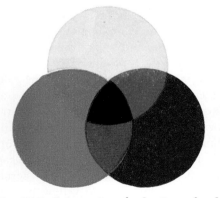

Fig. 17-7. Subtractive production of colors using the three primary pigments (color filters) and a single light source.

The effect of a combination of yellow and blue filters on a beam of white light is shown in Fig. 17-6.

When pigments are mixed, each one subtracts certain colors from white light, and the resulting color depends on the light waves that are not absorbed. *The primary pigments are the complements of the three primary colors.* They are, respectively, *cyan* (the complement of red), *magenta* (the complement of green), and *yellow* (the complement of blue). When the three primary pigments are mixed in the proper proportions, all the colors are subtracted from white light, and the mixture is black. See Fig. 17-7.

★ **8. The four-color printing process.** In the four-color printing process, all colors in the pictures are reproduced by depositing different proportions of three colors of printing ink—yellow, magenta, and cyan—with black added in shadow areas. Four negatives are first made of the subject to be reproduced in color. Differ-

Fig. 17-8. Left: a photograph taken with ordinary film and without a filter. Right: a photograph taken through an infrared filter on infrared sensitive film.

ent filters are used, so that each of these negatives records the amount of one of the colors that should print in the different areas of the picture. A blue filter is used for making the yellow-printer negative, a green filter for the magenta-printer negative, and a red filter for the cyan-printer negative. The filter makes the color to be printed by that particular plate photograph as black and the other two colors photograph as white. The negative for the black plate is made by partial ex-

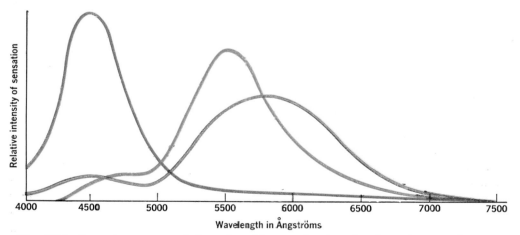

Fig. 17-9. Sensation curves of the color-vision mechanism for the primary colors according to the Young-Helmholtz theory.

posures through each of the three filters so that black will print mainly where all three colors are present.

Halftone printing plates are made from these four negatives in the normal manner. Each of the plates is printed in succession on white paper in the same position, each plate depositing one color of ink, the one for which it was made. Since there are no known printing inks which are pure enough in color to give accurate color reproduction directly, adjustments must be made in the amounts printed by certain areas of each plate, a process called *color correction*.

★ **9. Color photography.** There are a number of types of film available for taking colored still and motion pictures. While they differ in the physical composition of the film and in the method of development and color fixing they require, most of them reproduce colors by making three color records (red, green, and blue) in separate layers of film. These are developed to produce cyan, magenta, and yellow dye layers.

Color film consists of several layers, the top layer containing an emulsion which is sensitive only to blue light. Beneath this layer is a yellow filter layer which absorbs blue light, but transmits red and green light to the layers of film below. The middle layer of emulsion is sensitive only to green light. The lower layer of emulsion is sensitive only to red light. Beneath these three layers of emulsion is a black layer which prevents reflection of light back through the emulsion layers.

During the development and processing of the film, the portions of the blue-sensitive emulsion not affected by light are dyed yellow, the portions of the green-sensitive emulsion not affected by light are dyed magenta, and the portions of the red-sensitive emulsion not affected by light are dyed blue-green. The sensitive silver compounds on which the images are originally recorded, and the silver formed

during the development of the film, are removed during the final processing. This leaves only the colored dye images on the film.

★ **10. Infrared photography.** Photographs can be taken using electromagnetic waves which are just beyond the range of human visibility. Infrared waves reflected by objects are not so much affected as visible light by clouds, fog, and other atmospheric conditions which produce a haziness in photographs. Consequently, much clearer long-distance photographs may be taken with a camera equipped with an infrared filter and using infrared sensitive film. In Fig. 17-8, the picture on the left was taken by the usual method with visible light. The same scene photographed at the same time with an infrared filter and infrared film is shown in the picture on the right.

11. Color vision. Scientists still do not know exactly how our eyes react to light waves of different lengths to enable us to see colors. The most generally accepted theory of color vision was proposed by Thomas Young (1773–1829), an English physician and scientist. It was later elaborated on by Hermann Helmholtz (1821–1894), a great German physicist. According to the *Young-Helmholtz color vision theory*, the retina of the eye is provided with three types of nerve receptors with unequal sensitivity over the range of the visible spectrum. Maximum sensitivity for each type of receptor lies in a different region of the spectrum, so that there is one type for each of the primary colors. See Fig. 17-9.

If all three types of receptors are equally stimulated, we receive the sensation which the brain interprets as white. A lack of stimulation gives us the sensation of darkness or blackness. When red waves enter the eye, they stimulate chiefly the receptors that produce the sensation of red, and we see that color. If only those receptors sensitive to green are stimulated, the sensation of green is produced in the brain. When yellow light enters the eye, however, the receptors for both red and green are stimulated and we see yellow. We see purple if the receptors sensitive to red and blue are stimulated. Thus all colors, shades, and hues are seen through varying stimulation of one, two, or three types of color receptors.

A convenient diagram for mixing colors, called a *chromaticity diagram*, is shown in Fig. 17-10. The wavelengths of the spectral colors are listed around the perimeter in Ångstrom units. Any point not on the solid-line curve, but within the diagram, represents some additive mixture of colors and not a simple spectral color. White light, being such a mixture, is located within the bound area at point *C*. The primary colors are located at the three points of the curve.

A straight line joining any two points within the curve will indicate all of the color variations that can be obtained by combining these two colored lights in varying intensities, an addition process. The line *RG* is an example. Observe that straight lines passing through point *C* join colors which are complementary. Colors, shades, and hues that can be seen on a color television screen are inside the smaller triangle *BGR*.

Recent experiments in color vision, conducted by E. H. Land of the Polaroid Corporation, have shown the eye to be a far more versatile instrument than is indicated by the three-color theory. These experiments suggest that the rays of light themselves are not color-making, but that they are carriers of information which enable the eye to assign appropriate colors to the various parts of an image.

In the Land experiments two photographs of a multicolored object are taken simultaneously on black-and-white film with a special dual camera, the images being photographed through two different color filters. Black-and-white positive transparencies are then made from the two negatives. These transparencies have no color and, although they are photographs of the same scene, are not identical. The degree of transparency of corresponding areas of the two films is different since different wavelengths of light were used to form the two images originally. When the images of the two transparencies are projected and superimposed on a screen, the long-wavelength transparency being projected through a red filter and the short-wavelength transparency being projected with white light without a filter, the composite image reproduces the full range of color of the object originally photographed.

Certainly, red light and white light mixed on a screen produce pink. How then may the full range of color of this photographic image be explained? According to Land, the color of the image arises not from the choice of light wavelengths but from the relative balance of the longer and shorter wavelengths over the entire scene. This suggests that the eye needs information about the long and short wavelengths to see color, without regard to any particular wavelengths. The eye-brain mechanism may separate the incoming rays into long- and short-wavelength images, average together all those on the long side and all those on the short side, and then compare the two averaged images to develop the color sensation. Continuing research in this area of color may contribute substantially to our knowledge of the color-vision mechanism.

★ **12. Color blindness.** *A defect of the eye which causes some persons to confuse two or more colors which others can readily distinguish is known as* **color blindness**. About 6 to 7 percent of men and less than 1 percent of women are color blind. The defect is usually inherited, but certain diseases and large doses of certain drugs may produce temporary color blindness.

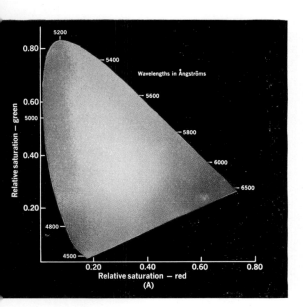

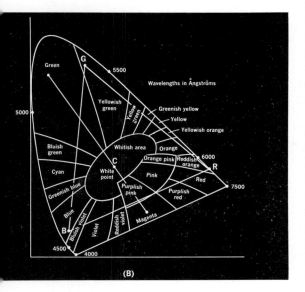

Fig. 17-10. In the chromaticity diagram colors are specified in terms of theoretical colored lights and all possible colors can be described mathematically.

Most color-blind persons cannot distinguish between reds, greens, and yellows, or between blue-greens, blues, and violets. The first group of colors appear to them as shades of yellow; the second group seem to be shades of blue. This type of color blindness is explained by the Young-Helmholtz theory as resulting from a defect in one of the three types of receptors required for complete color vision. Other, rarer, forms of color blindness seem to be caused by defects in two or even all three types of color receptors.

★ **13. Retinal fatigue.** Suppose that we suspend a bright red disk against a white background in strong sunlight and look intently at the disk for about one minute. Now, if the red disk is removed, we see on the white screen a blue-green (cyan) spot the size of the disk. This phenomenon is due to *retinal fatigue*. The red receptors in the retina tire of red and are no longer stimulated by it. The other six colors reflected by the white background combine to produce the sensation of the blue-green color, since red and blue-green are complementary colors. When we use a blue disk instead of a red one, the spot that appears after the eye tires of blue is yellow.

14. The prism spectroscope. We have seen how the sun's rays are separated into colors by a prism to form a spectrum. The light spectrum of a luminous source can be examined by means of an optical instrument known as a *prism spectroscope*, shown in Fig. 17-12. This instrument consists of a *collimator* for producing parallel light rays, a *prism* for dispersing the incident light, and a *telescope* for observing the spectrum produced.

The collimator is a tube with a converging lens at one end and a narrow slit opening at the other. The slit is located at the principal focus of the lens so that when the slit is illuminated, the light rays incident on the prism are parallel. The telescope is supported so that it can be rotated about the vertical axis of the prism table,

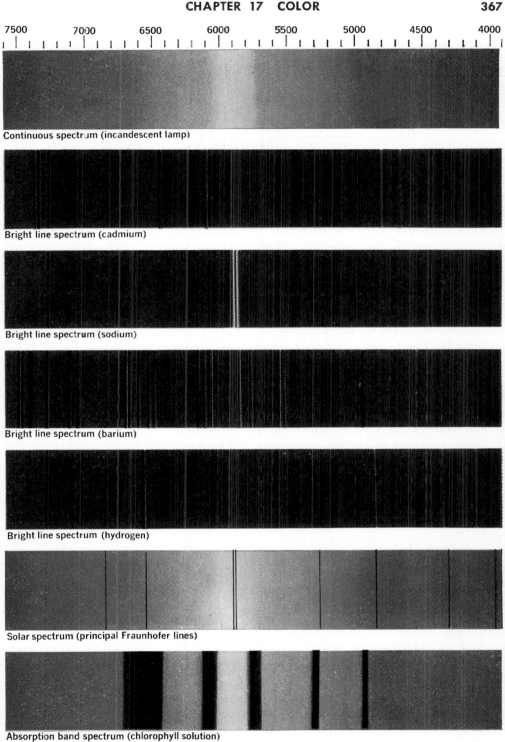

Fig. 17-11. Various types of spectra.

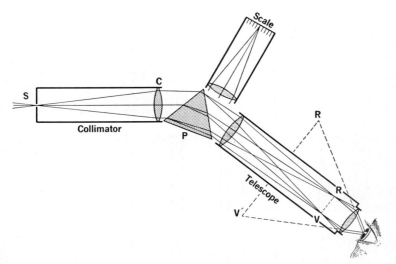

Fig. 17-12. Diagram of a prism spectroscope.

which may be graduated as a circular protractor. When the instrument is fitted for making precise measurements of spectra, it is called a *spectrometer;* when fitted for photographing spectra, it is called a *spectrograph.*

15. Kinds of spectra. Every luminous source emits a characteristic spectrum. The same substance may produce different spectra when excited to luminosity by different means. Optical spectra may be divided into two general types.

1. Emission spectra. When the slit of a spectroscope is illuminated by an incandescent substance, a slit image is formed for each frequency emitted by the source. *Optical spectra formed by the dispersion of light from incandescent solids, liquids, and gases are known as **emission spectra.*** Depending on the character of the source, emission spectra are of three kinds: *continuous, bright-line,* and *band spectra.*

a. Continuous spectra. Incandescent solids and liquids (and gases under very high pressure) produce continuous spectra consisting of a wide range of unseparated wavelengths. When all the wavelengths of visible light are present, the slit images formed by the spectroscope constitute an unbroken band of the six spectral colors.

A platinum wire held in the nonluminous Bunsen flame emits a continuous spectrum, the energy radiated at each frequency being dependent on the temperature of the platinum.

b. Bright-line spectra. If a solution of sodium chloride is introduced into the nonluminous flame of a Bunsen burner, the flame emits a bright yellow light that is characteristic of the vaporized sodium compound. Examination of this yellow flame through the spectroscope reveals two closely spaced yellow lines, each line being a narrow image of the collimator slit and having a definite position in the yellow region of the visible spectrum. (The two narrow lines may appear as one in an instrument of low resolving power.)

All gases and vapors, made luminous at atmospheric pressure, emit bright-line spectra consisting of monochromatic slit images having wavelengths characteristic of the atoms present. The number and intensities of the lines vary with the amount of energy supplied to the "excited" atoms. The composition of a metallic alloy can be analyzed quickly and accurately with the spectrograph. A small sample of the alloy is vaporized in an electric arc and the bright-line spectrum of the vapor is photographed and compared with a standard. Each chemical substance has its own characteristic spectrum which is not exactly like that of any other substance. Line spectra are characteristic of uncombined atoms.

c. Band spectra. Some emission spectra appear as fluted bands of color rather than sharply defined lines. The bands consist of groups of lines whose separation is so small that they are not easily resolved. Band spectra are characteristic of molecular structure.

2. Absorption spectra. Gases and vapors readily absorb energy of the same frequencies at which they would emit energy if heated to incandescence. If light from an incandescent platinum wire passes through an atmosphere of sodium vapor before reaching the slit of a spectroscope, the resulting spectrum lacks the wavelengths characteristic of luminous sodium vapor. Dark lines appear in the yellow region of the emission spectrum where the lines of sodium would be in a sodium bright-line spectrum. The nonluminous sodium vapor has absorbed these yellow wavelengths, producing an *absorption spectrum*. Bands of wavelengths are absorbed by nonluminous liquid or solid media, reflections from the remaining bands giving rise to the characteristic pigment coloration of these substances. Pure red glass absorbs all wavelengths except those in the red region of the visible spectrum. *Absorption spectra are continuous spectra interrupted by dark lines or bands which appear at points where absorbed frequencies would normally occur.*

16. The Fraunhofer lines. The solar spectrum appears to be a continuous spectrum on casual inspection. However, critical examination with proper instruments reveals the fact that it is actually a dark-line absorption spectrum.

In 1802, the English scientist William Hyde Wollaston (1766–1828) noticed that certain dark lines appear in the solar spec-

Fig. 17-13. Joseph Fraunhofer invented the prism spectroscope and first measured the dark lines of the solar spectrum.

trum. About ten years later, these dark lines were discovered independently by Joseph von Fraunhofer (1787–1826), a German physicist. With apparatus which he constructed himself, Fraunhofer charted the position of a number of these dark lines and observed that they always appear in the same positions in the spectrum. Furthermore, their positions are the same as those occupied by the bright lines in the spectra of the luminous vapors of certain elements. Fraunhofer charted approximately 600 of these absorption lines, which are appropriately called *Fraunhofer lines.*

Examination of Figs. 17-14 and 17-16 shows why the sun produces an absorption spectrum. The photosphere consists of highly compressed incandescent gases which form a continuous spectrum. The chromosphere consists of luminous gases under less pressure, which, alone, form bright-line spectra. In the outer portions of the sun's atmosphere (and to a lesser degree, in the earth's atmosphere) there are nonluminous gases which absorb some light waves and produce the dark lines in the sun's spectrum.

WHERE SPECTRUM LINES ORIGINATE

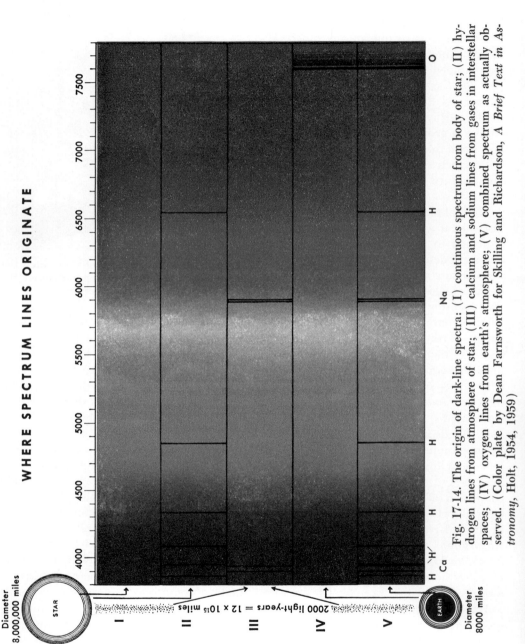

Fig. 17-14. The origin of dark-line spectra: (I) continuous spectrum from body of star; (II) hydrogen lines from atmosphere of star; (III) calcium and sodium lines from gases in interstellar spaces; (IV) oxygen lines from earth's atmosphere; (V) combined spectrum as actually observed. (Color plate by Dean Farnsworth for Skilling and Richardson, *A Brief Text in Astronomy*, Holt, 1954, 1959)

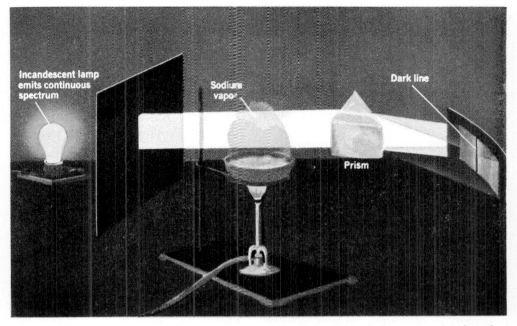

Fig. 17-15. Nonluminous sodium vapor absorbs yellow light of the same wavelength as that emitted by luminous sodium vapor.

★ **17. The production of rainbows.** When sunlight strikes drops of falling water a solar spectrum may be produced. Water disperses light in the same way a glass prism does, but reflection and refraction as well as dispersion are important in forming a rainbow. Figure 17-17 shows the path that a ray of sunlight takes in passing through a drop of water. As the ray enters the drop at *A* it is both refracted and dispersed. The red ray is reflected at *R* and the violet ray is reflected at *V*. When they leave the drop at *B*, both rays are again refracted. The angle which these refracted rays make with the sunlight coming over the shoulder of the observer to the drop is 40° for the violet and 42° for the red rays. In the actual bow which we see, the red rays come from drops of water at an angle of 42° and the violet rays from those at an angle of 40°. The other colors are formed by drops between these angles. A rainbow is an arc because the eye of the observer is at the apex of a cone from which

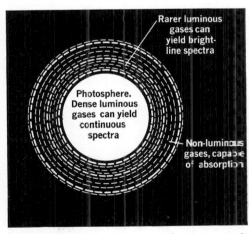

Fig. 17-16. The sun's atmosphere causes it to emit an absorption spectrum.

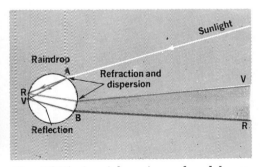

Fig. 17-17. A rainbow is produced by refraction, reflection, and dispersion of light.

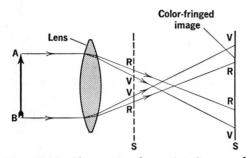

Fig. 17-18. Chromatic aberration is caused by unequal refraction of the different colors.

he sees the colored rays refracted from drops in all directions at angles of from 40° to 42°.

Sometimes a larger secondary bow is seen above the primary. The colors are reversed in the secondary bow, the violet being on the outside. The light is refracted from drops of water at an angle of from 51° to 54°. It enters the lower part of the drop and is refracted and dispersed as in the primary bow, but it is twice reflected before it leaves the drop. For this reason more light is absorbed, and the secondary bow is always fainter than the primary.

18. Chromatic aberration. The refraction of white light by a prism results in dispersion due to the difference in the index of refraction for the different colors. For the same reason, some dispersion occurs when light passes through a lens. Since violet light is bent more than the other colors, it is brought to a focus by a converging lens at a point nearer the lens than other colors. Because red is refracted

the least, the focus for the red rays is farthest from the lens. See Fig. 17-18. Images formed by ordinary spherical lenses are always fringed with spectral colors. *The non-focusing of light of different colors is called chromatic aberration.*

19. The achromatic lens. The fringe of colors around the image formed by an ordinary lens is often objectionable. John Dollond (1706–1761), an English optician, discovered that chromatic aberration could be remedied by means of a combination of lenses. A double convex lens of crown glass used with a suitable plano-concave lens of flint glass eliminates the dispersion of light without preventing refraction and image formation. A lens combination of this type is called an *achromatic* (without color) *lens.*

20. Interference of light waves. Sound waves may interfere with one another to produce beats, as stated in Chapter 12, Section 23. The interference of water waves is easily observed in the laboratory by the use of the common ripple tank. More precise studies of wave disturbances are made by photographing light reflections from the surface of a mercury ripple tank. Light shows a similar phenomenon, called *interference, which is the mutual effect of two beams of light resulting in a loss of energy in certain areas (destructive interference) and reinforcement of energy in others (constructive interference).*

In 1801, Thomas Young first demonstrated interference of light and showed its implications in support of the wave theory

Fig. 17-19. Double-slit interference.   Fig. 17-20. Double-slit interference fringes.

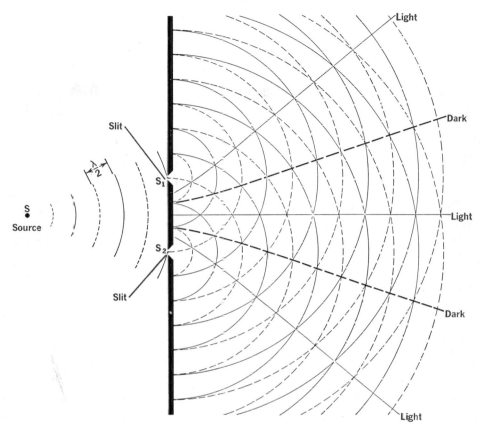

Fig. 17-21. A wave-front diagram of double-slit interference.

of Huygens. Suppose the two narrow slits of Fig. 17-19, about 1 mm apart in a piece of black paper, are used to observe a narrow source of light S placed 2 or 3 meters away. A series of alternately dark and light narrow bands is seen in the center of a fairly wide band of light similar to that of Fig. 17-20. A red filter interposed between the source and the slits provides a monochromatic light source, and a series of red and black bands is seen.

A wave-front diagram of double-slit interference with a monochromatic light source is shown in Fig. 17-21. Slits S_1 and S_2 are parallel to the source S and equidistant from it. As light from S reaches S_1 and S_2, each may be considered as a new light source producing new wave fronts in phase with each other. These waves travel out from S_1 and S_2, producing bright bands of reinforced light where constructive interference occurs, and dark bands due to cancellation where destructive interference occurs.

If two circular plates of glass, one *plane* and the other *very slightly convex*, are clamped together, a circular wedge-shaped film of air will be trapped between them. Near the actual point of contact, the film of air is about as thick as the length of a light wave. If monochromatic light from a sodium vapor lamp strikes this device, alternate yellow and dark bands of light are reflected. Reflection occurs at both surfaces of the glass. The wedge-shaped film of varying thickness causes some of the reflected waves to meet in the same phase, while others meet in opposite phase. Where they meet in the same phase, they form yellow bands; where they meet in opposite phase, they interfere and produce dark bands. When sunlight strikes this device, bands of different colors are visible, because the wedge-shaped air film causes different colors of *different wavelengths* to interfere at different positions. The color observed at a particular point is the complement of that removed by interference.

21. Diffraction of light waves. According to the wave theory of light, light waves should bend around corners. Our common experience with light shows that it travels in straight lines; however, under some conditions light waves do bend out of their straight course. When light waves encounter an obstruction which is small in comparison with their wavelengths, the light waves spread out and produce spectral colors due to interference. *The spreading of light into a region behind an obstruction is called* **diffraction.** A slit opening, a fine wire, a sharp-edged object, or a pinhole may serve as a suitable obstruction in the path of a beam of light from a point source.

Diffraction may also be produced by the reflection of light from a surface which is covered with exceedingly fine parallel lines. By means of a diamond point, 15,000 to 30,000 lines to the inch have been ruled on glass, or on special metallic surfaces. These ruled plates are called *diffraction gratings*. With a transparent grating, light is transmitted through the narrow space between the lines and

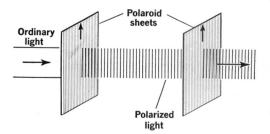

Fig. 17-23. Light is transmitted when the axes of the Polaroid sheets are parallel.

spreads out, or is diffracted. A grating is superior to a prism for examining spectra because the colors are spread out farther so that the spectrum produced may be several feet in length.

A beam of light traveling in dust-free air cannot be seen even in a darkened room. If, however, dust or smoke is introduced into the path of the beam, the beam becomes visible due to the ordinary reflection of light in all directions from the surface of the particles.

Suppose a beam of white light travels in a medium in which are suspended colloidal particles having diameters comparable to the mean wavelength of visible light. When observed at right angles to its path, the beam has a distinctly bluish cast. With certain concentrations of suspended particles, the bluish light sent off sideways becomes quite intense and the transmitted light acquires a red-orange shade. The conclusion is that an excess of shorter wavelengths is emitted at right angles to the path of the beam and an excess of longer wavelengths is transmitted along the path of the beam. This phenomenon is known as *scattering* and occurs when a beam of light encounters particles whose dimensions are comparable to the wavelengths in the beam.

Because of their size, the particles cannot reflect wave fronts of light, but act as centers from which new wave disturbances spread out in all directions, a *diffraction phenomenon*. It has been found that the intensity of the scattered light varies in-

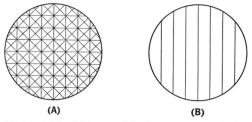

(A)   (B)

Fig. 17-22. (A) Possible appearance of the end of a beam of light. (B) Appearance of the end of a beam polarized in the vertical plane.

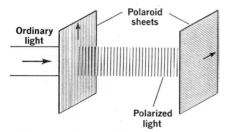

Fig. 17-24. Light is not transmitted when the axes of the Polaroid sheets are perpendicular.

versely with the fourth power of the wavelength; thus, in the case of white light, the scattered light must contain an excess of blue and violet wavelengths and the transmitted light must contain an excess of orange and red wavelengths.

Molecules in the atmosphere, and other particles having diameters smaller than the longest wavelengths of visible light, scatter the blue regions of sunlight. This accounts for the blue appearance of the sky and the reddish appearance of the setting sun. Scattering is responsible for certain other color phenomena seen in nature known as *structural colors*, in contrast to the *pigment colors* which we have already considered. The colors of many minerals are structural. The blue color of a bluejay's feathers results from scattering of light by tiny bubbles of air dispersed through the feather structure. The blue color in human eyes is also a structural color, since there is no blue pigment in the irises of blue eyes.

22. The polarization of light. If we could look at the end of a beam of light we would probably see some of its transverse waves vibrating horizontally, some vertically, and others at various angles as represented in Fig. 17-22(*A*). Certain crystals, such as tourmaline, and a synthetic material called *Polaroid*, primarily transmit light waves which vibrate in only one plane, as represented in Fig. 17-22(*B*). The light passing through such materials is said to be *polarized*.

Suppose we have two pieces of Polaroid arranged with their transmitting axes parallel, as shown in Fig. 17-23. A complex beam of light is polarized as it passes through the first sheet of Polaroid. Since the transmitting axis of the second sheet is parallel to that of the first, the polarized light from the first sheet passes through the second one also. If we now turn the transmitting axis of the second sheet of Polaroid through an angle of 90°, as shown in Fig. 17-24, the light that is polarized by the first sheet of Polaroid can no longer pass through the second sheet. As a result, little light passes through two pieces of Polaroid oriented in this fashion.

In order to understand how Polaroid acts, let us study Fig. 17-25. We can make a rope vibrate in a vertical plane through a picket fence, but we cannot make it vibrate in a horizontal plane. Through horizontal slots we can make the rope vibrate in a horizontal plane but not in a vertical plane. In a similar way, the first sheet of Polaroid permits only light waves vibrating in one plane to pass through. If the transmitting plane of the second sheet is oriented in the same direction as that of the first, the light waves pass on through, just as the vibrations of the rope pass through the second set of pickets. When we cross the sheets of Polaroid, the vibrating light waves are stopped by the second

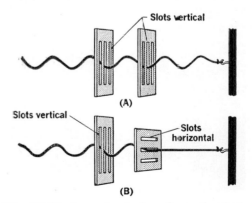

Fig. 17-25. A mechanical analogy of polarization.

sheet of Polaroid, just as the second set of pickets stops the vibrations of the rope.

★ **23. The polariscope.** A polariscope is an instrument which measures the angle of rotation of a beam of polarized light as it passes through a transparent solution. Light entering one end of the instrument is polarized by a piece of Polaroid or by some other polarizing device. The polarized light passes through the transparent solution and then through a second polarizer, called the *analyzer*. If the transparent solution is not itself a light polarizer, the polarized light will pass through the analyzer in the same plane in which it came through the original polarizer. However, if the solution also polarizes light, the analyzer must be rotated to allow the polarized light to pass through the instrument.

Chemical compounds such as glucose sugar and other organic substances cause rotation of the plane of polarized light.

Thus, by measuring the degrees of rotation of the analyzer, a technician can calculate the percentage of glucose or some other polarizing substance in a solution. The amount of rotation of the plane of polarized light varies according to the substance used and the concentration of the substance in the solution.

★ **24. Other uses of polarized light.** Because different substances vary in their ability to polarize light, chemists may use polarized light to identify small crystals of unknown substances. Manufacturers of automobiles, machine parts, and building materials use models made of Polaroid or other polarizing materials to study the effects of applied stresses on various structures, because the strains in the structures show clearly when polarized light passes through them. Polaroid sunglasses eliminate the annoying glare of bright sunlight reflected from the surface of a road or a smooth body of water.

Fig. 17-26. Two disks of Polaroid whose transmitting axes are perpendicular provide an effective means of demonstrating polarization of light. (Merrim from Monkmeyer)

ummary

Sunlight is shown to be composed of polychromatic light which undergoes dispersion when refracted by a prism. Six distinct elementary colors are recognized in dispersed white light. Color is a property of light that depends on the wavelength.

The removal of one elementary color from white light leaves a polychromatic color that is the complement of the one removed. Complementary colors produce white light by addition. White light is produced by the addition of three primary colors, any two of which produce the complement of the third. The primary pigments are the complements of the primary colors, their combination being a subtraction process. The Young-Helmholtz color vision theory is generally accepted as the explanation for the response of the human eye to colors. However, the newer Land theory of color vision suggests that the Young-Helmholtz theory may not be the whole story.

Light spectra are classified as emission or absorption, each being further classified as to types depending on the nature of the light source and the composition of the transmitting medium. Spectra are examined by means of a spectroscope. Each chemical substance has its own characteristic spectrum which is not exactly like that of any other substance.

Interference of light can be compared to that occurring in other disturbances known to consist of waves. The formation of double-slit interference fringes and the formation of interference fringes due to reflections from thin wedges of air can be analyzed on the basis of light waves.

Diffraction results in the spreading of light into the space behind an obstruction located in the path of the light rays. Scattering is a diffraction phenomenon which explains the existence of structural colors occurring in nature.

Polarization of light depends on the transverse nature of light waves. It is an important phenomenon from both a theoretical and a technological standpoint.

TERMS TO DEFINE

absorption spectra	continuous spectra	polarized light
achromatic lens	diffraction	Polaroid
addition process	diffraction grating	polychromatic light
band spectra	elementary colors	primary colors
chromatic aberration	emission spectra	primary pigments
color	four-color printing	prism
color blindness	Fraunhofer lines	retinal fatigue
color correction	infrared light	solar spectrum
color of opaque objects	infrared photography	spectroscope
color of transparent objects	interference	subtraction process
color photography	line spectra	ultraviolet light
complementary colors	monochromatic light	Young-Helmholtz theory

QUESTIONS

A 1. Why does a prism disperse sunlight into a band of colors?

2. What property of light determines its color?

3. (a) What name is given to electromagnetic waves which are slightly longer than visible light? (b) What name is given to waves which are slightly shorter than visible light?

4. If a black object absorbs all the light rays incident upon it, how can it be seen?

5. What is the appearance of a red dress in a closed room illuminated only by green light? Explain.

6. What will be the appearance of a yellow flower if viewed through a piece of blue glass? Explain.

7. What would you expect to see if you looked at the United States flag through (a) a piece of red glass; (b) a piece of blue glass?

8. (a) What are the primary colors? (b) Define a complementary color. (c) Name the complement of each primary color.

9. Why is it not possible to make white paint from orange paint by adding a pigment of another color?

10. Define and give examples of the following spectra: (a) bright line; (b) absorption; (c) continuous.

11. How could you demonstrate that a piece of white-hot iron gives off red light?

12. (a) What is chromatic aberration in lenses? (b) How may it be remedied?

13. How do sunglasses of Polaroid reduce the glare of bright sunlight?

14. Why is a blue dye added to some detergents to whiten clothes?

B 15. Why does the appearance of a person's complexion change when seen under the blue-green light of a mercury vapor lamp, or the bright yellow of a sodium vapor lamp?

16. Explain why the following appear red: (a) glowing charcoal; (b) a ripe cherry; (c) a neon sign; (d) the sunrise; (e) objects viewed through red sunglasses.

17. How do the colors of a soap bubble originate?

★ 18. Why are the inks used in four-color printing the complements of the primary colors?

★ 19. What are the advantages of photographing a broad landscape with infrared-sensitive film?

20. What is the origin of the Fraunhofer lines?

21. Suppose light from a Bunsen flame into which a salt has been introduced is made up of the following wavelengths: 6700 Å, 6100 Å, 5000 Å, and 4600 Å. Make a rough sketch of the spectrum as observed through a prism spectroscope.

22. What would be the color of the flame described in Question 21 as seen by the unaided eye?

23. Distinguish between a structural color and a pigment color.

24. What phenomenon provides evidence that light is a transverse wave disturbance?

RESEARCH ON YOUR OWN

1. Make up a number of color wheels and arrange a means of rotating them rapidly. Prepare a demonstration of the color-addition process.

2. Obtain samples of paper or cloth of various colors and view them through pieces of glass or cellophane of various colors. If your school has controllable stage lights of different colors, determine the color of different colored garments under the different lights singly and in combination. Explain your results in terms of the discussion in Section 3 of this chapter.

3. Investigate the new theory of color vision proposed by Edwin Land. Perform some of Land's experiments and report on your results.

4. Construct a prism spectroscope and demonstrate it.

5. Demonstrate the bright-line spectrum of sodium, using a piece of glass heated in a gas burner flame. If you can get a commercially made spectroscope, try to separate this bright line into two lines. A very interesting spectrum can be shown using a neon light operating on a 110-volt circuit.

6. Demonstrate an absorption spectrum. Put a few iodine crystals in an Erlenmeyer flask. Mount the flask horizontally, with its flat bottom near the slit of a spectroscope and a lighted incandescent lamp at its mouth. Adjust the apparatus so that you get a continuous spectrum from the lighted lamp. Then heat the flask gently until the iodine vaporizes. CAUTION: *Do not inhale the iodine vapor.*

7. Insert a piece of cobalt blue glass between a spectroscope and a lighted incandescent lamp. Can you detect any red in the spectrum obtained? How might a red object appear in light transmitted through cobalt glass?

8. Get a piece of heat-absorbing glass like that used in various types of optical projectors. Experiment to see if it absorbs any of the visible red wavelengths as well as the infrared.

9. Get two clean glass cover plates, such as those used in a chemistry laboratory. Put one on top of the other, horizontally, on a horizontal surface. Illuminate the top of the plates with a sodium flame obtained by heating glass tubing in a Bunsen flame. Observe the reflection of this flame from the glass plates. Can you explain the "zebra" pattern? Press on the top plate with your finger and explain the result.

10. Hold your hand horizontally about an inch in front of your eyes, with two fingers spread slightly apart so that they allow a narrow slit for the passage of light between them. Explain the narrow lines that you see. Try to adjust the slit between your fingers so as to produce one line, two lines, and three or more lines. Explain your results.

11. Obtain some of the new inexpensive replica grating material from a scientific supply house. Use it to illustrate the phenomena of diffraction.

12. Find out how a diffraction grating may be used to measure wavelengths of light. Using a diffraction grating, compare your measurement of a known wavelength of light with the accepted value for that wavelength.

13. Polarization of light was known to both Newton and Huygens. Explain why Huygens did not use polarization as a further proof of his theory.

14. Construct a polarimeter and use it to demonstrate the polarizing effects of solutions of various compounds.

15. Using small Polaroid disks, demonstrate some of the properties of polarized light. Under what circumstances would a Polaroid filter placed in front of a camera lens result in clearer photographs?

UNIT 7

Direct current electricity

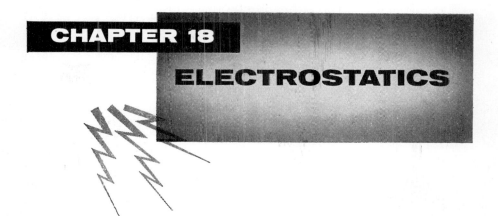

CHAPTER 18

ELECTROSTATICS

1 ELECTRIC CHARGE

1. Electrification. The phenomenon of *electrification* can be observed in a number of ways. You sometimes experience an annoying *shock* when you touch the door handle of an automobile after sliding over the plastic-covered seat. You feel a shock after shuffling over a woolen carpet and touching a doorknob or other metal object. The slight crackling sound that is heard when dry hair is brushed and the tendency of thin sheets of paper to resist separation are other common examples of the phenomenon.

Electrification is the process of producing an electric charge on an object. The object is said to be charged with *electricity*. Charged objects may attract small bits of cork, paper, or other lightweight particles. This phenomenon is most apparent when the air is cool and dry. Because the electric charge is confined to the object, it is said to be an *electrostatic* charge. Thus **static electricity** *is electricity at rest.* Static electricity is commonly produced by friction between two surfaces in intimate contact.

VOCABULARY

Capacitance. The ratio of the charge on either plate of a capacitor to the potential difference between the plates.

Capacitor. A combination of conducting plates separated by an insulator and used to store an electric charge.

Coulomb. The quantity of electricity equal to the charge on 6.25×10^{18} electrons.

Dielectric constant. The ratio of the capacitance with a particular material separating the plates of a capacitor to the capacitance with a vacuum between the plates.

Electric field. The region in which an electric force acts on a charge brought into the region.

Electroscope. A device used to observe the presence of an electrostatic charge.

Potential difference. The work done per unit charge as a charge is moved between two points in an electric field.

Static electricity. Electricity at rest.

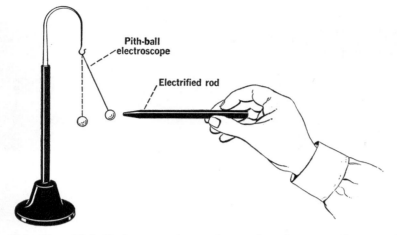

Fig. 18-1. The pith-ball electroscope may be used to detect an electrostatic charge.

2. The discovery of static electricity. Thales (*thay*-leez), one of the wise men of ancient Greece, is believed to have first discovered the effects of static electricity. About 600 B.C. he observed that amber, a fossilized resin from prehistoric soft wood, attracted thin wood shavings when rubbed with wool.

Centuries later, William Gilbert (1540–1603), an English scientist, discovered that many different kinds of materials behave like amber: when rubbed, they acquire the ability to attract lightweight objects. Gilbert is credited with giving the name *electricity* (from the Greek word for amber, *elektron*) to this property of matter.

3. Two kinds of electric charges. The presence of an electrostatic charge may be observed by means of a device called an *electroscope*. The simplest kind of electroscope is a small ball of wood pith suspended on a silk thread. Such an electroscope is more sensitive if the pith ball is coated with aluminum paint.

Suppose we charge a hard rubber or Bakelite rod by stroking it with flannel or fur. If we hold the end of the charged rod near a simple electroscope, we observe that the pith ball is attracted to the rod. See Fig. 18-1.

If the pith ball is allowed to come in contact with the charged rod, it immediately rebounds and is thereafter repelled by the rod. We may safely assume that some of the *charge* has been transferred to the pith ball so that both the ball and the rod are similarly charged.

Now suppose we charge a glass rod by stroking it with silk. If the glass rod is held near the charged electroscope, the pith ball is attracted rather than repelled as it was by the charged rubber rod. We may conclude that the charges produced on the two rods are opposite in nature.

Indeed, there are two kinds of electrification. That produced on the rubber rod when stroked with flannel or fur is called *negative* electrification and the rod is said to be charged negatively. That produced on the glass rod when stroked with silk is called *positive* electrification, and the rod is said to be charged positively.

From our study of atomic structure we know that all matter contains both positive and negative charges, but for simplicity, the drawings which follow will show only the excess charges. If a body is neutral, it will have no sign; if negative, it will be surrounded by minus signs; if positive, it will be surrounded by plus signs.

Fig. 18-2. Like charges repel each other and unlike charges attract each other.

Two pith balls which have acquired a negative charge through contact with a charged rubber rod will repel each other; similarly, two pith balls that have acquired a positive charge by contact with a charged glass rod will repel each other. However, if a negatively charged pith ball is brought near a positively charged pith ball, they will attract each other. See Fig. 18-2. These observations lead us to the *first law of electrostatics: objects that are similarly charged repel each other; those with unlike charges attract each other.*

4. Electrification and the structure of matter. To understand the nature of static electricity, it may be helpful to review briefly the structure of matter. (For a more comprehensive treatment of structure, see Chapter 6.) According to the modern concept, all matter is composed of atoms, of which there are many different kinds, one or more for each chemical element. Each atom consists of *protons, electrons,* and (except for the simplest hydrogen atom) *neutrons.*

The protons and neutrons are tightly packed into a very dense mass called the *nucleus.* The nuclear mass is positively charged since each proton possesses a single unit of positive electricity. Neutrons, as their name suggests, are neutral particles. The positive charge on the nucleus of an atom depends upon the number of protons it contains; that is, upon the *atomic number* of the element.

The electrons are larger, lighter particles that revolve about the nucleus at various distances. Each electron possesses a single unit of negative electricity; together the electrons constitute a negatively charged cloud surrounding the nucleus. An ordinary uncharged atom contains the same number of protons and electrons; it is electrically neutral.

The mass of an electron is 9.1083×10^{-28} g, while the mass of a proton or a neutron is about 1837 times as much. Thus the mass of an atom is almost entirely concentrated in the nucleus. Diagrams of some typical atomic structures are shown in Fig. 18-3.

The protons and neutrons are held together by a nuclear binding force. Little is known about the nature of this force, except that it is a tremendous force acting through very short distances on the positively charged protons and uncharged neutrons alike. The repelling forces due to the similarity of charge between the protons are relatively weak by comparison.

The negatively charged electrons revolve about the nucleus at great speeds,

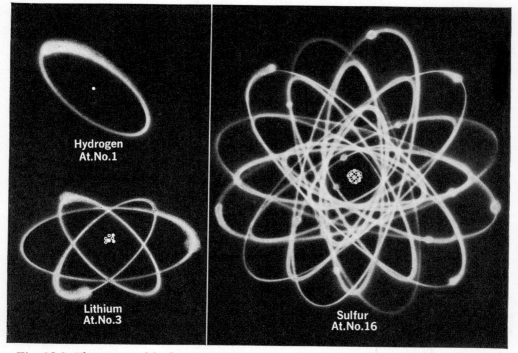

Fig. 18-3. The atoms of hydrogen, lithium, and sulfur, shown in approximately correct relative sizes. Hydrogen has one electron in the K shell; lithium has two electrons in the K shell and one electron in the L shell; sulfur has two electrons in the K shell, eight in the L shell, and six in the M shell.

those with higher energies having the greater mean radii. The centripetal forces which hold these electrons in their closed paths around the nucleus are due to the electrical attraction between them and the positively charged nucleus.

The force of attraction for each electron is dependent on the number of protons in the nucleus. This fact helps explain the difference in density of the lithium and sulfur atoms shown in Fig. 18-3. The outermost electron of lithium is very loosely held because the nuclear charge is weak. The atom of sulfur is much more compact because the nuclear charge is relatively strong. In general, the chemical properties of the elements are due to the number and arrangement of electrons revolving about the nuclei of the atoms.

It is now apparent that the forces involved in producing electrification cannot influence the protons, which are securely bound within the nucleus. When two appropriate materials are brought into intimate contact some of the loosely held electrons may be transferred from one material to the other. Thus, if a hard rubber rod is stroked with fur, some electrons can be transferred from the fur to the rod. The rubber rod thus becomes negatively charged, *due to a net excess of electrons*, and the fur becomes positively charged, *due to a deficiency of electrons*.

Similarly, when a glass rod is stroked with silk, some electrons are transferred from the glass to the silk. The glass rod is consequently positively charged, *due to a net deficiency of electrons*, while the silk has acquired an excess of electrons and so is negatively charged. *In general, the phenomenon of electrification occurs through the transfer of negative electricity.*

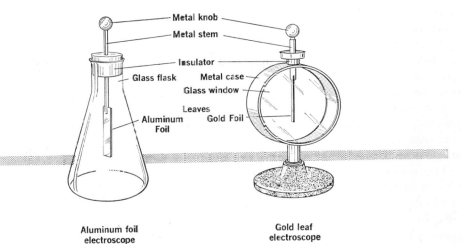

Fig. 18-4. Leaf electroscopes are sensitive laboratory instruments.

5. The leaf electroscope. An electroscope more sensitive than the simple pithball electroscope of Fig. 18-1 consists of very thin strips of gold leaf or aluminum foil hanging from a metal stem having a metal knob at the upper end. The leaves are protected by a glass flask or by a metal case with glass observation windows. The metal stem is carefully insulated from the metal case. See Fig. 18-4. When electrified, the leaves diverge, due to the force of repulsion of their similar charge.

The leaves of sensitive electroscopes are easily damaged by subjecting the instrument to an intense electrostatic charge. A *proof plane* is frequently used in conjunction with the leaf electroscope to test or transfer charges. The proof plane consists of a small metal disk attached to an insulating handle. You may easily make one by cementing a small coin to a glass rod. To transfer a charge with a proof plane, touch the coin to the charged object and then to the electroscope.

6. Conductors and insulators. Let us suspend an aluminum-coated pith ball by a silk thread and then join the ball to the knob of a leaf electroscope by means of a copper wire as shown in Fig. 18-6. If we now place a charge on the ball, the leaves of the electroscope diverge. Apparently the charge on the ball is transferred to the electroscope by means of the copper wire.

Suppose we repeat the experiment but substitute a silk thread for the copper wire. Now when we charge the ball, the leaves of the electroscope do not diverge because the charge has not been conducted to the electroscope by the silk.

A conductor is a material through which an electric charge is readily transferred. Most metals are good conductors. Silver is the best conductor; copper and aluminum

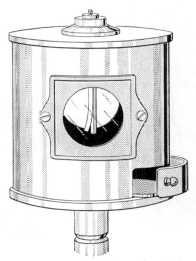

Fig. 18-5. The Hoag electroscope is used to detect radioactivity.

follow in that order. Certain solutions are good conductors, also.

An **insulator** *is a material through which an electric charge is not readily transferred.* Good insulators are such poor conductors that for all practical purposes they are considered to be *nonconductors.* Glass, mica, paraffin, hard rubber, Bakelite, sulfur, silk, shellac, dry air, and many plastics are good insulators.

The conductivity of solutions will be treated in Chapter 20, but in the study of electrostatics, we are primarily interested in the conductivity of solids. Let us apply what we know about the structure of matter to explain this phenomenon.

A solid piece of material is composed of a very large number of atoms arranged in a manner characteristic of that material. The atoms of metals are arranged in a close-packed crystal lattice structure. Each gram-atom of a metal contains the Avogadro number of atoms, 6.0238×10^{23} atoms. Thus 27.0 g of aluminum, 63.5 g of copper, and 108 g of silver each contain this extraordinarily large number of atoms.

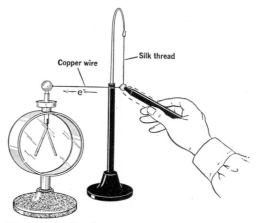

Fig. 18-6. A charge is conducted to the electroscope by the copper wire.

Some of the outermost electrons of these atoms, being loosely held by the nuclei, may become detached temporarily. As *free electrons,* their motions are completely random. If a free electron collides with a neutral atom, it may be retained, causing the ejection of another outer electron, which then becomes a free electron. *The number and freedom of motion of these free*

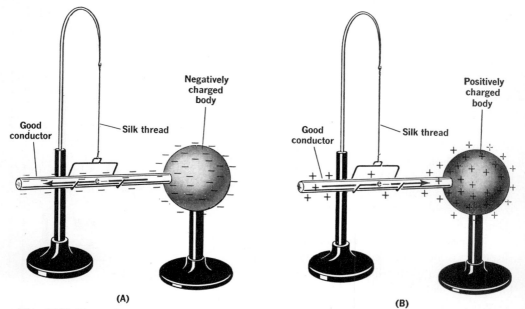

Fig. 18-7. Free electrons of a conductor surge in the direction which reduces the intensity of the charge.

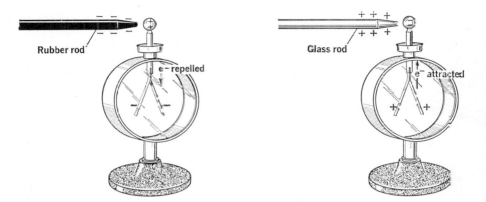

Fig. 18-8. An electroscope may be charged temporarily by induction due to a redistribution of the free electrons of the metallic conductor.

electrons determine the properties of a solid as a conductor of electricity.

A good conductor contains a large number of free electrons whose motions are relatively unimpeded by the atoms of the material. Since like charges repel, the free electrons spread throughout the material so as to relieve any local concentration of charge. Thus, if such a material is brought into contact with a charged body, the free electrons are caused to surge in a common direction. If the charged body is deficient in electrons (positively charged), this surge is in the direction of the body. If the charged body has an excess of electrons (negatively charged), the surge is directed away from the body. See Fig. 18-7. In either case, a transfer of charge continues until the repulsive forces of the free electrons are in equilibrium throughout the entire mass.

An insulator has few free electrons because the orbital electrons are firmly held within the atom structure. The motion of free electrons is greatly hampered by the strong nuclear charges; the transfer of charge through an insulator is usually negligible. If an excess of electrons is transferred to one region of such a material, the extra electrons remain in that region rather than being dispersed.

7. Methods of transferring an electrostatic charge. A charge may be trans-

ferred by induction. Suppose we charge a rubber rod by stroking it with fur. The rod retains an excess of electrons and thus is negatively charged. If we bring the rod *near* the knob on the electroscope, the leaves diverge. When the rod is withdrawn, the leaves collapse; no fixed charge remains on the electroscope.

We may reason that the negative charge on the rod, when brought near the metal knob on the conducting stem of the electroscope, repels free electrons in the conductor down to the leaves. The force of repulsion of the extra electrons on the leaves causes the leaves to diverge. The knob is then deficient in electrons and is consequently positively charged. As soon as the force of repulsion exerted by the charged rod is withdrawn, the excess free electrons on the leaves scatter throughout the conducting stem and knob, restoring the normal uncharged state throughout the electroscope.

Similarly, a glass rod that has been stroked with silk temporarily induces a positive charge on the leaves of an electroscope by attracting electrons through the conducting stem to the knob. See Fig. 18-8. (This experiment does not work well unless the air is quite dry, for a sufficient charge cannot be maintained.)

Any conducting object, when properly isolated in space, may be temporarily

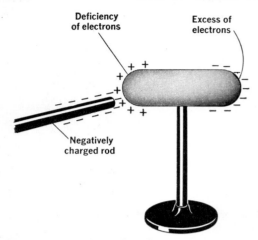

Fig. 18-9. A charged rod brought near an isolated conductor induces electricity of the same sign in the far end of the conductor. It induces electricity of the opposite sign in the near end of the conductor.

charged by induction. The region of the object nearest the charged body will acquire a charge of the *opposite* sign; the region farthest from the charged body will acquire a charge of the same sign. This is seen to be reasonable by recalling the *first law of electrostatics: like charges repel and unlike charges attract.* See Fig. 18-9.

A charge may be transferred by *conduction*. If we bring a negatively charged rubber rod into contact with the knob of an electroscope, the leaves diverge. When the rod is removed, the leaves remain apart, indicating that the electroscope has retained a charge. How may we de-

termine the nature of this residual charge on the electroscope?

We may reason that some of the excess electrons on the rod have been repelled onto the conducting knob of the electroscope. Certainly this would be true only for the region of the rod immediately in contact with the electroscope, since rubber is a very poor conductor and excess electrons do not migrate freely through such a material. Any free electrons thus transferred to the electroscope, together with other free electrons of the electroscope itself, would be repelled to the leaves by the excess electrons remaining on the regions of the rod not in contact with the electroscope. When the rod is removed, and with it the force of repulsion, the entire electroscope is left with a residual negative charge of a somewhat lower density. This deduction may be verified by bringing a positively charged glass rod near the electroscope to induce a positive charge on the leaves. The leaves collapse and diverge again when the glass rod is removed. This procedure is illustrated in Fig. 18-10.

Any conducting object, properly isolated in space, when charged by conduction, always acquires a residual charge of the same sign as that of the body touching it. Thus, when the sign of a residual charge on it is known, an electroscope may be used to identify the nature of the charge on another object. This second object need merely be brought

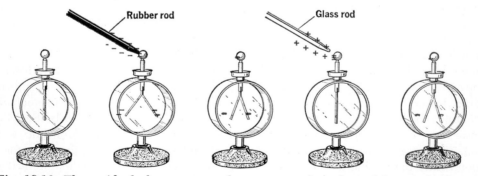

Fig. 18-10. The residual charge on an electroscope, when charged by conduction, is of the same sign as the charge on the object which touches it.

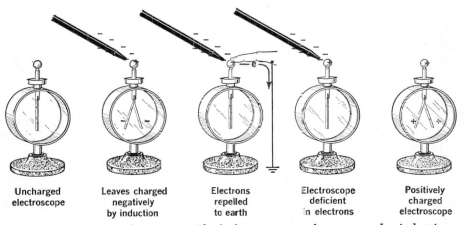

| Uncharged electroscope | Leaves charged negatively by induction | Electrons repelled to earth | Electroscope deficient in electrons | Positively charged electroscope |

Fig. 18-11. Steps in placing a residual charge on an electroscope by induction.

near the knob of the charged electroscope.

8. A residual charge by induction. When a charged rubber rod is held near the knob of an electroscope, there is no transfer of electrons between the rod and the electroscope. If, however, we provide a path over which electrons can flow from the electroscope while the repelling force is acting, free electrons will escape. Then, if we remove the escape path before removing the repelling force, the electroscope will be deficient in electrons and have a residual positive charge. We may verify this by bringing a positively charged glass rod near the knob of an electroscope charged in this manner. The steps in placing a residual charge on an electroscope by induction are shown in Fig. 18-11.

In a similar manner we may induce a residual negative charge on an electroscope using a positively charged glass rod. *When an isolated conductor is given a residual charge by the induction method, the charge is opposite in sign to that of the body inducing it.*

9. The force between charges. In Section 3 we recognized the first law of electrostatics: like charges repel and unlike charges attract. If a charge is uniformly dispersed over the surface of an isolated sphere, the influence on another charged body some distance away is the same as if the charge were concentrated at the center of the sphere. Thus, the charge on such a body may be considered to be located at a particular point and is called a *point charge.*

The quantity of charge a body possesses, designated by the letter Q, is determined by the number of electrons in excess of (or less than) the number of protons. In the MKS system of units, the practical system for the study of electricity, the quantity of charge is expressed in *coulombs* (coul), named for the French physicist, Charles Augustin de Coulomb (1736–1806).

$$1 \text{ coulomb} = 6.25 \times 10^{18} \text{ electrons}$$

Thus, the charge on one electron, expressed in coulombs, is the reciprocal of this number and the sign of Q is $-$.

$$e^- = 1.60 \times 10^{-19} \text{ coul}$$

Similarly, the charge on the proton is 1.60×10^{-19} coulomb and the sign of Q is $+$.

In the study of electrostatics, the coulomb is a very large unit of charge. Frequently, it is convenient to work with a submultiple of this unit called the *microcoulomb* (μcoul).

$$1 \text{ } \mu\text{coul} = 10^{-3} \text{ coul}$$

Coulomb performed many experiments with charged bodies which led him to

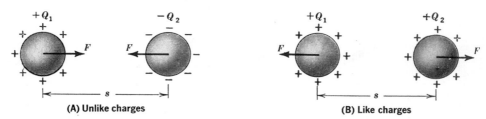

(A) Unlike charges   (B) Like charges

Fig. 18-12. When Q_1 and Q_2 are of opposite sign, F is negative and is interpreted as an attractive force. When Q_1 and Q_2 are of the same sign, F is positive and is interpreted as a repulsive force.

believe that the forces of attraction and repulsion obey a law similar to Newton's law of universal gravitation. We now recognize his conclusions as ***Coulomb's law of electrostatics:*** *the force between two point charges is directly proportional to the product of their magnitudes and inversely proportional to the square of the distances between them.* Charged bodies approximate point charges if the bodies are small compared to the distances separating them. See Fig. 18-12.

Coulomb's law may be expressed as follows:

$$F \propto \frac{Q_1 Q_2}{s^2}$$

If we introduce a *proportionality constant* which takes into account the properties of the medium separating the charged bodies, and which has the proper dimensions, Coulomb's law becomes

$$F = k \frac{Q_1 Q_2}{s^2}$$

In the MKS system k has the numerical value of 9×10^9 for air and the dimensions nt-m²/coul², Q_1 and Q_2 are in *coulombs* and of proper sign to indicate the nature of each charge. As s is in *meters*, F is expressed in *newtons of force*.

In Fig. 18-12(A) the charges Q_1 and Q_2 have opposite signs and the force F acts on each charge to move it towards the other. In (B), charges Q_1 and Q_2 have same sign and the force F acts on each charge to move it away from the other.

Observe that the force between the two charges is a vector quantity which acts on each charge.

Suppose the bodies of Fig. 18-12(B) are charged to 0.01 coulomb each and placed 10 meters apart. Since the charges are of like sign, the force between them is one of repulsion. Using the proportionality constant for air, the Coulomb's law expression for this force becomes

$$F = 9 \times 10^9 \; \frac{\text{nt-m}^2}{\text{coul}^2} \times \frac{(10^{-2} \text{ coul})(10^{-2} \text{ coul})}{(10 \text{ m})^2}$$

$$F = 9 \times 10^9 \; \frac{\text{nt-m}^2}{\text{coul}^2} \times \frac{10^{-4} \text{ coul}^2}{10^2 \text{ m}^2}$$

$$F = 9 \times 10^3 \text{ nt of repulsive force}$$

See the Sample Problem opposite.

10. Electric fields of force. The region surrounding a charged body is in a condition of stress because of the presence of the electrostatic charge. A second charge brought into this stressed region experiences a force according to Coulomb's law. Such a space contains an *electric field. An electric field exists in a region in which an electric force acts upon a charge brought into the region.*

Let us consider a positively charged sphere isolated in space, $+Q$ of Fig. 18-13(A). A small positive charge $+q$, which we shall call a *test charge*, is brought near the surface of the sphere. Since the test charge is located in the electric field of the sphere and the charges are similar, the charge experiences a repulsive force directed radially away from Q. Were the charge on the sphere negative, as in Fig.

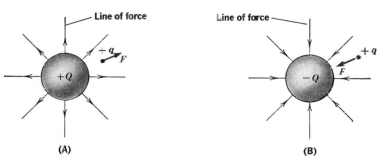

Fig. 18-13. The electric field surrounding a charged sphere isolated in space.

18-13(*B*), the force acting on the test charge would be directed radially towards *Q*.

The path described by a test charge moving in an electrostatic field is called a *line of force. An electric line of force is defined as a line so drawn that a tangent to it at any point indicates the orientation of the electric field at that point.* By convention, electric lines of force *originate* at the surface of a positively charged body and *terminate* at the surface of a negatively charged body, the lines of force being the paths followed by a positive test charge. A line of force must therefore be *normal* to the surface of the charged body where it joins that surface.

The *intensity*, or strength, of an electrostatic field, as well as its direction, may be represented graphically by lines of force. *The electric field intensity is proportional to the number of lines of force per unit area normal to the field.* Where the intensity is high, the lines of force will be spaced close

Sample Problem

Find the force between charges of $+100.$ μcoul and -50.0 μcoul located 50.0 cm apart in air.

Solution

The charges must be expressed in coulombs and the distance in meters.

$+100.$ μcoul $= 100. \times 10^{-6}$ coul $= 1.00 \times 10^{-4}$ coul
-50.0 μcoul $= -50.0 \times 10^{-6}$ coul $= -5.00 \times 10^{-5}$ coul
50.0 cm $= 0.500$ m

$$F = k \frac{Q_1 Q_2}{s^2}$$

$$F = 9 \times 10^9 \frac{\text{nt-m}^2}{\text{coul}^2} \times \frac{(1.00 \times 10^{-4} \text{ coul})(-5.00 \times 10^{-5} \text{ coul})}{(0.500 \text{ m})^2}$$

$$F = 9 \times 10^9 \frac{\text{nt-m}^2}{\text{coul}^2} \times \frac{-5.00 \times 10^{-9} \text{ coul}^2}{2.5 \times 10^{-1} \text{ m}^2}$$

$F = -180$ nt of force, the minus sign indicating attraction between the two charges

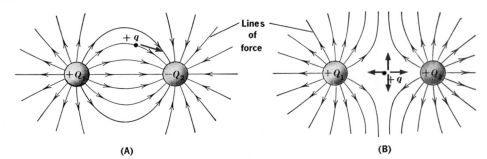

Fig. 18-14. Lines of force show the nature of the electric field near two equal charges of opposite sign (*A*), and near two equal charges of the same sign (*B*).

together. Where the intensity is low, the lines of force will be more widely separated.

In Fig. 18-14(*A*), electric lines of force are used to show the electric field near two equally but oppositely charged bodies. At any point in this field the resultant force acting on a test charge may be represented by a vector drawn tangent to the line of force at that point.

The electric field near two bodies of equal charge of the same sign is shown by the lines of force in Fig. 18-14(*B*). The resultant force acting on a test charge placed at the midpoint between these two

similar charges would be zero. *The electric field intensity, $\mathcal{E}$, at any point in an electric field is the force per unit positive charge at that point.* In the MKS system the unit for electric field intensity is the *newton per coulomb.* Thus,

$$\mathcal{E} = \frac{F}{+Q}$$

where $\mathcal{E}$ is the electric field intensity and F is the force in newtons acting on the charge Q in coulombs.

The Sample Problem below illustrates the use of this equation.

Sample Problem

A charge of 2 μcoul placed in an electric field experiences a force of 0.08 nt. What is the magnitude of the electric field intensity?

Solution

The charge of 2 μcoul must be expressed in coulombs.
$Q = 2 \times 10^{-6}$ coul
The force is then most conveniently expressed as
$F = 8 \times 10^{-2}$ nt
Since
$$\mathcal{E} = \frac{F}{Q}$$
$$\mathcal{E} = \frac{8 \times 10^{-2} \text{ nt}}{2 \times 10^{-6} \text{ coul}}$$
$\mathcal{E} = 4 \times 10^{4}$ nt/coul, the electric field intensity

2 POTENTIAL DIFFERENCE

11. Electric potential. Let us consider the work being done by gravity on a wagon coasting down a hill. The wagon is within the gravitational field of the earth and experiences a gravitational force causing it to travel downhill. Work is done by the gravitational field, so the energy expended comes from within the system. The wagon has less potential energy at the bottom of the hill than it possessed at the top, and in order to return the wagon to the top, work must be done on it. However, in this instance, the energy must be supplied from an outside source to pull against the gravitational force. The energy expended is stored in the wagon, imparting to it more potential energy at the top of the hill than it possessed at the bottom.

Similarly, a charge located in an electric field experiences an electric force according to Coulomb's law. If it moves in response to this force, work is done by the electric field. If this charge is moved against the Coulomb force of the electric field, work is done on it using energy from some outside source, this energy being stored in the system.

If work is done as a charge moves from one point to another in an electric field, or if work is required to move a charge from one point to another, these two points are said to *differ in electric potential. The magnitude of the work is a measure of this difference of potential.* The concept of potential difference is of utmost importance in the understanding of electric phenomena. We see that it is analogous to gravitational potential in mechanical energy transformations. *The potential difference (V) between two points is the work done per unit charge as a charge is moved between these points.*

$$\text{potential difference } (V) = \frac{\text{work } (W)}{\text{charge } (Q)}$$

The unit of potential difference in the MKS system is the *volt* (v). *One **volt** is the potential difference between two points in an electric field such that 1 joule of work moves a charge of 1 coulomb between these points.*

$$1 \text{ volt} = \frac{1 \text{ joule}}{1 \text{ coulomb}}$$

Small differences of potential are expressed in *millivolts* (mv) or *microvolts* (μv). Large differences of potential are expressed in *kilovolts* (kv) and megavolts (Mv).

$$
\begin{aligned}
1 \ \mu v &= 10^{-6} \ v \\
1 \ mv &= 10^{-3} \ v \\
1 \ kv &= 10^{3} \ v \\
1 \ Mv &= 10^{6} \ v
\end{aligned}
$$

See the Sample Problem on page 394.

Since a joule of work involves a force of 1 newton applied through a distance of 1 meter, it follows that

$$v = \frac{\text{joule}}{\text{coul}} = \frac{\text{nt-m}}{\text{coul}}$$

and

$$\frac{v}{m} = \frac{\text{nt}}{\text{coul}}$$

In Section 10 we learned that $\mathcal{E}$, the electric field intensity, is expressed in newtons per coulomb. Thus,

$$\mathcal{E} = \frac{\text{nt}}{\text{coul}} = \frac{v}{m}$$

The electric field intensity is commonly expressed in terms of *volts per meter* and may be referred to as the *potential gradient. The **potential gradient** of an electric field is the change in potential per unit of distance.*

We may consider the earth to be an inexhaustible source of electrons, or limitless *sink* into which electrons can be "poured" without changing its potential. For all practical purposes, the potential of the earth is arbitrarily taken as *zero*. Any conducting body connected to the earth must be at the same potential as the earth; that is, the potential difference

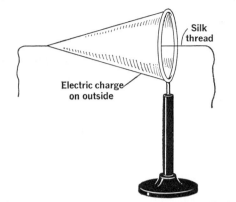

Fig. 18-15. The type of conical silk bag used by Faraday to demonstrate that electric charges reside on the outside.

between them is zero. Such a body is said to be *grounded*.

The potential at any point in an electric field is in reality the potential difference between the point and earth taken as the zero reference potential. This potential may be either positive or negative depending on the nature of the charge producing the electric field.

12. The distribution of the electrostatic charge. Michael Faraday performed several significant experiments to demonstrate the distribution of charge on an isolated body. He charged a silk bag of conical shape, like that of Fig. 18-15, and found that the charge was on the outside of the bag. By pulling on the silk thread, Faraday turned the bag inside out and found that the charge was again on the outside. The inside of the bag showed no electrification in either position.

Faraday connected the outer surface of an insulated metal ice pail to an electroscope by means of a conducting wire, as shown in Fig. 18-16(*A*). He then lowered into the pail a positively charged ball, supported by a silk thread. The leaves of the electroscope diverged (*B*), indicating a charge by induction: the positively charged ball attracted the free electrons in the pail to the inner surface, leaving the outside of the pail and the electroscope positively charged. The leaves remained apart without change when the ball was allowed to contact the inside of the pail (*C*). The positive charge on the ball was exactly neutralized by the equal and opposite charge induced on the inside of the pail; the charge on the ball was therefore lost. After the ball was removed, it was evident that the outside of the pail (and the electroscope) had acquired all the charge originally placed on the ball (*D*).

Sample Problem

The difference of potential between two points in an electric field is 6.0 volts. How much work is required to move a charge of 300. microcoulombs between these points?

Solution

300. μcoul may be expressed as 3.00×10^{-4} coul.

$$V = \frac{W}{Q}$$

$W = V \times Q$

$W = 6.0 \text{ v} \times 3.00 \times 10^{-4} \text{ coul}$

$W = 1.8 \times 10^{-3}$ joule, the work required

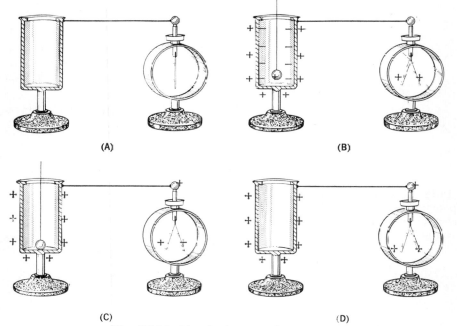

(A)

(B)

(C)

(D)

Fig. 18-16. Faraday's ice-pail experiment.

From these and other experiments, we may conclude that

1. All the static charge on a conductor lies on its surface. Electrostatic charges are at

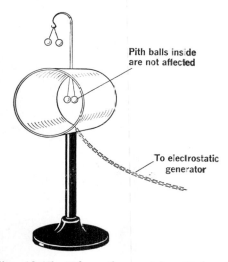

Pith balls inside are not affected

To electrostatic generator

Fig. 18-17. When the metal cylinder is charged by the electrostatic generator, the pith balls outside diverge, while those inside are not affected. What does this tell us about the location of the charge?

rest. If the charge were beneath the surface, so that an electric field existed within a conductor, free electrons would be acted upon by the Coulomb force of this field. Work would be done, the electrons would move because of a difference of potential, and energy would be given up by the field. Since movement is not consistent with a *static* charge, the charge must be on the surface and the electric field must exist only externally to the surface of a conductor.

2. There can be no potential difference between two points on the surface of a charged conductor. A difference of potential is a measure of the work done in moving a charge from one point to another. As no electric field exists within the conductor, no work is done in moving a charge between two points on the same conductor. No difference of potential can exist between such points.

3. The surface of a conductor is an equipotential surface. All points on a conductor are at the same potential and no work is

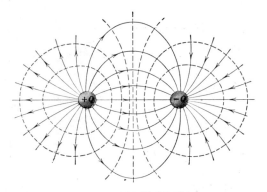

Fig. 18-18. Lines of force (solid lines) and equipotential lines (dashed lines) define the electric field near two equal but opposite charges.

done by the electric field in moving a charge residing on a conductor. If points of equal potential in an electric field near a charged body are joined, an *equipotential line* or *surface* within the field is indicated. No work is done when a test charge is moved in an electric field along an equipotential line.

4. Electric lines of force are normal to equipotential lines or surfaces. A line of force shows the direction of the force acting on a test charge in an electric field. It can be shown that there is no force acting normal to this direction. Thus no work is done when a test charge is moved in an electric field normal to the lines of force.

5. Lines of force originate or terminate normal to the surface of a charged body. Since the surface of a conductor is an equipotential surface, lines of force must start out perpendicularly from the surface. For the same reason a line of force cannot originate and terminate on the same conductor.

13. The effect of the shape of a conductor. A charged spherical conductor, when perfectly isolated in space, has a uniform charge density over the outer surface. Lines of force extend radially from the surface in all directions and the equipotential surfaces of the electric field are spherical and concentric. Such symmetry is not

to be found in all cases of charged conductors.

Suppose we charge an ellipsoidal conductor like that shown in Fig. 18-19. When we test it with a proof plane and electroscope we find that the charge density is not uniform over the surface. There is a greater density of charge in the region of larger curvature (smaller radius of curvature). If we increase the curvature at the small end by making it more pointed, the density of the charge increases, also. *The charge density, or quantity of charge per unit area, is greatest at the point of greatest curvature.*

14. The discharging effect of points. In Fig. 18-19, the lines of force and equipotential lines are shown more concentrated at the small end of the charged conductor. This is the way of indicating that the intensity of the electric field, or potential gradient, in this region is greater than elsewhere around the conductor. If this surface is reshaped to a sharply pointed end the field intensity may become great enough to cause the gas molecules in the air to *ionize*. Ionized air consists of electrically charged particles responsive to the

———— Lines of force
– – – – Equipotential lines

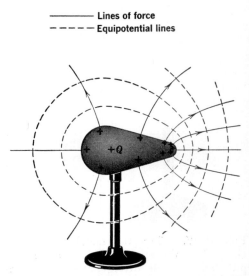

Fig. 18-19. The charge density is greatest at the point of greatest curvature.

electric force. When the air is ionized, the point of the conductor is rapidly discharged.

When a molecule of a gas loses electrons due to some stress condition, it becomes a positively charged *ion*. There are always a few of these positive ions and free electrons present in the air. The intense electric field near a sharp point of a charged conductor will set these charged particles in motion, the electrons being driven in one direction and the positive ions in the opposite direction. Violent collisions with other gas molecules will knock out some electrons and produce more charged particles. In this way air may be quickly ionized when subjected to sufficient electric stress.

In dry air at atmospheric pressure, a potential gradient of 30 kv/cm is required between two charged surfaces to ionize the intervening column of air. When such an air gap is ionized, a *spark discharge* occurs. There is a rush of free electrons across the ionized gap, discharging the surfaces and producing heat, light, and sound. Usually the quantity of static electricity involved is quite small and the time duration of the spark discharge is very short. Atmospheric lightning, however, is a spark discharge in which the quantity of charge may be great.

The intensity of an electric field near a charged body may be sufficient to produce ionization only at sharp projections or sharp corners of the body. A slow leakage of charge will occur at these locations, producing a *brush* or *corona discharge*. A faint violet glow is sometimes emitted by the ionized gases of the air. A glow discharge, called St. Elmo's fire, may be observed at night at the tips of the masts of ships and at the trailing edges of wing and tail surfaces of aircraft. Flexible "pigtails" are usually attached to the trailing edges of aircraft wings to aid in removing the charges acquired by the plane in flight.

The fact that sharply pointed conduc-

Fig. 18-20. Lightning frequently strikes the Empire State building. Why are the occupants perfectly safe? (United Press International Photo)

tors allow charges to escape from them is of great importance in the operation of electrostatic generators and in the design of lightning rods.

Lightning is a gigantic electric discharge in which a surge of electric charges rush to meet their opposites. The interchange may occur between clouds or between a cloud and the earth. According to the Lightning Protection Institute, a hundred bolts of lightning bombard the earth every second, each bolt initiated by a potential difference of millions of volts.

There are no known ways of preventing lightning. However, there are effective means of protection from its destructiveness. Lightning rods, an invention of Benjamin Franklin, are often used to protect buildings made of wood or masonry from lightning damage. The sharply pointed rods are strategically located above the

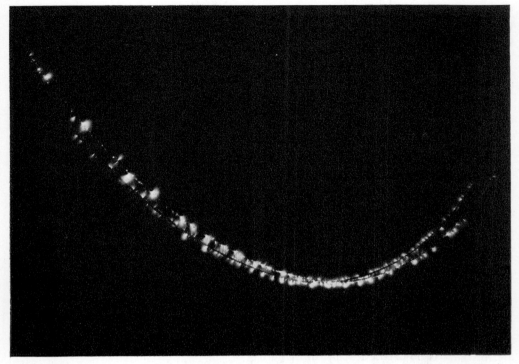

Fig. 18-21. A corona discharge photographed by its own light. (General Electric Co.)

highest projections of the building, and by their discharging effect, normally prevent the accumulation of a dangerous electrostatic charge. Lightning rods are thoroughly grounded and in the event of a strike, they provide a good conducting path into the ground. The steel frames of large buildings offer excellent protection from lightning damage.

Television receiving antennas, even though equipped with lightning arresters, do not protect a building from lightning.

3 CAPACITANCE

15. Capacitors. Any isolated conductor is able to retain an electrostatic charge to some extent. If we place a positive charge on such a conductor by removing electrons, the potential is raised to some positive value with respect to ground. On the other hand, a negative charge placed on the conductor results in a negative potential with respect to ground. By doubling the charge we double the potential of the body. This is true since the potential of an isolated conductor is a measure of the work done in placing a charge on the conductor. It is evident that we may continue to increase the charge until the magnitude of the potential, with respect to ground or other conducting surface, is such that corona or spark discharges occur.

Suppose we connect a charged conductor to an electroscope as shown in Fig. 18-22(A). The leaves of the electroscope will diverge, thus indicating the potential of the charged conductor, because there can be no difference of potential between different regions of a single charged conducting surface.

Now suppose we bring a grounded conductor near the charged conductor, as shown in Fig. 18-22(B). A positive charge is induced on this second conductor as free electrons are repelled to ground by the negative field of the first conductor. The leaves of the electroscope partially collapse. The closer we move the grounded plate the more pronounced is this effect. Due to the attractive force of the induced charge on the grounded plate, less work is required to place the same negative charge on the first conductor. Its potential is consequently reduced accordingly. A greater charge may now be placed on this conductor to raise the potential back to the initial value.

*A combination of conducting plates separated by an insulator and used to store an electric charge is known as a **capacitor**.* The area of the plates, their degree of separation, and the character of the insulating material separating them determine the extent to which a capacitor is capable of being charged. This is *constant* for a given capacitor and is known as its *capacitance* (C). ***Capacitance** is the ratio of the charge on either plate of a capacitor to the potential difference between the plates.*

$$C = \frac{Q}{V}$$

where C is the capacitance of a capacitor, Q is the quantity of charge on either plate, and V is the potential difference between the conducting plates.

In the MKS system, the unit of capacitance is the *farad* (f), named in honor of Michael Faraday. *The capacitance is 1 **farad** when a charge of 1 coulomb on a capacitor results in a potential difference of 1 volt between the plates.* The farad is, consequently, an extremely large unit of capacitance. Practical capacitors have capacitances of the order of *microfarads*, μf, or *micromicrofarads*, μμf.

$$1 \ \mu f = 10^{-6} \ f$$
$$1 \ \mu\mu f = 10^{-12} \ f$$

If we replace the air separating the plates of the charged capacitor of Fig. 18-22(B) with a glass plate, the electroscope leaves again partially collapse. This indicates that the potential difference between the plates has been further reduced. The ratio Q/V is consequently higher, and so the capacitance has been increased accordingly. Other materials, such as mica, paraffin, oil, or paraffined paper may be substituted for the glass. For each material the resulting capacitance will have a different value.

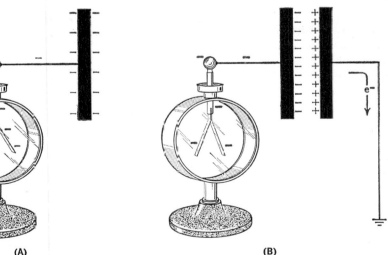

(A)   (B)

Fig. 18-22. The principle of operation of a capacitor.

Dielectric	Dielectric constant (typical value)	Proportionality constant (nt–m²/coul²)
Air	1	9×10^9
Paper (oiled)	2	4.5×10^9
Paraffin	2.25	4×10^9
Polyethylene	2.3	3.9×10^9
Polystyrene	2.5	3.6×10^9
Hard rubber	2.8	3.2×10^9
Mica	6	1.5×10^9
Glass	8	1.1×10^9

Materials used to separate the plates of capacitors are known as dielectrics. *The ratio of the capacitance with a particular material separating the plates of a capacitor to the capacitance with a vacuum between the plates is called the* **dielectric constant** *of the material.* Dry air at atmospheric pressure has a dielectric constant of 1.00060. In practice this is taken as *unity* (the same as vacuum) for dielectric constant determinations. The dielectric constants are pure numbers (numbers without dimension) ranging from 1 to 10 for materials commonly used in capacitors. Typical dielectric constants are given in the table for some common dielectrics above, together with the corresponding MKS proportionality constants for Coulomb's law relationships. Remember that these proportionality constants do have dimensions.

16. Types of capacitors. The earliest form of capacitor was devised at the University of Leyden, Holland, in the middle of the eighteenth century. It consists of a glass jar coated with metal foil about halfway up the sides, both inside and out. A metal knob and stem are supported by an insulating cap and connected to the inner metal foil by means of a metal chain. See Fig. 18-23.

We may charge the *Leyden jar* by connecting one terminal of an electrostatic generator to the knob. The outer foil is connected either directly to the other terminal of the generator or indirectly through a ground. Thus, electrons will be removed from one foil coating and added to the other.

A highly charged Leyden jar may be capable of producing a severe and dangerous shock. The jar should be discharged by connecting the outer coating to the knob using a bent conductor held by an insulated handle.

Capacitors find wide application in all kinds of electronic circuits, ignition systems, and telephone and telegraph equipment. Large capacitances are achieved by using large plate areas, insulators with high dielectric constants, and small separation of the plates. Physical size limits the plate area while cost limits the choice of dielectric. *Dielectric strength* of the insulator limits the reduction in spacing between the plates.

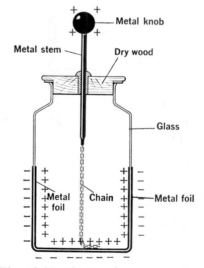

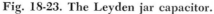

Fig. 18-23. The Leyden jar capacitor.

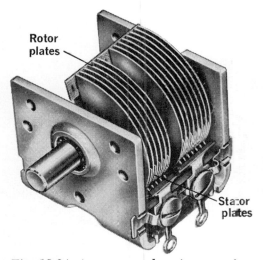

Fig. 18-24. A two-ganged tuning capacitor designed for a radio receiver.

Dielectric strength should not be confused with the dielectric constant of a material. The dielectric strength defines the quality of the material as an insulator; that is, the potential gradient it will withstand without being punctured by a spark discharge. Some typical values are given in the following table.

Dielectric material	Dielectric strength (kv/cm to puncture)
Air	30
Oil	75
Paraffin	350
Paper (oiled)	400
Mica	500
Glass	1000

For *variable* capacitors used in the tuning circuits of a radio, air is used as the dielectric. See Fig. 18-24. Capacitance is varied by rotating a set of movable plates (*rotor plates*) so as to vary the plate area enmeshed with a set of stationary plates (*stator plates*). Capacitances are usually of the order of 10 to 400 $\mu\mu$f.

In small, high quality capacitors, mica is used as the dielectric, and a multiplate arrangement achieves maximum plate area within a very small space. See Fig. 18-25. Because mica has high dielectric

strength, very thin sheets can be used and plate separation is very small. *Mica* capacitors molded in Bakelite and having capacitances of the order of 100 to 1000 $\mu\mu$f are common. They are able to withstand potential differences of the order of 500 v (called the *working voltage*).

Inexpensive capacitors for general use in electronic circuits are made of long strips of aluminum foil separated by impregnated paper. These are rolled into tight cylinders and sealed in Bakelite tubes or metal cans, or simply dipped in wax. *Paper* capacitors may have capacitances up to 10 μf and working voltages up to 1000 volts.

Electrolytic capacitors generally have capacitances ranging from 10 μf to 2000 μf and working voltages from 500 v to 6 v respectively. Aluminum foil is used as one of the plates; a paste electrolyte constitutes the other plate. Chemical action between the metal and the electrolyte produces the dielectric which insulates the metal from the electrolyte. Electrolytic capacitors are sealed in metal cans and are made large in size to provide either a large capacitance or a high working voltage. It is obvious that only a capacitor of inordinate dimensions could provide both large capacitance and high working voltage.

17. Combinations of capacitors. Suppose we connect three capacitors in *parallel;* that is, with one plate of each capacitor connected to one conductor while the other plate is connected to a second conductor.

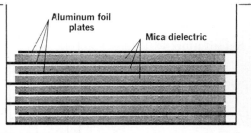

Fig. 18-25. The mica capacitor using a multiplate arrangement.

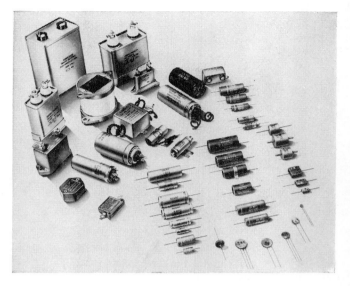

Fig. 18-26. Capacitors are designed to perform highly specialized functions in a great variety of circuits. (Cornell-Dubilier Electric Corp.)

See Fig. 18-27. The plates connected to the + conductor are parts of one conducting surface. Those connected to the − conductor form the other conducting surface. If the three capacitors are charged, it is apparent that they must have the same difference of potential, V, across them. The quantity of charge on each must be respectively

$$Q_1 = C_1 V, \quad Q_2 = C_2 V, \quad \text{and} \quad Q_3 = C_3 V$$

The total charge, Q_T, must be the sum of the separate charges on the three capacitors.

$$Q_T = Q_1 + Q_2 + Q_3$$

then

$$Q_T = C_1 V + C_2 V + C_3 V$$

Since the total charge is equal to the product of the total capacitance, C_T, and the potential difference, V, we can see that

$$Q_T = C_T V$$

Substituting,

$$C_T V = C_1 V + C_2 V + C_3 V$$

and

$$C_T = C_1 + C_2 + C_3$$

For capacitors connected in parallel, the total capacitance is the sum of all the separate capacitances.

Now suppose we connect the three capacitors in *series* as shown in Fig. 18-28. A positive charge placed on C_1 from the + conductor induces a negative charge on the second plate, the electrons being attracted away from the plate of C_2 connected to C_1. A positive charge of the same magnitude is left on the + plate of C_2. Similarly, the plates of C_3 become charged to the same magnitude. Thus

$$Q = Q_1 = Q_2 = Q_3$$

The negative plate of C_1 must be at the same potential with respect to ground as the positive plate of C_2, since they are connected and are parts of the same conducting surface. Similarly, the negative plate of C_2 must be at the same potential as the positive plate of C_3. Thus the total difference of potential, V_T, across the three

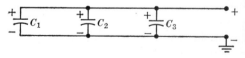

Fig. 18-27. Capacitors in parallel.

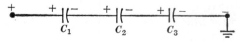

Fig. 18-28. Capacitors in series.

series capacitors must be equal to the sum of the separate potential differences across each capacitor: V_1, V_2, and V_3.

$$V_T = V_1 + V_2 + V_3$$

It is true that

$$V_T = \frac{Q}{C_T}$$

and

$$V_1 = \frac{Q}{C_1}, \quad V_2 = \frac{Q}{C_2}, \quad V_3 = \frac{Q}{C_3}$$

Substituting,

$$\frac{Q}{C_T} = \frac{Q}{C_1} + \frac{Q}{C_2} + \frac{Q}{C_3}$$

or

$$\frac{1}{C_T} = \frac{1}{C_1} + \frac{1}{C_2} + \frac{1}{C_3}$$

For capacitors connected in series, the reciprocal of the total capacitance is equal to the sum of the reciprocals of all the separate capacitances.

See the Sample Problem on page 404.

18. Electrostatic generators. There are three main types of electrostatic generators.

1. Electrophorus. The electrophorus (eh-lek-*trof*-er-us), shown in Fig. 18-29, is one of the simplest electrostatic generators. It was invented by the Italian physicist, Alessandro Volta (1745–1827). The instrument has a nonconducting base made of hard rubber, wax, or sulfur, and a metal plate equipped with an insulated handle.

The base acquires a negative charge on being rubbed with fur. When the metal plate is placed on the base, the plate is strongly charged by induction, Fig. 18-29(A). Charging by conduction is not significant, as the plate may actually be in contact with the insulating material composing the base at only a few points. If the upper surface of the plate is momentarily grounded, as in Fig. 18-29(B), electrons will be repelled to ground, leaving the plate positively charged.

The metal plate is removed by means of the insulated handle. The positive charge on the plate may be sufficient to provide a spark discharge when a source of electrons is brought near enough, as in Fig. 18-29(C). This process can be repeated a great number of times without appreciable loss of charge from the base.

2. Wimshurst machine. The Wimshurst induction machine is in reality a continuously acting electrophorus. See Fig. 18-30. It has two glass disks carrying a large number of tin-foil strips that rotate in opposite directions. In the course of its rotation, each metal strip acts alternately to induce a charge and to carry a charge. Sharp-pointed collector combs remove the charges, which are taken up by two Leyden jars having adjustable knobs. Sufficient charges of opposite sign can be built up in the Leyden jars to ionize an air gap of 75 to 100 mm between their knobs.

3. Van de Graaff generator. The Van de Graaff generator is capable of producing very high voltages of the order of 10 Mv with respect to ground. It accelerates

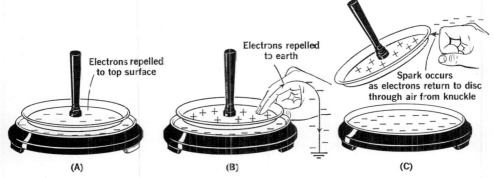

Electrons repelled to top surface

Electrons repelled to earth

Spark occurs as electrons return to disc through air from knuckle

(A)   (B)   (C)

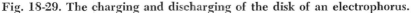

Fig. 18-29. The charging and discharging of the disk of an electrophorus.

Sample Problem

Three capacitors have capacitances of 0.200 μf, 0.300 μf, and 0.500 μf. (a) If they are connected in parallel and charged to a potential difference of 100. v, what is the charge on each capacitor? (b) What is the total charge acquired? (c) If these three capacitors are discharged, then connected in series, and a charge of +30.0 μcoul is transferred to the ungrounded terminal, what potential difference appears across each? (d) What total potential difference exists across the three capacitors?

Solution

(a) The diagram of Fig. 18-27 applies to this part of the problem. In parallel,

$$V = V_1 = V_2 = V_3 = 100 \text{ v}$$

Then,

$$Q_1 = C_1 V = 0.200 \text{ } \mu f \times 100. \text{ v} = 20.0 \text{ } \mu coul$$

$$Q_2 = C_2 V = 0.300 \text{ } \mu f \times 100. \text{ v} = 30.0 \text{ } \mu coul$$

$$Q_3 = C_3 V = 0.500 \text{ } \mu f \times 100. \text{ v} = 50.0 \text{ } \mu coul$$

(b) In parallel,

$$Q_T = Q_1 + Q_2 + Q_3$$

$$Q_T = (20.0 + 30.0 + 50.0) \text{ } \mu coul$$

$$Q_T = 100.0 \text{ } \mu coul$$

(c) The diagram of Fig. 18-28 applies to this part of the problem. In series,

$$Q = Q_1 = Q_2 = Q_3 = 30.0 \text{ } \mu coul$$

Thus each capacitor is charged to 30.0 μcoul, the ungrounded terminal being positive.

Then,

$$V_1 = \frac{Q}{C_1} = \frac{30.0 \text{ } \mu coul}{0.200 \text{ } \mu f} = 150. \text{ v}$$

$$V_2 = \frac{Q}{C_2} = \frac{30.0 \text{ } \mu coul}{0.300 \text{ } \mu f} = 100. \text{ v}$$

$$V_3 = \frac{Q}{C_3} = \frac{30.0 \text{ } \mu coul}{0.500 \text{ } \mu f} = 60.0 \text{ v}$$

(d) In series,

$$V_T = V_1 + V_2 + V_3$$

$$V_T = 150. \text{ v} + 100. \text{ v} + 60.0 \text{ v}$$

$$V_T = 310. \text{ v (positive with respect to ground)}$$

Fig. 18-30. A Wimshurst machine commonly found in the physics laboratory. (Stansi Scientific Co.)

either positively or negatively charged particles and is useful in experiments in nuclear physics. A simplified schematic diagram of the Van de Graaff generator is shown in Fig. 18-31.

A large hollow metal sphere is supported by an insulating cylinder. A wide belt made of an insulating material is driven at high speed from a pulley in the base over an idler pulley mounted in the sphere. A high negative potential is maintained on a series of needle points mounted close to the belt in the base of the machine. A continuous corona discharge around these points sprays electrons onto the belt as it moves upward. A second set of needle points collects these free electrons and transfers them to the sphere. The charge on the sphere is steadily increased as the machine operates and is limited only by the rate at which the charge leaks off to surrounding bodies. The charge leakage is sometimes retarded by enclosing the entire generator in a pressure tank containing a suitable gas, such as freon, at high pressure. Van de Graaff generators are used in nuclear physics experiments as particle accelerators. They generate steady, high-intensity beams of electrons or positive ions.

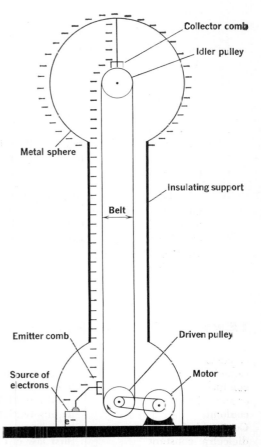

Fig. 18-31. A simplified schematic diagram of a Van de Graaff generator. See also Figs. 7-10 and 7-11.

Summary

Electric charges are of two kinds, positive and negative. Like charges repel and unlike charges attract. Electrification results from the transfer of free electrons. The leaf electroscope may be used to detect the presence of a static charge.

Metallic substances generally are known as good conductors. Nonmetals are very poor conductors, and are called insulators. Isolated conductors may be charged either by induction or conduction methods.

The force between electrostatic charges is defined by Coulomb's law of electrostatics. The unit of charge in the MKS system is the coulomb. The electric field is a region near a charge in which the coulomb force acts. Both the direction and the intensity of the electric field may be defined.

Potential difference is defined in terms of work and quantity of charge. The MKS unit is the volt. The earth is considered to have zero potential. Potentials may be either positive or negative with respect to earth, and unless otherwise stated, are assumed to be referred to earth as zero potential.

Electrostatic charge resides on the surface of a body. Any isolated conducting surface is an equipotential surface. The charge density is related to the surface curvature. The intensity of the electric field near sharp points on a charged body may be great enough to ionize the surrounding air, which then discharges the body.

A capacitor may be used to store a static charge. The MKS unit of capacitance is the farad. Capacitance is dependent on the area of the plates, the nature of the dielectric, and the amount of plate separation. The capacitance of a group of capacitors connected together is dependent on the manner of their connection.

There are several types of electrostatic generators capable of producing charges at high potentials. These are the electrophorus, the Wimshurst machine, and the Van de Graaff generator. The Wimshurst machine is in reality a mechanically operated electrophorus. The Van de Graaff machine may produce voltages of the order of 10 Mv and is used as a particle accelerator in experiments in nuclear physics.

TERMS TO DEFINE

capacitance	electric line of force	nonconductor
capacitor	electrification	potential difference
conductor	electroscope	potential gradient
corona discharge	equipotential line	proof plane
coulomb	equipotential surface	rotor plates
Coulomb's law	farad	spark discharge
dielectric constant	first law of electrostatics	static electricity
dielectric strength	free electron	stator plates
electric field	induction	volt
electric field intensity	insulator	working voltage

QUESTIONS

A 1. List five examples (other than those given in this chapter) in which electrification occurs.

2. A hard rubber rod is rubbed with fur. What kind of charge is acquired (a) by the rubber rod; (b) by the fur?

3. A glass rod is rubbed with silk. What kind of charge is acquired (a) by the glass rod; (b) by the silk?

4. A pith ball suspended on a silk thread is attracted to a charged rubber rod. Does this indicate that the pith ball is oppositely charged? Explain.

5. State the law of electrostatics which governs the attraction and repulsion of charged bodies.

6. Why do the leaves of an uncharged electroscope diverge when a charged object is brought near?

7. Why is it necessary to ground an electroscope temporarily while inducing a residual charge on it with a negatively charged object?

8. What determines the property of a metal as a conductor of electricity?

9. How can you explain the fact that sulfur is a very poor conductor?

10. What is the unit of electric charge in the MKS system?

11. State Coulomb's law of electrostatics.

12. Define an electric field.

13. In what region of an insulated ellipsoidal conductor is the greatest charge found to be concentrated?

14. What determines whether a difference of potential exists between two points?

15. Define (a) potential difference; (b) the MKS unit of potential difference.

16. Any conducting body connected to the earth is said to be grounded. Explain.

17. Is work required to move a charge on the surface of a charged conductor insulated in space? Explain.

18. How does a spark discharge occur between two charged surfaces?

19. (a) Define capacitance. (b) What is the MKS unit of capacitance?

20. What is the effect of connecting capacitors (a) in parallel; (b) in series?

B 21. (a) How can you explain the presence of a charge on a rubber rod after it has been rubbed with fur? (b) How can you explain the charge remaining on the fur?

22. Which would you consider offers the more conclusive proof of the presence of a charge on a pith-ball electroscope, an observed force of repulsion or one of attraction? Explain your answer.

23. Given a charged sphere, describe a simple experiment which would enable you to determine conclusively the nature of the charge on the sphere.

24. A negatively charged rod is brought near the knob of a charged electroscope. The leaves first collapse and then, as the rod is brought nearer, they again diverge. (a) What is the residual charge on the electroscope? (b) Explain the action of the leaves.

25. In order for a coulomb force to be expressed in newtons, what must be the dimensions of the MKS proportionality constant in the Coulomb's-law equation, $F = k \dfrac{Q_1 Q_2}{r^2}$? Demonstrate.

26. Given a solid metal sphere and a hollow metal sphere of the same dimensions, which will hold the larger charge? Justify your answer.

27. A very small sphere is given a positive charge and is then brought near a large negatively charged plate. Draw a diagram of the system showing the appearance of the electric lines of force.

28. Express the dimensions of the volt in fundamental MKS units. Demonstrate that the electric field intensity may have the dimensions of volt per meter.

29. (a) Why is it not possible to maintain a charge on an electroscope indefinitely? (b) What shape should the knob have for a minimum rate of loss of charge?

30. Why are the tips of lightning rods shaped into sharp points?

31. Why are the occupants of a modern steel-frame building not harmed when the building is struck by lightning?

32. Would you expect to be very successful in conducting experiments with static electricity on a humid day? Explain.

33. The metal plate of an electrophorus may be charged and discharged repeatedly without a noticeable loss of charge from the base. Explain.

34. Impregnated paper may have a dielectric constant of 2. Its corresponding Coulomb's law proportionality constant is then one-half that for air. Explain.

PROBLEMS

B **1.** A small sphere is given a charge of +20. μcoul and a second sphere of equal diameter located 10. cm away is given a charge of −5.0 μcoul. What is the force of attraction between the charges?

2. The two spheres of Problem 1 are allowed to touch and are again spaced 10. cm apart. What force exists between them?

● **3.** Two small spheres, each having a mass of 0.050 g, are suspended by silk threads from the same point. When given equal charges, they separate, the threads making an angle of 10° with each other. What is the force of repulsion acting on each sphere? (Suggestion: Construct the vector diagram and solve for the horizontal component of the force on one thread.)

● **4.** Two small spheres, each having a mass of 0.10 g, are suspended from the same point on silk threads 20. cm long. When given equal charges they are found to repel each other, coming to rest 24 cm apart. Find the charge on each sphere. (Suggestion: Construct a vector diagram and determine the force of repulsion by similar triangles.)

5. A charge of 0.52 μcoul is placed in an electric field where the field intensity is 4.5×10^5 nt/coul. What is the magnitude of the force acting on the charge?

6. A force of 0.032 nt is required to move a charge of 42 μcoul in an electric field between two points 25 cm apart. What potential difference exists between the two points?

7. An electron is accelerated in a machine in which it is subjected to a potential difference of 50. megavolts. What energy has the electron acquired?

8. (*a*) What is the potential gradient between two parallel plates 0.50 cm apart when charged to a potential difference of 1.2 kv? (*b*) Convert your result to an expression of electric field intensity in terms of nt/coul.

9. A capacitor consisting of two parallel plates separated by a layer of air 0.3 cm thick and having a capacitance of 15.0 μμf is connected across a 150.-volt source. (*a*) What is the charge on the capacitor? The air dielectric is replaced by a sheet of mica 0.3 cm thick. (*b*) What is the capacitance with the mica dielectric? (*c*) What additional charge does the capacitor take up?

10. Three paper capacitors having capacitances of 0.15 μf, 0.22 μf, and 0.47 μf are connected in parallel and charged to a potential difference of 240 volts. (*a*) Determine the charge on each capacitor. (*b*) What is the total capacitance of the combination? (*c*) What is the total charge acquired?

RESEARCH ON YOUR OWN

1. Cut a slender diamond-shaped piece of cardboard 1 in. long. Put a silk thread through its center and tie the ends of the thread to a yoke made of plastic or to a glass Y tube. Trim the cardboard "needle" with scissors so that it hangs balanced evenly on the thread. This device can be used to investigate a static electric field, much as a magnet is used to investigate a magnetic field.

2. Repeat the Faraday ice-pail experiment described in Section 12 of this chapter, and prepare a report on your results.

3. Try the effect of a static charge on soap bubbles suspended in air and on bubbles made by blowing air through a straw into a cup of soapsuds. Explain the results.

4. Visit a local industry which has a dust-precipitation installation and report on its operation.

5. Construct a small electroscope using strips of the thinnest foil you can find. Make full use of your ingenuity to devise a really good electroscope. Compare its sensitivity to the instrument in your physics laboratory. Many interesting experiments can be carried out at home with the electroscope.

6. Study carefully the operation of a Wimshurst machine. Try to construct an electro-static generator on the same principle, using a phonograph record and auxiliary parts that you can easily fabricate.

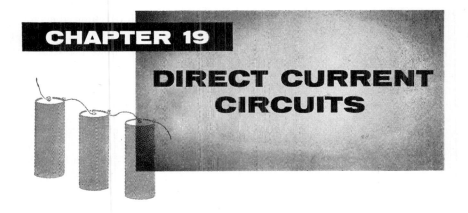

CHAPTER 19

DIRECT CURRENT CIRCUITS

1 SOURCES OF DIRECT CURRENT

1. Electric charges in motion. The quantity of charge on a given capacitor is indicated by the potential difference between the plates.

$$Q = CV$$

If the capacitance C is a constant, as it will be in any given capacitor, then the charge Q is proportional to the potential difference V.

$$Q \propto V$$

The potential difference across a charged capacitor, and therefore the charge on the capacitor, may be indicated by an electroscope connected across the plates. See Fig. 19-1. Suppose we connect the two plates of the capacitor by means of a heavy piece of copper wire as shown in Fig. 19-2(A). The leaves of the electroscope immediately collapse, indicating that the capacitor has been discharged rapidly. Free electrons flow from the negative plate of the capacitor, and from the electroscope, through the copper wire to the positive plate. This action quickly establishes the distribution of electrons characteristic of an uncharged capacitor.

Suppose we substitute for the copper

VOCABULARY

Ampere. The unit of current in the MKS system, one coulomb per second.

Anode. The positive electrode of an electric cell.

Cathode. The negative electrode of an electric cell.

Electric current. The rate of flow of charge past a given point in an electric circuit.

emf. The energy per unit charge supplied by a source of electricity, called the electromotive force.

Ohm. The unit of resistance in the MKS system, one volt per ampere.

Parallel circuit. One in which two or more components are connected across two common points in the circuit so as to provide separate conducting paths for current.

Resistance. The opposition to the flow of electricity.

Series circuit. One in which the components are arranged to provide a single conducting path for current.

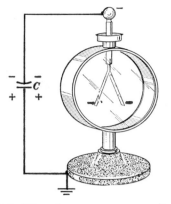

Fig. 19-1. The charge on a capacitor may be indicated by an electroscope.

wire connecting the plates of the charged capacitor a long, fine wire made of nichrome, which has few free electrons compared to copper. The leaves of the electroscope collapse more gradually than before. See Fig. 19-2(*B*). This means, of course, that a longer time is required to completely discharge the capacitor. When any conducting wire connects the plates of the capacitor, electrons move from the negative plate through the conductor to the positive plate. This acts to decrease the charge on each plate and the difference of potential between the plates.

We have seen that the charge *Q* on either plate of a capacitor is proportional to the potential difference *V* between the plates. The *rate* at which the charge decreases, in coul/sec, is proportional to the *rate* at which the potential difference decreases, in v/sec. Now the rate of decrease of charge on the capacitor must represent the rate of flow of the charge, in coul/sec, through the conductor. Thus the rate at which the leaves of the electroscope collapse indicates the rate of flow of the charge through the conductor. During the time the capacitor is discharging, a *current* is said to exist in the conducting wire. *An* **electric current** (*I*) *is the rate of flow of charge past a given point in an electric circuit.*

$$\text{current } (I) = \frac{\text{charge } (Q)}{\text{time } (t)}$$

The unit of current in the MKS system is the *ampere* (amp). *An* **ampere** *is a current of 1 coulomb per second.*

$$1 \text{ ampere} = \frac{1 \text{ coulomb}}{1 \text{ second}}$$

You will recall that 1 coulomb of charge consists of 6.25×10^{18} electrons, or a like number of protons. Small currents may be expressed in *milliamperes* (ma) or *microamperes* (μa):

$$1 \text{ ma} = 10^{-3} \text{ amp}$$
$$1 \text{ μa} = 10^{-6} \text{ amp}$$

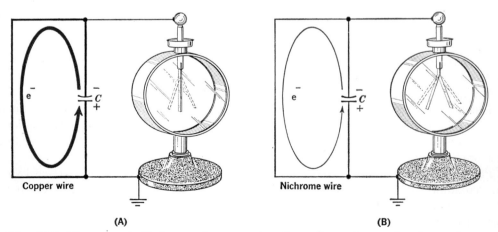

Copper wire

Nichrome wire

(A)   (B)

Fig. 19-2. The rate of discharge of a capacitor depends on the conducting path provided.

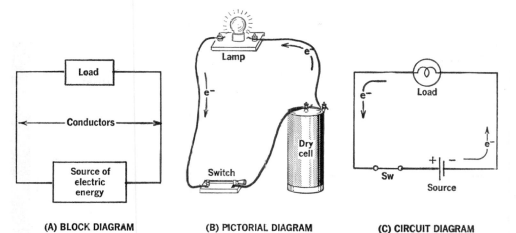

(A) BLOCK DIAGRAM   **(B) PICTORIAL DIAGRAM**   **(C) CIRCUIT DIAGRAM**

Fig. 19-3. An electric circuit is a conducting loop in which a current may transfer electric energy from a suitable source to a useful load.

Any conductor offers some opposition to the flow of electricity through it. Some of the surging electrons which constitute the current collide with the bound atoms of the material and electric energy is dissipated in the process. *This opposition to the flow of electricity is called* **resistance** (R). The practical MKS unit of resistance is the *ohm*, represented by the Greek letter omega, Ω. Laws governing electrical resistance will be discussed in Section 15.

2. Continuous current. The current from a discharging capacitor persists for a very short interval of time; it is known as a *transient* current. The effects of such a current are of course transient also, but transient currents are very important in certain types of electronic circuits. In the general applications of electricity, currents of a more continuous character are required.

The effects of current electricity are quite different from those of static electricity studied in Chapter 18. The electric current is one of our most convenient means of transmitting energy. A *closed-loop* conducting path is needed if energy is to be utilized outside the source; this conducting loop is known as an *electric circuit*, and the device utilizing the electric energy

is called the *load*. The basic components of an electric circuit are illustrated in simple form in Fig. 19-3. Some conventional symbols used in schematic diagrams of electric circuits are shown in Fig. 19-4.

The capacitor would be useful as a source of continuous current over a prolonged period of time only if some means were available for keeping it continuously charged. We would need to supply electrons to the negative plate of the capacitor as rapidly as they were removed by the current in the conducting loop. Similarly, we would need to remove electrons from the positive plate of the capacitor as rapidly as they were deposited by the current. This is to say, *we must maintain the potential difference across the capacitor during the time a continuous current is in the circuit.*

This is an energy-consuming process in which work is done on the electrons in opposition to the force of the electric field between the charged plates. Some of this energy becomes available to do useful work in the external circuit. What is needed is some kind of "electron pump." We could use a Wimshurst machine to achieve our purpose; however, there are more practical means utilizing available

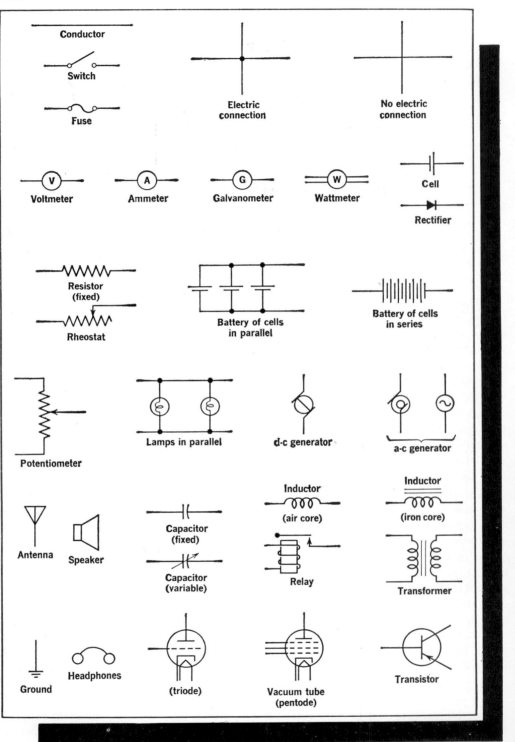

Fig. 19-4. Conventional symbols used in schematic diagrams of electric circuits.

energy sources to maintain a difference of potential across an operating electric circuit.

3. Sources of continuous current. The current sources are of various kinds.

1. Chemical. Certain chemical reactions, called *oxidation-reduction reactions*, involve a transfer of electrons from one reactant to the other. Oxidation-reduction reactions that occur *spontaneously* can be used as sources of continuous current. During the chemical action, electrons are removed from one reactant, which is said to be *oxidized*. A like number of electrons is added to the other reactant, which is said to be *reduced*. By separating the reactants in a conducting solution, the transfer of electrons may take place through an external circuit connected between them. Such an arrangement is known as an *electrochemical cell*. Chemical energy is transformed into electric energy during the chemical action.

Electrochemical cells are of two general types, *primary* cells and *storage* cells. *A* **primary cell** *is an electrochemical cell in which the reacting materials must be replaced after a given amount of energy has been supplied to the external circuit.* The dry cell is the only primary cell in general use today, because a continuous current of electricity can be produced more economically and more conveniently in other ways for most applications. However, we can better understand the energy transformations in the production of electric currents through study of primary cells. These will be considered in more detail in Section 4.

A **storage cell** *is an electrochemical cell in which the reacting materials are renewed by the use of a reverse current from an external source.* The chemical reaction of a storage cell is completely reversible. The *forward* reaction occurs *spontaneously* when a load is placed across the cell. The storage cell is said to be *discharging* as chemical energy is converted to electric energy during this reaction. The *reverse* reaction must be

driven by replacing the load with a source of reverse current. The cell is said to be *charging* as electric energy from the external source is converted to chemical energy within the storage cell. Storage cells will be studied in Section 7.

2. Photoelectric. The *photoelectric effect* was discovered by Heinrich Rudolph Hertz (1857–1894), a German physicist, while studying spark discharges between two charged metal spheres. He observed that the discharge occurred more readily when the spheres were illuminated by another spark discharge.

Electrons are emitted from the surface of a metal illuminated by light of sufficiently short wavelength. For most metals, the light must contain wavelengths in the ultraviolet region. The alkali metals are particularly sensitive to this action; potassium and cesium oxide will respond to rays of ordinary visible light. When a photon of the incident light is absorbed by the metal, its energy is imparted to an electron, which may then possess sufficient energy to break away from the forces which bind it within the surface of the metal.

The metal surface, if properly isolated, of course acquires a positive charge as *photoelectrons* are emitted. As the charge increases, other electrons are prevented from escaping from the metal and the action is stopped. If, however, the metal is placed in an evacuated tube and made part of a circuit, as shown in Fig. 19-5, it may act as a source of current whenever light is incident upon its surface. Such a tube is called a *photoelectric cell*.

To construct the photoelectric cell shown in Fig. 19-5, a coating of potassium metal is placed on the inner surface of a glass tube, leaving an aperture through which light may enter. A metallic ring near the focus of the emitter surface acts as a collector of photoelectrons. The emitter is connected externally to the negative terminal of a battery and the

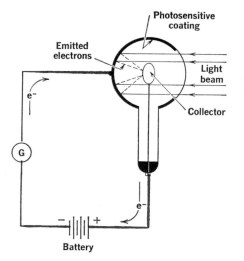

Fig. 19-5. The circuit of a photoelectric cell.

collector is connected to the positive terminal. The collector is thus maintained at a positive potential with respect to the emitter. The force of the resulting electric field acts on the emitted electrons, driving them to the collector and producing a small current in the external circuit. A *galvanometer*, a meter sensitive to very feeble currents, may be placed in the circuit to indicate the relative magnitude and direction of the current.

A bright light causes the ejection of many electrons from the surface of the photosensitive metal, while light of lower intensity produces fewer photoelectrons. Thus the current produced by the photoelectric cell is determined by the intensity of the incident light; this is a case in which radiant energy is transformed into electric energy. Some form of photosensitive cell must be used in devices that are controlled or operated by light.

3. Thermoelectric. Suppose we form a conducting loop consisting of a length of iron wire and a length of copper wire and including a sensitive galvanometer. We may arrange the loop as shown in Fig. 19-6. One copper-iron junction is placed in a beaker of ice and water to maintain

a low constant temperature; the other junction is placed in a Bunsen flame. As the second junction is heated, the galvanometer indicates a current in the loop. Such junctions are known as a *thermocouple.*

The magnitude of the current is related to the nature of the two metals forming the junctions and the temperature difference between the junctions. We can use a thermocouple as a type of thermometer, known as a thermoelectric *pyrometer*. The iron-copper junction is useful for temperatures up to about 275° C. Junctions of copper and constantan (a copper-nickel alloy) are widely used in the lower temperature ranges. Junctions of platinum and rhodium are used to indicate temperatures ranging up to 1600° C.

The thermocouple illustrates a thermoelectric source of current, since heat energy is transformed directly into electric energy. If a sensitive galvanometer is properly calibrated, temperatures may be read directly. Thus the hot junction can be placed in a remote location where it would not be possible to read an ordinary mercury thermometer.

4. Piezoelectric. When certain crystals, such as Rochelle salt and quartz, are subjected to a mechanical stress, the opposite surfaces become electrically charged. The difference of potential between the stressed surfaces is proportional to the amount of stress applied to the crystal. A reversal of the stress reverses the charges also.

If the crystal is suitably supported and a conducting circuit is connected between the surfaces having the difference of potential, electricity will flow through the circuit. Thus, mechanical energy is transformed into electric energy. This transformation is known as the *piezoelectric effect*, and the crystal with its supporting mechanism is called a *piezoelectric cell*.

Crystal microphones make use of the piezoelectric effect to transform the alternating pressure of sound waves into an

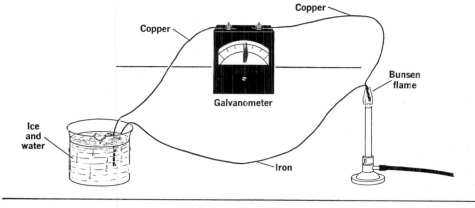

Fig. 19-6. A thermocouple.

electric current that varies as the pressure of the sound waves. A phonograph pickup responds in a similar manner to the varying stress caused by the needle riding in the groove of the record.

The piezoelectric effect is reversible; that is, the crystal undergoes a mechanical strain when subjected to an electric stress. An alternating difference of potential properly placed across the crystal will cause a mechanical vibration proportional to the varying voltage. Crystal headphones make use of this reciprocal effect.

5. *Electromagnetic.* The major source of electric current in practical circuits today depends upon the principle of *electromagnetic induction.* If a conducting loop is rotated in a magnetic field, the free electrons of the conductor are forced to move around the loop and constitute a current. This is the basic principle of operation of electric generators; it is an example of the transformation of mechanical energy into electric energy. Electromagnetic induction and the electric generator will be studied in Chapter 22.

4. The simple voltaic cell. Luigi Galvani (1737–1798), a professor of anatomy at the University of Bologna in Italy, made an important discovery which led to the development of the first primary cell. He observed that frog legs, freshly dissected and suspended on copper hooks,

twitched vigorously when touched with an iron scalpel. Galvani erroneously believed that the twitching was due to "animal" electricity contained in the frog's leg.

Volta, who was a professor of physics at the University of Pavia at this time, undertook a series of experiments to investigate Galvani's discovery. These experiments provided Volta with the correct explanation for the strange behavior of the frog legs: *two dissimilar metals immersed in a conducting fluid cause a chemical reaction capable of producing an electric current.* As a consequence of his investigations, Volta invented the first primary cell, now called the *simple voltaic cell.* Many versions of the voltaic cell using different materials and

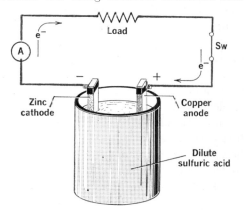

Fig. 19-7. A simple voltaic cell with external load.

different physical arrangements have been devised. Of these the *Daniell* cell, the *gravity* cell, the *Leclanché* cell, and the *dry* cell are common types. Only the dry cell has practical significance today.

We may prepare a simple voltaic cell by placing a strip of zinc and a strip of copper in a small battery jar of water containing a little sulfuric acid as an electrolyte. *An* **electrolyte** *is a substance whose water solution conducts the electric current.* If the zinc and copper strips, called *electrodes*, are kept apart in the solution and are connected externally to a load, bubbles of hydrogen gas form on the copper electrode. A *voltmeter* placed across the cell indicates a potential difference between the electrodes. As the action proceeds, the zinc electrode is consumed.

Zinc atoms in contact with the electrolytic solution have a strong tendency to give up electrons and pass into the solution as zinc ions. This is an *oxidation* reaction that leaves the zinc electrode negatively charged. *The negative electrode of a cell is called the* **cathode.** In the cathode reaction,

$$Zn^0 \rightarrow Zn^{++} + 2e^-$$

one zinc atom	yields	one zinc ion	and	two electrons

Hydrogen ions are present in the solution due to the slight ionization of the water itself and the extensive ionization of the sulfuric acid, H_2SO_4. The hydrogen ion, or proton, is known to be *hydrated* in water solution and is correctly represented as the *hydronium ion*, H_3O^+. This fact should be kept in mind in discussion of electrolytic solutions, since free protons are no more likely to exist in solution than free electrons. For the sake of simplicity, however, we shall use the notation, H^+, to represent the hydrogen ion,

$$H_2SO_4 \rightarrow 2H^+ + SO_4^=$$

one sulfuric acid molecule	yields	two hydrogen ions	and	one sulfate ion

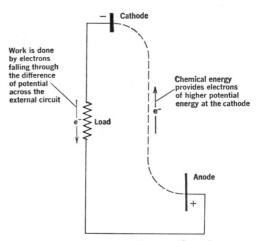

Fig. 19-8. A voltaic cell provides electrons of higher potential energy because of chemical action in the cell.

The H^+ ions are repelled toward the copper electrode by the high density of Zn^{++} ions near the cathode. The H^+ ions are discharged at the copper electrode, by removing electrons from the copper. This is a *reduction* reaction that leaves the copper electrode positively charged. *The positive electrode of a cell is called the* **anode.** In the anode reaction,

$$2H^+ + 2e^- \rightarrow H_2 \uparrow$$

two hydrogen ions	and	two electrons	yield	one hydrogen molecule

Electrons move through the external circuit from cathode to anode because of the difference in potential between the two electrodes. Thus the voltaic cell acts as a kind of electron pump. It removes electrons with low potential energy from the anode and supplies electrons with high potential energy to the cathode in an effort to maintain the potential difference between the electrodes while current is in the external circuit. Observe that electricity flows through the external circuit in the same direction, from cathode to anode, throughout the life of the cell. This unidirectional current produced by voltaic cells is an example of *direct current* (dc).

If we open the external circuit and stop

the flow of electricity, the reduction reaction continues only until the positive charge on the anode is sufficient to repel the H^+ ions with a force equal to that repelling them to the anode. Similarly, the oxidation reaction continues only until the negative charge on the cathode successfully opposes further ionization of the zinc atoms. Thus an equilibrium of electric forces is quickly established within the cell after the circuit is opened. The *maximum* potential difference across a cell is reached when no current flows through it; the magnitude of this *open circuit* potential difference is dependent solely on the materials that make up the electrodes.

The *open circuit* potential difference may be referred to as the emf, or *electromotive force* of the cell. The MKS symbol for emf is E and the unit is, of course, the *volt*. Obviously this is not exactly a force, and so the term "emf" is preferable to the expression "electromotive force." The cell itself must supply a definite amount of energy for each unit of charge that is stored on either electrode; *the emf of a source is the energy per unit charge supplied by the source.* Thus the potential difference across the cell on *open circuit* is equal to the emf of the cell.

$$V_{open\ ckt} = E$$

We will see in Section 10 that V across a source of emf on *closed circuit* is less than E.

The emf of a copper-zinc cell is approximately 1.1 volts; of a carbon-zinc cell, approximately 1.5 volts. A variety of combinations of electrode materials is possible for use in voltaic cells. A list of metals, known as the *Electrochemical Series*, or *Electromotive Series*, indicates their relative activities, the metals being arranged in descending order according to the ease with which their atoms give up electrons to form ions. The voltages listed in the Series which follows are referred to hydrogen as zero. The difference between the voltages of two metals indicates the

ELECTROMOTIVE SERIES	
Element	**Voltage**
Lithium	-2.96
Potassium	-2.92
Calcium	-2.76
Sodium	-2.71
Magnesium	-2.40
Aluminum	-1.70
Zinc	-0.76
Iron	-0.44
Cadmium	-0.40
Nickel	-0.23
Tin	-0.14
Lead	-0.13
Hydrogen	0.00
Copper	$+0.35$
Mercury	$+0.80$
Silver	$+0.80$
Gold	$+1.36$

emf of an ideal voltaic cell in which these metals form the electrodes. The metal which is higher on the table will form the cathode of the pair.

5. Defects of the simple voltaic cell. One defect of the simple cell is *local action.* Commercial zinc usually has carbon particles distributed through it, since coke is used in extracting the zinc from its ores. As the zinc electrode is used up in the cell, carbon particles appear at the surface of the zinc cathode. They act as tiny anodes, setting up miniature circuits within the cell itself. See Fig. 19-9. Such action continues whether or not the external circuit is closed. Zinc is used up in the process, some hydrogen gas is liberated at the cathode, and energy is wasted within the cell. This destructive action is called *local action.*

We may prevent local action by using chemically pure zinc, an expensive product, or by coating the surface of the impure zinc plate with mercury. Mercury dissolves zinc, forming an *amalgam*. As zinc is used up, more zinc is dissolved by the mercury layer and brought to the surface. The carbon particles do not amalgamate but remain covered and out of contact with the electrolyte.

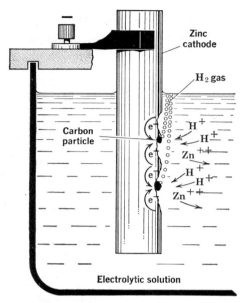

Fig. 19-9. Local action in a voltaic cell.

Polarization is another defect of the simple cell. If we connect a voltmeter across a voltaic cell, we may observe that the expected potential difference of about 1 volt is indicated. This approximates the emf of the cell since only a very small current is in the meter circuit. We allow the cell to operate for a time with the voltmeter serving as the load while we observe both the voltmeter reading and the cell action.

We notice a gradual decrease in voltage as the cell operation continues. If we examine the electrodes, we find an accumulation of tiny gas bubbles on the anode. The anode has been virtually isolated from the cell by a plating of hydrogen gas, which greatly increases the *internal resistance* of the cell and, in effect, substitutes a hydrogen anode for the copper one. The cell is said to be *polarized*. Polarization is responsible for the reduction in potential difference across the cell and thus for a reduction in current in the circuit.

Polarization may be prevented by the addition of an *oxidizing agent* which reacts with the hydrogen at the anode to form

water. Potassium dichromate may be used in the wet cell we are discussing. Manganese dioxide is the oxidizing agent used in the dry cell and the Leclanché cell.

Polarization may also be prevented by modifying the voltaic cell so that metal ions rather than hydrogen ions are discharged at the anode. In the *Daniell* cell a copper anode is immersed in a solution of cupric sulfate. The zinc cathode is immersed in a solution of zinc sulfate. The two solutions are prevented from diffusing by means of a porous partition. Cupric ions plate out on the copper anode; thus, the nature of the electrode is not changed and polarization does not occur.

In the *gravity* cell the same advantage is gained by layering the lighter zinc sulfate solution above the cupric sulfate solution. See Fig. 19-11. This type of cell requires a small continuous current to prevent diffusion of the two solutions. It is known as a closed-circuit cell.

6. The dry cell is a practical voltaic cell. The dry cell is the only primary voltaic cell which has practical significance today. It is used in a great variety

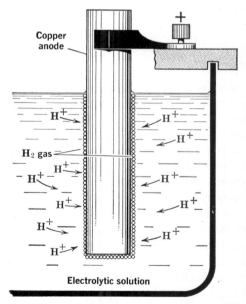

Fig. 19-10. Polarization in a voltaic cell.

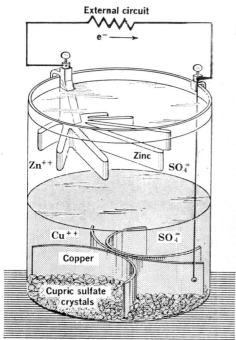

Fig. 19-11. The gravity cell is a nonpolarizing voltaic cell.

Ammonium ions remove electrons from the anode, leaving it positively charged. If manganese dioxide were not present, hydrogen gas would be formed.

$$2NH_4^+ + 2e^- \rightarrow 2NH_3^0 + H_2^0 \uparrow$$

| two ammonium ions | two electrons | two ammonia molecules | one hydrogen molecule |

However, hydrogen is oxidized to water by the manganese dioxide, and manganese, rather than hydrogen, is reduced at the anode.

$$2MnO_2 + 2NH_4^+ + 2e^- \rightarrow$$

| manganese dioxide | ammonium ions | electrons |

$$Mn_2O_3 + 2NH_3 + H_2O$$

| dimanganese trioxide | ammonia | water |

(anode reaction)

The ammonia, NH_3, is taken up by the zinc chloride present in the electrolyte.

Since carbon and zinc are used as the electrodes, the dry cell has an emf of approximately 1.5 volts, regardless of the

of applications as a convenient source of direct current. The dry cell is the modern counterpart of the Leclanché cell. The only significant difference is that the electrolyte in the *dry* cell is in the form of a moist paste instead of a solution.

A diagram of a standard dry cell commonly used in the physics laboratory is shown in Fig. 19-12. A zinc cup serves as the cathode and a carbon rod serves as the anode. The carbon rod is surrounded with a mixture of manganese dioxide as the depolarizer and powdered carbon to reduce the internal resistance of the cell. The electrolyte is a moist paste of ammonium chloride containing some zinc chloride.

When the external circuit is closed, zinc is oxidized at the cathode giving it a negative charge.

$$Zn^0 \rightarrow Zn^{++} + 2e^-$$

| one zinc atom | one zinc ion | two electrons |

(cathode reaction)

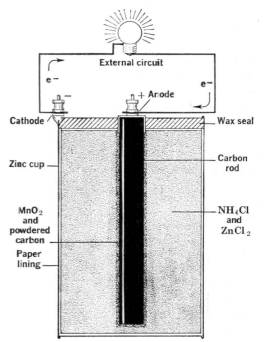

Fig. 19-12. The dry cell is a practical source of direct current in the physics laboratory.

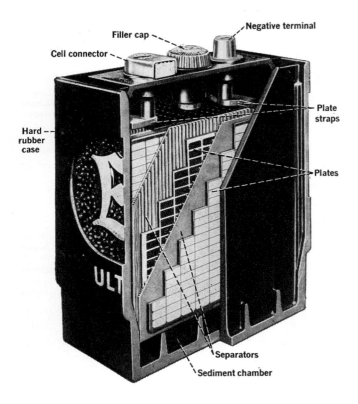
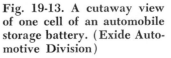

Fig. 19-13. A cutaway view of one cell of an automobile storage battery. (Exide Automotive Division)

physical size of the cell. However, the larger the electrode surfaces the higher the capacity of the cell for delivering current. The standard No. 6 dry cell commonly used in the laboratory is capable of supplying a *momentary* current up to 35 amperes. It should not be required to furnish more than 0.25 ampere of *continuous* current, however. The internal resistance may vary from less than 0.1 ohm in the No. 6 cell to over 1 ohm in very small special-purpose cells.

When an excessive continuous current is drawn, polarization does develop. This increases the internal resistance of the cell and results in a lower difference of potential across the terminals. The polarization soon disappears after the circuit is opened. Thus the dry cell is primarily useful in circuits requiring *intermittent* currents.

7. Storage cells. A storage cell is a voltaic cell that can be restored or re-charged repeatedly to its original condition. Storage cells of three types are now in general use: the lead-acid cell, the Edison cell, and the nickel-cadmium cell. The lead-acid storage cell used in automobile batteries is by far the most widely used type. The emf of each cell is approximately 2.2 volts.

The electrodes of lead-acid cells are initially composed of the same materials. A paste consisting of a combination of oxides of lead and sulfuric acid is pressed into grids made of lead. These are immersed in a forming solution of sulfuric acid and a direct current of electricity is passed through the cell. The cathode is formed into a plate of spongy lead, and the anode is formed into lead dioxide. The electrodes have been formed by chemical action into dissimilar materials, and when immersed in a sulfuric acid electrolyte, constitute a voltaic cell. The plate area is large and the plates are close together to provide good conduction and a very low internal resistance, about 0.001 ohm.

During the *discharge cycle*, chemical energy is transformed to electric energy. Both the cathode and anode are largely converted to lead sulfate, and water is also produced. The chemical action is summarized by the following equations:

$$Pb^0 - 2e^- + SO_4^= \rightarrow PbSO_4 \qquad \text{(cathode reaction)}$$
$$2H^+ + 2e^- + PbO_2 + H_2SO_4 \rightarrow PbSO_4 + 2H_2O \qquad \text{(anode reaction)}$$
$$\overline{Pb + PbO_2 + 2H_2SO_4 \rightarrow 2PbSO_4 + 2H_2O} \qquad \text{(cell reaction)}$$

This chemical action is reversible, and the cell may be recharged by passing a direct current from an external source in the reverse direction through the cell.

During the *charge cycle*, electric energy is converted to chemical energy and the cell is restored. The chemical action is summarized by the following equations:

$$PbSO_4 + 2e^- \rightarrow Pb^0 + SO_4^= \qquad \text{(cathode reaction)}$$
$$PbSO_4 + 2H_2O - 2e^- \rightarrow PbO_2 + H_2SO_4 + 2H^+ \qquad \text{(anode reaction)}$$
$$\overline{2PbSO_4 + 2H_2O \rightarrow Pb + PbO_2 + 2H_2SO_4} \qquad \text{(cell reaction)}$$

You will observe that the cell reaction on charge is the reverse of the cell reaction on discharge. These two equations may be written as one to show the reversibility of the action in the storage cell. The chemical action is shown in Fig. 19-14.

$$\xrightarrow{\quad \text{discharging} \quad}$$
$$Pb + PbO_2 + 2H_2SO_4 \rightleftharpoons 2PbSO_4 + 2H_2O$$
$$\xleftarrow{\quad \text{charging} \quad}$$

Sulfuric acid is used up as the cell is discharged, and water is formed. The specific gravity of the electrolytic solution is approximately 1.300 in a fully charged cell; the specific gravity of the acid solution in the discharged cell may be as low as 1.100. The state of charge of the lead-acid storage cell may thus be determined by testing the specific gravity of the acid solution. The lead-acid cell efficiency is quite high at normal operating temperatures; it drops off rapidly at low temperatures.

The *nickel-cadmium* cell offers some advantages over the lead-acid cell for use in automobile batteries. The cell is ruggedly constructed, is capable of delivering the high starting current required, and is not subject to freezing when discharged. The initial cost, however, is quite high compared to the lead-acid cell.

The cathode is made of nickel hydroxide on a nickel-plated steel grid. The anode is of cadmium containing some iron oxide on a steel grid. The electrolyte is potassium hydroxide, which remains at a constant specific gravity throughout the life of the cell. The emf of the nickel-cadmium cell is about 1.2 volts. See Fig. 19-15 on page 423.

Thomas A. Edison (1847–1931) developed a light-weight, strong, and durable storage cell now known as the *Edison cell*. The anode consists of hydrated nickel oxide and nickel. The cathode is iron oxide, and the electrolyte potassium hydroxide.

The emf of the Edison cell is approximately 1.3 volts and the internal resistance is about 10 times that of the lead-acid cell. It holds a charge for long periods of time and stands up well under neglect and abuse. Batteries of Edison cells of practical size are not capable of delivering the high starting currents required by automobile engines. They are used to provide direct current in remote and unattended locations.

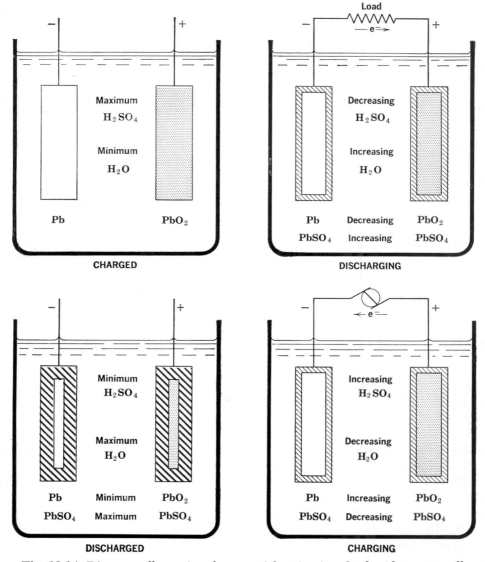

Fig. 19-14. Diagrams illustrating the essential action in a lead-acid storage cell.

8. Combinations of cells. Energy-consuming devices constituting the loads of electric circuits are designed to draw the proper current for their operation when a specific potential difference exists across their terminals. For example, a lamp designed for use in a 6-volt electric system of an automobile would draw an excessive current and burn out if placed in a 12-volt system. A lamp that is in-tended for use in a 12-volt system, on the other hand, would not draw sufficient current at 6 volts to function as intended.

Voltaic cells are sources of emf. Each cell furnishes a certain amount of energy to the circuit for each coulomb of charge that is moved. It is often necessary to combine cells in order to provide the proper emf to the circuit, or an adequate source of current. Groups of cells may be connected in *series*, in *parallel*, or in *series-parallel* combinations. *Two or more cells connected together form a battery.* The emf of a battery depends on the emf of the individual cells and the manner in which the cells are connected.

In a *series* combination of cells, the positive terminal of one cell is connected to the external circuit and the negative terminal is connected to the positive terminal of the second cell. The negative terminal of this cell is connected to the positive terminal of the third cell, and so on. The negative terminal of the last cell in the series is then connected to the load to complete the circuit. Thus the cells are joined end to end and *the same quantity of electricity must flow through each cell.* See Fig. 19-16.

Let us think of the battery as a group of electron pumps connected in *series* (aiding). Each electron pump (cell) removes electrons of lower potential energy from its anode and supplies electrons of

Fig. 19-15. A cutaway view of one cell of a nickel-cadmium storage battery often used in European automobiles. (Nife)

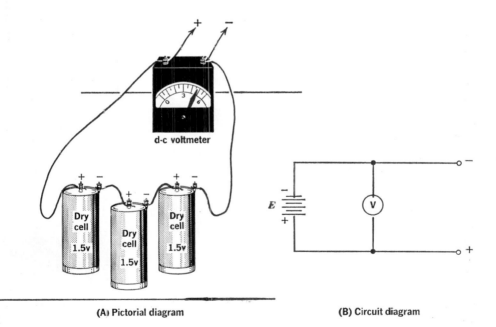

(A) Pictorial diagram	(B) Circuit diagram

Fig. 19-16. Dry cells connected in series to form a battery. The same quantity of electricity flows through each cell.

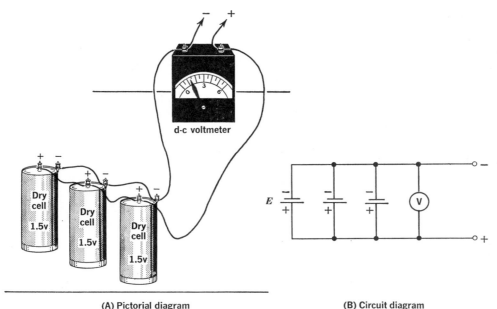

(A) Pictorial diagram   (B) Circuit diagram

Fig. 19-17. Dry cells connected in parallel to form a battery.

higher potential energy to its cathode. The first pump lifts electrons to a certain level of potential energy, the second pump takes them from this level to the next higher level, the third lifts them to a still higher potential energy, and so on. We can readily see that the emfs of the cells are added to give the emf of the battery.

A battery made up of cells connected in series has the following characteristics:

1. The emf of the battery is equal to the sum of the emfs of the individual cells.

2. The current in each cell and in the external circuit is the same.

3. The internal resistance of the battery is equal to the sum of the internal resistances of the individual cells.

In a *parallel* combination of cells, all negative terminals are connected together. One side of the external circuit is then connected to any one of these common terminals. The positive terminals are connected together and the other side of the external circuit may be connected to any one of these common terminals to complete the circuit. This, in effect, simply

increases the total cathode and anode surface areas. The battery is then roughly the equivalent of a single cell with greatly enlarged electrodes in contact with the electrolyte and a lower internal resistance.

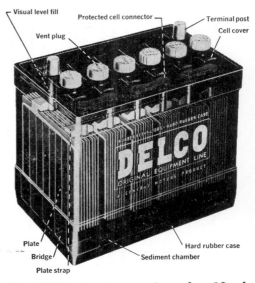

Fig. 19-18. A cutaway view of a 12-volt lead-acid storage battery.

Each cell of a group in parallel merely furnishes its proportionate share of the total circuit current. Cells should not be connected in parallel unless they have the same emfs.

A battery of identical cells connected in parallel has the following characteristics:

1. The emf is equal to the emf of each separate identical cell.

2. The total current in the circuit is divided equally among the separate cells.

3. The reciprocal of the internal resistance of the battery is equal to the sum of the reciprocals of the internal resistances of the separate cells.

The lead-acid storage battery for automobiles with 6-volt electric systems consists of three cells connected in series. The emf is approximately 6.6 volts. Six cells are connected in series to make up the

battery for 12-volt systems. See Fig. 19-18.

In Section 6 we mentioned that a No. 6 dry cell, if properly used, is not required to deliver more than 0.25 ampere of continuous current. Let us suppose we have an electric device designed to perform in a 3-volt circuit and requiring a continuous current of 0.75 ampere. How may we use dry cells to operate this device?

Certainly, 2 dry cells in series would provide an emf of 3 volts for the circuit. Three cells in parallel would require no more than 0.25 ampere from each cell. Thus we see that a series-parallel arrangement of dry cells is appropriate. The battery consisting of this series-parallel arrangement of cells is shown in Fig. 19-19.

9. Batteries are rated in ampere-hours. The quantity of chemical energy stored in a battery depends on the magnitude of the charging current and the time

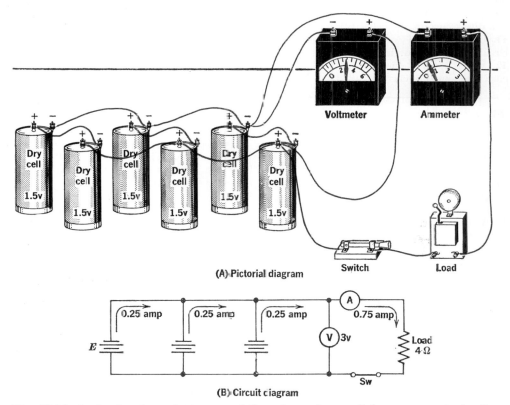

(A) Pictorial diagram

(B) Circuit diagram

Fig. 19-19. A circuit using a battery consisting of a series-parallel arrangement of cells.

the current flows to bring it to a fully charged state.

The *capacity* of a battery is usually rated in ampere-hours. One having a capacity rating of 90 ampere-hours could supply a current of 1 ampere for 90 hours, 2 amperes for 45 hours, 3 amperes for 30 hours, and so on, assuming the efficiency remains the same for all rates of delivery. Unfortunately, the efficiency of the storage battery decreases rapidly at high rates of discharge. This explains the rapid decline in battery power when a driver tries to start a balky engine in very cold weather.

QUESTIONS

A 1. What is an electric current?
2. What is the MKS unit of current?
3. Define the unit of current in terms of fundamental MKS units.
4. What is electric resistance?
5. Name 5 basic sources of continuous current.
6. Name a practical current-producing device for each source named in Question 5.
7. What are the essential parts of a simple voltaic cell?
8. Define an electrolyte.
9. What term is used to identify (a) the negative electrode of an electric cell; (b) the positive electrode?
10. What is the distinguishing characteristic of a direct current of electricity?
11. Distinguish between the terms "open circuit" and "closed circuit."
12. What is the open-circuit potential difference of a source of current called?

B 13. (a) Referring to the Electromotive Series, what should be the emf of a voltaic cell having electrodes of iron and copper? (b) Which metal would form the anode, and which the cathode?
14. What change in the energy of an electron is produced (a) by a source of emf; (b) by a load connected across a source of emf?
15. What is the distinguishing difference between a primary cell and a storage cell?

16. Explain the meaning of the expression "spontaneous oxidation-reduction reaction."
17. Distinguish between potential difference and emf.
18. (a) Explain local action in a primary cell. (b) In what two ways may local action be prevented?
19. How is polarization commonly prevented in the dry cell?
20. Why is it possible to determine the state of charge of a lead-acid storage battery by the use of a hydrometer?
21. (a) How would you connect 1.5-volt dry cells to provide a 6-volt battery to supply a continuous current of 0.25 ampere to a load? (b) Draw a circuit diagram of the battery you describe.
22. (a) How would you connect 1.5-volt dry cells to provide a 6-volt battery to supply a continuous current of 0.50 ampere to a load? (b) Draw a circuit diagram showing the battery connected to a resistance load, a voltmeter connected to read the potential difference across the load, and an ammeter connected to read the current in the circuit.
23. An automobile storage battery may be rated at 120 ampere-hours. Explain the meaning of this rating.
24. How does the temperature affect the efficiency of a lead-acid storage battery?
25. Does a storage battery store electricity? Justify your answer.

2 SERIES AND PARALLEL CIRCUITS

10. Ohm's law for d-c circuits. In Section 1 we defined *resistance* (R) as the opposition to the flow of electricity. Metallic substances in general are classed as good conductors of electricity. Silver and copper, because of their abundance of free electrons, are excellent conductors, but even these metals offer some opposition to the surge of electricity through them. There is some inherent resistance, or opposition to the current, in every conductor, and therefore every device or component in an electric circuit offers some resistance to the current in the circuit.

Copper wire is used in electric circuits to connect various circuit components because ordinarily its resistance is low enough to be neglected. Certain metallic alloys offer unusually high resistance to the flow of electricity; *nichrome* and *chromel* are notable examples. Spools wound with wire made from these alloys may be used in an electric circuit to provide either *fixed* amounts of resistance, or *variable* resistance in definite amounts. Such devices are called *wire-wound resistors*.

Carbon granules may be mixed with varying amounts of clay and molded into cylinders having a definite resistance. These devices are called *carbon resistors* and are commonly used in electronic circuits.

Georg Simon Ohm (1787–1854), a German physicist, discovered experimentally that *the ratio of the emf applied to a closed circuit to the current in the circuit is a constant.* This constant is the *resistance* of the circuit. The above statement is known as *Ohm's law of resistance,* a relationship of the utmost importance in the study of current electricity. Ohm's law may be stated mathematically as follows:

$$\frac{E}{I} = R$$

Or, when transposed into the usual form:

$$E = IR$$

The MKS units are the volt, ampere, and ohm respectively. The *ohm* (Ω) has the dimensions nt-m-sec/coul² as we can readily see from the following:

$$1 \, \Omega = \frac{1 \text{ v}}{1 \text{ amp}} = 1 \frac{\frac{\text{nt-m}}{\text{coul}}}{\frac{\text{coul}}{\text{sec}}}$$

$$1 \, \Omega = 1 \frac{\text{nt-m-sec}}{\text{coul}^2}$$

See the Sample Problem on page 429.

The emf, E, applied to a circuit equals the drop in potential across the *total* resistance of the circuit, but Ohm's law applies equally well to *any part* of a circuit that does not include a source of emf. Suppose we consider the circuit shown in Fig. 19-20. Points A and B are the terminals of the battery, which supplies an emf of 12.0 volts to the circuit. The total resistance of the circuit is 12.0 ohms. Of this total, 0.20 ohm is *internal resistance* (r) of the battery and is conventionally represented as a lumped resistor in series with the battery inside the battery terminals. The remaining 11.8 ohms of resistance consists of a *load resistor* (R_L) in the external circuit.

For the entire circuit, the total resistance (R_T) is equal to the sum of internal and external resistances.

$$R_T = R_L + r$$

The current through the entire circuit is

$$I = \frac{E}{R_T} = \frac{E}{R_L + r}$$

$$I = \frac{12.0 \text{ v}}{11.8 \, \Omega + 0.20 \, \Omega}$$

$$I = 1.00 \text{ amp}$$

When we apply Ohm's law to a part of a circuit that does not include a source of emf, we are concerned with the potential difference V, the current I, and the resistance R that apply only to that part of the circuit. Thus, Ohm's law for a part of the circuit becomes

$$V = IR$$

The drop in potential across the exter-

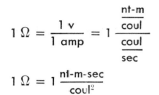
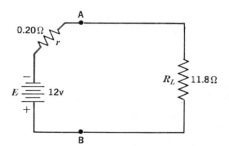

Fig. 19-20. Ohm's Law applies equally well to all or any part of an electric circuit.

Sample Problem

An emf of 12 v is applied across an electric circuit. (*a*) What is the current in the circuit if the resistance is 30. Ω?   (*b*) If the resistance of the circuit is doubled, what is the current?

Solution

(*a*) According to Ohm's law

$E = IR$

Solving for I

$I = \dfrac{E}{R}$

$I = \dfrac{12 \text{ v}}{30. \ \Omega}$

$I = 0.40$ amp, the current in the circuit.

(*b*) If the resistance is doubled, that is, if the opposition to the flow of electricity is doubled, and the applied emf remains the same, we should expect the current in the circuit to be reduced to half the former value.

$I = \dfrac{12 \text{ v}}{60. \ \Omega}$

$I = 0.20$ amp, the current in the circuit

nal circuit of Fig. 19-20 (to the right of A–B) must be

$V_L = IR_L$
$V_L = 1.00 \text{ amp} \times 11.8 \ \Omega$
$V_L = 11.8$ volts

The drop in potential across the internal resistance of the battery due to current in the battery may be found by a similar application of Ohm's law.

$V_r = Ir$
$V_r = 1.00 \text{ amp} \times 0.20 \ \Omega$
$V_r = 0.20$ volt

This is a fall of potential across the battery resistance, which removes energy from the electrons. It is, therefore, opposite in sign to the emf of the battery and subtracts from the emf to give the potential difference across the battery terminals on closed circuit with a current I.

$V = E - Ir$

The closed-circuit potential difference across the terminals of a source of emf which is applied to the external circuit will always be less than the emf by the amount Ir volts. For a source of emf of low internal resistance, this is not an important difference unless an excessive current is in the circuit. (In much of the discussion that follows the next section, the internal resistance of a source of emf will be neglected and the emf will be assumed to be applied to the external circuit.)

11. Determining internal resistance. A good quality voltmeter is an instrument of very high resistance. When a voltmeter is connected across the terminals of a source of emf, even one with low internal resistance, negligible current is drawn from the source. For all practical purposes the meter reading is an "open-circuit" reading and indicates the emf of the source.

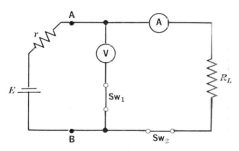

Fig. 19-21. A circuit for measuring the internal resistance of a cell.

This provides us with a convenient method of measuring the internal resistance of a cell or battery. The Sample Problem on page 430, based on Fig. 19-21, illustrates this method.

12. Resistances in series. If several electric devices are connected end to end in a circuit, electricity must flow through each in succession. There is only a single path for the moving charge, and so the *same* current must be in each device: otherwise there would be an accumulation of charge at different points around the conducting circuit. We know that a charge can be accumulated on a conductor only if it is isolated. *An electric circuit with components arranged to provide a single conducting path for current is known as a series circuit.*

Series-circuit operation has several inherent limitations. If one element of a series connection fails to provide a conducting path, the circuit is opened. Also, each component of the circuit offers resistance to the flow of electricity, and resistance in a circuit acts to limit the current in the circuit according to Ohm's law. When connected in series, the resistance effect is cumulative; the more resistive components, the higher the total resistance, and the smaller the current in the circuit for a given applied emf. Obviously, since there must be a single magnitude of current in the circuit, *all devices connected in series must be designed to function at the same current.*

From Ohm's law, the drop in potential across each component of a series circuit is the product of the current in the circuit and the resistance of the component. Electrons lose energy as they fall through a difference of potential; in a series circuit these losses occur in succession and are therefore cumulative. *The drops in potential across successive components in a series circuit are additive, and their sum is equal to the potential difference across the whole circuit.*

We may summarize these observations by stating **three cardinal rules** for resistances in series:

1. The current in all parts of a series circuit has the same magnitude.

$$I_T = I_1 = I_2 = I_3 = \text{etc.}$$

2. The sum of all the separate drops of potential around a series circuit is equal to the applied emf.

$$E = V_1 + V_2 + V_3 + \text{etc.}$$

3. The total resistance in a series circuit is equal to the sum of all the separate resistances.

$$R_T = R_1 + R_2 + R_3 + \text{etc.}$$

Let us apply these rules to a circuit consisting of several resistors connected in series as shown in Fig. 19-22. The computations are shown at the right of the circuit diagram. Observe that the "positive" side of R_1 is 3.0 volts positive with respect to the cathode of the battery and is 9.0 volts negative with respect to the anode of the battery. The algebraic sum of all the voltages around the circuit is equal to zero.

13. Resistances in parallel. We have recognized some of the limitations of series operation of electric devices. It would be quite disconcerting to have all lights go out in your home each time one lamp "burned out." It is more satisfactory to have each lamp on a separate branch of the lighting circuit, so that each lamp may be operated independently of the others. Such lamps are said to be connected in *parallel. A **parallel circuit** is one in which two or more components are connected across*

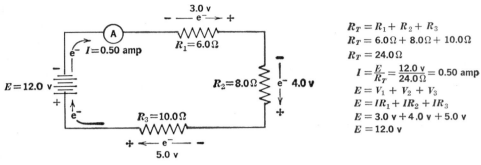

$$R_T = R_1 + R_2 + R_3$$
$$R_T = 6.0\,\Omega + 8.0\,\Omega + 10.0\,\Omega$$
$$R_T = 24.0\,\Omega$$
$$I = \frac{E}{R_T} = \frac{12.0\text{ v}}{24.0\,\Omega} = 0.50\text{ amp}$$
$$E = V_1 + V_2 + V_3$$
$$E = IR_1 + IR_2 + IR_3$$
$$E = 3.0\text{ v} + 4.0\text{ v} + 5.0\text{ v}$$
$$E = 12.0\text{ v}$$

Fig. 19-22. A series circuit.

two common points in the circuit so as to provide separate conducting paths for current.

Since there can be only one difference of potential between any two points in an electric circuit, *electric devices or appliances connected in parallel should usually be designed to operate at the same voltage.* The current in the separate branches must vary in-

Sample Problem

A dry cell gives an open-circuit voltmeter reading of 1.5 v. The voltmeter is then removed and an external load of 2.8 ohms is connected across the cell. An ammeter in the external circuit reads 0.50 ampere. (*a*) Find the internal resistance of the cell. (*b*) What would the voltmeter have read if it had been left connected while the current was in the load?

Solution

(*a*) We are given the following information: the emf of the cell, $E = 1.5$ v; $I = 0.50$ amp; and $R_L = 2.8\ \Omega$. We are asked to find r.

We know that E is the work done per coulomb of charge moved through the total resistance of the circuit.

Thus $E = IR_T$

But $R_T = R_L + r$

Then $E = I(R_L + r)$

Solving for r, $r = \dfrac{E - IR_L}{I}$

Substituting, $r = \dfrac{1.5\text{ v} - (0.50\text{ amp} \times 2.8\ \Omega)}{0.50\text{ amp}}$

$r = 0.20\ \Omega$, the internal resistance

(*b*) $V = E - Ir = 1.5$ v $- (0.50$ amp $\times 0.20\ \Omega)$
$V = 1.4$ v, the potential difference across the circuit

versely with their separate resistances since the same potential difference exists across each branch of the parallel circuit.

By Ohm's law, which may be applied to any part of a circuit, the current in each branch is

$$I = \frac{V}{R}$$

But V is constant for all branches in parallel. Then

$$I_{\text{(for each branch)}} \propto \frac{1}{R_{\text{(of that branch)}}}$$

In Fig. 19-23 it is apparent that there is more opportunity for the flow of electricity between points A and B with two parallel branches in the circuit than with one branch removed. The current entering point A (I) must be the same as the current leaving point A ($I_1 + I_2$). Similarly, the current entering point B ($I_1 - I_2$) must be the same as the current leaving point B (I). Then I must be equal to $I_1 + I_2$.

Let us assume that $R_1 = 10.\ \Omega$, $R_2 = 15$ Ω, and $V = 30.$ v. According to Ohm's law the current in R_1 is

$$I_1 = \frac{V}{R_1} = \frac{30.\ \text{v}}{10.\ \Omega} = 3.0\ \text{amp}$$

The current in R_2 is

$$I_2 = \frac{V}{R_2} = \frac{30.\ \text{v}}{15\ \Omega} = 2.0\ \text{amp}$$

and $I = I_1 + I_2 = 5.0\ \text{amp}$

According to Ohm's law, the current

from A to B, which is I, is the quotient of the potential difference across A–B divided by the effective resistance between A and B. It is convenient to think of the effective resistance due to resistances in parallel as a single *equivalent resistance* (R_{eq}) which, if substituted for the parallel resistances, would provide the same current in the circuit.

$$I = \frac{V}{R_{eq}}$$

Then

$$R_{eq} = \frac{V}{I} = \frac{30.\ \text{v}}{5.0\ \text{amp}} = 6.0\ \Omega$$

The equivalent resistance for the parallel combination of R_1 and R_2 is *less than* either resistance present. As the current before (and after) dividing *must be larger* than either branch current, we can see that the equivalent resistance of the parallel circuit *must be smaller* than the resistance of any branch.

It can be shown that the sum of the reciprocals of the resistances in parallel is equal to the reciprocal of their equivalent resistance. Then

$$\frac{1}{R_{eq}} = \frac{1}{R_1} + \frac{1}{R_2}$$

$$R_1 R_2 = R_{eq}(R_1 + R_2)$$

$$R_{eq} = \frac{R_1 R_2}{R_1 + R_2}$$

$$R_{eq} = \frac{10.\ \Omega \times 15\ \Omega}{10.\ \Omega + 15\ \Omega} = \frac{150\ \Omega^2}{25\ \Omega}$$

$$R_{eq} = 6.0\ \Omega$$

Let us summarize these observations by stating *three cardinal rules* for resistances in parallel.

1. The total current in a parallel circuit is equal to the sum of the currents in the separate branches.

$$I_T = I_1 + I_2 + I_3 + \text{etc.}$$

2. The potential difference across all branches of a parallel circuit must have the same magnitude.

$$V = V_1 = V_2 = V_3 = \text{etc.}$$

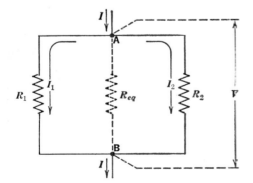

Fig. 19-23. Two resistances in parallel.

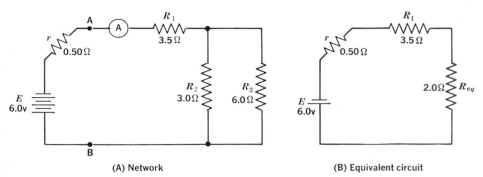

(A) Network   (B) Equivalent circuit

Fig. 19-24. A simple network and its equivalent circuit.

3. *The reciprocal of the equivalent resistance is equal to the sum of the reciprocals of the separate resistances in parallel.*

$$\frac{1}{R_{eq}} = \frac{1}{R_1} + \frac{1}{R_2} + \frac{1}{R_3} + etc.$$

14. Resistances in series-parallel combinations—simple networks. Practical circuits may be quite complex compared to the series and parallel circuits we have considered. There may be resistances in series, other resistances in parallel, and different sources of emf. Such complex circuits are commonly called *networks*.

A very simple network is shown in Fig. 19-24(*A*). There is a single source of emf and one resistor in series with the combination of two resistors in parallel. We will use this circuit to demonstrate the steps that can be taken to simplify a network and reduce circuit problems to simple relationships.

We are given the emf of the battery and the resistance of each component resistor in the circuit. The first step is to find the total current in the circuit. To do this we must know the total resistance. To find the total resistance we must reduce the parallel resistances to an *equivalent* value.

$$\frac{1}{R_{eq}} = \frac{1}{R_2} + \frac{1}{R_3}$$
$$\frac{1}{R_{eq}} = \frac{1}{3.0\ \Omega} + \frac{1}{6.0\ \Omega}$$
$R_{eq} = 2.0\ \Omega$, the equivalent resistance of R_2 and R_3 in parallel

We may now draw a simpler *equivalent* circuit showing this equivalent resistance in series with R_1 and r. See Fig. 19-24(*B*). The total resistance is now readily seen to be 6.0 ohms.

$$R_T = R_1 + R_{eq} + r = 6.0\ \Omega$$
And
$$I_T = \frac{E}{R_T} = \frac{6.0\ v}{6.0\ \Omega} = 1.0\ amp$$

The drop in potential across R_1 is
$$V_1 = I_T R_1 = 1.0\ amp \times 3.5\ \Omega$$
$$V_1 = 3.5\ v$$

Since R_2 and R_3 are in parallel, the same potential drop must appear across each. This is found by considering the total current in the equivalent resistance of the parallel segment.

$$V_{eq} = I_T R_{eq} = 1.0\ amp \times 2.0\ \Omega$$
$$V_{eq} = 2.0\ v$$

The potential difference across the terminals of the battery is the difference between the emf and the $I_T r$ drop.

$$V = E - I_T r = 6.0\ v - (1.0\ amp \times 0.50\ \Omega)$$
$$V = 5.5\ v$$

This is verified by the fact that V must equal $V_1 + V_{eq}$.

The current in R_2 may be found since the potential difference, V_{eq}, is known.

$$I_2 = \frac{V_{eq}}{R_2} = \frac{2.0\ v}{3.0\ \Omega}$$
$$I_2 = 0.67\ amp$$

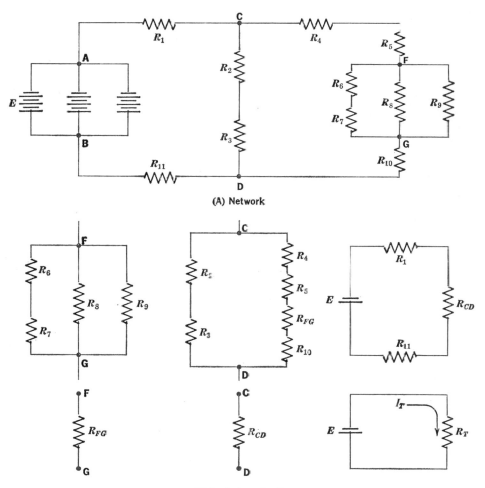

(A) Network

(B) Equivalent circuit

Fig. 19-25. A network may be reduced to a simple circuit by the use of equivalent circuit analysis techniques.

The current in R_3 is

$$I_3 = \frac{V_{eq}}{R_3} = \frac{2.0 \text{ v}}{6.0 \ \Omega}$$

$$I_3 = 0.33 \text{ amp}$$

This is verified by the fact that I_3 must equal $I_T - I_2$.

A more complex network is shown in Fig. 19-25(A). The battery is a series-parallel arrangement of similar cells, so the magnitude of the emf will depend on the number of cells in *series*. The total current must be known. The attack is the same as that in our earlier example. First,

reduce the segment F–G to its equivalent value. We will label this R_{FG}. Now R_{FG} is in series with R_4, R_5, and R_{10} to form one branch of the segment C–D. When these are reduced to their equivalent, R_{CD}, we may consider R_1, R_{CD}, and R_{11} to be in series. This provides R_T, and I_T may be calculated. These circuit reductions are shown in Fig. 19-25(B).

Let us suppose that we need to know the magnitude of current in R_7 and the drop in potential across this resistor. Now the current in R_{CD} must be I_T and the drop in potential across C–D must be $I_T R_{CD}$, or V_{CD}. The current in the branch of C–D containing R_{FG} is the quotient of V_{CD} divided by the sum of $(R_4 + R_5 + R_{FG} + R_{10})$. This current (we will label it I_{FG}) is in R_{FG} and the potential drop, V_{FG}, across R_{FG} is the product $I_{FG}R_{FG}$.

Since R_6 and R_7 are in series, the resistance of this branch of F–G is equal to their sum. The current in R_7 is V_{FG} divided by $(R_6 + R_7)$. With I_7 known, the drop in potential across R_7 is the product I_7R_7. You will observe that we have depended on Ohm's law and the six extensions of Ohm's law we listed as cardinal rules for series and parallel circuits in Sections 12 and 13.

15. The laws of resistance. Various factors affect the resistance of a conductor.

1. Temperature. The electric resistance of all substances changes to some degree with changes in temperature. *In the case of pure metals and most metallic alloys, the resistance increases rapidly with a rise in temperature.* Carbon, semiconductors, and many electrolytic solutions, on the other hand, show a decrease in resistance as their temperature is raised. A few special alloys, such as constantan and manganin, show very slight changes in resistance over a considerable range of temperatures. For practical purposes, the resistance of these alloys may be considered independent of temperature.

Thermal agitation of the particles composing a metallic conductor rises rapidly as we heat the metal. As we lower the temperature, thermal agitation diminishes. We may relate the electric resistance of metals to this thermal agitation; their resistance approaches zero as the temperature approaches absolute zero ($0°$ K). The graph of resistance against temperature of a metallic conductor is essentially linear over the full temperature range of the solid state of the metal. Thus, when we refer to the electric resistance of a conductor, we should state the temperature of the material at which this resistance applies. See Fig. 19-26.

2. Length. In Section 12 we learned that

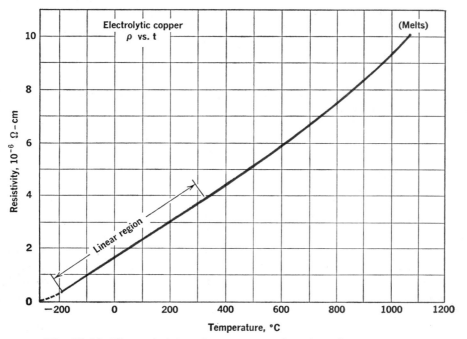

Fig. 19-26. The resistivity of copper as a function of temperature.

resistances in series are added to give the total resistance of the series circuit. From this we may conclude that 10 meters of a certain conductor should have a resistance 10 times that of 1 meter of the same conductor. Indeed, experiments prove this to be true; *the resistance of a uniform conductor is directly proportional to its length.*

$$R \propto l$$

where l is the length of the conductor.

3. *Cross-sectional area.* If we place three equal resistances in parallel in an electric circuit, the equivalent resistance will be one-third the resistance of any one branch (Section 13). The equal currents in the three branches add to give the total current in the circuit.

Assuming the three resistances to be three similar wires 1 meter in length, each having a cross-sectional area of 0.1 cm², we may think of the equivalent resistance as a similar wire of the same length but having a cross-sectional area of 0.3 cm². This is reasonable, since a wire carrying a direct current of constant magnitude has a constant current density throughout its cross-sectional area. If the parallel resistances are designated R_1, R_2, and R_3, then

$$\frac{1}{R_{eq}} = \frac{1}{R_1} + \frac{1}{R_2} + \frac{1}{R_3}$$

But

$$R_1 = R_2 = R_3$$

So

$$\frac{1}{R_{eq}} = \frac{3}{R_1}$$

And

$$R_1 = 3R_{eq}$$

We may conclude that the resistance of the large wire, R_{eq}, is one-third the resistance of the small wire, R_1, and experiments prove this to be true. *The resistance of a uniform conductor is inversely proportional to its cross-sectional area.*

$$R \propto \frac{1}{A}$$

where A is the cross-sectional area of the conductor.

Fig. 19-27. The German physicist Georg Simon Ohm. (Culver Service)

4. *Nature of the material.* A copper wire having the same length and cross-sectional area as an iron wire offers about one-sixth the resistance to the flow of electricity. A similar silver wire presents even less resistance. *The resistance of a given conductor depends on the material out of which it is made.*

Taking these four factors into account, we come to several useful conclusions. For a uniform conductor of a given material and temperature, the resistance is directly proportional to the length and inversely proportional to the cross-sectional area.

$$R \propto \frac{l}{A}$$

Suppose we introduce a proportionality constant, called *resistivity* and represented by the Greek letter ρ (rho). The *laws of resistance* for wire conductors may then be summarized by the following expression:

$$R = \rho \frac{l}{A}$$

Resistivity is dependent only on the material composing the wire and its temperature. See Fig. 19-26. If R is in ohms, l is in centimeters, and A is in centimeters^2, then ρ has the dimensions *ohm-centimeter*.

$$\rho = \frac{RA}{l}$$

$$\rho = \frac{\Omega\text{-cm}^2}{\text{cm}} = \Omega\text{-cm}$$

Resistivity, ρ, is equal to the resistance of a wire 1 cm long and having a uniform cross-sectional area of 1 cm^2. If the resistivity of a material is known, the resistance of any other wire composed of the same material can be calculated. See the Sample Problem below.

In the English system, the *circular mil* (circ mil) is the standard unit of cross-sectional area of round wires. A wire that is 0.001 in. in diameter is said to be *1 mil in diameter*. A **circular mil** *is the area of a circle 1 mil in diameter*. The advantage of the circular mil as a unit is that cross-sectional areas of round wires expressed in this unit bear a very simple relationship to the diameters expressed in mils. The area of a round wire of diameter d, in mils, is

$$A = d^2, \text{ in circ mil}$$

If a wire has a diameter of 0.025 in., then its diameter is 25 mils. The cross-sectional area is 25^2 circular mils. You will observe that the factor π does not enter the computation of cross-sectional areas with the circular mil as the unit.

The resistivity constant, ρ, in the English system is the resistance of a round wire *1 foot* long and having a uniform cross-sectional area of *1 circular mil*. This unit is frequently expressed as *ohms per mil foot*. It is obvious that this is dimensionally incorrect since

$$\rho = \frac{RA}{l} = \frac{\Omega\text{-circ mil}}{\text{ft}}$$

Resistivity in the English system is properly

Sample Problem

What is the resistance of a copper wire 20. m long and 0.81 mm in diameter at 20° C? The resistivity of annealed copper at 20° C is 1.72 × 10^{-6} Ω-cm.

Solution

We are given the resistivity of copper at 20° C, ρ = 1.72 × 10^{-6} Ω-cm. The length of wire may be converted to centimeters and is most conveniently expressed as l = 2.0 × 10^3 cm. The diameter of the wire in millimeters may be converted to 0.081 cm.

The area, A, of a circle with diameter, d, = $\frac{\pi d^2}{4}$.

$$R = \rho \frac{l}{A}$$

$$R = 1.72 \times 10^{-6}\ \Omega\text{-cm} \times \frac{2.0 \times 10^3 \text{ cm}}{\dfrac{\pi (0.081 \text{ cm})^2}{4}}$$

$$R = \frac{1.72 \times 10^{-6}\ \Omega\text{-cm} \times 4 \times 2.0 \times 10^3 \text{ cm}}{\pi \times 6.56 \times 10^{-3} \text{ cm}^2}$$

R = 0.67 Ω, the resistance of the wire

expressed in Ω-*circ mil/ft*. Table 16, Appendix B, gives the value of ρ at 20° C for several commonly used conductors. Table 19, Appendix B, gives some useful properties of copper wire. See the Sample Problem below.

16. Semiconductors. The enormous range of resistivities of common materials is shown in Fig. 19-28. The resistance of the best insulator may be greater than that of the best conductor by a factor of approximately 10^{25}. Insulators and semiconductors may decrease in resistivity with increasing temperature and with increasing potential gradient. We may interpret this latter behavior to mean that Ohm's law is not obeyed by these materials.

A small group of *semiconductors* are assuming increasing importance because of their unusual variations in resistance with changes in temperature and potential gradient. Copper oxide rectifiers known as *varistors* will pass a current when a potential difference is applied in one direction but not in the opposite direction. Silicon and germanium *transistors* are excellent substitutes for vacuum tubes in many electronic circuit applications. These will be discussed in Chapter 25.

17. The measurement of resistance. There are several methods of measuring the resistance of a circuit component. Two methods utilizing apparatus normally available in the physics laboratory will be discussed here. These are the *voltmeter-ammeter* method and the *Wheatstone bridge* method.

1. The voltmeter-ammeter method. Ohm's law applies equally well to any part of an electric circuit which does not contain a source of emf and to an entire circuit to which an emf is applied. For a part of a circuit:

$$V = IR \quad \text{and} \quad R = \frac{V}{I}$$

If the potential difference V across a resistance component is measured with a voltmeter and the current I in the resistance is measured with an ammeter, the resistance R can be computed.

Suppose we wish to measure the resistance of R_1 in the circuit shown in Fig. 19-29. We connect the ammeter *in series* with the resistance R_1 to determine the current in R_1. We connect the voltmeter in *parallel* with R_1 to determine the potential difference across R_1.

If the resistance of R_1 is very low, it may have an excessive loading effect on

Sample Problem

Find the resistance of 150. ft of No. 24 copper wire, using appropriate wire data from the Appendix.

Solution

From Table 16, Appendix B, we find the resistivity for copper, $\rho = 10.37$ Ω-circ mil/ft. From Table 18 we find the diameter of No. 24 gauge wire, $d = 20.1$ mils.

$$R = \rho \frac{l}{A}$$

$$R = \frac{10.37 \ \Omega\text{-circ mil}}{\text{ft}} \times \frac{150. \ \text{ft}}{(20.1)^2 \ \text{circ mil}}$$

$R = 3.85$ Ω, the resistance of the wire

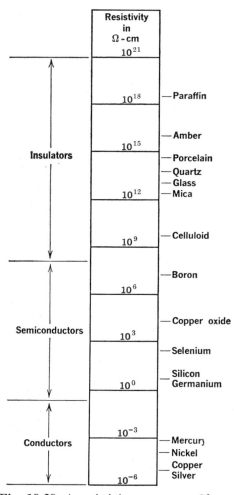

Fig. 19-28. A resistivity spectrum. Observe the enormous range of resistivities of different substances.

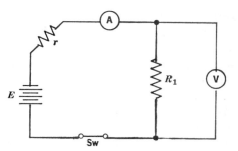

Fig. 19-29. Determining resistance by the voltmeter-ammeter method.

particularly precise. A voltmeter is a high resistance instrument. However, as it is connected in parallel with the resistance to be measured, there is a small current in it. The ammeter reading is actually the sum of the currents in these two parallel branches. Precision is limited by the extent to which the resistance of R_1 exceeds the equivalent resistance of R_1 and the meter in parallel.

2. *The Wheatstone bridge method.* A very precise means of determining resistance utilizes a simple *bridge* circuit known as the *Wheatstone bridge*. It consists of a source of emf, a galvanometer, and a network of four resistors. If three are of known resistance, the resistance value of the fourth can be calculated.

The circuit diagram of a Wheatstone bridge is shown in Fig. 19-31, in which an unknown resistance, R_x may be balanced against known resistances R_1, R_2, and R_3. A galvanometer is *bridged* across the paral-

the source of emf, causing an excessive current in the circuit. We may avoid this difficulty by placing a variable resistance, called a *rheostat*, in series with R_1. The rheostat provides additional series resistance and acts to limit the current in the circuit. By adjusting the rheostat we may provide an appropriate magnitude of current in the circuit. See Fig. 19-30. Observe that the voltmeter is connected across that part of the circuit for which resistance is to be determined.

The voltmeter-ammeter method of measuring resistance is convenient but not

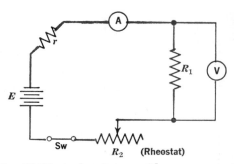

Fig. 19-30. A rheostat provides a means of limiting the current in a circuit.

lel branches ADB and ACB. By adjusting R_1, R_2, and R_3, the bridge circuit may be balanced, and the galvanometer shows zero current.

When the bridge is balanced, there can be no potential difference between C and D, since the galvanometer indicates zero current. Thus

$$V_{AD} = V_{AC}$$

and

$$V_{DB} = V_{CB}$$

The current in the branch ACB is I_1, and the current in ADB is I_2. Then

$$I_2R_x = I_1R_1$$

and

$$I_2R_3 = I_1R_2$$

Dividing one expression by the other, we have

$$\frac{R_x}{R_3} = \frac{R_1}{R_2}$$

or

$$R_x = R_3\frac{R_1}{R_2}$$

In the laboratory form of the Wheatstone bridge, the resistances R_1 and R_2 usually consist of a uniform resistance

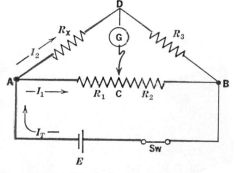

Fig. 19-31. The electric circuit of the Wheatstone bridge.

wire, such as constantan, mounted on a meter stick. See Fig. 19-32. The length of wire comprising R_1, and the length comprising R_2, are determined by the position of the contact C. If we let l_1 be the length of wire forming R_1 and l_2 the length of wire forming R_2, it is apparent that

$$\frac{l_1}{l_2} = \frac{R_1}{R_2}$$

We do not need to know the resistances of R_1 and R_2, for the lengths of wire, l_1 and

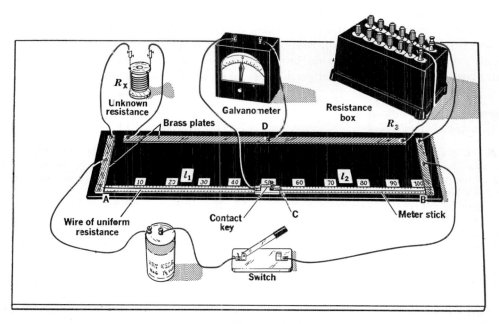

Fig. 19-32. The Wheatstone-bridge method of measuring resistance.

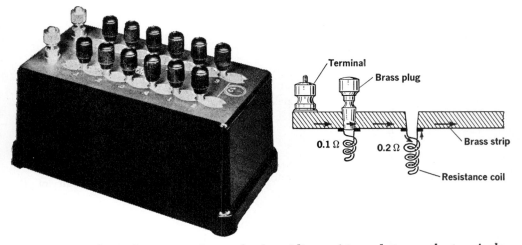

Fig. 19-33. Left: A plug-type resistance box providing resistance between the terminals from 0.1 ohm to 111 ohms in 0.1-ohm steps. (Cenco) Right: The total resistance across the terminals of a resistance box depends on which plugs are removed.

l_2, may be taken directly from the meter stick. Our Wheatstone bridge expression then becomes

$$R_x = R_3 \frac{l_1}{l_2}$$

A precision *resistance box* of the type shown in Fig. 19-33 is often used to provide a suitable known resistance, R_3, in the bridge circuit. The internal arrangement is shown in the diagram. Resistance coils are wound with manganin or constantan wire to minimize changes in resistance with temperature. The free ends of each resistance coil are soldered to heavy brass blocks which can be electrically connected by inserting brass plugs between them. Each plug in place provides a low-resistance path across a resistance coil and thus effectively removes it from the circuit. Each plug removed places a coil in the circuit. The resistance between the terminals of the box is the sum of the resistances of all coils whose plugs are removed.

QUESTIONS

A **1.** State Ohm's law (*a*) verbally; (*b*) mathematically.
2. What is the mathematical expression for Ohm's law as it applies to a part of a circuit which does not contain a source of emf?
3. What is the identifying characteristic of a series circuit?
4. State the three cardinal rules for resistances in series.
5. Define a parallel circuit.
6. What change occurs in the total resistance of a circuit as additional resistances are added (*a*) in series; (*b*) in parallel?
7. State the three cardinal rules for resistances in parallel.

8. (*a*) What is the usual relationship between resistance and temperature of metallic conductors? (*b*) Is this true of all conducting materials in general?
9. How does the resistance of a conductor vary with its length?
10. What is the relationship between the resistance of a conductor and its cross-sectional area?
11. Define the resistivity constant, rho, which appears in the mathematical expression for the Laws of Resistance.
12. (*a*) What is the standard unit of cross-sectional area for round wires in the English system? (*b*) Define this unit.

B 13. How can you explain the fact that the fall of potential across the internal resistance of a source of emf when a current is in the circuit is always opposite in sign to the emf of the source?

14. What condition must be assumed in order to determine the emf of a battery by placing a voltmeter across it?

15. What is the objection to having lamps in a house-lighting circuit connected in series?

16. What would happen if a 6-volt lamp and a 120-volt lamp were connected in parallel across a 120-volt circuit?

17. Draw a diagram of an electric circuit which would be classed as a simple network. Include the internal resistance of the source of emf. Assign values to all resistances and to the source of emf, and be prepared to analyze your network for the class.

18. Demonstrate that the proportionality constant, called resistivity, has the dimensions "ohm-centimeter."

19. What are the dimensions of the resistivity constant, rho, when the cross-sectional area and the length of a conductor are expressed in English units? Demonstrate.

20. Explain how the voltmeter-ammeter method is used for measuring resistance.

21. Why is the voltmeter-ammeter method not a particularly precise way to measure resistance?

22. In the laboratory form of the Wheatstone bridge as shown in Fig. 19–32, resistors R_1 and R_2 are simply lengths of wire. What fact enables us to use the lengths of wire rather than their actual resistances in determining the unknown resistance once the bridge is balanced?

PROBLEMS

A 1. A resistance of 18 ohms is connected across a 4.5-volt battery. What is the current in the circuit?

2. The load across a 12-volt battery consists of a series combination of three resistances R_1, R_2, and R_3 which are 15 ohms, 21 ohms, and 24 ohms respectively. (a) Draw the circuit diagram. (b) What is the total resistance of the load? (c) What is the magnitude of the circuit current?

3. What is the potential difference across each of the three resistances of Problem 2?

4. A small lamp is designed to draw 300. ma in a 6.0-v circuit. What is the resistance of the lamp filament?

5. Resistances R_1 of 2 ohms and R_2 of 4 ohms are connected in series across a combination of 1.5-volt dry cells. An ammeter in the circuit reads 0.5 amp. (a) What potential difference is applied across the circuit by the battery? (b) If the continuous current of each cell is limited to 0.25 amp, how many cells are used and how are they arranged? (c) Draw the circuit diagram.

6. The resistance of an electric lamp filament is 230 ohms. The lamp is switched on when the line voltage is 115 volts. What current is in the lamp circuit?

7. If the line voltage of Problem 6 rises to 120 volts, what current is in the lamp circuit?

8. What would be the filament resistance of a lamp designed to draw the same current as the lamp in Problem 6, but in a 230-volt circuit?

9. Prove algebraically that the equivalent resistance of two resistances, R_1 and R_2, connected in parallel is:

$$R_{eq} = \frac{R_1 R_2}{R_1 + R_2}$$

10. Two resistances, one 12 ohms and the other 18 ohms, are connected in parallel. What is the equivalent resistance of the parallel combination?

11. Solve the following expression algebraically for R_{eq}:

$$\frac{1}{R_{eq}} = \frac{1}{R_1} + \frac{1}{R_2} + \frac{1}{R_3}$$

12. Three resistances of 12 ohms each are connected in parallel. What is the equivalent resistance?

13. (a) What potential difference must be applied across the parallel combination of resistances in Problem 12 to produce a total current of 1.5 amperes? (b) What is the current in each branch?

14. A 3-ohm, a 5-ohm, and an 8-ohm resistance are connected in parallel. What is the equivalent resistance?

15. A 4.0-ohm resistance, R_1, and a 6.0-ohm resistance, R_2, are connected in parallel across a 6.0-volt battery. (a) Draw the circuit diagram. (b) What is the total current in the circuit? (c) What is the current in R_1? (d) What is the current in R_2?

16. A 24-volt lamp has a resistance of 8.0 ohms.

What resistance must be placed in series with it, if it is to be used on a 117-volt line?

17. At 20° C, 100. ft of No. 18 gauge copper wire has a resistance of 0.639 ohm. What is the resistance of 500. ft of this wire?

18. The diameter of the copper wire in Problem 17 is 40.30 mils. What is the resistance of 100. ft of No. 30 gauge copper wire which has a diameter of 10.03 mils?

19. What is the resistance of 500. ft of aluminum wire which has a diameter of 31.96 mils at 20° C? (ρ = 17.01 Ω-circ mil/ft)

20. No. 24 gauge German silver wire has a diameter of 20.1 mils at 20° C. How many feet are needed to make a resistance spool of 100. ohms? (ρ = 198 Ω-circ mil/ft)

B   21. Three cells of a storage battery, each with a resistance of 0.0100 ohm and an emf of 2.20 volts, are connected in series with a load resistance of 3.27 ohms. (a) Draw the circuit diagram. (b) Determine the current in the circuit. (c) What is the potential difference across the load?

22. Two dry cells connected in series provide an emf of 3.1 volts. When a load of 5.8 ohms is connected across the battery an ammeter in the external circuit reads 0.50 ampere. Find the internal resistance of each cell.

23. A load connected across a 12.0-volt battery consists of the resistance R_1, of 40.0 ohms in series with the parallel combination of R_2 and R_3 of 30.0 ohms and 60.0 ohms respectively. (a) Draw the circuit diagram. (b) What is the total current in the circuit? (c) What is the potential difference across R_1? (d) What is the current in the R_2 branch?

24. A 6.0-ohm, a 9.0-ohm, and an 18.0-ohm resistance are connected in parallel and the

combination is connected across a battery having an internal resistance of 0.10 ohm and an emf of 6.2 volts. (a) Draw the circuit diagram and the equivalent circuit. (b) Determine the total current in the circuit. (c) What is the potential difference across the load? (d) What is the current in each of the three load resistances?

25. Resistors R_1, R_2, and R_3 have resistances of 15.0 ohms, 9.0 ohms, and 8.0 ohms respectively. R_1 and R_2 are in series and the combination is in parallel with R_3 to form the load across two 6-volt batteries connected in parallel. (a) Draw the circuit diagram. (b) Determine the total current in the circuit. (c) What is the current in the R_3 branch? (d) What is the potential drop across R_2?

26. A battery with an internal resistance of 1.5 ohms is connected across a load consisting of two resistances, 3.0 ohms and 3.5 ohms, in series. The potential difference across the 3.0-ohm resistance is 9.0 volts. What is the emf of the battery?

27. Two resistances, R_1 and R_2, of 12.0 ohms and 6.00 ohms are connected in parallel and this combination is connected in series with a 6.25-ohm resistance, R_3, and a battery which has an internal resistance of 0.250 ohm. The current in R_2, the 6.00-ohm resistance, is 800. milliamperes. (a) Draw the circuit diagram. (b) Determine the emf of the battery.

28. The resistance of a uniform copper wire 50.0 meters long and 1.15 mm in diameter is 0.830 ohm at 20° C. What is the resistivity of the copper at this temperature?

29. In determining the resistance of a component of an electric circuit by the voltmeter-ammeter method, the voltmeter reads 1.4 volts and the ammeter reads 0.28 ampere. What is the resistance of the component?

 **S**ummary

Electric current is the rate of flow of charge in a circuit. A continuous current requires a source of emf. There are several sources of emf, each transforming energy in some form to electric energy. The dry cell and storage cell are two common sources of emf which supply direct current to a circuit; both are forms of voltaic cells which convert chemical energy to electric energy. Cells may be combined in series and in parallel to form batteries of suitable characteristics for a given circuit.

All circuit components offer some resistance to the flow of electricity. The relationship between resistance, current, and potential difference is expressed by Ohm's law, which applies to an entire circuit or to any part of a circuit.

Resistances may be connected in series, in parallel, or in series-parallel arrangements called networks. Networks may be reduced to simple equivalent circuits and solved by proper applications of Ohm's law.

The resistance of a metal conductor depends on the temperature, length, cross-sectional area, and the nature of the material. From the knowledge of these influencing factors the Laws of Resistance were formulated. Resistivity is an important and useful property of a material dependent only on the nature of the material and its temperature.

Resistance may be measured by the voltmeter-ammeter method or by the Wheatstone bridge method, the latter method being more precise.

TERMS TO DEFINE

amalgam	equivalent circuit	piezoelectric effect
ampere	hydronium ion	polarization
anode	internal resistance	primary cell
battery	load	reduction
cathode	local action	resistance
closed circuit	network	resistivity
circular mil	ohm	semiconductor
electric circuit	Ohm's law	series circuit
electric current	open circuit	storage cell
electrochemical cell	oxidation	thermocouple
Electromotive Series	parallel circuit	voltaic cell
emf	photoelectric effect	Wheatstone bridge

RESEARCH ON YOUR OWN

1. Construct a "light counter" using Fig. 19-5 as the basic circuit. A high-vacuum type of photoelectric cell such as is used in sound movie projectors may serve as a light-sensitive source of current. The galvanometer of Fig. 19-5 may be replaced by a common neon lamp, in which case a paper capacitor is connected in parallel with the neon lamp. The capacitance of this capacitor may be of the order of 0.001 f. The flashing rate of the neon lamp is a function of the intensity of the light incident upon the cell. A little experimenting will establish the optimum constants for the desired circuit sensitivity.

2. Make a thermocouple of two pieces of iron wire and piece of copper wire, connecting the ends of the iron wire to a sensitive galvanometer. Gradually heat one of the junctions while keeping the other cold. Does the galvanometer show a continuous flow of current? Explain.

3. Make a voltaic pile, alternating pieces of copper and zinc, and putting pieces of blotting paper soaked with vinegar or sodium bicarbonate solution between the pieces of metal. See how high a voltage you can build up. Can you detect any effects by touching opposite terminals of the pile simultaneously with your fingers?

4. Arrange a visit to your telephone company to obtain information about the bridge circuits used in making resistance measurements.

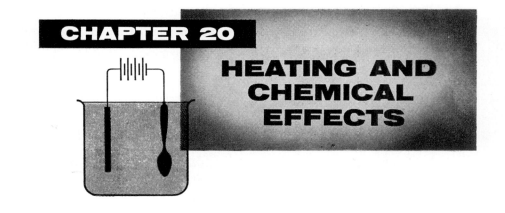

CHAPTER 20

HEATING AND CHEMICAL EFFECTS

1 ELECTRIC POWER

1. Energy of an electric current. The basic concept in physics is that of *energy*, which has been described as the ability to do work and expressed in units of work and heat. In order to maintain an electric current in a circuit, energy must be supplied. Chemical energy, which we may think of as a kind of potential energy, is transformed into electric energy in a voltaic cell. Thus an electric current acquires energy within a generating cell, or other source of emf, and expends this energy in an electric circuit.

In Chapter 18, Section 12, it was stated that one joule of work is done when one coulomb of charge is moved through a potential difference of one volt. We may always express this transfer of charge by the equation

$$W = QV$$

In a source of emf, the charge is moved in opposition to the potential difference, and work W is done *by the source* upon the electrons. As the charge moves through the circuit in response to the potential difference, work W is done *by the electrons* upon the components of the circuit. It is this electric energy, expended in the

VOCABULARY

Chemical equivalent. The quantity of an element, expressed in grams, equal to the ratio of its atomic weight to its valence.

Circuit breaker. A safety device, other than a fuse, for interrupting an electric circuit under an overload condition.

Electrochemical equivalent. The mass of an element, in grams, deposited by 1 coulomb of electricity.

Electrolysis. The conduction of electricity through a solution of an electrolyte or through a fused ionic compound, together with the resulting chemical changes.

Fuse. A safety device consisting of a strip of a low-melting-point alloy inserted in an electric circuit to melt and thus open the circuit under an overload condition.

Short circuit. An electric circuit through a negligible resistance which usually shunts a normal load and overloads the circuit.

$W \rightarrow$ heat + light $W \rightarrow$ heat + motion $W \rightarrow$ heat + chemical action $W \rightarrow$ heat

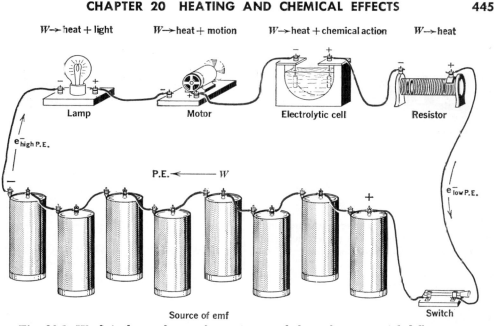

Lamp   Motor   Electrolytic cell   Resistor

$e_{\overline{\text{high P.E.}}}$

P.E. $\longleftarrow W$

$e_{\overline{\text{low P.E.}}}$

Source of emf   Switch

Fig. 20-1. Work is done when a charge is moved through a potential difference.

external circuit, that is available for use.

We may observe the work done by an electric current in a variety of ways. If a lamp is in the circuit, part of the work appears as light; if an electric motor is in the circuit, part of the work appears as rotary motion; if an electroplating cell is in the circuit, part of the work promotes the chemical action in the cell. In all cases, *part* of the work W appears as *heat* due to the inherent resistance of the circuit components. If an ordinary resistor comprises the circuit, *all* of the work goes to the production of heat, since no mechanical work or chemical work is done.

2. Electric energy is converted to heat in a resistance. Suppose we connect short lengths of No. 30 gauge copper wire and German silver wire in series and place them in a circuit as shown in Fig. 20-2. When we close the switch, the German silver wire may become red hot and melt. The copper wire will become warm, but is less likely to melt. The melting point of German silver is only about 30 C° higher than that of copper, but its resistivity is nearly 20 times higher than that of copper. Since

the two wires were connected in series, the same magnitude of current was in each. We may infer that *a greater quantity of electric energy was converted to heat in the wire having the higher resistance.*

Now let us connect a single piece of No. 30 copper wire in the circuit in place of the copper-German silver link. When the switch is closed, the copper wire may warm to a red heat and even melt. Since

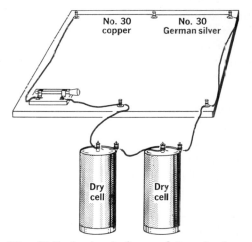

No. 30 copper   No. 30 German silver

Dry cell   Dry cell

Fig. 20-2. A circuit for studying the heating effect of an electric current.

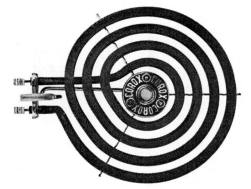

Fig. 20-3. A view showing construction of the heating element of an electric range. (Westinghouse Electric Corp.)

the resistance of this copper wire is less than that of the copper-German silver link, the current in the circuit is higher. We may infer that *the quantity of electric energy converted to heat in the wire is greater when the current is increased.* We may reason also that *the longer the switch is closed* (assuming the wire does not melt), *the greater will be the quantity of electric energy converted to heat.*

3. Joule's law. James Prescott Joule, the English physicist who first studied the relationship between heat and work, also pioneered in studying the heating effect of an electric current. From the results of his experiments he formulated the law that enables us to calculate the quantity of heat developed in a conductor carrying a current. The following statement is known as **Joule's law:** *The heat developed in a conductor is directly proportional to the resistance of the conductor, the square of the current, and the time the current is maintained.*

All of the work done by a current in a resistor appears as heat. Thus the electric energy consumed in the resistance is equal to the heat energy that appears.

$$W = H$$

where W is the electric energy in joules and H is the heat energy in joules. Thus, from Section 1,

$$H = QV \text{ joules}$$

Here Q is the charge in coulombs flowing through the resistance and V is the potential difference across the resistance when a source of emf is applied to the circuit. Now

$$Q = It$$

According to Ohm's law,

$$V = IR$$

By substituting these values for Q and V our equation becomes an expression of Joule's law.

$$H = I^2Rt \text{ joules}$$

In Chapter 11, Section 2, we stated that 1 calorie is the equivalent of 4.19 joules of work. Hence, the heat in calories is

$$H = \frac{I^2Rt \text{ joules}}{4.19 \text{ joules/cal}}$$

Joule's law now becomes

$$H = 0.24 \ I^2Rt \text{ cal}$$

where I is the current in amperes, R is the resistance in ohms, and t is the time in seconds during which the electricity flows. Since the constant *0.24* has the dimensions cal/joule, H is the heat developed in a resistance in calories. See the Sample Problem on the opposite page.

4. Electric heating appliances. Many of the electrically operated appliances we use in our homes today are basically heating devices: irons, toasters, percolators, grills, ranges, and deep-fat fryers are heated by electricity. The heating element in an appliance usually consists of a length of nichrome wire that will provide the proper resistance according to Joule's law when the prescribed voltage is impressed across it.

From our experiment with the small copper and nichrome wires in Section 2, we see one result of excessive currents in conductors. Electric circuits such as those in our homes are supplied by pairs of insulated copper wires led through the walls; we connect appliances in parallel across these lines. The more devices we connect in parallel, the lower the equivalent resistance across the source of current, and thus, the higher the current in the supply lines. See Fig. 20-4.

When more current is drawn in a circuit than the conductors can safely carry, the circuit is said to be *overloaded*. If the circuit is not protected by a *fuse* or *circuit breaker*, the heat produced may burn away the insulation from the overloaded conductors. The conductors may even melt or make contact with one another and form a *short circuit*. Such a short circuit may set fire to the house.

The National Electric Code establishes safety standards for the interior wiring of homes. Circuits fused according to this standard are protected from overloads. For example, the code requires that a branch circuit using 14 gauge copper wires be fused at 15 amperes. Then if an excessive load is placed across this circuit, the fuse will melt when the current rises above 15 amperes, opening the circuit and preventing a dangerous overload.

5. Power in an electric circuit. In Chapter 5, Section 3, we defined power as the rate of doing work. The symbol for power is P, and in the MKS system the unit of power is the *watt* (w), a rate of one joule of work per second. In electric circuits, it is convenient to think of power

Sample Problem

The heating element in a percolator has a resistance of 22.0 ohms and is designed for use across a 110.-volt circuit. How long will it take to heat 1 liter of water from 20.0° C to the boiling point, 100.0° C, assuming no loss of heat to the surroundings?

Solution

From Ohm's law we first determine the current in the heating element.

$$I = \frac{E}{R} = \frac{110. \text{ v}}{22.0 \text{ } \Omega} = 5.00 \text{ amp}$$

One liter of water has a mass of 1000. g. We must determine the quantity of heat required to raise the temperature of this amount of water from 20° C to 100° C.

$$H = m \times \text{sp. ht.} \times \Delta t$$

$$H = 1000. \text{ g} \times \frac{1 \text{ cal}}{\text{g-°C}} \times (100.0° - 20.0°) \text{ C}$$

$$H = 8.00 \times 10^4 \text{ cal}$$

We now have the necessary data for Joule's law.

$$H = 0.24 \text{ cal/joule } I^2Rt$$

and

$$t = \frac{H}{0.24 \text{ cal/joule } I^2R}$$

$$t = \frac{8.00 \times 10^4 \text{ cal}}{0.24 \text{ cal/joule} \times (5.00 \text{ amp})^2 \times 22.0 \text{ } \Omega}$$

$t = 606$ sec, or 10.1 minute, the time required

Observe that dimensionally the time is in seconds.

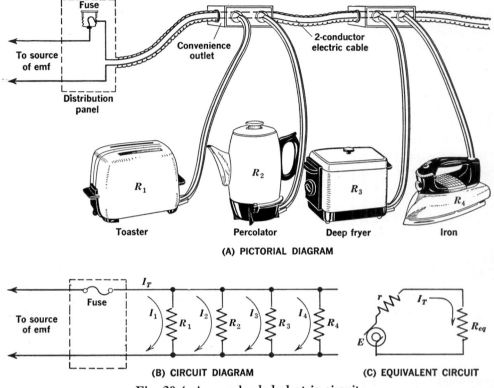

Fig. 20-4. An overloaded electric circuit.

as *the rate at which electric energy is delivered to the circuit.* Returning again to our basic expression of Section 1 and remembering that electric charge is current × time, we have

$$W = QV = ItV$$

and

$$\frac{W}{t} = IV$$

Hence

$$P = IV$$

If I is in amperes (coul/sec) and V is in volts (joule/coul), then P is in watts (joule/sec).

By Ohm's law, the potential difference across a load resistance in a circuit is equal to the product IR_L. Substituting for V in the last equation,

$$P_L = I \times IR_L$$

or

$$P_L = I^2R_L$$

This shows us that *the power expended by a*

current in a resistance is proportional to the square of the current in the resistance.

Similarly, the power dissipated in the internal resistance of a source of emf is

$$P_r = I^2r$$

The total power consumed in a circuit must be the sum of the power dissipated within the source of emf and the power expended in the load constituting the external circuit.

$$P_T = I_T^2R_T = I_T^2(R_L + r)$$

Recall that

$$E = I_T(R_L + r)$$

Therefore

$$P_T = I_TE$$

There are instances in which the current in a circuit is unknown or of no interest. Power may then be expressed in terms of voltage and resistance since, by Ohm's

battery in a short time. Other less familiar examples are the transfer of audio-frequency power from the output stage of a radio to the speaker, and the transfer of radio-frequency power from the transmission line to the antenna.

Let us use the circuit of Fig. 20-6 to study how maximum power from a given source of emf may be expended in the load. Observe that in all three circuits the same source of emf is used, and that loads greater than, less than, and equal to the internal resistance of the source are supplied. In each circuit I_T, P_L, P_r, and P_T may be determined by inspection, using relationships presented in Section 5. These values are listed below for comparison.

	CIRCUIT (A)	CIRCUIT (B)	CIRCUIT (C)
$I_T =$	2.0 amp	5.0 amp	3.0 amp
$P_L =$	4.0 w	2.5 w	4.5 w
$P_r =$	2.0 w	12.5 w	4.5 w
$P_T =$	6.0 w	15.0 w	9.0 w

It is apparent that the maximum power from this source of emf is transferred to the load in circuit (C). In (B) most of the power generated is dissipated as heat in the source of the emf. This is wasted power, constituting a severe overload that could permanently damage the source. In (A) little power is lost in the internal resistance of the source; however, the power expended in the load is not as high as in circuit (C). *Maximum power is transferred to the load when the load resistance is equal to the internal resistance of the source of emf.*

law, current I_T is equal to the quotient E/R_T. Then

$$P_T = \frac{E^2}{R_T}$$

and

$$P_L = \frac{V^2}{R_L}$$

6. Maximum transfer of power. There are some electric-circuit applications in which the transfer of *maximum* power to the load is of great importance. An example is the starting circuit of an automobile engine. To start the engine, a large amount of electric energy must be supplied by a

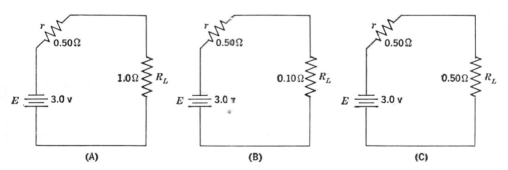

(A)   (B)   (C)

Fig. 20-6. In which circuit is the most power expended in the load?

Under such circumstances, the source and the load are said to be *matched*.

7. We purchase electric energy. If an operating circuit requires 100 watts of power, it means simply that 100 joules of energy are being consumed per second. Obviously, the longer this circuit continues to operate, the larger will be the total quantity of energy consumed. Since

$$\text{power} = \frac{\text{energy}}{\text{time}}$$

then $\text{energy} = \text{power} \times \text{time}$

In the MKS system, current, potential difference, and resistance are measured in amperes, volts, and ohms; power is ex-

Sample Problem

A small electric furnace operating on 100. v expends 2.0 kw of power. (*a*) What current is in the circuit? (*b*) What is the resistance of the furnace? (*c*) What is the cost of operation for 24 hr at $0.050 per kw-hr? (*d*) What quantity of heat, in kcal, is developed in 1.0 hr?

Solution

(*a*) The potential difference across the furnace and the power expended in the furnace are given. We may find the current since

$$P = IV \text{ whence } I = \frac{P}{V}$$

$$I = \frac{2.0 \text{ kw}}{100. \text{ v}} \times \frac{1000. \text{ w}}{\text{kw}}$$

$I = 20.$ amp, the current in the circuit

(*b*) Knowing both the current in the furnace and the potential drop across it, we may apply Ohm's law to find the resistance.

$$R = \frac{V}{I} = \frac{100. \text{ v}}{20. \text{ amp}}$$

$R = 5.0 \ \Omega$, the resistance of the furnace

(*c*) We are given the power requirement of the furnace, the time of operation, and the cost per kw-hr.

$$\text{cost} = \text{kw-hr} \times \frac{\text{cost}}{\text{kw-hr}}$$

$$\text{cost} = \frac{2.0 \text{ kw} \times 24 \text{ hr} \times \$0.050}{\text{kw-hr}}$$

$\text{cost} = \$2.40$ for 24 hr

(*d*) We are given the time of operation and we have found the current and the resistance.

$$H = 0.24 \text{ cal/joule } I^2Rt$$

$$H = \frac{0.24 \text{ cal/joule} \times (20. \text{ amp})^2 \times 5.0 \ \Omega \times 1.0 \text{ hr} \times 3600. \text{ sec/hr}}{1000. \text{ cal/kcal}}$$

$H = 1.7 \times 10^3$ kcal, the heat in 1 hr

pressed in watts and time in seconds. The energy may be expressed in *watt-seconds* (w-sec). The MKS watt-second is an inconveniently small unit for electric energy sold on a commercial scale. For example, a 100-watt lamp operated for 1 hour consumes 3.6×10^5 watt-seconds of energy. By dividing by 3.6×10^3 sec/hr we may convert this quantity to 1×10^2 w-hr. By dividing again by 1×10^3 w/kw we arrive

at 1×10^{-1} kw-hr (0.1 kilowatt-hour), a more practical unit of electric energy. Observe the magnitude of this combined conversion constant:

$$\text{kw-hr} = \text{w-sec} \times \frac{1 \text{ kw-hr}}{3.600 \times 10^6 \text{ w-sec}}$$

A kilowatt-hour of electric energy usually costs between 1 and 6 cents.

See the Sample Problem on the opposite page.

2 ELECTROLYSIS

8. Electrolytic cells. We have already mentioned the close relationship between chemical energy and electric energy. In Chapter 19, Section 3, we described spontaneous oxidation-reduction reactions which involve the transfer of electrons from one reactant to the other. Such reactions can be sources of emf. In the voltaic cell, chemical energy is converted to electric energy while the spontaneous oxidation-reduction reaction proceeds. The products of the reaction have less energy than did the reactants.

Oxidation-reduction reactions *that are not spontaneous* may be forced to occur if electric energy is supplied from an external source, as in the charging of a storage cell. In such forced reactions, the products have more chemical energy than did the reactants. This means, of course, that electric energy from the external source of emf is transformed into chemical energy while the reaction proceeds. An arrangement in which a forced oxidation-reduction reaction occurs is known as an *electrolytic cell.*

The basic requirements for an electrolytic cell are shown in Fig. 20-7. The conducting solution contains an *electrolyte*, furnishing positively and negatively charged ions. Two electrodes are immersed in the electrolytic solution. The negative terminal of a battery or other source of direct current is connected to one electrode, forming the *cathode* of the cell; the positive terminal of the source is

connected to the other electrode to form the *anode* of the cell.

When the circuit of an electrolytic cell is closed, the cathode becomes negatively charged and the anode positively charged. Positive ions migrate to the cathode, where they acquire electrons of high potential energy from the cathode and are discharged. This is a *reduction* process. Negatively charged ions migrate to the anode and are discharged by giving up electrons of low potential energy to the anode. This is an *oxidation* process. You will recall that the electrode reactions in the electrochemical cells studied in Chapter 19, Section 4, are just the reverse of these occurring in the electrolytic cell.

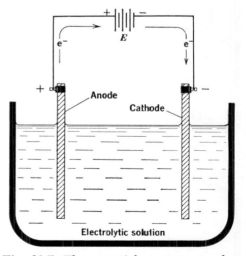

Fig. 20-7. The essential components of an electrolytic cell.

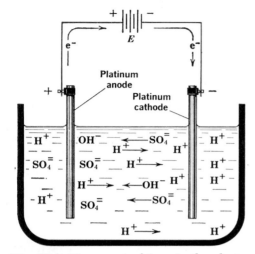

Fig. 20-8. Movement of ions in the electrolytic solution during electrolysis of water.

The loss of electrons by the cathode and the acquisition of a like number of electrons by the anode is, in effect, the conduction of electricity through the cell. *The conduction of electricity through a solution of an electrolyte or through a fused ionic compound, together with the resulting chemical changes, is called* **electrolysis.** The end result of electrolysis is dependent on the nature of the electrolyte, the kinds of electrodes, and to some extent, the emf of the battery. Electrolytic cells are useful in decomposing compounds, plating metals, refining metals, and extracting metals from ores.

9. The electrolysis of water. Pure water is a very poor conductor of electricity. Approximately two molecules of

Fig. 20-9. The electrolysis of water.

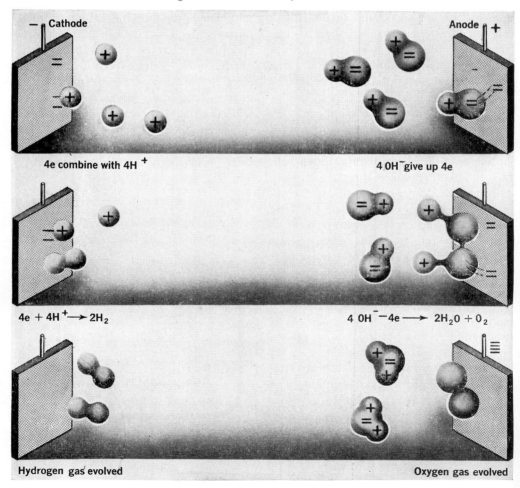

water in a billion ionize to form a positively charged hydrogen ion, H^+ (existing as H_3O^+), and a negatively charged hydroxide ion, OH^-. If we add a small amount of an electrolyte, such as sulfuric acid, H_2SO_4, the resulting solution is a good conductor, each molecule of sulfuric acid in dilute solution ionizing to form two hydrogen ions, $2H^+$, and one sulfate ion, $SO_4^=$.

Suppose we place the dilute sulfuric acid solution in an electrolytic cell using platinum electrodes, which do not react chemically with the acid. See Fig. 20-8. In this electrolytic solution there are H^+ ions from the acid and the water. There are $SO_4^=$ ions from the acid and some OH^- ions from the water. When the circuit is closed the positively charged H^+ ions migrate to the negatively charged cathode. Negatively charged $SO_4^=$ ions and OH^- ions migrate to the positively charged anode.

At the cathode, each hydrogen ion acquires an electron and is discharged, forming a hydrogen atom. This is a reduction reaction. Two hydrogen atoms join to form a diatomic molecule of hydrogen gas, and molecules accumulate on the anode, finally escaping as bubbles of hydrogen gas.

$$4H^+ + 4e^- \rightarrow 2H_2 \uparrow$$
(cathode reaction)

At the anode, both $SO_4^=$ ions and OH^- ions are present. Although the concentration of $SO_4^=$ ions from the sulfuric acid is greater, the OH^- ions from the water are more easily discharged; thus hydroxide ions are preferentially discharged, each ion giving up an electron to the anode. This is an oxidation process. For every four OH^- ions discharged, two molecules of water and one diatomic molecule of oxygen gas are formed, the oxygen escaping as gas bubbles.

$$4OH^- - 4e^- \rightarrow 2H_2O + O_2 \uparrow$$
(anode reaction)

The removal of OH^- ions from the water solution disturbs the ionization equilibrium of the water, and additional molecules ionize, supplying more H^+ ions and OH^- ions to the solution. Thus we can see that it is the water which is decomposed in this electrolytic process. The net chemical reaction in the cell is shown by the following chemical equation.

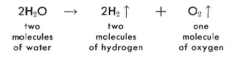

$$2H_2O \quad \rightarrow \quad 2H_2 \uparrow \quad + \quad O_2 \uparrow$$

| two molecules of water | two molecules of hydrogen | one molecule of oxygen |

We may collect the two decomposition products of the electrolysis of water by using an apparatus similar to that shown in Fig. 20-10. Observe that the volume of hydrogen gas collected over the cathode is twice that of the oxygen gas collected over the anode. (Why?)

10. Electroplating metals. Suppose positively charged metallic ions, such as cupric (Cu^{++}) or silver (Ag^+) ions, are in the conducting solution of an electrolysis cell. Either of these ions is more easily discharged than the H^+ ion and is reduced at the cathode in preference to hydrogen

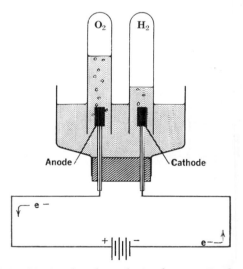

Fig. 20-10. The electrolysis of water. In the electrolytic cell, reduction occurs at the cathode and oxidation occurs at the anode.

when a small potential difference is placed across the cell.

$$Cu^{++} + 2e^- \rightarrow Cu^0$$

or
$$Ag^+ + e^- \rightarrow Ag^0$$
(cathode reaction)

The copper or silver atoms formed will plate out on the cathode surface.

This is the basic action which enables an electrolytic cell to be used for the *electrolytic deposition* or *electroplating* of one metal on the surface of another. *The metallic object to be plated is used as the cathode of the cell. The conducting solution contains a salt of the metal to be plated out;* for example, cupric sulfate or silver nitrate. *The anode consists of the plating metal,* copper or silver for the examples given.

The metal atoms of the anode are more easily oxidized than the negative ions of the solution that migrate to the anode. Instead of oxygen being formed, as in the electrolysis of water, metallic ions are formed to replace those being plated out. Metallic ions pass into solution from the anode at the same rate as similar metallic ions leave the solution to form the plate. Thus, the anode is used up in the plating process to maintain the concentration of

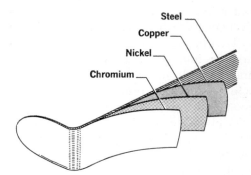

Fig. 20-12. An automobile bumper is electroplated to improve its appearance and its durability.

metallic ions in the electrolytic solution.

$$Cu^0 - 2e^- \rightarrow Cu^{++}$$
or
$$Ag^0 - e^- \rightarrow Ag^+$$
(anode reaction)

Because each metal has its own optimum current density for best plating results, it is important that the proper current be determined and supplied to the cell. A simple copper plating cell is shown in Fig. 20-11.

The commercial plating processes use highly specialized techniques. Cyanide salts (dangerous compounds) may be included in the solution to reduce the concentration of metallic ions. In chromium plating cells, a lead anode is used and chromium ions are supplied by occasionally adding chromic acid to the electrolytic solution. Steel is usually plated first with copper, then with nickel, and finally with chromium. Nonmetallic objects may be coated with a conductive powder and then plated in the same manner as metal objects; this last process was used in making the page plates for the printing of this textbook. About eighteen metallic elements have been successfully used for electroplating. Those of considerable commercial importance are copper, nickel, chromium, silver, gold, zinc, cadmium, tin, and lead.

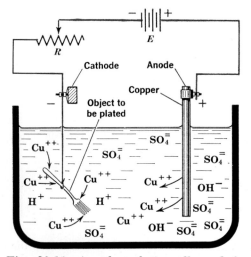

Fig. 20-11. An electrolytic cell used for copper plating.

11. Extracting metals by electrolysis. Many metals are extracted by a method

Fig. 20-13. An industrial electroplating installation. (General Motors)

that requires heating of the ores in the presence of coke or carbon. For some metals, such as aluminum, this process does not work. About seventy-five years ago a method of extracting aluminum by electrolysis was developed by Charles M. Hall (1863–1914) while he was still a student at Oberlin College. The chief ore of aluminum is bauxite, which consists largely of aluminum oxide, Al_2O_3. After the aluminum oxide is freed of impurities, it is dissolved in fused cryolite, sodium aluminum fluoride, and is then decomposed by electrolysis.

In the Hall process, an iron box of the type shown in Fig. 20-14 is used as the cathode. The anode consists of several carbon rods which dip down into the electrolyte, the solution of aluminum oxide in fused cryolite. The negative oxygen ions migrate to the carbon rods; the aluminum ions migrate to the cathode, where they are discharged to form aluminum atoms. The fused aluminum collects in the bottom of the box, from which it is withdrawn.

Other metals, such as sodium, magnesium, and potassium, are extracted from their ores by electrolysis, as is the nonmetal chlorine. Either a solution of common salt in water, or the fused salt itself, may be used as the electrolyte from which chlorine is set free at the anode.

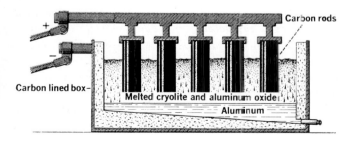

Fig. 20-14. Producing aluminum by the electrolysis of fused aluminum oxide.

Certain metals are refined by electrolysis. Copper, for example, is purified by using a bar of impure copper as the anode of an electrolytic cell, and a thin sheet of very pure copper as the cathode. The electrolyte is cupric sulfate in a sulfuric acid solution. A small difference of potential is maintained across the cell. During the electrolysis, copper and other metals above copper in the Electromotive Series (Chapter 19, Section 4) are oxidized from the anode and enter the solution as ions.

$$Cu^0 - 2e^- \rightarrow Cu^{++}$$
$$Fe^0 - 2e^- \rightarrow Fe^{++}$$
$$Zn^0 - 2e^- \rightarrow Zn^{++}$$
$$\text{(anode reaction)}$$

Any silver and gold in the anode will fall to the bottom of the cell as a sludge as the anode is used up, for these less active metals would require higher voltages to become oxidized to ions along with the copper. Of the metallic ions present in the solution along with H^+ ions, only the Cu^{++} ions are discharged at the cathode at the small potential difference that exists across the cell.

$$Cu^{++} + 2e^- \rightarrow Cu^0$$
$$\text{(cathode reaction)}$$

Thus, of all the metals present, only copper plates out on the cathode. Electrolytic copper is over 99.9 percent pure.

Crude copper is usually refined electrolytically for two reasons.

1. The silver and gold impurities are easily recovered from the sludge which forms beneath the anode.

2. Very small amounts of impurities in copper markedly increase its electric resistance.

12. Faraday's laws of electrolysis. Michael Faraday found that a current that deposited a half-pennyweight of silver in ten minutes would deposit one pennyweight of silver in twenty minutes. This suggests a very important relationship between the quantity of electricity which passes through an electrolytic cell and the

quantity of a substance liberated by the chemical action.

Let us consider the quantitative significance of Faraday's discovery by imagining several cells to be connected in series and supplied by a source of emf. Each cell has a pair of inert platinum electrodes immersed in an electrolyte. See Fig. 20-16. Each cell has a different electrolyte: cell No. 1 has sulfuric acid (hydrogen sulfate), cell No. 2 has silver nitrate, No. 3 has cupric sulfate, and No. 4 has aluminum sulfate. Since this is a *thought experiment* we need not be concerned with the possibility of running out of ions in the cells. The cells are in series, so a certain current in the circuit for a given time will mean that *the same quantity of charge has passed through each cell.*

Hydrogen, silver, copper, and aluminum are liberated at the respective cathodes. The quantity of each liberated substance must be proportional to the quantity of charge that passed through each cell, that is, to the product of the current and the time.

Faraday's first law: The mass of an element deposited during electrolysis is proportional to the quantity of charge that passes.

$$m \propto Q \quad (Q = It)$$

By varying either current or time we merely vary the quantity of charge passing through each cell. By Faraday's first law, the masses of the elements deposited vary accordingly. It follows that whatever the charge through the cells, the relationship between the quantities of the elements deposited remains *constant.* Such quantities of the elements may be said to be *electrochemically equivalent. The **electrochemical equivalent** (z) of an element is the mass of the element, in grams, deposited by 1 coulomb of electricity.*

Suppose we allow the charge to flow through our cells until 1 g of hydrogen has been liberated in cell No. 1. We would find 108 g of silver deposited in No. 2,

Fig. 20-15. The principle
of electrolytic refining of
copper is illustrated by
the action in this sim-
ple electroplating cell.
(F. W. Goro—courtesy
LIFE. © 1949, Time
Inc.)

31.8 g of copper in No. 3, and 9 g of
aluminum in No. 4.

Using this information, we may make
two very interesting and important observations. *First*, the hydrogen ion, H^+,
and silver ion, Ag^-, are deficient by 1
electron and carry 1 unit of positive
charge. These elements are said to have
a *valence* of 1, which means they lose (or
gain) 1 electron per atom in a chemical
action. Similarly the valence of the cupric
ion, Cu^{++}, is 2 and that of the aluminum
ion, Al^{+++}, is 3. *The quantity of each element
deposited, in grams, is numerically equal to the*
ratio of its atomic weight to its valence. This
ratio is known as the *chemical equivalent*
of an element.

$$\text{chemical equivalent} = \frac{\text{atomic weight}}{\text{valence}} \text{ grams}$$

Thus, the chemical equivalents of hydrogen, silver, copper, and aluminum are
respectively 1, 108, 31.8, and 9 grams.

Second, the product of the current in
amperes, and the time in seconds during
which the cells operated to deposit the
chemical equivalents of these elements, is
found to be approximately 96,500 coulombs. This product is a constant and is

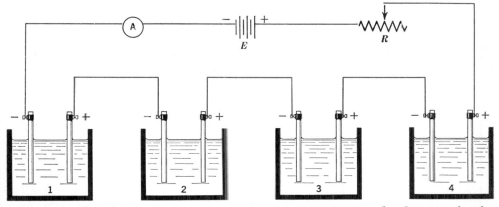

Fig. 20-16. Electrolytic cells in series must have the same magnitude of current for the
same length of time.

called a *faraday:*

1 faraday = 96,500 coulombs

One faraday, 96,500 coulombs, is the quantity of electricity required to deposit one chemical equivalent of an element. This unit has many significant applications in electrolysis and electrochemistry in general.

Faraday's second law: *The mass of an element deposited during electrolysis is proportional to the chemical equivalent of the element.*

m ∝ chemical equivalent

From our definition of the electrochemical equivalent of an element, we can see that

$$z = \frac{\text{chemical equivalent}}{\text{faraday}}$$

and has the dimensions g/coul. The electrochemical equivalent z is a constant for a given element, but of course is different for different elements.

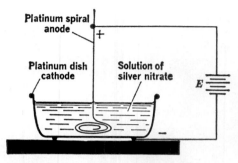

Fig. 20-17. A silver coulombmeter.

We may combine Faraday's Laws of Electrolysis into the following equation:

$$m = zIt$$

where m is the mass in grams of an element deposited, z is the electrochemical equivalent in g/coul of the element, I is the current in amperes, and t is the time in seconds. See the Sample Problem below.

Sample Problem

How long must an electroplating cell be operated to plate out 152 mg of nickel if an average current of 0.500 ampere is maintained?

Solution

We are given the current in amperes and the mass of nickel in milligrams.

$$152 \text{ mg} \times \frac{1 \text{ g}}{1000 \text{ mg}} = 0.152 \text{ g of nickel}$$

From Table 17, Appendix B, we find the electrochemical equivalent of nickel to be 0.000304 g/coul.

$$m = zIt$$

$$t = \frac{m}{zI}$$

$$t = \frac{0.152 \text{ g}}{\dfrac{3.04 \times 10^{-4} \text{ g}}{\text{coul}} \times 0.500 \text{ amp}}$$

$$t = \frac{1.00 \times 10^3 \text{ coul}}{\text{amp}}$$

$$t = 1.00 \times 10^3 \text{ sec or } 16.7 \text{ min, the time}$$

★ **13. The silver coulombmeter.** Faraday's laws give us a precise method of measuring the quantity of electricity flowing through a circuit. If we know the length of time the electricity flows, we may determine the average current magnitude. A platinum dish is connected with the negative terminal of a source of about 2 volts emf and then the dish is partly filled with a solution of silver nitrate. A platinum spiral rod is connected to the positive terminal of the source of current and dipped into the silver solution. See Fig. 20-17.

One coulomb of electricity (one ampere-second) flowing through such a silver solution will deposit on the walls of the dish 0.001118 g of silver. If the average current in the circuit is one ampere for one hour, 3600 coulombs will have deposited 4.025 g of silver. From the weight of the silver deposited the number of coulombs of electricity can be easily and accurately determined.

Summary

The electric energy expended in a resistance goes into the production of heat. By Joule's law we recognize the relationship between the heat developed in a conductor, the resistance, the current in the resistance, and the time the current is maintained. The heat produced in a conductor according to Joule's law, when the circuit is overloaded, may produce disastrous fires, but when circuits are properly fused, the dangers from overloads and short circuits are largely eliminated.

Electric power expended in the resistance of a circuit is proportional to the current squared. Power dissipated in the internal resistance of a generator is wasted. Where it is important to deliver maximum power to the load, the load and the source of emf must be matched.

Electrolytic cells involve chemical reactions that can be driven by electric energy. From their study we recognize the relationship between chemical energy and electric energy. Electrolytic cells are useful in decomposing compounds and plating, refining, and extracting metals.

Faraday's Laws of Electrolysis provide us with an insight into the quantitative significance of the energy transformations in chemical reactions. These laws relate the mass of an element deposited during electrolysis to the quantity of charge that passes through the cell and to the chemical equivalent of the element. The faraday is an important constant in electrochemistry. The silver coulombmeter provides a precise method of measuring the quantity of electricity flowing in an electric circuit.

TERMS TO DEFINE

atomic weight	electrolytic deposition	overload
chemical equivalent	faraday	short circuit
circuit breaker	Faraday's laws	silver coulombmeter
electrochemical equivalent	fuse	valence
electrolysis	Joule's law	watt
electrolytic cell	kilowatt-hour	watt-second

QUESTIONS

A   **1.** State four ways in which the work done by an electric current in a load may be observed, and name the kind of load responsible in each instance.

2. Equal lengths of silver wire and iron wire having the same diameters are connected in series to form the external circuit across a dry cell. Which wire becomes hotter? Explain.

3. One length of platinum wire is connected across the terminals of a single dry cell. A second platinum wire, identical with the first, is connected across a battery of two dry cells in series. Which wire becomes hotter? Explain.

4. State Joule's law.

5. What is meant by an overloaded circuit?

6. What precaution is taken to protect an electric circuit from becoming overloaded?

7. How may electric power be defined?

8. (a) What change occurs in the heating effect of a certain electric circuit in which the total resistance is cut in half? (b) Devise a simple circuit problem to prove your answer.

9. If a battery is short-circuited by means of a heavy copper wire, its temperature rises. Explain.

10. Under what circumstance is the power expended in a load the maximum the source is capable of delivering?

11. Suppose you have just paid the electric utility bill for your home. (a) What did you purchase? (b) In what units was it measured?

12. What change occurs in the resistance in the external circuit connected to a source of emf when the load across the source is increased?

13. How can oxidation-reduction reactions that are not spontaneous be forced to occur?

14. What is an electrolytic cell?

15. What may be the effect of the conduction of electricity through a fused ionic compound?

16. In the electrolysis of water, what action occurs (a) at the cathode; (b) at the anode?

17. What are the basic requirements for a silver-plating cell?

18. Why is electrolytically refined copper used to make copper conductors?

19. State Faraday's Laws of Electrolysis.

20. What part of a silver coulombmeter is used as the cathode?

B   **21.** (a) Demonstrate that the constant 0.24 in Joule's law has the dimensions cal/joule. (b) Demonstrate that H in Joule's law is properly expressed in calories.

22. What is the objection to placing a copper one-cent piece behind a fuse in a house-lighting circuit to avoid "blowing" the fuse?

23. What is the objection to replacing a 15-ampere fuse with a 30-ampere fuse in a house-lighting circuit to avoid frequent fuse "blowing"?

24. Why is it important that an automobile battery have a very low internal resistance?

25. Distinguish between an electrochemical cell and an electrolytic cell.

26. In the electrolysis of water, explain why oxygen is given up at the anode even though there is a greater concentration of sulfate ions than hydroxide ions in the anode region.

27. How can you explain the fact that an electrolytic cell used for copper plating does not act instead to cause the electrolysis of water since the electrolytic solution is mainly water?

28. The atomic weight of aluminum is 27 and of gold is 197; both have a valence of 3. Which has the higher electrochemical equivalent? Justify your answer.

29. Demonstrate that the mass of an element deposited according to Faraday's laws is expressed in grams.

30. How could you define the ampere in relation to Faraday's laws and the silver coulombmeter?

PROBLEMS

A   **1.** The current in an electric heater is 7.5 amperes. What quantity of electricity flows through the heater in 15 minutes?

2. Determine the current in a lamp circuit if 4800 coulombs of electricity flow through the lamp in 25 minutes.

3. An electric lamp connected across a 117-volt line has a current of 0.52 ampere in it. How much work is done in 12 minutes?

4. What is the approximate wattage rating of the lamp in Problem 3?

5. How many calories of heat are liberated by a resistance of 55 ohms connected across a 110-volt line for 10. minutes?

6. A heating coil across a 117-volt line draws 9.00 amperes. How many calories of heat are liberated if the heater is connected for 30.0 minutes?

7. The heating element of an electric iron has a resistance of 24 ohms and draws a current of 5.0 amperes. How many calories of heat are developed if a housewife uses the iron for 45 minutes?

8. A battery has an emf of 26.4 volts and an internal resistance of 0.300 ohm. A load of 3.00 ohms is connected across the battery. (a) How much power is delivered to the load? (b) What power is dissipated in the battery?

9. (a) To what value would the load resistance of Problem 8 have to be changed in order for maximum power to be delivered to the load using the same source of emf? (b) What is the magnitude of the maximum power delivered to this load? (c) What power is now dissipated in the battery?

10. How much silver can be deposited by a steady current of 0.500 ampere in 8.00 minutes?

11. An electroplating cell connected across a source of direct current for 15.0 minutes deposits 0.750 g of copper. What is the average current in the cell?

12. How many hours are required for an electrolysis cell to liberate 0.160 g of oxygen when supplied with a steady current of 0.300 ampere?

B 13. If electric energy costs 5.0¢ per kw-hr, what is the cost of heating 4.6 kg of water from 25° C to the boiling point, assuming no energy is wasted?

● 14. A coffee percolator having a heating coil of 20.0 ohms resistance is connected across

a 120.-volt line. (a) What quantity of heat is liberated per second? (b) If the percolator contains 500. g of water at 22.5° C, how much time is required to heat the water to the boiling point, assuming no loss of heat?

● 15. An electric iron has a mass of 1.50 kg. The heating element consists of a 2.00-m length of No. 24 gauge nichrome wire. What time is required for the iron to be heated from 20.0° C to 150.° C when connected across a 115-volt line, assuming no loss of heat?

● 16. An electric hotplate draws 10.0 amperes on a 120.-volt circuit. In 7.00 minutes the hotplate can heat 600. g of water at 20.0° C to the boiling point, and boil away 60.0 g of water. What is the efficiency of the hotplate?

17. Each coil of a plug-type resistance box is capable of dissipating heat energy at the rate of 4.0 watts. What is the maximum voltage that should be applied across (a) the 2.0-ohm coil; (b) the 20.0-ohm coil?

18. A dial-type rheostat of 10.0 ohms resistance is capable of dissipating heat energy at the rate of 4.0 watts. (a) What is the maximum current the rheostat can carry? (b) What is the maximum voltage that can be applied across it?

19. How many feet of No. 30-gauge nichrome wire will be needed to form the heating element of a 1000.-watt electric iron to be used on a 117-volt line?

● 20. An electrolysis-of-water cell is operated until 1 faraday of electricity has been passed. How many atoms of hydrogen have been liberated?

RESEARCH ON YOUR OWN

1. As a class or demonstration experiment, determine the efficiency of a hotplate or coffee percolator. See how long it takes to bring a known quantity of water from room temperature to boiling. From the voltmeter and ammeter readings and the elapsed time, find the amount of heat input. From the mass of water and the temperature change, find the heat output. How is heat wasted in this experiment?

2. Draw a diagram of the electric distribution panel or fuse box in a home-wiring installation. Show the ratings of all fuses. Identify the mains feeding into the panel, the ground line, and all branch circuits in use. CAUTION: Do not probe in the fuse box or come in contact with any terminals.

3. Heat the end of an empty test tube and use it to melt two holes through the bottom of a soft plastic dish. Insert one-hole stoppers fitted with electrodes suitable for the electrolysis of water. Test tubes filled with water and inverted over the electrodes may be used for the collection of the gases resulting from the electrolysis.

4. Electroplate an iron or brass object with copper. (Cuprous salts usually work better than cupric salts.) Clean the plated object with fine sandpaper, dip it momentarily into nitric acid, and then rinse.

CHAPTER 21

MAGNETIC EFFECTS

1 MAGNETISM

1. The relation between magnetism and electricity. The performance of many types of electric devices depends on both magnetism and electricity and the relationship between them. This relationship makes possible generators to produce the vast quantities of electricity that we use and electric motors to transform electric energy into mechanical energy. Many electric measuring instruments depend on the relationship of magnetism to electricity.

Before taking up the study of the magnetic effects of electric currents, it is necessary to know something about the magnetic properties of various substances and the characteristics of magnetic fields.

2. Magnetic substances. In a section of Turkey formerly called Magnesia, there are deposits of a magnetic iron ore which was discovered by the Greeks many centuries ago. It is called *magnetite*. Other deposits of magnetite are found in the

VOCABULARY

Diamagnetism. The property of a substance by which it is feebly repelled by a strong magnet.

Domain. A microscopic magnetic region composed of a group of atoms whose magnetic fields are aligned in a common direction.

Ferromagnetism. The property of a substance by which it is strongly attracted by a magnet.

Flux density. The number of flux lines per unit area which permeate a magnetic field.

Hysteresis. The lagging of the magnetization of ferromagnetic material behind the magnetizing force.

Line of flux. A line so drawn that a tangent to it at any point indicates the direction of the magnetic field.

Magnetic field. A region in which a magnetic force can be detected.

Magnetic flux. Lines of flux in a magnetic field, considered collectively.

Magnetic force. A force associated with the motion of electric charges.

Paramagnetism. The property of a substance by which it is feebly attracted by a strong magnet.

Adirondack Mountains of northern New York and in other regions of the world. Pieces of magnetite are known as *natural magnets*. A suspended piece of magnetite aligns itself with the magnetic field of the earth. About the twelfth century men began to use these natural magnets, which they called lodestones (leading stones), as the first magnetic compasses.

A few materials, notably iron and steel, are strongly attracted by magnets; cobalt and nickel are attracted to a lesser degree. These substances are said to have *ferromagnetic* properties. Special alloys, such as *permalloy* and *alnico*, have extraordinary ferromagnetic properties. Physicists are intensely interested in the structure of materials possessing the property of *ferromagnetism*.

Today very strong and versatile *artificial* magnets are made from ferromagnetic substances. Some alnico-type magnets will support a weight over 1000 times that of the magnets themselves. Ferromagnetic substances are usually referred to simply as "magnetic substances."

3. Nonmagnetic substances. We commonly classify materials as magnetic or nonmagnetic. Those which do not demonstrate the strong ferromagnetic properties characteristic of the Iron Family of elements are said to be "nonmagnetic." However, if we subject these materials to the influence of a very strong magnet, we may observe that some are slightly repelled by the magnet, while others may be very slightly attracted.

Zinc, bismuth, sodium chloride, gold, and mercury are a few of the substances that are feebly repelled, and are said to be *diamagnetic*. The property of *diamagnetism* is an important concept in the modern theory of magnetism as we shall see in Section 4.

Wood, aluminum, platinum, oxygen, and cupric sulfate are examples of substances which are very slightly attracted by a strong magnet. Such materials are

Fig. 21-1. Alnico-type magnets will support heavy objects. (Crucible Steel Co.)

said to be *paramagnetic*, and this type of magnetic behavior is *paramagnetism*.

4. The domain theory of magnetism. William Gilbert's report on his experiments with natural magnets, published in 1600, probably represents the first scientific study of magnetism. In the years that followed, discoveries by Ampère, Oersted, and Coulomb added much to our knowledge of the behavior of magnets and the nature of magnetic forces. However, only within the last twenty years have physicists begun to understand the true nature of magnetism. Magnetism in matter is now believed to stem from the

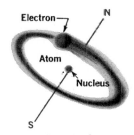

Fig. 21-2. Revolving electrons impart a magnetic property to the atom.

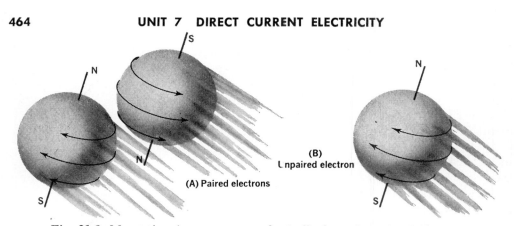

Fig. 21-3. Magnetism in matter stems basically from the spin of electrons.

movements of electrons within the atoms of substances. Since the electron is an electrically charged particle, this theory implies that *magnetism is a property of a charge in motion.* If so, we can account for the energy associated with magnetic forces by using known laws of physics, some of which we have already stated in the chapter on electrostatics.

Two kinds of electron motions are important in the modern concept of magnetism. *First,* an *electron revolving in its orbit about the nucleus of an atom imparts a magnetic property to the atom's structure.* When the atoms of a substance are subjected to the magnetic force of a strong magnet, the force affects this magnetic property of the atom in such a way as to oppose the revolving motion of the electrons. The atoms are thus repelled by the magnet; this is diamagnetism. If the electron's revolving motion were its only motion, all substances would be diamagnetic. Diamagnetic repulsion is quite feeble in its action on the total mass of a substance, because thermal motions within the substance keep the atom magnets knocked about in random directions so they tend to neutralize one another.

*The **second** kind of electron motion is the spinning of the electron on its own axis.* The magnetic property of matter stems basically from the spin of electrons; *each spinning electron acts as a tiny permanent magnet.* Oppo-

site spins are designated as + and − spins; electrons spinning in opposite directions tend to form *pairs* and so neutralize their magnetic character. The magnetic character of an atom as a whole may be weak due to the mutual interaction among the electron spins.

Magnetic properties are associated with both kinds of electron motion. The atoms of some substances may possess permanent-magnet characteristics due to an imbalance between orbits and spins. These atoms act like tiny magnets, called *dipoles,* and are attracted by strong magnets. Substances in which this effect exceeds the diamagnetism common to all atoms show the property of paramagnetism.

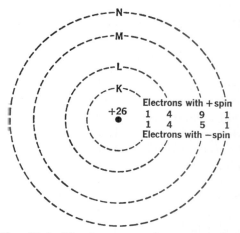

	Electrons with + spin
+26	1 4 9 1
	1 4 5 1
	Electrons with − spin

Fig. 21-4. The iron atom has strong ferromagnetic properties.

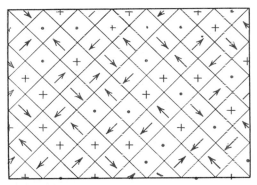

Fig. 21-5. The domains of an unmagnetized ferromagnetic substance are polarized along the crystal axes. Dots and plus signs represent arrows going out and in the page respectively.

In the atoms of substances that show ferromagnetism, there are unpaired electrons whose spins are oriented in the same way. Iron, cobalt, and nickel, special alloys, and certain metallic oxides called ferrites show very strong ferromagnetic properties.

The complete inner electron shells of the atom structures of most elements contain only paired electrons. The outer shell of each of the inert gases consists of a *stable octet* of electrons made up of four electron pairs. The atoms of other elements achieve this stable-octet configuration in their valence shells by forming chemical bonds. Only in certain transition elements, which have incomplete inner shells, do unpaired electrons result in ferromagnetic properties. The electron configuration of the iron atom, Fig. 21-4, shows four unpaired electrons in the M shell. The similarly oriented spins of these unpaired electrons account for the strong ferromagnetism of iron.

Why then does not every piece of iron behave as a magnet? The iron atoms are grouped into microscopic magnetic regions called *domains*. The atoms in each domain are magnetically polarized parallel to a crystal axis. Ordinarily, these domains point in every possible direction parallel to the crystal axes, so that they

cancel one another and the net magnetism is zero. In Fig. 21-5 the polarity of each domain in an unmagnetized material is represented by an arrow.

The material becomes magnetized when an external force, stronger than the thermal agitation of the atoms, aligns the domains in the same direction. The stronger the force, the greater will be the number of domains aligned, and the stronger will be the magnetization. When all domains are aligned, the material is said to have reached *magnetic saturation*. The material forms a *permanent* magnet if some domain alignment is retained after the external magnetizing force is removed. When the material is heated so that its thermal energy is high enough, the magnetism is lost.

Physicists have developed a technique which enables them to see and photograph the microscopic domains in a ferromagnetic material, the domains being outlined with colloidal particles of iron oxide. This technique can be used to show what goes on inside a magnet when it is subjected to various experimental manipulations.

A new magnet technology, under development now, is based on a group of ferromagnetic substances known as *ferrites*. The ferrites are iron oxides combined with oxides of other metals such as manganese, cobalt, nickel, copper, and magnesium. The combined oxides are powdered,

Fig. 21-6. A photomicrograph of magnetic domains. (Bell Telephone Laboratories)

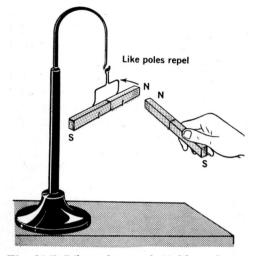

Fig. 21-7. Like poles repel. Unlike poles attract.

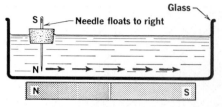

Fig. 21-8. The path followed by a floating magnet is approximately that of an independent N pole.

formed into the desired shape under pressure, and fired. They form strong hard magnets with some very unique properties. As oxides, the ferrites have very high electric resistance, a property that is extremely important in some applications of ferromagnetic materials. The original lodestone is a material of this type. Chemically, it is a combination of ferrous oxide, FeO, and ferric oxide, Fe_2O_3. It is usually called magnetic iron oxide but is more correctly called ferrous ferrite, $Fe(FeO_2)_2$.

5. Force between magnet poles. The fact that iron filings cling mainly to the

ends of a bar magnet tells us that the magnetic force is acting on the filings primarily in these regions or *poles;* it does not mean that the middle region of the magnet is unmagnetized. The pole which points toward the north, when the magnet is free to swing about a vertical axis, is commonly called the *north-seeking pole* or simply the N pole. The opposite pole, which points toward the south, is called the *south-seeking pole* or S pole.

Suppose we suspend a bar magnet as shown in Fig. 21-7. When we bring the N pole of a second magnet near the N pole of the suspended magnet, we observe that the two repel each other. We see a similar action with the two S poles. Now let us bring the S pole of one magnet near the N pole of the other magnet; we find that they attract each other. From these observations we conclude that *like poles repel; unlike poles attract.*

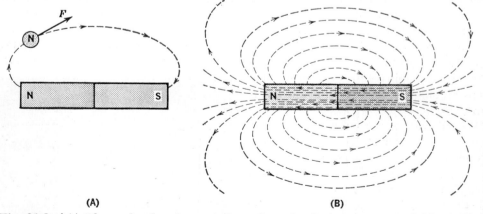

(A)　　　　　　　　　　　　　　　　(B)

Fig. 21-9. (A) The path taken by an independent N pole in a magnetic field is called a line of flux. (B) Magnetic flux about a bar magnet.

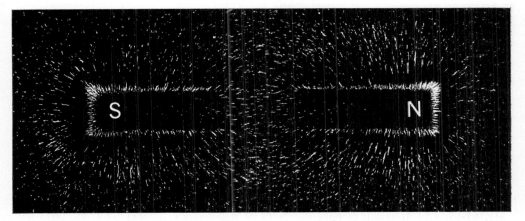

Fig. 21-10. Iron filings near a single bar magnet.

Magnets usually have two well-defined poles, one N and one S. Long bar magnets sometimes acquire more than two poles. An iron ring may have no poles at all when magnetized. A single isolated pole is not a physical possibility since a magnet must have an equal S pole for every N pole. An isolated N pole of unit strength is frequently *assumed*, however, in theoretical considerations using "thought experiments." *A **unit** pole is one which repels an exactly similar pole placed 1 centimeter away with a force of 1 dyne.*

The first quantitative study of the force between two magnets is generally credited to Coulomb, who found this magnetic force to be governed by the same inverse-square relationship that applies to gravitational force and electrostatic force. ***Coulomb's law for magnetism*** states that *the force between two magnetic poles is directly proportional to the strengths of the poles and inversely proportional to the square of their distance apart.* The force is one of repulsion or attraction, depending on whether the poles are alike or different.

6. Magnetic field of force. In Chapter 18, Section 10, we stated that an electric field of force exists near an electrically charged body. The situation of a magnet is analogous. If an independent N pole is brought into the region near a magnet, the independent pole experiences a force according to Coulomb's law, because such

Fig. 21-11. Iron filings near the unlike poles of two bar magnets.

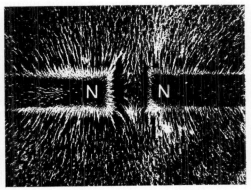

Fig. 21-12. Iron filings near like poles of two bar magnets.

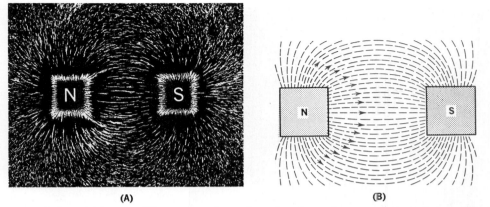

Fig. 21-13. (A) Iron filings near the poles of a horseshoe magnet, end on. (B) An idealized drawing of (A) showing lines of flux.

a region contains a *magnetic field. A magnetic field exists in a region in which a magnetic force acts on an independent pole brought into the region.* While an electric field and a magnetic field have similar characteristics, it would be a mistake to assume that they are equivalent. An electrically charged particle in motion is influenced by a magnetic field but not in the same way that it is influenced by an electric field.

The behavior of an independent N pole in a magnetic field may be approximated by using a magnetized darning needle as shown in Fig. 21-8. The needle passes through a piece of cork large enough to float it, with the N pole below the surface of the water. The S pole is far enough away to have negligible influence on the movement of the needle. A bar magnet placed under the glass dish so that its N pole is near the needle causes the floating magnet

to move approximately along the path that would be followed by an isolated N pole.

The path described by the motion of an independent N pole in a magnetic field is called a *line of flux. A line of flux is a line so drawn that a tangent to it at any point indicates the direction of the magnetic field.* Flux lines emerge from a magnet in the region of the N pole and enter the magnet in the region of the S pole, every line being a closed path running from S pole to N pole within the magnet. *Flux lines are sometimes loosely called lines of force.* See Fig. 21-9.

The lines of flux in a magnetic field are referred to collectively as the *magnetic flux.* The symbol for magnetic flux is the Greek letter Phi, Φ. The unit of magnetic flux in the MKS system is the *weber.*

$$1 \text{ weber} = 10^8 \text{ lines of flux}$$

*The **magnetic flux density** (B) is the number*

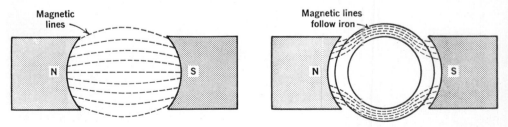

Fig. 21-14. At left, magnetic flux crosses the air gap between the poles of a magnet. At right, magnetic flux follows the soft iron ring, which is more permeable than air.

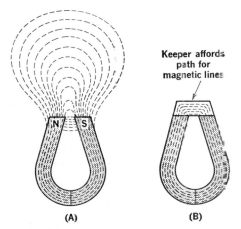

Fig. 21-15. (A) Magnetic flux about the poles of a horseshoe magnet. (B) The effect of a keeper on the path of the magnetic flux.

of flux lines per unit area that permeate the magnetic field, a field expressible as a vector because it has both magnitude and direction. Flux density in the MKS system is expressed in *webers per meter²*, and determines the *field intensity* (H) at any point within the magnetic field. *Magnetic field intensity is the force exerted by the field on a unit N pole situated in the field.*

The field of a single magnet or a group of magnets is suggested by the pattern formed by iron filings sprinkled on a glass plate laid over the magnet. Photographs of such patterns are shown in Figs. 21-10 through 21-13.

7. Magnetic permeability. In Section 6 we observed the effect of a magnetic field of force acting on iron filings and a magnetized needle through glass and water. Nonmagnetic materials, in general, are *transparent* to magnetic flux; that is, their effect on the lines of flux is not appreciably different from that of air. *The property of a material by which it changes the flux density in a magnetic field from the value in air is called its permeability* (μ). The permeability of air is unity. The permeabilities of diamagnetic substances are slightly less than unity, while permeabilities of paramagnetic substances are slightly greater than unity. Permeability is a ratio and therefore a pure number.

If a sheet of iron lies over a magnet, we find that there is no magnetic field above the iron sheet, as the flux enters the iron and follows a path entirely within the iron itself. Figure 21-14 illustrates this principle. The flux density in iron is *greater* than it is in air; therefore, iron is said to have a *high* permeability. The permeabilities of other ferromagnetic substances are also very high.

When a horseshoe magnet is not in use, a small bar of soft iron, called a *keeper*, should be placed across its poles as shown in Fig. 21-15. The magnetic flux is gathered into the *keeper*, which provides a closed path of highly permeable ferromagnetic material for the flux lines, thus helping to maintain the magnet strength. The strength of bar magnets may be maintained by placing them side by side with opposite poles together and with keepers across each pair of poles.

8. Induced magnetism. Suppose a bar of soft iron lies in a magnetic field, as in Fig. 21-16. Due to the high permeability of the iron, the field is distorted, the magnetic flux passing through the iron in preference to the air. The soft iron bar

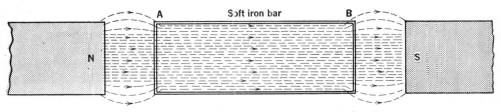

Fig. 21-16. Magnetizing an iron bar by induction.

becomes a magnet under these circumstances. End A is the S pole and end B is the N pole; the bar is said to be magnetized by *induction*. *Magnetism produced in a ferromagnetic substance by the influence of a magnetic field is called* **induced magnetism**.

If we remove the magnetic field by withdrawing the two bar magnets, the magnetic character of the iron bar largely disappears. Most of the induced magnetism is lost. Magnets produced by induction are called *temporary* magnets. A piece of hardened steel is not so strongly magnetized by induction, but retains a greater *residual* magnetism when removed from the induction field.

There is no significant difference in the induction process if we bring the iron bar of Fig. 21-16 in contact with one of the magnet poles. The magnetization process is somewhat more efficient due to the reduction of the air gap. This is sometimes referred to as *magnetization by contact*. See Fig. 21-17.

★ **9. Magnetic hysteresis.** The magnetic field intensity, H, acts as the *magnetizing force* in the process of magnetic induction. As a ferromagnetic material is subjected to an increasing magnetizing force, the flux density, B, increases until the material is *saturated*. See curve *ab* of Fig. 21-18. If the magnetizing force is then reduced to zero, the magnetization does not return to zero but lags behind the magnetizing force, segment *bc*. *The lagging of the magnetization behind the magnetizing force is known as* **hysteresis**. The greater the lag, the greater is the residual magnetism retained by the material, ordinate *Oc*.

The flux density, and thus the magnetization, can be reduced to zero only by reversing the magnetic field and building up the magnetizing force in the opposite direction, segment *cd*. The reverse magnetizing force, if increased enough, causes the material to reach saturation again, but with its poles reversed, segment

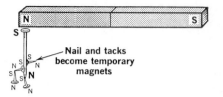

Fig. 21-17. The nail becomes a magnet by induction. What about the tacks?

de. Reducing the magnetizing force to zero and then increasing it in the original direction again merely completes the segment *eft*. This process may be repeated and the magnetization of the material follows the closed loop *bcef*, a curve called a *hysteresis loop*.

Hardened steel has a thick-loop hysteresis characteristic since the residual magnetism is high. Soft iron has a thin-loop characteristic. The *area* enclosed by a hysteresis loop gives an indication of the quantity of energy that is dissipated in taking a ferromagnetic substance through a complete cycle of magnetization. In the operation of many electric devices, this energy is wasted and appears as heat; the hysteresis characteristic of a ferromagnetic material is therefore an important design consideration in such electric devices.

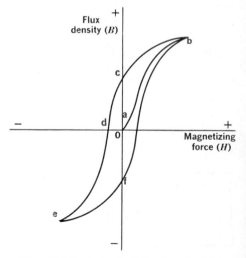

Fig. 21-18. A typical hysteresis loop.

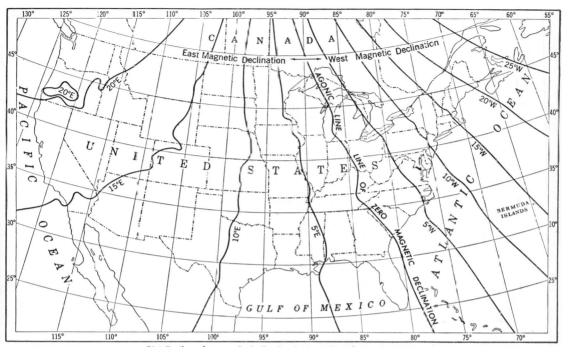

Distribution of magnetic declination in the United States for 1955.

Fig. 21-19. A map of the United States showing magnetic declination for 1955. (U.S. Dept. of Commerce, Coast and Geodetic Survey)

★ **10. Terrestrial magnetism.** The earth behaves as a large magnet, but its magnetic poles unfortunately do not coincide with the geographic poles, the North Magnetic Pole being about 1100 miles south of the North Geographic Pole. Thus the N pole of the compass needle does not point due north from most locations on the earth. *The angle of compass variation from true north is called the* **angle of declination.** See Fig. 21-19. A succession of points of equal declination form an *isogonic* line, and a line of zero declination is called an *agonic* line.

A compass needle mounted on a horizontal axis and provided with a means by which the angle of the needle with the horizontal can be measured is called a *dipping* needle. See Fig. 21-20. At certain places on the earth's surface, approximately midway between the magnetic poles, the angle of dip is zero and the needle is horizontal. A line drawn through a succession of such points identifies the *magnetic equator;* it is the *aclinic* line. Lines drawn through places of equal dip are called *isoclinic* lines. *The dip, or deviation between the equilibrium position of a dipping needle and the horizontal, is known as* **magnetic inclination.**

Fig. 21-20. A dipping needle. (Cenco)

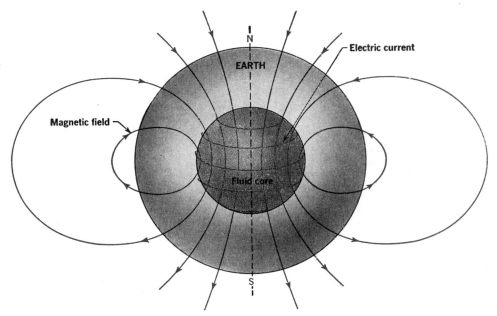

Fig. 21-21. The magnetic field of the earth may be due to electric currents in the earth's core.

William Gilbert published in 1600 a scientific paper, *De Magnete*, dealing with the magnetism of the earth. This was one of the earliest papers ever written on experimental science. Gilbert naturally inferred that the earth behaved as a large magnet because the interior consisted of magnetic material. Scientists know today, however, that the core of the earth is much too hot to be a permanent magnet.

Karl Friedrich Gauss (1777–1855), a German physicist, proved that the magnetic field of the earth must originate inside the earth. Walter M. Elsasser, a German physicist now a professor of theoretical physics at the University of California, suggested in 1939 that the earth's magnetic field results from currents generated by the flow of matter in the fluid core of the earth. This promising hypothesis may someday provide us with the answer to an ancient question. It follows on the assumption that magnetism is a property of an electric charge in motion (Section 4). In the remainder of this chapter, we shall concern ourselves with the relationship between a current of electricity and a magnetic field.

2 ELECTROMAGNETISM

11. The link between electricity and magnetism. In 1819, Hans Christian Oersted (*er*-stet) (1777–1851), a Danish physicist, found that a small compass needle is deflected when brought near a conductor carrying an electric current. Here was the first evidence of a link between electricity and magnetism that had long been suspected. Oersted determined that the compass deflection was due to a magnetic field established around the conductor by the current in the conductor.

A description of Oersted's famous experiment will help you to understand its significance. A dry cell, compass, switch, and conducting wire are arranged as shown in Fig. 21-23(*A*). With the switch open, a straight section of the conductor is supported *above* the compass in the vertical plane of the compass needle. In (*B*) the dry-cell connection is such that the electron flow will be from north to south. When the switch is closed, the N pole of the compass is deflected toward the west. When the dry-cell connections are reversed so electron flow is from south to north, the N pole of the compass is deflected to the east. *There is a magnetic field in the region near the conductor when the circuit is closed; and the direction of the field is dependent on the direction of the current in the conductor.*

If the experiment is repeated with the conductor placed *below* the compass needle, the compass deflection is opposite to that in the first experiment. This suggests, but does not prove, that the magnetic field encircles the conductor.

12. The magnetic field surrounding an electric charge in motion. Shortly after Oersted's discovery, the French physicist André Marie Ampère (1775–1836) determined the shape of the magnetic field about a conductor carrying a current. He had discovered that forces exist between two parallel conductors in an electric circuit, the force being one of attraction if the two currents are in the same direction, and one of repulsion if the currents are in opposite directions.

Fig. 21-22. Hans Christian Oersted discovered the relationship between magnetism and electricity. (Bettmann Archive)

These attractive and repulsive forces between current-carrying conductors prove to be directly proportional to the currents in the conductors, thus providing a precise method of defining the practical unit of current, the ampere. In this sense, the **ampere** may be defined as *the current in each of two long, parallel conductors, spaced one meter apart, which causes a magnetic force of 2×10^{-7} newton per meter length of conductor.*

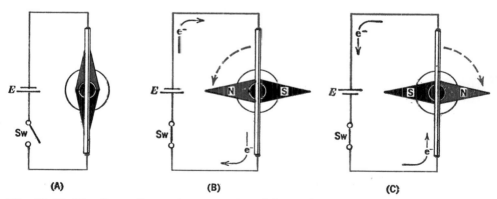

Fig. 21-23. The Oersted experiment as viewed from above. In each diagram the compass needle is located below the conductor.

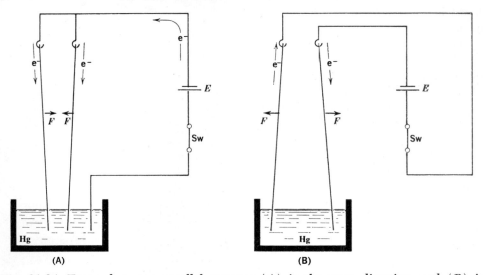

Fig. 21-24. Forces between parallel currents (A) in the same direction, and (B) in opposite directions.

Following this scheme, the **coulomb** as a quantity of charge (an ampere-second), may be defined as *the quantity of electricity which passes a given point on a conductor in one second when the conductor carries a constant current of one ampere.*

Ampère investigated the magnetic fields about conductors to find an explanation of the magnetic forces. Suppose a heavy copper wire passes vertically through the center of a sheet of stiff cardboard that is in a horizontal position. When the ends of the vertical conductor are connected to a dry cell and iron filings are sprinkled over the surface of the cardboard, the iron filings form a pattern of concentric circles around the conductor. If a small compass is placed at various points on a circle of filings, the N pole always comes to rest tangent to the circle.

If the direction of current in the vertical conductor is reversed, the N pole of the

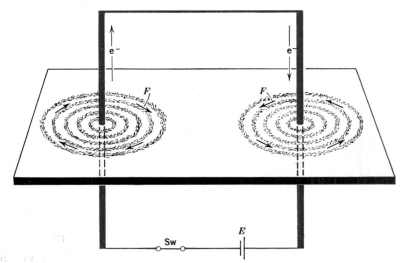

Fig. 21-25. The magnetic field encircling a current in a straight conductor.

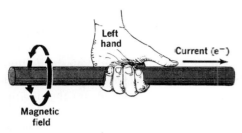

Fig. 21-26. Ampère's rule for a straight conductor.

of this rule takes into account the fact that an electric current consists of a flow of electrons through a conductor.

> **Ampère's rule for a straight conductor:** Grasp the conductor in the left hand with the thumb extended in the direction of the electron current. The fingers then will circle the conductor in the direction of the magnetic flux.

compass needle again becomes aligned tangent to the circle of filings, but in the *opposite* direction. From these observations, we may conclude that *a magnetic field encircles an electric charge in motion.* The lines of flux are closed concentric circles lying in a plane perpendicular to the conductor with the axis of the conductor as their center. The direction of the magnetic field is everywhere tangent to the flux and is dependent on the direction of the current.

Ampère was able to show that the strength of the magnetic field around a conductor carrying a current varies directly with the magnitude of the current and inversely with the distance from the conductor. He devised a rule, now known as *Ampère's rule,* for predicting the direction of the magnetic field around a current in a straight conductor once the direction of the current is known. The modern version

13. Magnetic field about a conducting loop. Keeping Ampère's rule in mind, let us consider a loop in a conductor carrying a current. The magnetic flux from all segments of the loop must pass through the inside of the loop in the same direction, that is, *the faces of the loop must show polarity.* See Fig. 21-27.

The pole strength of this magnet will be stronger if the flux density is increased. As the magnetic field around a conductor varies with the current, *one way* to increase the pole strength would be to increase the magnitude of the current in the conducting loop. A *second way* would be to form additional loops in the conductor, similar to the original loop and closely oriented with it.

A straight-line arrangement of such conducting loops takes the form of a *helix*. A long helically wound coil is called a

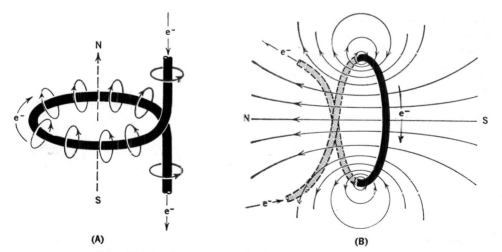

(A)   (B)

Fig. 21-27. The magnetic field through a current loop.

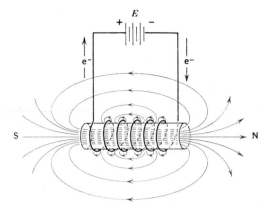

Fig. 21-28. Magnetic field about a solenoid.

solenoid. The cylindrical column of air inside the loops and extending the length of the coil is called the *core.* When a current is in the solenoid, the core of each loop, or *turn,* becomes a magnet, and the core of the solenoid is a magnetic tube through which practically all the magnetic flux passes. See Fig. 21-28.

Since a solenoid carrying a current acts like a bar magnet, we may determine its polarity by means of a compass; however, the magnetic flux in the core of the solenoid is derived from the magnetic field of each turn of the conductor. Thus we may modify Ampère's rule to fit this special case of a conductor carrying a current.

> **Ampère's rule for a solenoid:** Grasp the coil in the left hand with the fingers circling the coil in the direction of the electron current. The extended thumb will point in the direction of the N pole of the core.

14. The electromagnet. A solenoid having a core of air, wood, or some other nonmagnetic material does not produce a very strong electromagnet, for the permeability of all nonmagnetic substances is essentially equal to that of air, unity. Substitution of such materials for air does not appreciably change the flux density.

Soft iron, on the other hand, has a high permeability, and if an iron rod is sub-

stituted for air as the core material, the flux density is greatly increased. Strong electromagnets therefore have a ferromagnetic core with high permeability. Once the core is selected, the strength of the electromagnet depends on the magnitude of the current and the number of turns; that is, on *the number of ampere-turns.*

15. Uses of electromagnets. For use where very strong magnetic fields must be maintained continuously, permanent magnets made of special ferromagnetic alloys are usually best. There are a great many operations, however, that require intermittent or controlled magnetic fields; for these, electromagnets are most useful.

Joseph Henry (1797–1878), an American physicist, made the first practical electromagnets. Many of the applications of electromagnets are familiar to you. They range in complexity from the simple door bell to highly specialized components of complex electronic devices. Strong electromagnets that can lift several tons are used in handling scrap iron and steel. Surgeons use electromagnets to remove steel splinters from wounds. The electric bell, the telegraph, the electric generator, and the electric motor all employ electromagnets. Recordings, including complete television programs, are made on magnetic tapes by means of electromagnets. The remaining portion of this chapter deals with combinations of permanent magnets and electromagnets as they are used in certain electric measuring instruments.

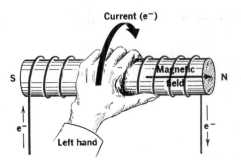

Fig. 21-29. Ampère's rule for a solenoid.

3 d-c METERS

16. The galvanoscope. If we form a wire into a loop, place a compass needle in the center of it, and allow a current to flow through the loop, the needle is deflected, as shown in Fig. 21-23. If we increase the number of turns sufficiently, even a feeble current produces a marked deflection of the needle. This device is called a *galvanoscope*, and may be used to detect the presence of an electric current or to determine its direction. See Fig. 21-30.

17. Construction of a galvanometer. A more versatile instrument for detecting feeble currents is the *galvanometer*, the essential parts of which are shown in Fig. 21-31. In the galvanometer, a coil of wire is pivoted on jeweled bearings between the poles of a permanent horseshoe magnet. The coil is a helix which becomes a magnet whenever current passes through it. Thus our instrument has two magnets: (*1*) a permanent horseshoe magnet that is in a fixed position; and (*2*) an electromagnet that is free to turn on its axis. Electric connections to the helix are made through the two control springs, which hold the coil in such a position that the pointer attached to the electromagnet shows a zero reading when no current is present. In a galvanometer, the zero position is often located at the midpoint of the scale.

When there is a current in the movable coil, its faces acquire polarity and are attracted and repelled by the poles of the permanent magnet. A torque acts upon the coil, which rotates in an attempt to align its plane perpendicular to the line joining the two poles of the permanent magnet. As the coil rotates, however, it must do work against the two control springs, and its final position is reached when the torque acting on it is just neutralized by the reaction of the springs. The permanent field flux being constant, the torque on the coil is proportional to the current in it. We may assume, for small excursions, that the reaction of the springs is proportional to the deflection angle. When the coil reaches its equilibrium position, these two opposing torques are equal, and the deflection angle of the coil is therefore proportional to the current in it.

The scale of the galvanometer is marked at intervals on either side of the zero center. Readings are made on this scale by means of a small, lightweight pointer attached to the coil. For a coil current in one direction, the needle deflection is to the left. If the current direction is reversed, the needle is deflected to the right.

The galvanometer is a sensitive instrument for detecting feeble currents of the order of microamperes, the scale graduations giving relative magnitudes of current. For translation of a reading into absolute current values, the *current sensitivity* of the specific instrument must be known. Current sensitivity is usually expressed in *microamperes per scale division*.

The pointer deflection, *s*, of a galvanometer is proportional to the current, I_M, in the coil.

$$I_M \propto s$$

or

$$I_M = ks$$

and

$$k = \frac{I_M}{s}$$

where *k* is the current sensitivity in microamperes per scale division.

The galvanometer movement, of course, has resistance. By Ohm's law, we see that a potential difference appears across the resistance of the meter when a current is in the coil. We may easily express the *voltage sensitivity* of the instrument, since it must be equal to the product of the meter resistance and the current per scale division.

Voltage sensitivity $= kR_M = \dfrac{I_M}{\text{div}} \times R_M$

where R_M is the resistance of the meter movement. Voltage sensitivity is given in microvolts per scale division.

If provision is made to prevent excessive currents from entering the coil, the galvanometer can easily be adapted for service as either a d-c ammeter or d-c voltmeter.

The Sample Problems below illustrate calculations involving the galvanometer.

Sample Problem

What current is required for full-scale deflection (50. divisions) of a galvanometer having a current sensitivity of 50. μamp per scale division?

Solution

We are given the current sensitivity, $k = 50.$ μamp/div, and the number of divisions on either side of mid-scale (zero) position, $s = 50.$ div.

$I_M = ks$

$I_M = \dfrac{50.\ \mu\text{amp}}{\text{div}} \times 50.\ \text{div}$

$I_M = 2500\ \mu\text{amp}$, or 2.5×10^{-3} amp, the required current

Sample Problem

What potential difference appears across a galvanometer having a current sensitivity of 50. μamp/div when the pointer is fully deflected? The meter resistance is 10. Ω.

Solution

We are given the current sensitivity, $k = 50.$ μamp/div, the resistance of the meter, $R_M = 10.$ Ω, and the number of divisions of deflection, $s = 50.$ div.

$V_M = I_M R_M$

But

$I_M = ks$

Then

$V_M = ksR_M$

$V_M = \dfrac{50.\ \mu\text{amp}}{\text{div}} \times 50.\ \text{div} \times 10.\ \Omega$

$V_M = 2.5 \times 10^4\ \mu\text{v}$ or 2.5×10^{-2} v, the potential difference across the meter

Fig. 21-30. A simple galvanoscope.

18. The d-c voltmeter. We have seen in Section 17 that the potential difference across a galvanometer is quite small even when the meter is fully deflected. If a galvanometer movement is to be used as a voltmeter to measure voltages of ordinary magnitudes, we must convert it to a high-resistance instrument.

If a high resistance is added in series with the moving coil, most of the potential drop appears across this series, or *multiplier*, resistor. Since a voltmeter is connected in *parallel* with the part of a circuit across which the potential difference is to be measured, a high resistance prevents an appreciable loading effect. By the proper choice of resistance, we can calibrate the meter to read any desired voltage.

Suppose we convert the galvanometer movement used in the sample problems of Section 17 to a voltmeter reading 100.0 volts cn full-scale deflection. The current required for full deflection has been found to be 2.500×10^{-3} ampere, and the resistance of the meter coil is 10. ohms. We must determine the value of the resistor to be placed in series with the moving coil. Figure 21-33 illustrates this problem.

Since R_M and R_S (of Fig. 21-34) are in series,

$$V = I_M R_M + I_M R_S$$

Then

$$R_S = \frac{V}{I_M} - R_M$$

$$R_S = \frac{100.0 \text{ v}}{2.500 \times 10^{-3} \text{ amp}} - 10. \ \Omega$$

$R_S = 39{,}990 \ \Omega$, the value of the series resistor

Observe that the total resistance between the terminals of the meter is 40,000 ohms. *The voltmeter sensitivity may be expressed in terms of ohms per volt.* When the ohms-per-volt sensitivity of a voltmeter is known, we may quickly estimate the loading effect it will have when placed across a known resistance component of a circuit. For example, at 400 ohms per volt, our meter which reads from 0 to 100 volts has 40,000 ohms between the terminals. If

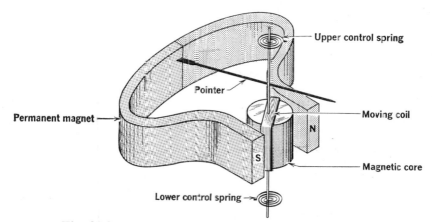

Fig. 21-31. Magnet and moving coil of a galvanometer.

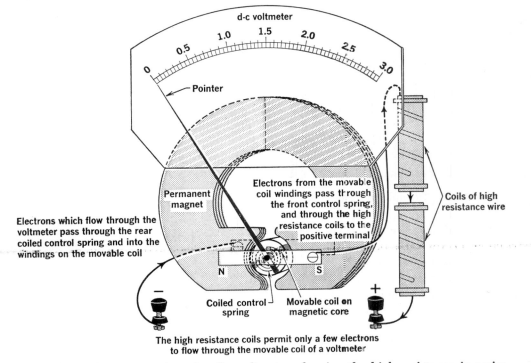

d-c voltmeter

Pointer

Permanent
magnet

Electrons from the movable
coil windings pass through
the front control spring,
and through the high
resistance coils to the
positive terminal

Coils of high
resistance wire

Electrons which flow through the
voltmeter pass through the rear
coiled control spring and into the
windings on the movable coil

N   S

Coiled control
spring

Movable coil on
magnetic core

The high resistance coils permit only a few electrons
to flow through the movable coil of a voltmeter

Fig. 21-32. The construction of a d-c voltmeter, showing the high resistance in series with the windings of the movable coil.

it were placed across resistances greater than about 4000 ohms, the loading effect would result in serious errors. See Chapter 19, Section 17.

19. The d-c ammeter. We could use our basic galvanometer movement of Section 17 as a microammeter merely by recalibrating the graduated scale to read directly in microamperes. However, the meter would not be useful in circuits in which the current exceeded 2500 microamperes; larger current magnitudes would ruin the meter movement since no energy could

be expended to produce movement beyond the full deflection. A larger current than that required for full-scale deflection would simply heat the coil. Recall that this is an I^2R loss and so we should expect the meter to *burn out*.

To convert the galvanometer movement so as to read larger currents, we provide an alternate (parallel) path for current, called a *shunt*, across the terminals. By the proper choice of shunt resistances, we can calibrate the meter to read over the range of current magnitudes we may require.

Suppose we wish to convert the galvanometer movement previously considered to an ammeter reading 10.0 amperes full scale. As before, the current required for the full deflection of the moving coil is 2.5×10^{-3} ampere and the resistance is 10. Ω. We must determine the resistance of the shunt to be used across the coil. Figure 21-35 applies.

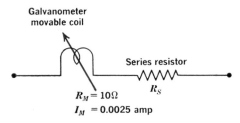

Galvanometer
movable coil

Series resistor

$R_M = 10\,\Omega$

R_S

$I_M = 0.0025$ amp

Fig. 21-33. Converting a galvanometer to a voltmeter.

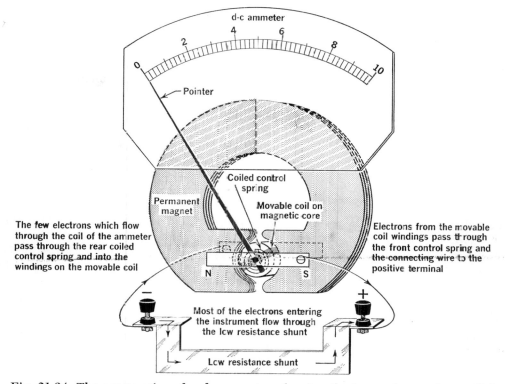

d-c ammeter

Pointer

Coiled control spring

Permanent magnet

Movable coil on magnetic core

The few electrons which flow through the coil of the ammeter pass through the rear coiled control spring and into the windings on the movable coil

Electrons from the movable coil windings pass through the front control spring and the connecting wire to the positive terminal

N   S

Most of the electrons entering the instrument flow through the low resistance shunt

Low resistance shunt

Fig. 21-34. The construction of a d-c ammeter, showing the low resistance in parallel with the windings on the movable coil.

Since R_M and R_S are in parallel,

$$I_M R_M = I_S R_S$$

But

$$I_S = I_T - I_M$$

Then

$$R_S = \frac{I_M R_M}{I_T - I_M}$$

$$R_S = \frac{0.0025 \text{ amp} \times 10. \, \Omega}{9.9975 \text{ amp}}$$

$R_S = 0.0025 \, \Omega$, the value of the shunt resistor

The total resistance of the ammeter is the equivalent value of 10 ohms and 0.0025 ohm in parallel. This must be *less than* 0.0025 ohm. We see immediately why it is essential that an ammeter be connected in *series* in a circuit, and why its presence does not materially affect the amount of current in the circuit.

20. The ohmmeter. The circuit of a simple ohmmeter is shown in Fig. 21-36. An ohmmeter provides a convenient means of measuring the resistance of a circuit component, but its accuracy limitation is approximately the same as the voltmeter-ammeter method. Actually, it is simply a modified version of this method. *It is essential that the ohmmeter be used only on a completely de-energized circuit.*

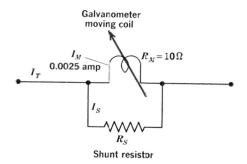

Galvanometer moving coil

I_M
0.0025 amp
$R_M = 10\,\Omega$
I_T
I_S
R_S
Shunt resistor

Fig. 21-35. Converting a galvanometer to an ammeter.

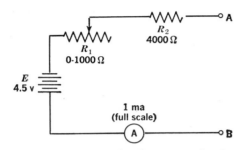
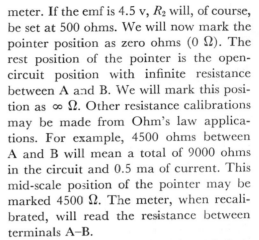

Fig. 21-36. A simple ohmmeter circuit.

In the ohmmeter circuit of Fig. 21-36, we have a milliammeter requiring 1 ma for full-scale deflection. With an emf of 4.5 volts, by Ohm's law, 4500 ohms of resistance will provide 1 ma of current when terminals A–B are short-circuited. We have provided a fixed resistor, R_2 of 4000 ohms and a rheostat, R_1, of 0–1000 ohms.

Suppose we bring terminals A and B into direct contact. We may adjust R_2 to give precisely full deflection on the meter. If the emf is 4.5 v, R_2 will, of course, be set at 500 ohms. We will now mark the pointer position as zero ohms (0 Ω). The rest position of the pointer is the open-circuit position with infinite resistance between A and B. We will mark this position as ∞ Ω. Other resistance calibrations may be made from Ohm's law applications. For example, 4500 ohms between A and B will mean a total of 9000 ohms in the circuit and 0.5 ma of current. This mid-scale position of the pointer may be marked 4500 Ω. The meter, when recalibrated, will read the resistance between terminals A–B.

Each time the ohmmeter is used, it is first shorted across A–B and R_2 is adjusted to zero the meter. This calibrates the meter and accommodates any decrease in the terminal voltage of the battery with age. The resistance R_2 allows the ohmmeter to be used until E drops below 4.0 volts.

Summary

Materials fall into one of three classes according to their magnetic properties. Ferromagnetic substances may be strongly magnetized, diamagnetic substances are slightly repelled, and paramagnetic substances are slightly attracted by magnets. Ferromagnetic materials have high permeabilities. The domain theory explains magnetism on the basis of electric charges in motion. Coulomb's law applies to the force between magnet poles. There are many similarities between a magnetic field and its relation to a hypothetical independent N pole, and an electric field and its relationship to a positive test charge. A ferromagnetic substance becomes magnetized in a magnetic field by induction. The magnetism of the earth is thought to result from electric currents in the earth itself.

A moving charge is always surrounded by a magnetic field. The core of a coil carrying an electric current becomes a magnet. By winding a coil on a ferromagnetic core very strong electromagnets are produced. The strength of an electromagnet is dependent on the number of ampere-turns.

The galvanometer is a basic meter movement used for d-c measurements. By placing a high resistance in series with a galvanometer coil, the meter may be calibrated as a voltmeter. If a very low resistance shunt is placed across a galvanometer coil, the instrument may be calibrated as an ammeter. An ohmmeter may consist of a source of emf, an adjustable resistance, and a sensitive ammeter so arranged that the resistance to be measured is connected in series with the ohmmeter resistance and the ammeter.

TERMS TO DEFINE

diamagnetism
dipping needle
domain
electromagnet
electron spin
ferrites
ferromagnetism
field intensity
flux density
galvanometer

galvanoscope
hysteresis
hysteresis loop
induced magnetism
isogonic line
keeper
line of flux
magnetic declination
magnetic field
magnetic flux

magnetic force
magnetic inclination
magnetic saturation
magnetism
paramagnetism
permeability
solenoid
unit pole
voltmeter sensitivity
weber

QUESTIONS

A 1. (a) What is a lodestone? (b) Why are lodestones sometimes called natural magnets?
2. What is the distinguishing property of ferromagnetic materials?
3. Distinguish between diamagnetic and paramagnetic materials.
4. What two kinds of electron motion are important in determining the magnetic property of a material?
5. What are electron pairs and how are they formed?
6. (a) What three metals are the most important ferromagnetic materials? (b) What special alloy is often used to make very strong magnets?
7. How can you account for the ferromagnetic properties of the metals of the Iron Family?
8. What are magnetic domains?
9. Describe the condition of a ferromagnetic material which is said to be in a state of magnetic saturation.
10. State Coulomb's law for magnetism.
11. Under what circumstances will a magnetic force be (a) one of repulsion; (b) one of attraction?
12. Describe a simple way to examine the fields of small magnets.
13. What determines the field intensity at any point in a magnetic field?
14. (a) What is the advantage of making a magnet in the shape of a horseshoe? (b) What is the purpose of a keeper?
15. Describe an experiment which illustrates induced magnetism.
16. Distinguish between a north-seeking pole and the North Magnetic Pole.
17. Why is a declination angle involved in the use of a compass over most of the earth's surface?

18. What important discovery was made by the Danish physicist, Oersted?
19. A conductor carrying a current is arranged so that electrons flow in one segment from north to south. A compass is held over this segment of the wire. In what direction is the compass needle deflected?
20. Describe a simple experiment which will show the nature of the magnetic field about a straight conductor carrying a current.
21. Suppose an electron flow in a conductor passing perpendicularly through this page is represented by a dot inside a small circle when the direction of flow is up out of the page. What is the direction of the magnetic flux about this current?
22. Upon what factors does the strength of an electromagnet depend?
23. What prevents the movable coil of a galvanometer from aligning its magnetic field parallel to that of the permanent magnet each time a current is in the coil?
24. (a) Why is it necessary that an ammeter be a low-resistance instrument? (b) Why must a voltmeter be a high-resistance instrument?

B 25. Explain, on the basis of atomic structure, the property of diamagnetism.
26. Explain paramagnetism on the basis of imbalance between orbits and spins.
27. Assume the pan in Fig. 21-8 to be located in the northern hemisphere. Will the magnetized needle be attracted to the north edge of the pan? Explain.
28. How would you prove that a steel bar is magnetized?

29. A solenoid is suspended by a thread so that the core can rotate in the horizontal plane. A current is maintained in the coil such that the electron flow is clockwise from end A to end B. How will the coil align itself in the earth's magnetic field?

30. A stream of electrons is projected horizontally to the right. A straight conductor carrying a current is supported parallel to the electron stream and above it. (a) What is the effect on the electron stream if the direction of the current in the conductor is from left to right; (b) if the direction of the current is reversed?

31. Suppose the conductor in Question 30 is replaced by a magnet which produces a magnetic field directed downward. What is the effect on the electron stream? Explain.

32. What is the significance of the area enclosed by the hysteresis loop of a ferromagnetic material?

33. If a watch mechanism is to be magnetically "insulated," should the case be made of diamagnetic, paramagnetic, or ferromagnetic material? Explain.

34. Why might the potential difference indicated by a voltmeter placed across a circuit load be different from the potential difference with the meter removed?

35. Suppose the resistance of a high-resistance load is to be determined using the voltmeter method. Considering the design characteristics of ammeters and voltmeters, how would you arrange the meters in the circuit to reduce the error to a minimum? Draw your circuit diagram and justify your arrangement.

36. Suppose the resistance of a low-resistance load is to be determined using the voltmeter-ammeter method. How would you arrange the meters in this circuit to reduce the error to a minimum? Draw your circuit diagram and justify your arrangement.

PROBLEMS

B 1. Two parallel conductors 2 m long and 1 m apart experience a total force of 1.6×10^{-6} nt. What magnitude of current is in each conductor?

2. An ammeter which has a resistance of 0.01 ohm is connected in a circuit and indicates a current of 10 amperes. A shunt having a resistance of 0.001 ohm is then connected across the meter terminals. What is the new reading on the meter?

3. A galvanometer has a zero-center scale with 20.0 divisions on each side of zero. The pointer deflects 15.0 scale divisions when a current of 375 μamp is in the movable coil. (a) What

is the current sensitivity of the meter? (b) What current will produce a full-scale deflection?

4. A galvanometer has a resistance of 75 ohms and requires 75 milliamperes to produce a full-scale deflection. What value of resistance must be connected in series with the galvanometer in order to use it as voltmeter for measuring a maximum of 250 volts?

5. A galvanometer movement has a resistance of 2.5 ohms and when fully deflected has a potential difference of 50. millivolts across it. What shunting resistance is required to enable the instrument to be used as an ammeter reading 7.5 amperes full scale?

RESEARCH ON YOUR OWN

1. Alnico magnets can be bought quite cheaply from various sources. Devise experiments using such magnets. Use them to make a magnetic door catch or some other magnetic device. Why should you use brass screws to hold the magnets in place?

2. Hold a strong alnico magnet near a lighted 110-volt carbon filament lamp on an alternating current circuit. Explain your results. If possible, try the same experiment with a 110-volt direct current circuit. What is the effect of holding the magnet in different positions?

3. Wrap about 30 turns of bell wire around a glass tank and connect the ends of the wire to a 6-volt source of direct current. Magnetize eight needles and thrust them horizontally through cork wafers made by slicing thin pieces from a large cork. Float the corks, one at a time, in the water in the tank. Explain the symmetry of the patterns produced.

4. Make an electromagnet out of a short piece of soft-steel rod and a piece of insulated wire several feet long. See how many small carpet tacks you can pick up with the electromagnet when it is connected to a dry cell.

5. Get three electric-meter movements and construct from them an ammeter, a voltmeter, and an ohmmeter. Demonstrate these meters and explain the reasons for the differences in construction.

6. Design and make a current balance to demonstrate the definition of an ampere. (The current balance need not measure an ampere.)

7. Look up a Barlow's wheel in a scientific supply house catalog and construct one for yourself. Demonstrate it and explain its principle of operation.

UNIT **8**

Alternating current electricity

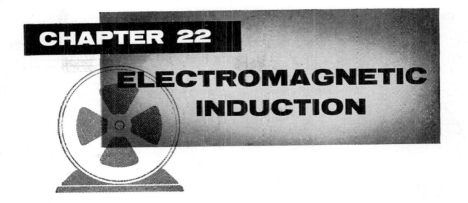

CHAPTER 22
ELECTROMAGNETIC INDUCTION

1. The discovery of electromagnetic induction. Shortly after the beginning of the nineteenth century, Oersted discovered the link between magnetism and electricity. He learned that a magnetic field exists about a conductor carrying an electric current. A moving charge constitutes an electric current; thus magnetic fields are the result of charges in motion, and magnetic forces are associated with the motions of charges.

Soon after Oersted's discovery, his contemporaries attempted to find out whether an electric current could be produced by the action of a magnetic field. In 1831, Michael Faraday discovered that *an emf is set up in a conductor located in a magnetic field, when the magnetic flux is cut by the conductor.* Joseph Henry, working independently in America, made a similar discovery at about the same time. This phenomenon is known as *electromagnetic induction.* The emf is called an *induced emf* and the resulting current in the conducting loop is called an *induced current.*

Our present-day technology is largely the result of the production and distribution of inexpensive electric power. These were made feasible by the discoveries of Faraday and Henry, which led to the invention of electric generators and transformers.

VOCABULARY

Alternating current. A current which has one direction during one part of a generating cycle and the opposite direction during the remainder of the cycle.

Electric generator. A device for converting mechanical energy into electric energy.

Electric motor. A device for converting electric energy into mechanical energy.

Electromagnetic induction. The process by which an emf is set up in a conductor located in a magnetic field, when the magnetic flux is cut by the conductor.

Inductance. The property of an electric circuit by which a varying current induces an emf in that circuit or a neighboring circuit.

Instantaneous current. The magnitude of a varying current at any instant of time.

Instantaneous voltage. The magnitude of a varying voltage at any instant of time.

Transformer. A device for changing an alternating voltage from a low potential to a high potential or vice versa.

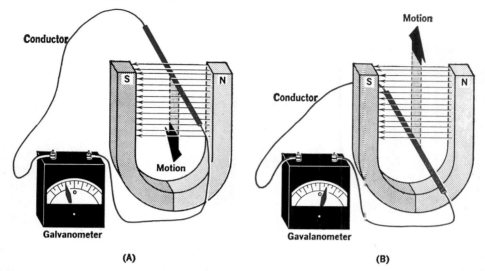

Fig. 22-1. A current is induced in a conducting loop cutting through the flux of a magnetic field.

1 INDUCED CURRENTS

2. Faraday's induction experiments.
Let us repeat some of Faraday's experiments in order that we may better understand the significance of his contribution. Suppose we connect a sensitive galvanometer in a conducting loop as shown in Fig. 22-1. A segment of the conductor is poised in the field of a strong magnet. In Fig. 22-1(*A*), as the conductor is moved down between the poles of the magnet, we observe a momentary deflection of the galvanometer needle, indicating a current. The fact that the needle shows no deflec-

tion when the conductor is stationary in the magnetic field leads us to conclude *that the induced current is related to the motion of the conductor in the field.*

Raising the conductor between the poles of the magnet, as in Fig. 22-1(*B*), we again observe a momentary deflection on the galvanometer, but this time in the opposite direction. We may conclude that *the direction of the induced current in the conductor is related to the direction of motion of the conductor in the field.* The emf induced in the conductor this time must be of

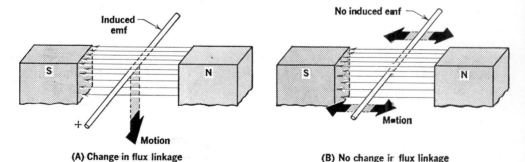

(A) Change in flux linkage   **(B) No change in flux linkage**

Fig. 22-2. An emf is induced in a conductor when there is a change of flux linked by the conductor.

opposite polarity to that in our first experiment.

Faraday found that he could induce an emf in a conductor either by moving the conductor through a stationary field or by moving the magnetic field near a stationary conductor. He observed that the direction of the induced current in the conducting loop is reversed with a change in the direction of motion or the direction of the magnetic field.

Supporting the conducting loop of Fig. 22-1 in a fixed position and lifting the magnet, we observe a deflection similar to that of Fig. 22-1(*A*). When we lower the magnet, the galvanometer needle is momentarily deflected as in Fig. 22-1(*B*). The relative motion between the conductor and the magnetic flux is the same whether we raise the conductor through the stationary field or lower the field near the stationary conductor.

So far we have considered the relative motion of the conductor to be essentially *perpendicular* to the magnetic flux; if the conductor is moved in the magnetic field *parallel* with the flux lines, no emf is induced and no deflection is observed on the galvanometer. *When a conductor cuts across lines of flux, the magnetic flux linking the conductor changes;* but a conductor moving parallel with the flux experiences no change in flux linkage. Hence, we may conclude that *relative motion between a conductor and a magnetic field, which produces a change of magnetic flux linked by the conductor, results in an induced emf in the conductor.*

Suppose the conductor is looped so that several turns are poised in the magnetic field, as in Fig. 22-4. When we move the coil down between the poles of the magnet as before, we observe a deflection of greater magnitude on the galvanometer. By increasing the rate of motion of the coil across the magnetic flux, or by substituting a stronger magnetic field, greater deflections are produced. In each of these cases the effect is to increase the number of

Fig. 22-3. Michael Faraday was a distinguished physicist and chemist. He liquefied certain gases, formulated the laws of electrolysis, and discovered the principle of electromagnetic induction. (Bettmann Archive)

flux lines cut by turns of the conductor in a given length of time. We may conclude that *the magnitude of the induced emf, and of the induced current in a closed loop, is related to the rate at which the flux linked by the conductor changes.*

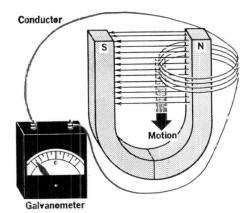

Fig. 22-4. A greater change in flux linkage occurs when several turns of a conductor cut through the magnetic flux.

3. Factors affecting induced emf. The magnitude of an induced emf is proportional to the following factors: the rate of relative motion between the conductor and the magnetic flux, the flux density, and the number of turns of the conductor linking the magnetic flux.

The rate of change in magnetic flux Φ (Phi) linked by the conductor in an interval of time t is increased either by increasing the rate of motion of the conductor or by increasing the magnetic flux density. The magnitude of induced emf then is dependent on

1. *The time rate of change of magnetic flux linkage,* and

2. *The number of turns of the conductor linking the magnetic flux.*

$$E = -N\frac{\Delta\Phi}{\Delta t}$$

where N is the number of turns of the conductor and $\Delta\Phi/\Delta t$ is the change in flux linkage in a given interval of time. If $\Delta\Phi/\Delta t$ is expressed in *webers per second,* the induced emf is given in *volts.* The negative sign merely indicates the relative polarity of the induced emf. See the Sample Problem below.

4. The cause of an induced emf. A length of conductor moving in a magnetic field has an emf induced across it proportional to the rate of change of flux linkage,

but an induced current exists as a consequence of this emf *only* if the conductor is a part of a closed circuit. In order to understand the cause of an induced emf we shall make use of several facts you have already learned.

A length of copper wire poised in a magnetic field, as shown in Fig. 22-5, of course contains many free electrons, and moving charges constitute an electric current. In Chapter 21, Section 17, we stated that a force acts on the movable coil of a galvanometer situated in a magnetic field when a current is in the coil, a force, in effect, acting on the moving charges themselves.

Suppose we push the copper wire of Fig. 22-5 downward through the magnetic field of flux density B with a velocity v. The free electrons of the copper conductor may be considered as moving perpendicular to the flux with the velocity v as a consequence of the motion of the wire, and a force F acts on them in a direction perpendicular to both B and v. These electrons move in response to the force toward end a and away from end b, end b of the wire being left with a positive charge and end a acquiring a negative charge. Thus a difference of potential is established across the conductor with a the negative end and b the positive end.

Sample Problem

A conductor has 150 turns linking magnetic flux. The coil is moved perpendicular to the flux for 0.010 sec and experiences a change in flux linkage of 3.0×10^{-5} weber. What is the induced emf?

Solution

$$E = -N\frac{\Delta\Phi}{\Delta t}$$

$$E = -150 \times \frac{3.0 \times 10^{-5} \text{ weber}}{1.0 \times 10^{-2} \text{ sec}}$$

$$E = -0.45 \text{ volt, the induced emf}$$

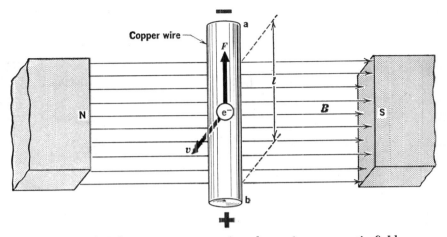

Fig. 22-5. A force acts on a moving charge in a magnetic field.

An electric field opposing the movement of electrons through the wire is consequently established between the ends of the conductor. Since the ends of the wire are not connected in a circuit, the force of the electric field soon balances the force due to the motion of the conductor, and the flow of electrons ceases. The equilibrium potential difference across the open conductor constitutes the induced emf, and depends on the length l of wire linking the magnetic flux, the flux density B of the field, and the velocity v imparted to the wire.

$$E = Blv$$

When B is in webers/m², l in meters, and v in meters/sec, the emf is given in volts.

In Fig. 22-5 a force equaling but opposite to F will act on the positively charged protons in the copper nuclei, but since these are in the bound parts of the copper atoms, they will not move. If either the motion of the wire or the magnetic field is reversed, the direction of F will be reversed and an emf will be induced so that end a is positive and end b is negative. See the Sample Problem below.

5. The direction of induced current. If the wire of Fig. 22-5 is part of a conducting circuit, there will be an induced current in the circuit when the wire is moved. We may think of the length of wire linked

Sample Problem

A conductor 7.5 cm long moves perpendicularly to the flux in a magnetic field, having flux density of 0.040 weber/m². The velocity of the wire is 1.5 m/sec. Find the induced emf.

Solution

7.5 cm = 0.075 m
$E = Blv$
$E = (0.040 \text{ weber/m}^2)(0.075 \text{ m})(1.5 \text{ m/sec})$
$E = 0.0045$ v or 4.5 mv, the induced emf

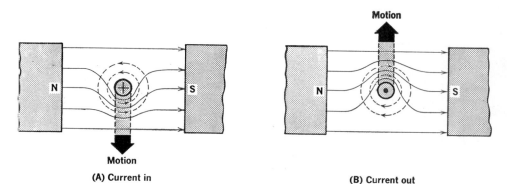

Fig. 22-6. An induced current always produces a magnetic force which opposes the force causing the motion.

with the magnetic flux as the *internal circuit* and the rest of the conducting path as the *external circuit.*

When the movement of the straight conductor is downward, as shown in Fig. 22-5, electrons will move from the negative end *a* through the *external circuit* to the positive end *b* and through the *internal circuit* from end *b* to end *a*. Work done by the current in the external circuit expends energy acquired by the electrons as potential energy in the internal circuit, and thus we must do work on the free electrons of the wire to move it in the magnetic field. *This movement must be opposed by a force if the free electrons are to acquire potential energy.* We will discuss the source of this opposing force in the study of Lenz's law.

6. Lenz's law. By Ampère's rule (see Chapter 21, Section 12) we know the direction of the magnetic field encircling a current. Let us apply this rule to the induced current we have been considering in Section 5.

In Fig. 22-6 we have a cross-sectional view of a wire poised in a magnetic field. The wire is a part of a closed circuit, which of course cannot be shown in this cross-sectional diagram. We are, in effect, looking at end *b* of the wire shown in Fig. 22-5. As this conductor is moved downward through the magnetic field, Fig. 22-6(*A*), the induced electron current is

directed into the page, symbolized by the arrow tail shown in the wire cross section. By Ampère's rule the magnetic field of this induced current is found to be in the counterclockwise direction.

It is apparent in Fig. 22-6(*A*) that the permanent magnetic field and the induced field are opposed in the region above the wire, reducing the total flux. Below the wire, however, the two fields are in the same direction and the total flux is increased. The magnetic field is stronger in the region into which the conductor is moving; thus the direction of the induced current is such as to weaken the field behind it and strengthen the field ahead of it. *This results in an unbalanced force which acts on the induced current in opposition to the motion of the conductor.* Figure 22-6(*B*) shows that a similar force opposes the reverse motion of the conductor.

This very significant relationship between an induced current and the action inducing it was first recognized in 1834 by the German physicist H. F. E. Lenz (1804–1864). *Lenz's law,* true of all induced currents, may be stated very simply: *An induced current is in such direction that its magnetic effect opposes the change by which the current is induced.*

Lenz's law provides us with another example of the conservation principle so prominent in our study of physics. Work must be done to induce a current in a conducting circuit; the energy thus expended comes from outside the system and potential energy is stored within the system. The induced current can produce heat or do mechanical or chemical work in the external circuit; this is accomplished by electrons of high potential energy falling through a difference of potential in the electric circuit.

2 GENERATORS

7. The simple generator. An emf is induced in a conductor whenever it experiences a change in flux linkage, and when the conductor is made a part of a closed circuit, we may detect an induced current in the circuit. Since, according to Lenz's law, work must be done to induce a current in a conducting circuit, we have a practical source of electric energy.

Moving a conductor up and down in a magnetic field is not a convenient method for producing an induced current; a more practical way is to shape the conductor into a loop which can be rotated in the magnetic field. The ends of the loop can be connected to the external circuit by means of *slip rings*. See Fig. 22-7.

Such an arrangement is a simple *generator*. The loop across which an emf is induced is called the *armature*. The ends of the loop are connected to slip rings which rotate as the armature is turned.

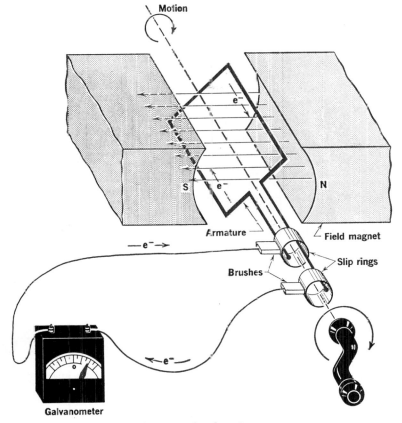

Fig. 22-7. A simple electric generator.

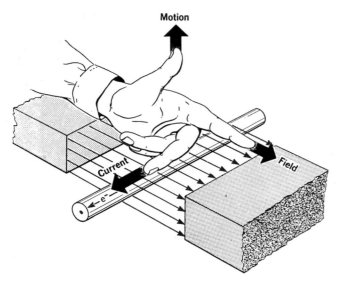

Fig. 22-8. The left-hand generator rule.

A graphite *brush* rides on each slip ring connecting the armature to the external circuit. *An **electric generator** converts mechanical energy into electric energy.* The essential components of a generator are *(1) a field magnet, (2) an armature, and (3) slip rings and brushes.*

The induced emf across the armature, and the induced current in the closed circuit, are consequences of relative motion between the conducting loop and the magnetic flux resulting in a change in the flux linkage. Thus either the armature or the magnetic field may be rotated, and in some commercial generators the field magnet is rotated and the armature is the stationary element.

8. The generator rule. According to Lenz's law, the direction of an induced current must oppose the motion producing it. We may easily determine the direction of induced current in the armature loop of a generator by the use of a *left-hand rule* known as the *generator rule*, which takes into account Lenz's law and the fact that an electric current consists of a flow of electrons. See Fig. 22-8.

> **The generator rule:** Extend the thumb, forefinger, and middle finger of the left hand at right angles to each other. Let the forefinger point in the direction of the magnetic flux and the thumb in the direction the conductor is moving; then the middle finger points in the direction of the induced electron current.

9. The simple a-c generator. The two sides of the conducting loop in Fig. 22-7 move through the magnetic flux in oppo-

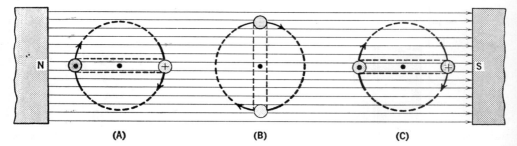

Fig. 22-9. An emf is induced only when there is a change in the flux linking a conductor.

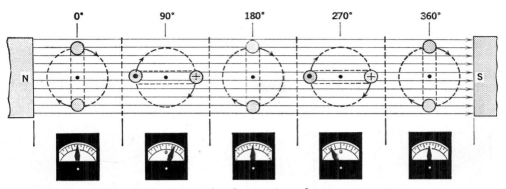

Fig. 22-10. One cycle of operation of an a-c generator.

site directions when the armature is rotated; by the generator rule as applied to each side of the loop, the direction of the induced current is shown to be toward one slip ring and away from the other. Thus a single-direction current loop is established in the closed circuit. However, as the direction of each conductor changes with respect to the magnetic flux, the direction of the induced current is reversed. As the armature rotates through a complete cycle there are two such reversals in direction of the induced current.

In Fig. 22-9 one side of a conducting loop rotating in a magnetic field is shown cross sectionally in red, the other side in black. In (A) the red conductor is moving down and cutting through the magnetic flux; by the generator rule, the induced current is directed into the page. The black conductor's motion induces a current directed out of the page.

In (B), since an emf is induced in a conductor as a result of a change in the flux linking the conductor, and since both conductors are moving parallel to the flux and there is no change in linkage, there is no emf induced across the loop and no current in the closed circuit.

In (C) the black conductor is moving down, cutting through the flux; the induced current is directed into the page. Since the red conductor is moving up through the flux, the induced current is

directed out of the page. The direction of the current in the circuit is therefore the reverse of that in (A). One quarter cycle later the emf again drops to zero and there is no current in the circuit. The emf induced across the conducting loop reaches a maximum value when the conductors are moving perpendicular to the magnetic flux. See Section 2.

It is not difficult to see from Fig. 22-9 that the magnitude of the induced emf across the conducting loop must vary between zero and a maximum during a half cycle of rotation. The emf must then vary in magnitude between zero and this

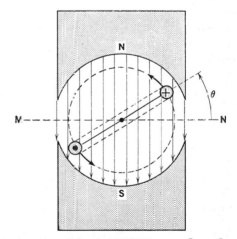

Fig. 22-11. The instantaneous value of an induced voltage varies with the sine of the displacement angle of the loop in the magnetic field.

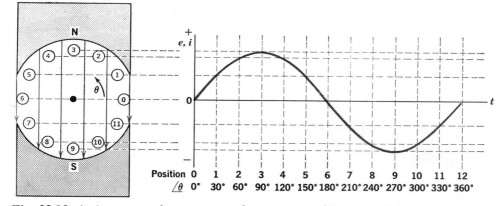

Fig. 22-12. A sine curve of current or voltage generated by a single-loop armature rotating at a constant rate in a uniform magnetic field.

maximum during the second half cycle but with the opposite polarity across the loop. The emf thus *alternates* in polarity across the loop.

Similarly, the current in a circuit connected to the rotating armature by way of the slip rings alternates in direction, electrons flowing in one direction during one half cycle and in the opposite direction during the other half cycle. *A current which has one direction during part of a generating cycle and has the opposite direction during the remainder of the cycle is called an* **alternating current** *(ac)*. A generator which produces an alternating current must, of course, produce an alternating emf.

Commercial electric power is usually supplied by the generation of alternating currents and voltages. Such power is referred to as *a-c power*. The expressions *a-c* and *d-c* are commonly used in discussions of electric circuits as prefixes to distinguish between alternating-current and direct-current properties. Examples are *a-c voltage*, *d-c voltage*, *a-c current*, and *d-c current*. Although some terms may not be strictly correct in their literal interpretations, all are meaningful.

10. Instantaneous values of current and voltage. The open-circuit voltage across a battery has a constant magnitude characteristic of the composition of its electrodes. The voltage across an armature rotating in a magnetic field, however, has no constant magnitude. It varies from zero through a maximum in one direction and back to zero during one half cycle, then rises to a maximum in the opposite direction and back to zero during the other half cycle of the armature rotation. During successive instants of time, different magnitudes of induced voltage exist across the rotating armature. *The magnitude of a varying voltage at any instant of time*

Fig. 22-13. A small laboratory magnetic generator. (Cenco)

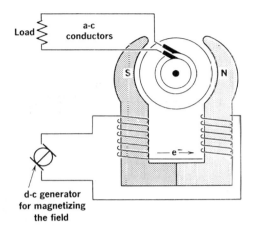

Fig. 22-14. The field of an alternating current generator is produced by an electromagnet.

is called the **instantaneous voltage.** The symbol for instantaneous voltage is e.

The maximum voltage, E_{max}, is obtained when the conductor is moving perpendicular to the magnetic flux, since during this time the flux linking the conductor is maximum. *If the armature is rotating at a constant rate in a magnetic field of uniform flux density, the magnitude of the induced voltage will vary sinusoidally (as a sine wave) with respect to time.*

In Fig. 22-11 a single loop is rotating in a uniform magnetic field. When the plane of the loop is perpendicular to the flux (MN of Fig. 22-11) the conductors are moving parallel to the flux lines; the displacement angle of the loop is said to be zero. We shall refer to this angle between the plane of the loop and the perpendicular to the magnetic flux as θ (theta). When $\theta = 0°$ and $180°$, $e = 0$ v. When $\theta = 90°$, $e = E_{max}$ and when $\theta = 270°$, $e = -E_{max}$. These relationships are apparent from Fig. 22-10. In general the instantaneous voltage e varies with the sine of the displacement angle of the loop.

$$e = E_{max} \sin \theta$$

The current in the external circuit of the simple generator consisting of pure resistance will vary in a similar way, the

maximum current, I_{max}, occurring when the induced voltage is maximum. From Ohm's law

$$I_{max} = \frac{E_{max}}{R}$$

The *instantaneous current* (i) is accordingly

$$i = \frac{e}{R}$$

but

$$e = E_{max} \sin \theta$$

so

$$i = \frac{E_{max}}{R} \sin \theta$$

and

$$i = I_{max} \sin \theta$$

11. Commercial a-c generators. The simple generator discussed consists of a coil rotated in the magnetic field of a permanent magnet. Any small generator employing a permanent magnet is commonly referred to as a *magneto*. Small magnetos are often used in the ignition systems of small gasoline engines for lawnmowers, motorbikes, and boats.

The generator output is increased in the practical generator by increasing the number of turns on the armature or increasing the field strength. The field magnets of large generators are strong electromagnets; in a-c generators they are ordinarily supplied with direct current from an auxiliary d-c generator called an *exciter*.

The performance of large a-c generators (often called alternators) is generally more satisfactory if the armature is stationary and the field rotates inside the armature. Such stationary armatures are called *stators* and the rotating field magnets are called *rotors*. Circuit current is taken from the stator at the high generated voltage without the use of slip rings and brushes, while the exciter voltage, which is much lower than the armature voltage, is applied to the rotor through slip rings and brushes.

In the simple two-pole generator one cycle of operation produces one cycle or two alternations of induced emf as shown in Fig. 22-12. If the armature (or the field) rotates at the rate of 60 cycles per second,

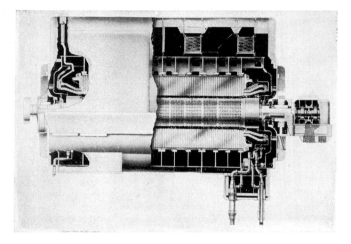

Fig. 22-15. Cutaway view of a conductor-cooled turbine generator with a gas-cooled rotor and liquid-cooled stator. (General Electric Co.)

the *frequency*, *f*, of the generated voltage sine wave is 60 cycles per second, the period T being $\frac{1}{60}$ second.

The **frequency** *of an alternating current or voltage is the number of cycles the sine wave makes per second.* If a generator has a 4-pole field magnet, 2 cycles of emf will be generated during 1 revolution of the armature or field. Such a generator turning at 30 rps would generate a 60 cps voltage. In general

f (in cps) = No. pairs of poles × speed (in rps)

Practically all commercial power is generated by *three-phase* alternators having three armature coils spaced symmetrically and producing emfs spaced 120 degrees apart. The coils are usually connected so that these generated currents may be carried by a system of only three conductors.

It is evident from Fig. 22-16(*B*) that three-phase power is smoother than the single-phase power of Fig. 22-12. Electric power is transmitted in three-phase form but is commonly supplied to the consumer in single-phase form.

12. The d-c generator. The output of an a-c generator is not suitable for some applications. For example, we could not charge an automobile battery with an a-c generator. An a-c generator can be made to supply a *unidirectional* current to the external circuit by terminating the armature turns in a *commutator* instead of slip rings. *A* **commutator** *is a split ring, each segment of which is connected to an end of a corresponding armature loop.*

The current and voltage generated in the armature are alternating, as we would expect. However, by means of the com-

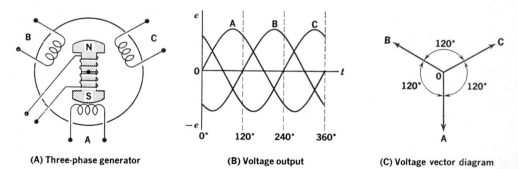

(A) Three-phase generator   (B) Voltage output   (C) Voltage vector diagram

Fig. 22-16. The principle of the three-phase alternator.

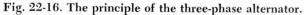

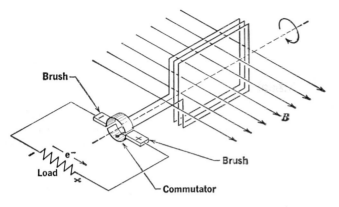

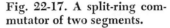

Fig. 22-17. A split-ring commutator of two segments.

mutator, the connections to the external circuit are reversed at the same instant that the direction of the induced emf reverses in the loop. See Fig. 22-17. The alternating current in the armature appears as a *pulsating* direct current in the external circuit, and a pulsating d-c voltage appears across the load. A graph, plotted against time, of the instantaneous values of the pulsating current from a d-c generator with a two-segment commutator is shown in Fig. 22-18, and a graph of the voltage across a resistance load would have a similar form. Compare this pulsating d-c output to that of the a-c generator shown in Fig. 22-12.

The electrons in the external circuit of a d-c generator flow through the circuit in one direction, but this current is quite different from the direct current supplied by a battery, in that it is not steady. The split-ring commutator *rectifies* the alternating current induced in the armature, which is, at any displacement angle θ, $I_{max} \sin \theta$. *The average of all the instantaneous currents induced during one cycle of rotation is the equivalent of a steady battery current which would do the same work in the external circuit.* For the rectified sine wave shown in Fig. 22-18, the average value is 0.636 of the maximum value induced.

$$I_{av} = 0.636\ I_{max}$$

Similarly, *the average of all the instantaneous emfs induced during one cycle of rotation is the equivalent of a steady battery emf which would provide the same potential difference across the external circuit.* For the rectified voltage of Fig. 22-18

$$E_{av} = 0.636\ E_{max}$$

To secure a more constant voltage from a d-c generator, and thus an average value which approaches the magnitude of E_{max}, many coils are wound on the armature. Each coil is terminated in a different pair of commutator segments, the two brushes being placed so that they are in contact with successive pairs of commutator segments while the induced emf is in the E_{max} region in their respective coils.

The voltage output of one cycle of a three-coil armature is shown graphically in Fig. 22-19. Observe that the output wave form has a *ripple* frequency three times the rotating frequency of the armature. The average value of the voltage is very nearly that of the E_{max} of each coil.

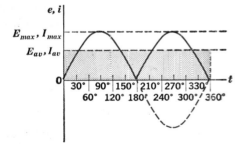

Fig. 22-18. The variation of current or voltage with time in the external circuit of a simple generator with a two-segment commutator.

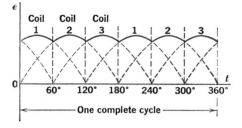

Fig. 22-19. The output of a d-c generator having three armature coils and a six-segment commutator is fairly constant.

Each pair of commutator segments remains in contact with the brushes during only 60 degrees in each half cycle of armature rotation.

13. d-c generators are self-excited. Most d-c generators employ part of the induced power to energize their field magnets, and are said to be *self-excited*.

The field magnets may be connected in *series* with the armature loops, so that all of the generator current passes through the coil windings. In the *series-wound* generator an increase in the load increases the magnetic field and consequently the induced emf. See Fig. 22-20.

The field magnets may also be connected in parallel with the armature so that only a portion of the generated current is used to excite the field. In this *shunt-wound* generator, Fig. 22-21, an increase in load results in a decrease in the field and hence a decrease in the induced emf.

By using a combination of both series and shunt windings to excite the field magnets, the potential difference across the external circuit of a d-c generator may be maintained fairly constant, an increase in load causing an increase in current in the series windings and a decrease in current in the parallel windings. With the proper number of turns of each type of winding, a constant flux density may be maintained under varying load conditions. A compound-wound generator is shown in Fig. 22-22.

14. Ohm's-law and d-c generator circuits. We may think of the armature turns

as the source of emf in the d-c generator circuit. If the field magnet were separately excited, this emf would appear across the armature terminals on open-circuit operation since there would be no induced armature current.

However, in a self-excited generator the armature circuit is completed through the field windings. The resistance of the armature turns (r_a) is in this current loop, producing a situation analogous to that of a battery with internal resistance furnishing current to an external circuit. A potential drop $I_a r_a$, of opposite polarity to the induced emf, must appear across the armature, the armature potential difference, V, being

$$V = E - I_a r_a$$

The resistance circuit of the series-wound generator is shown in Fig. 22-23. The resistance of the field windings, R_f, is in series with the internal resistance of the armature and the load resistance, so that the armature current is in all three resistances.

In Fig. 22-21, the resistance of the shunt windings is in parallel with the load. The resistance circuit of a shunt-wound generator is diagrammed in Fig. 22-24, the resistance of the shunt windings being shown as R_f. The total current of the circuit, I_a, must be in r_a producing an $I_a r_a$ drop across the armature. The potential difference V, which has been shown to be $E - I_a r_a$, then appears across the network consisting of R_f and R_L in parallel. The following Ohm's law relationships hold:

$$I_f = \frac{V}{R_f}$$

$$I_L = \frac{V}{R_L}$$

and $$I_a = I_f + I_L$$

The total electric power in the generator circuit, P_T, derived from the mechanical energy source which turns the armature, is the product of the armature current, I_a, and the induced emf, E.

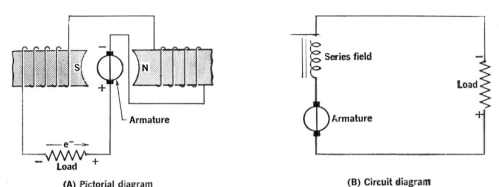

(A) Pictorial diagram

(B) Circuit diagram

Fig. 22-20. A series-wound d-c generator.

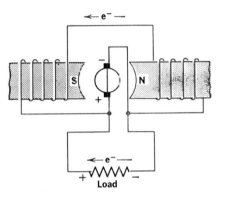

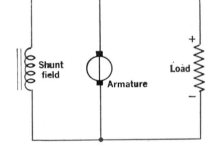

(A) Pictorial diagram

(B) Circuit diagram

Fig. 22-21. A shunt-wound d-c generator.

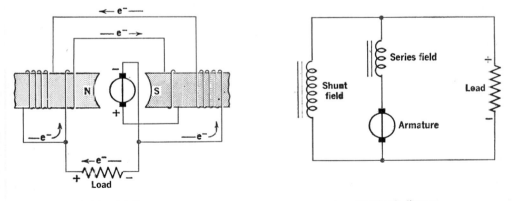

(A) Pictorial diagram

(B) Circuit diagram

Fig. 22-22. A compound-wound d-c generator.

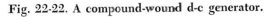

$$P_T = EI_a$$

Some of this power is dissipated as heat in the armature resistance, and some is consumed in the field windings; the remaining power is delivered to the load.

$$P_T = P_a + P_f + P_L$$
or $$EI_a = I_a^2 r_a + I_f^2 R_f + I_L^2 R_L$$

The application of these relationships to the d-c shunt-wound generator is illustrated in the Sample Problem given below.

In Fig. 22-25 we have the resistance circuit of a compound-wound generator. Observe the similarity between this circuit and the resistance network shown in

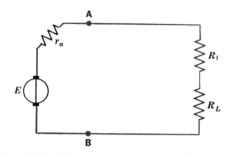

Fig. 22-23. The resistance circuit of a series-wound d-c generator.

Fig. 19-25 in Chapter 19. How would you proceed to analyze this resistance circuit of the compound-wound d-c generator?

Sample Problem

The armature resistance of a shunt-wound generator is 0.50 ohm and the resistance of the shunt winding is 60. ohms. What is the emf of the generator if 0.96 kilowatt is delivered to a 15-ohm load?

Solution

The resistance diagram of Fig. 22-24 applies to this problem. We are given the power delivered to the load, $P_L = 0.96\,kw = 960\,w$; and we are given the resistance of the load, $R_L = 15\ \Omega$. Since

$$P_L = I^2 R_L = \frac{V^2}{R_L}$$

$V = \sqrt{P_L R_L}$
$V = \sqrt{960\ w \times 15\ \Omega}$
$V = 120\ v$, the potential difference across AB

$$I_a = I_f + I_L = \frac{V}{R_f} + \frac{V}{R_L}$$

$$I_a = \frac{120\ v}{60.\ \Omega} + \frac{120\ v}{15\ \Omega}$$

$I_a = 2.0\ amp + 8.0\ amp.$
$I_a = 10.\ amp.$, the total current in the circuit

We know that the potential difference across the terminals of the armature is
$V = E - I_a r_a$
$E = V + I_a r_a$
$E = 120\ v + (10.\ amp \times 0.50\ \Omega)$
$E = 125\ v$, the emf of the generator

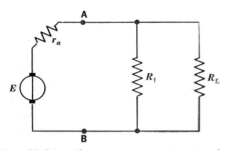

Fig. 22-24. The resistance circuit of a shunt-wound d-c generator.

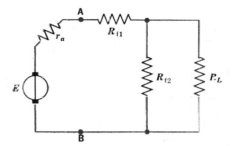

Fig. 22-25. The resistance circuit of a compound-wound d-c generator.

3 MOTORS

15. The motor effect. We have learned that a current is induced in a conducting loop when it is moved in a magnetic field so that the conductor cuts across the magnetic flux. This is the generator principle. By Lenz's law, we have seen that work must be done against a magnetic force as an induced current is generated in the conducting loop. This opposition force is due to a distortion of the magnetic field caused by the current itself. The effect was shown earlier in Fig. 22-6.

Instead of employing a mechanical effort to move a conductor poised in the magnetic field, suppose we *supply* a current to the conductor from an external source. The magnetic field must be distorted as we have seen before in Section 6. The resulting magnetic force tends to expel the conductor from the magnetic field, an action known as the *motor effect*, and illustrated in Fig. 22-26.

If a current is supplied to an armature loop poised in a uniform magnetic field as in Fig. 22-26, the field around each conductor is distorted. A repulsion force acts on each conductor, proportional to the flux density and the current in the armature loop, the forces being equal in magnitude but opposite in direction. These two forces constitute a *couple*, producing a torque which causes the armature loop to rotate about its axis. The magnitude of this torque is equal to the product of the force and the *perpendicular* distance between the two forces. See Chapter 3, Section 18.

You can readily see, from Fig. 22-27, that the perpendicular distance between

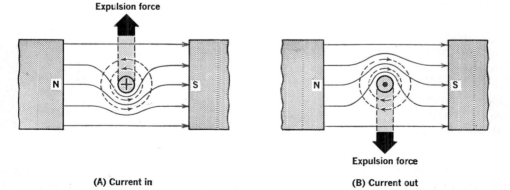

(A) Current in

(B) Current out

Fig. 22-26. The motor effects: a current in a magnetic field distorts the field and experiences an expulsion force resulting from this distortion.

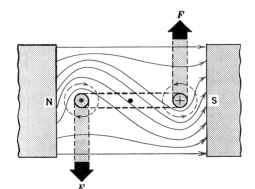

Fig. 22-27. The forces acting on a current loop in a magnetic field.

the torque-producing forces is maximum when the conductors are moving perpendicular to the magnetic flux. This distance is equal to the width of the armature loop. When the loop is in any other position with respect to the flux lines, however, the perpendicular distance between the forces is less than the width of the loop, and consequently the resulting torque must be less. See Fig. 22-28.

We shall refer to the angle between the plane of the loop and the magnetic flux as angle α (alpha). When the angle is zero, the plane of the loop is parallel to the flux lines and the torque is maximum.

$$\text{Maximum torque} = Fw$$

where F is the magnetic force acting on either conductor and w is the width of the conducting loop.

As the armature turns, the angle α approaches 90° and the torque diminishes, since the perpendicular distance between the couple approaches zero. In general, the perpendicular distance between the forces acting on the two conductors is equal to $w \cos \alpha$, as shown in Fig. 22-28. Hence

$$\text{Torque} = Fw \cos \alpha$$

When the plane of the loop is perpendicular to the magnetic flux, angle α is 90°, and since the cosine of 90° = 0, the torque is zero. As the inertia of the con-

ductor carries it beyond this point, a torque develops which reverses the motion of the conductor and returns it to the zero-torque position. In order to prevent this action, the direction of the current in the armature loop must be reversed at the proper instant. The conducting loop terminates in a commutator to reverse the current when the neutral position is reached.

16. The motor rule. An electric motor performs the reverse function of a generator. *Electric energy is converted to mechanical energy* using the same electromagnetic principles employed in the generator. We may easily determine the direction of motion of the conductor on a motor armature by use of a *right-hand rule* known as the *motor rule*, which is illustrated in Fig. 22-29.

> **The motor rule:** Extend the thumb, forefinger, and middle finger of the right hand at right angles to each other. Let the forefinger point in the direction of the magnetic flux and the middle finger in the direction of the electron current; then the thumb points in the direction of the motion of the conductor.

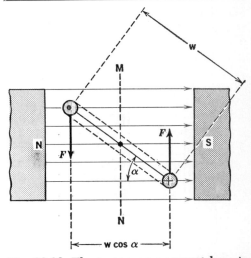

Fig. 22-28. The torque on a current loop in a magnetic field is proportional to the perpendicular distance between the forces acting on the conductors.

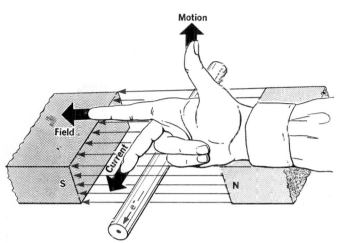

Fig. 22-29. The right-hand motor rule.

17. Back emf in a motor. The simple d-c motor does not differ essentially from the generator; it has a field magnet, an armature, and a commutator ring. In fact, *the operating motor must also act as a generator.* As the conducting loop of the armature rotates in a magnetic field, an emf must be induced across the armature turn, the magnitude of the emf depending on the speed of rotation.

Let us connect an incandescent lamp and an ammeter in series with the armature of a small battery-driven motor. If the motor armature is held so that it cannot rotate as the circuit is closed, the lamp glows and the circuit current is indicated on the meter. Releasing the armature allows the motor to gain speed, and the lamp dims; the ammeter indicates a smaller current.

According to Lenz's law, the induced emf must be opposed to the motion inducing it. The emf induced by the generator action of a motor consequently opposes the voltage applied to the armature. *Such an induced emf is called the* **back emf** *of the motor.* The difference between the applied voltage and the back emf determines the current in the motor circuit.

A motor running at full speed under a no-load condition generates a back emf nearly equal to the applied voltage; thus a small current is required in the circuit.

The more slowly the armature turns, the smaller is the back emf and consequently the larger is the voltage difference and the circuit current. A motor starting under full-load conditions has a large initial current which decreases due to the generation of a back emf, as the motor gains speed.

The induced emf in a generator is equal to the terminal voltage *plus* the voltage drop across the armature resistance.

$$E = V + I_a r_a$$

However, in the motor the induced emf is equal to the terminal voltage *minus* the voltage drop across the armature resistance.

$$E = V - I_a r_a$$

Hence, the back emf in a motor must always be less than the voltage impressed across the armature terminals.

18. Three types of d-c motors. A simple motor with a single armature coil would be impractical for many purposes because it has neutral positions and a pulsating torque. In practical motors a large number of coils are used in the armature; in fact there is little difference in the construction of motor and generator armatures. Multiple-pole field coils may be used to aid in the production of a uniform torque. The amount of torque produced in any given motor is proportional

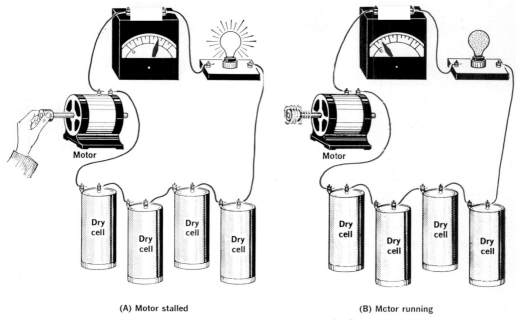

(A) Motor stalled   (B) Motor running

Fig. 22-30. Demonstrating the back emf of a motor.

to the armature current and to the flux density.

Practical d-c motors are of three general types, depending on the method of exciting the field magnets. These are the *series*, *shunt*, and *compound* motors. The excitation methods are similar to those of the d-c generators discussed in Section 12.

19. Starting circuits for d-c motors. The armatures of small motors have low inertia and gain speed very rapidly when current is applied, but a temporary overload condition always exists before sufficient back emf is generated to reduce the armature current to the working magnitude.

The armature resistance of a 10-hp, 110-v motor is approximately 0.05 ohm, and its operating current is about 90 amperes. The armature is large and has considerable inertia. If it were connected directly across 110-v supply lines, the initial current would tend to be about 2200 amperes (110 v ÷ 0.05 Ω = 2200 amp). The disadvantages of such a venture are obvious.

To prevent the destruction of a large d-c motor when it is started, resistance must be connected in series with the armature. A heavy rheostat is generally used, the resistance being gradually cut out of the armature circuit as the speed builds up and back emf is developed. A typical starting circuit for a series motor is shown in Fig. 22-31.

20. Types of a-c motors. Nearly all commercial distributors of electric power now supply alternating-current power. Thus a-c motors are in far more common use than d-c motors, except in certain applications. Unfortunately much of the theory and technology of a-c motors is quite complex. We will outline very briefly some important generalizations on three common types of a-c motors: *the universal motor, the induction motor,* and *the synchronous motor.*

1. The universal motor. Any small d-c series motor may be operated from an a-c supply. When this is done, the current in the field windings and armature reverses direction simultaneously, maintaining

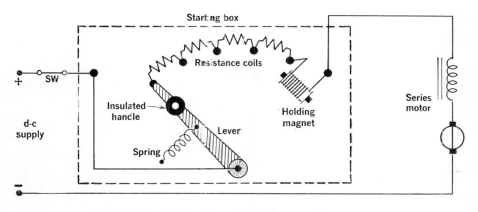

Fig. 22-31. A starting circuit for a series motor.

torque in the same direction throughout the operating cycle. However, heat losses in the field windings are extensive unless certain design changes are incorporated in the motor. With laminated pole pieces and special field windings small series motors operate satisfactorily on either a-c or d-c power. They are known as *universal* motors.

2. *The induction motor.* Induction motors are the most widely used a-c motors, for they are rugged, simple to build, and well adapted to constant speed requirements. Induction motors consist of two essential parts, a stator of field coils and a rotor. The rotor is usually built of copper bars laid in slotted, laminated iron cores. The ends of the copper bars are shorted by a copper ring to form a cylindrical cage; this common type is known as a *squirrel-cage* rotor.

By using three pairs of poles and a three-phase current the magnetic field of the stator is caused to rotate electrically, and currents are induced in the rotor, which, by Lenz's law, will then rotate so as to follow the rotating field. Since induction requires relative motion between the conductor and the field, the rotor must *slip* or lag behind the field in order for a torque to be developed. An increase in the load causes a greater slip, a greater induced

current, and consequently a greater torque.

An induction motor depends on a rotating magnetic field for its operation. Thus a single-phase induction motor is not self-starting without auxiliary means because the magnetic field of its stator merely reverses periodically and does not rotate electrically. Single-phase induction motors may be started by hand, by an auxiliary motor, or by a *split-phase winding*, a *capacitor*, a *shading coil*, or a *repulsion winding*. The name of the motor usually indicates the auxiliary means for starting it.

3. *The synchronous motor.* We may illus-

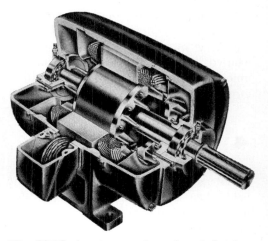

Fig. 22-32. A cutaway view of an induction motor. (General Electric Co.)

Fig. 22-33. A 4500-hp synchronous motor driving pumps at an Atomic Energy Commission installation. The field magnets of the rotor are supplied with d-c power and the armature coils of the stator are supplied with a-c power. (General Electric Co.)

trate the principle of synchronism by placing a thoroughly magnetized compass needle in a rotating magnetic field. The magnetized needle aligns itself with the magnetic field and rotates in synchronization with the rotating field.

The synchronous motor is a constant speed motor, running in synchronism with the a-c generator which supplies the stator current. However, it is not self-starting; the rotor must be brought up to synchronous speed by auxiliary means.

Electric clocks are operated by small single-phase synchronous motors. In older types the small magnetized rotor was whirled by hand to start the clock, and unfortunately the clock would run either forward or backward depending on which way the rotor was whirled. The modern electric-clock motor starts automatically as a form of induction motor, and once synchronism is attained, runs as a synchronous motor. Electric power companies exercise very accurate control of the 60 cps frequency of commercial power now that electric clocks are in wide use.

In large industrial synchronous motors, the permanent-magnet rotor is replaced by an electromagnetic rotor supplied with d-c power, and the stator is commonly supplied with three-phase alternating current. Improved designs of synchronous motors are used in ship propulsion, in driving d-c generators, in compressors, and in grinding and milling operations.

4 INDUCTANCE

21. Mutual inductance. An emf is induced across a conductor in a magnetic field when there is a change in the flux linking the conductor. In our study of the generator we observed that an induced emf appears across the armature loop whether the conductors move across a stationary field, or the magnetic flux moves across stationary conductors. *In either action there is relative motion between conductors and magnetic flux.*

This relative motion between conductors and magnetic flux can be produced in another way. By connecting a battery

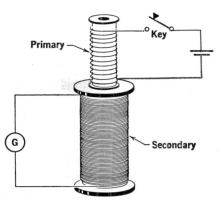

Fig. 22-34. Varying the current in the primary induces an emf in the secondary coil.

to a solenoid through a contact key, we produce an electromagnet with a magnetic field similar to that of a bar magnet. When the key is open, there is no magnetic field. As the key is closed, the magnetic field builds up from zero to some steady value determined by the number of ampere-turns, the magnetic flux reaching out and permeating the field about the coil. *An expanding magnetic field is a field in motion.* When the key in the solenoid circuit is opened, the magnetic flux collapses to zero. *A collapsing magnetic field is also a field in motion;* however, the motion is in the opposite direction to that of the expanding field.

Let us insert the solenoid into a second coil whose terminals are connected to a galvanometer as in Fig. 22-34. The coil connected to a current source is called the *primary;* the coil connected to the load is called the *secondary.* At the instant the contact key is closed we observe a deflection on the galvanometer; there is no deflection, however, while the key remains closed. When the key is opened, we again observe a galvanometer deflection, but in the opposite direction. An emf is induced across the secondary turns whenever the flux linking the secondary is increasing or decreasing.

The relative motion between conductors and flux is in one direction when the field

expands, and in the opposite direction when the field collapses. Thus the emf induced across the secondary as the key is closed is of opposite polarity to that induced as the key is opened. The more rapid this relative motion, the greater the magnitude of the induced emf; the greater the number of turns on the secondary, the greater the magnitude of the induced emf. Of course a soft iron core placed in the primary increases the flux density and the induced emf decidedly.

Two circuits so arranged that a change in magnitude of current in one causes an emf to be induced in the other show *mutual inductance. The **mutual inductance,** M, of two circuits is the ratio of the induced emf in one circuit to the rate of change of current in the other circuit.*

The unit of mutual inductance in the MKS system is called the *henry* (h) after the American physicist Joseph Henry. The mutual inductance of two circuits is *one henry* if *one volt of emf* is induced in the secondary when the current in the primary changes at a rate of *one ampere per second.*

$$M = \frac{-E_S}{\Delta I_P / \Delta t}$$

Here M is the mutual inductance of the two circuits in henrys, E_S is the average induced emf across the secondary in volts, and $\Delta I_P / \Delta t$ is the time rate of change of current in the primary in amperes per second. The minus sign indicates that the induced voltage opposes the change in current according to Lenz's law. From this equation we may express the emf induced in the secondary as follows:

$$E_S = -M \frac{I_P}{t}$$

See the Sample Problem on page 510.

22. Self-inductance. Suppose we form a coil by winding a large number of turns of insulated copper wire on an iron core and connect it in a circuit to a 6-volt battery, a neon lamp, and a switch as

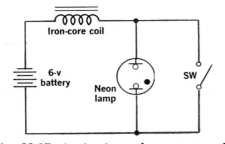

Fig. 22-35. A circuit to demonstrate self-inductance.

shown in Fig. 22-35. Since the neon lamp requires about 85-vdc to fire, it does not conduct in a 6-volt circuit but acts initially as an open switch.

When the switch is closed, a conducting path is completed through the coil; the fact that the lamp does not fire is evidence that it is not in the conducting circuit. If now the switch is quickly opened, the neon lamp is observed to conduct for an instant, producing a flash of light. This means, of course, that the lamp is subjected to a potential difference considerably higher than that of the battery. What is the source of this higher voltage?

Any change in the magnitude of current in a conductor causes a change in the magnetic flux about the conductor. If the conductor is wound into a coil, a changing magnetic flux about one turn cuts across adjacent turns and induces a voltage across them. According to Lenz's law, the polarity of this induced voltage is such that it opposes the motion of the flux inducing it. The sum of the induced voltages of all the turns constitutes a *counter* emf across the coil.

If a rise of current with its expanding magnetic flux is responsible for the counter emf, this rise of current will be opposed. Therefore the counter emf is opposite in

Sample Problem

Two coils have a mutual inductance of 1.25 henrys. Find the average emf induced in the secondary if the current in the primary builds up to 10.0 amperes in 0.0250 second after the switch is closed.

Solution

The primary current must build up from zero to 10.0 amp during the 0.0250 sec, so

$$\frac{I_P}{t} = \frac{10.0 \text{ amp}}{0.0250 \text{ sec}}$$

The mutual inductance is given as 1.25 h.

$$E_S = -M \frac{I_P}{t}$$

$$E_S = -1.25 \text{ h} \times \frac{10.0 \text{ amp}}{0.0250 \text{ sec}}$$

$$E_S = -500. \text{ v, the emf induced in the secondary}$$

Observe that since $h = \dfrac{v}{amp/sec}$

the units $h \times \dfrac{amp}{sec} = \dfrac{v \times sec \times amp}{amp \times sec} = v$

Fig. 22-36. Joseph Henry, who was an American physicist, discovered self-induction and developed the electromagnet. (Culver Service)

polarity to the applied voltage. When the switch in Fig. 22-35 was closed the rise of current from zero to the steady-state magnitude was opposed by the counter emf induced across the coil. Once the current reached a steady value, the magnetic field ceased to expand and the opposition voltage fell to zero.

If a fall in current with its collapsing flux is responsible for the induced voltage across the coil, the fall of current is opposed. In this case the induced emf has the same polarity as the applied voltage and tends to sustain the current in the circuit. A very rapid collapse of the magnetic field may cause a very high voltage to be induced. *It is the change in current, not the current itself, which is opposed by the induced emf.* The greater the rate of change of current in a circuit containing a coil, the greater is the magnitude of the induced emf across the coil which opposes this change of current.

The property of a coil which causes a counter emf to be induced across it by the change in current in it is known as *self-inductance*, or simply *inductance*. The

self-inductance, L, *of a coil is the ratio of the induced emf across the coil to the rate of change of current in the coil.*

The unit of self-inductance in the MKS system is the *henry*, the same unit we use for mutual inductance. Self-inductance is *one henry* if *one volt of emf* is induced across the coil when the current in the circuit changes at the rate of *one ampere per second*.

$$L = \frac{-E}{\Delta I / \Delta t}$$

Here L is the inductance in henrys, E is the average emf induced in volts, and $\Delta I / \Delta t$ is the rate of change of current in amperes per second. The minus sign merely shows that the induced voltage is in opposition to the change of current. From this expression the induced emf is given by the following:

$$E = -L \frac{\Delta I}{\Delta t}$$

Once a coil has been wound, its inductance is a constant property which depends on *the number of turns, the diameter of the coil, the length of coil,* and *the nature of the core.* Because of its property of inductance, a coil is commonly called an *inductor.*

Inductance in electricity is analogous to inertia in mechanics, which, you will recall, is the property of matter that opposes a *change* of velocity. If a mass is at rest, its inertia opposes a change which imparts a velocity; if the mass has a velocity, its inertia opposes a change which brings it to rest. The flywheel of mechanics illustrates the property of inertia. We know that energy is stored in a flywheel as its angular velocity is increased, and is removed as its angular velocity is decreased.

In an electric circuit inductance has no effect as long as the current is steady. An inductance does, however, oppose any change in the circuit current. An increase in current is opposed by the inductance and energy is stored in its magnetic field

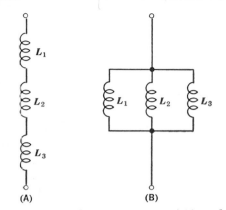

Fig. 22-37. Inductors in series (A) and in parallel (B).

since work is done by the source against the counter emf induced. A decrease in current is opposed by the inductance and energy is removed from its field, tending to sustain the current. *We may think of inductance as imparting a flywheel effect in a circuit having a varying current.* This concept is very important in alternating-current circuit considerations.

23. Inductors in series and parallel. The total inductance of a circuit consisting of inductors in series or parallel can be calculated in the same manner as total resistance. When inductors are connected in series the total inductance (L_T) is equal to the sum of the individual inductances, providing there is no mutual inductance between them.

$$L_T = L_1 + L_2 + L_3 + \text{etc.}$$

However, when two inductors are in series and so arranged that the magnetic flux of each links the turns of the other, the total inductance is

$$L_T = L_1 + L_2 \pm 2M$$

The $\pm$ sign is necessary in the general expression because the counter emf induced in one coil by the flux of the other may either aid or oppose the counter emf of self-induction. The two coils may be connected either in series "aiding" or series "opposing" depending on the manner in which their turns are wound.

Inductors connected in parallel so that each is unaffected by the magnetic field of another provide a total inductance according to the following general expression:

$$\frac{1}{L_T} = \frac{1}{L_1} + \frac{1}{L_2} + \frac{1}{L_3} + \text{etc.}$$

24. The induction coil. The ignition systems of automobile engines and numerous devices in the physics laboratory require high voltages. These voltages are ordinarily produced from low voltage d-c batteries by means of an *induction coil.*

The induction coil, shown in Fig. 22-38, is constructed around a core composed of a bundle of soft-iron wires. A primary coil of perhaps 200 turns of coarse copper wire is wound on the core and is connected to a battery through an automatic switch consisting of an *armature* and a *threaded contact, T.* This switch *makes* and *breaks* the primary circuit at a rapid rate as in an electric bell or other simple electromagnetic device. A capacitor is connected across the switching device to prevent excessive sparking between the armature and the contact T each time the primary circuit is opened.

A secondary coil composed of thousands of turns of fine copper wire surrounds the primary and is terminated in a pair of discharge points S and S'. A high counter emf induced across the secondary wind-

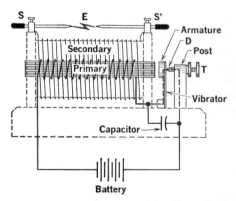

Fig. 22-38. An induction coil will produce a high voltage from a low-voltage d-c source.

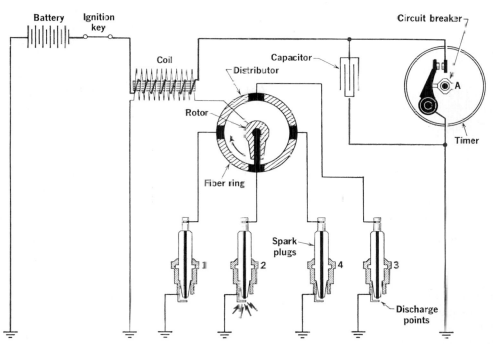

Fig. 22-39. A diagram of the ignition system of an automobile engine.

ings may ionize the air between the discharge points and produce a spark discharge.

In the operation of the induction coil the primary circuit is automatically closed and opened at D by the vibrating action of the armature. Since primary current builds up gradually due to self-inductance, the primary flux cuts across the secondary turns relatively slowly when the switch closes.

If the capacitor were not connected across the switch, a spark discharge would occur between the armature and contact as the switch opened. This discharge would sustain the primary current and the field would collapse slowly. However, because of the capacitor, the primary current collapses very quickly and a very high counter emf, of the order of 10^5 volts, is induced across the secondary. An alternating emf exists in the secondary; however, a spark discharge occurs across the points only at the *break* of the primary circuit. Hence, the electron flow across

the gap E always occurs in the same direction.

A spark discharge is used in the gasoline engine to ignite the explosive mixture. It must occur in the proper cylinder at the proper time. The ignition system of an automobile engine is shown in Fig. 22-39. Can you explain the functions of the *timer, distributor, coil,* and *spark plug?*

25. The transformer. Because an alternating current is continuously varying, we could operate an induction coil with a low voltage a-c source. The switching mechanism would no longer be needed and the essential parts remaining would be (1) *the iron core,* (2) *the primary coil* to which a-c power is supplied, and (3) *the secondary coil* from which a-c power may be delivered. Such an arrangement operating from an alternating-current source is called a *transformer. In principle, the transformer consists of two coils electrically insulated from each other and wound on the same ferromagnetic core.* Electric energy is transferred from the primary to the secondary by means of the

Load

High-voltage
secondary

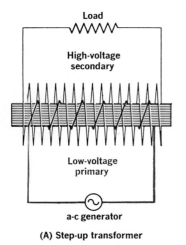

Low-voltage
primary

a-c generator

(A) Step-up transformer

Load

Low-voltage
secondary

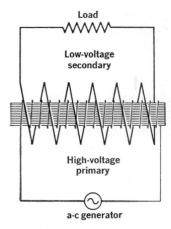

High-voltage
primary

a-c generator

(B) Step-down transformer

Fig. 22-40. The transformer in its simplest forms.

magnetic flux in the core. A transformer is shown in its simplest form in Fig. 22-40.

Let us turn back to Fig. 22-12 and examine the current sine wave as produced by the a-c generator. The current is changing at its maximum rate as it passes through zero. The emf induced across the secondary winding of a transformer is maximum, therefore, as the primary current passes through zero. The polarity of the secondary emf reverses each time the primary current passes through a positive or negative maximum, since at these instants the current is changing at its minimum rate.

In the power transformer, a *closed* core is used to provide a continuous path for the magnetic flux, insuring that practically all of the primary flux links turns of the secondary. Since the same flux links both primary and secondary turns, the same emf per turn is induced in each, the ratio of secondary to primary emf being equal to the ratio of secondary to primary turns. Neglecting losses, we may assume the terminal voltages to be equal to the corresponding emf's. Thus

$$\frac{V_S}{V_P} = \frac{N_S}{N_P}$$

where V_S and V_P are the secondary and primary terminal voltages, and N_S and N_P are the number of turns in the secondary and primary windings respectively.

If there are 20 turns in the secondary winding for every turn of the primary, the transformer is said to have a *turns ratio* of 20.

$$\text{Turns ratio} = \frac{N_S}{N_P} = \frac{20}{1} = 20$$

If the primary voltage is 110 volts, the secondary terminal voltage is 2200 volts, the transformer being called a *step-up transformer*. If the connections are reversed and the coil with the larger number of turns is made the primary, the transformer becomes a *step-down transformer*. The same primary voltage now produces a voltage across the secondary of 5.5 volts.

It can be shown that when power is delivered to a load in the secondary circuit, the product of the secondary current and secondary turns is essentially equal to the product of the primary current and primary turns.

$$I_S N_S = I_P N_P$$

or

$$\frac{I_S}{I_P} = \frac{N_P}{N_S}$$

Thus when the voltage is stepped up, the current is stepped down; there is no power

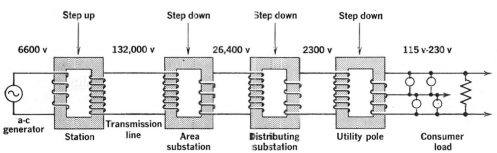

Fig. 22-41. A simplified diagram of a typical a-c power distribution system.

gain as a result of transformer action. Ideally, primary and secondary power are equal, but actually there are power losses as in any machine. Transformer efficiencies above 90 percent are common.

26. Transformer losses. Power losses in the transformer are of three types: (1) *copper losses*, (2) *hysteresis losses*, and (3) *eddy-current losses*. All represent wasted energy and show up in the form of heat.

1. Copper losses. These are the result of the resistance of the copper wires making up the primary and secondary turns. Copper losses are I^2R heat losses and cannot be avoided.

2. Hysteresis losses. Energy is consumed in reversing the magnetic polarity of the transformer core. The loss is minimized by the proper choice of core material, one having a narrow hysteresis loop. See Chapter 21, Section 9.

3. Eddy-current losses. When a mass of conducting metal is moved in a magnetic field or is subjected to a changing magnetic flux, induced currents circulate in the mass. These are closed-loops of induced current circulating in planes perpendicular to the magnetic flux and are known as *eddy currents*.

Eddy currents in motor and generator armatures and transformer cores produce heat due to the I^2R losses in the resistance of the iron. They are induced currents which do no useful work, and they waste energy by opposing the change which induces them according to Lenz's law

Eddy-current losses are reduced by *laminating* the armature frames and cores. Thin sheets of metal with insulated surfaces are used to build up the armatures and cores, the laminations being set in planes parallel to the magnetic flux, so that eddy-current loops are confined to the width of the individual laminations.

27. Electric power transmission. Electric power may be transmitted economically over long lines when the voltage is high and the current is low, because the power loss in the resistance of the conductors is proportional to I^2. It is impractical, however, to generate electricity at a high transmission voltage because of the insulation problems created in the generating equipment.

Alternating-current electricity is generated and distributed very efficiently and economically by the use of power transformers, a three-phase system being commonly employed in generation and either three-phase or single-phase systems in distribution. Single-phase power is commonly supplied to the residential consumer.

A typical a-c power system might include the following major steps.

1. Generation. Power is generated at 6600 volts.

2. Transmission. Voltage is increased by transformer action to 132,000 volts. Power is then transferred to the long transmission lines which supply a distant substation near the consumer area.

3. Area substation. Voltage is stepped down to 26,400 volts. The power is then delivered to various distributing substations by underground cables or overhead lines.

4. Distributing substation. Voltage is stepped down to 2300 volts for distribution to consumers.

5. Utility pole. Voltage is stepped down to 230–115 volts. Power is supplied from the transformer on the utility pole to the consumer by a 3-wire, single-phase system.

ummary

An emf is induced in a conductor when relative motion between the conductor and a magnetic field produces a change in the flux linkage. The greater the rate of relative motion, the greater is the magnitude of the induced emf. If the conductor is a part of a closed circuit, a current is induced in the circuit. The direction of an induced current is always in accord with Lenz's law.

An electric generator converts mechanical energy into electric energy. The direction of induced current in the armature turns is determined by use of a left-hand generator rule. The generator induces a sinusoidal emf across the armature turns. The current in the armature circuit alternates. The frequency of the generated current or emf is given in cycles per second.

An a-c generator is converted to yield a pulsating d-c output by the use of a split-ring commutator. The d-c generator is self-excited, three methods being used.

The electric motor converts electric energy into mechanical energy. The motor effect is the result of a current moving in a magnetic field; it is the reverse of the generator effect. The direction of motion of the armature turns is determined by using the right-hand motor rule. Every motor produces a back emf which subtracts from the applied voltage. Practical d-c motors are of three types: series, shunt, and compound wound. Three common types of a-c motors are the universal motor, the induction motor, and the synchronous motor. Of these the induction motor is the most widely used.

If a change in current in one circuit induces an emf in a second circuit, the two have a property of mutual inductance. An emf is induced across a coil by a change of current in the coil; this is known as self-inductance. The unit of inductance is the henry. The induced emf across a given inductance is dependent on the time rate of change of current in the inductance. Inductance is a kind of electric inertia.

The induction coil can produce high voltages from small d-c voltages. It has a primary and a secondary wound on a single soft iron core, and an automatic switch to make and break the primary circuit rapidly.

Transformers are a-c versions of the induction coil. The primary and secondary windings have a common core. For a given primary voltage, the turns ratio determines the secondary voltage. The transformer may either step up or step down the a-c voltage of the primary circuit. Efficient and economical distribution of a-c power is possible through the use of the transformer principle.

TERMS TO DEFINE

alternating current
alternator
armature
back emf
brushes
commutator
eddy currents
electric generator
electric motor
electromagnetic induction
field magnets
generator rule
induced current

induced emf
inductance
induction coil
induction motor
inductor
instantaneous current
instantaneous voltage
Lenz's law
magneto
motor rule
mutual inductance
primary
pulsating dc

ripple frequency
rotor
secondary
self-inductance
single-phase system
slip rings
stator
step-down transformer
step-up transformer
synchronous motor
three-phase system
transformer
universal motor

QUESTIONS

A **1.** What is the essential condition under which an emf is induced in a conductor?
2. What determines the magnitude of the emf induced in a length of conductor moving in a magnetic field?
3. In what two ways may the rate of change of magnetic flux linking a conductor be increased?
4. Distinguish between an induced emf and an induced current.
5. What is the source of the energy expended as work is done in a load by an induced current resulting from the movement of the conductor in a magnetic field?
6. State Lenz's law.
7. What are the essential components of an electric generator?
8. State the rule which helps us determine the direction of the induced current in the armature loops of a generator.
9. Distinguish between a direct current and an alternating current.
10. Under what circumstances does a simple generator produce a sine-wave variation of induced voltage?
11. What does the term θ (theta) represent in the expression $e = E_{max} \sin \theta$?
12. (a) What is a magneto? (b) For what is it used?
13. What is the function of an *exciter* in the generation of a-c power?
14. (a) What is meant by the frequency of an alternating current? (b) Under what circumstances will the frequency of a generated current be the same as the rps of the armature?
15. How can a generator be made to supply a direct current to its external circuit?

16. In what way is the output of a d-c generator different from the d-c output of a battery?
17. (a) What methods are used to energize the field magnets of d-c generators? (b) Draw a circuit diagram of each method.
18. What are the three power-consuming parts of a d-c generator circuit?
19. What is meant by the term α (alpha) in the expression Torque $= Fw \cos \alpha$?
20. State the rule which helps us determine the direction of motion of the armature loops of a motor.
21. (a) What is meant by back emf? (b) How is it induced in an electric motor?
22. What two quantities influence the amount of torque produced in a given motor?
23. What are the three common types of a-c motors?
24. Define (a) mutual inductance; (b) self-inductance.
25. What types of losses occur in the transformer?

B **26.** If a bar magnet is held in a vertical position with the N pole down and is dropped through a closed-loop coil whose plane is horizontal, what is the direction of the induced current as the N pole approaches the loop?
27. What is the direction of the force acting on the loop of Question 26 as the N pole approaches?
28. What is the advantage of having a 4- or 6-pole field magnet in a generator producing a 60-cps output?
29. What physical quantities are measured in (a) webers; (b) webers per meter²; (c) webers

per second; (*d*) henrys; and (*e*) joules per coulomb?

30. Explain how Lenz's law illustrates conservation of energy.

31. How does an increase in the load on a series-wound d-c generator affect the induced emf? Explain.

32. How does an increase in the load on a shunt-wound d-c generator affect the induced emf? Explain.

33. How is torque produced on the armature loops of a motor?

34. Why is it true that an operating motor is also a generator?

35. The torque in a series motor increases as the load increases. Explain.

36. Explain why a single-phase induction motor is not self-starting.

37. Why are synchronous motors used in electric clocks?

38. Why is an inductor in an electric circuit said to impart a flywheel effect?

39. Why is a transformer considered to be an a-c circuit device?

40. Two conducting loops, identical except that one is silver and the other aluminum, are rotated in a magnetic field. In which case is the larger torque required to turn the loop?

PROBLEMS

A **1.** A coil of 325 turns moving perpendicular to the flux in a uniform magnetic field experiences a change in flux linkage of 1.15×10^{-5} weber in 0.00100 sec. What is the induced emf?

2. How many turns are required to produce an induced emf of 0.25 volt for a coil which experiences a change in flux linkage at the rate of 5.0×10^{-3} weber per sec?

3. A straight conductor 10. cm long is moved through a magnetic field perpendicular to the flux at a velocity of 75 cm/sec. If the flux density is 0.025 weber/m², what emf is induced in the conductor?

4. A simple d-c generator having an armature with a single coil produces an instantaneous current of 25 ma in the load when the coil is moving perpendicularly across the flux. What steady battery current would do the same work in this load?

5. A step-up transformer is used on a 120-volt line to provide a potential difference of 2400 volts. If the primary has 75 turns, how many turns must the secondary have (neglecting losses)?

B **6.** A coil of 75 turns and an area of 4.0 cm² is removed from the gap between the poles of a magnet having a uniform flux density of 15,000 lines per cm² in 0.025 sec. What voltage is induced across the coil?

7. A rod 15 cm long is perpendicular to a magnetic field of 4.5×10^3 flux lines/cm² and is moved at right angles to the flux at a rate of 30. cm/sec. Find the emf induced in the rod.

8. A series-wound d-c generator turning at its rated speed develops an emf of 28 volts. The current in the external circuit is 16 amperes and the armature resistance is 0.25 ohm.

What is the potential drop across the external circuit?

9. A d-c generator delivers 150 amperes at 220 volts when operating at normal speed connected to a resistance load. The total losses are 3200 watts. Determine (*a*) the efficiency of the generator and (*b*) the horsepower required to drive the generator.

10. A shunt generator has an armature resistance of 0.15 ohm and a shunt winding of 75.0-ohms resistance. It delivers 18.0 kw at 240. v to a load. (*a*) Draw the circuit diagram. (*b*) What is the armature current? (*c*) What is the generator emf? (*d*) What is the total power developed by the armature?

● **11.** A magnetic force of 3.5 nt acts on one conductor of a conducting loop in a magnetic field. A second force of equal magnitude but opposite direction acts on the opposite conductor of the loop. The conducting loop is 15 cm wide. (*a*) Find the torque acting on the conducting loop when the plane of the loop is parallel to the magnetic flux. (*b*) What is the torque after the loop has rotated through 30°?

● **12.** The maximum torque which acts on the armature loop of a motor is 10 m-nt. At what positions of the loop with respect to the magnetic flux will the torque be 5 m-nt?

13. A shunt-wound motor connected across a 117-v line generates a back emf of 112 v when the armature current is 10. amp. What is the armature resistance?

14. An initial rise of current in a coil occurs at the rate of 7.5 amp/sec at the instant a potential difference of 16.5 v is applied across it. (*a*) What is the self-inductance of the coil? (*b*) At the same instant a potential difference of 50. v is induced across an adjacent coil. Find the mutual inductance of the two coils.

● **15.** A coil with an inductance of 1.2 h and a resistance of 65 ohms is connected across an 80.-vdc line. What is the rate of current rise at the instant it is connected to the line? (Suggestion: Consider the inductance and resistance of the coil to be in series.)

● **16.** A coil with an inductance of 0.42 h and a resistance of 25 ohms is connected across a 110-vdc line. (*a*) What is the rate of current rise at the instant the circuit is closed? (*b*) At what rate is the current rising at the instant it reaches 85% of its steady-state value?

RESEARCH ON YOUR OWN

1. Explain how you can use Lenz's law and the rules for the field about a wire or a helix to determine the direction of an induced current.
2. Make a pendulum by attaching a disk of aluminum or copper to the end of a 30-cm stick. Note the period of the pendulum. Then place the pendulum so that the disk swings between the poles of a strong U magnet. Account for any differences in the period of the pendulum. Replace the disk with a loop made up of several turns of copper wire. Repeat the experiment with the ends of the wire loop connected to each other and again with the ends disconnected. Explain your results.
3. Consult references on selsyn motors (sometimes called synchros or autosyns). Obtain one of these motors and demonstrate that you can get a three-phase power supply from it. (Note that the current will not be very great.)
4. Use your knowledge of magnetism and the field about a wire to determine the direction of the motion of a conductor in a field. A wire carrying a current tends to move away from the side where the fields are in the same direction. Is this in agreement with the motor rule? Explain.
5. Study the diagram of the electric system of an automobile to find applications of the use of electricity. What advantages would be realized if the electric system were converted to ac? What disadvantages would be encountered? Investigate the present status of development of a-c electric systems for automobiles and report your findings.
6. Carefully take apart an old electric clock that does not run and try to repair it. Explain why it runs synchronously.

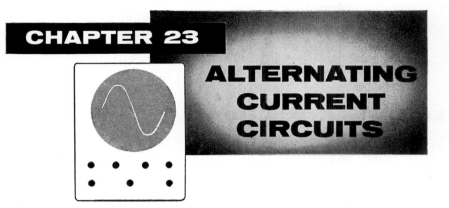

CHAPTER 23

ALTERNATING CURRENT CIRCUITS

1 a-c MEASUREMENTS

1. Sine waves of current and voltage. A single conducting loop rotating at a constant speed in a uniform magnetic field generates an alternating emf. The magnitude of this emf varies with the sine of the angle which the plane of the loop makes with the perpendicular to the magnetic flux. The instantaneous value of the emf, as given in Chapter 22, Section 10, is

$$e = E_{max} \sin \theta$$

The current in a pure resistance load comprising the external circuit of the generator is similarly expressed as

$$i = I_{max} \sin \theta$$

This current is a consequence of the alternating voltage impressed across the load, and its maxima and minima occur at the same instants as the voltage maxima and minima. The alternating current and voltage are said to be *in phase*, this in-phase

VOCABULARY

Capacitive reactance. Reactance in an a-c circuit, due to capacitance, which produces a lagging voltage.

Effective value of current. The magnitude of an alternating current which, in a given resistance, produces heat at the same average rate as that magnitude of steady direct current.

Electrodynamometer. A device, similar to a galvanometer movement, in which a moving coil rotates in a magnetic field created by a pair of fixed coils carrying a magnetizing current.

Impedance. The joint opposition of reactance and resistance to the current in an a-c circuit.

Inductive reactance. Reactance in an a-c circuit, due to inductance, which produces a lagging current.

Power factor. The cosine of the phase angle between current and voltage in an a-c circuit.

Reactance. The nonresistive opposition to current in an a-c circuit.

Root-mean-square (rms) current. The same as the effective value of alternating current; the square root of the mean of the instantaneous values squared.

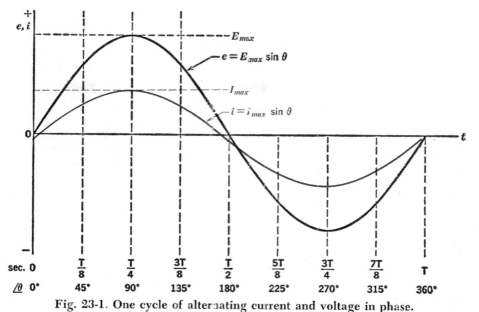

Fig. 23-1. One cycle of alternating current and voltage in phase.

relationship being characteristic of a resistance load to which an alternating voltage is applied. Sine curves of alternating current and voltage which are in phase are shown in Fig. 23-1.

2. Power in an a-c circuit. Electric power in a d-c circuit is the product of E and I. In an a-c circuit the instantaneous power, p, is the product of e and i. These relationships are shown in Fig. 23-2.

The voltage and current in Fig. 23-2(B) are shown in phase as in a resistance load. The instantaneous power curve then varies between some positive maximum and zero and has an average value labeled P. The instantaneous power gives a cosine curve with a frequency twice that of e and i, whose ordinates are always positive since e and i are in phase. During the first half cycle e and i are both positive, and of course their products are positive. During the second half cycle both e and i are negative, but again their products are positive.

3. Effective value of an alternating current. If we were to place a d-c ammeter of the galvanometer type in an a-c circuit, the pointer would attempt to swing in

both the positive and negative directions. At any but the very lowest frequencies, the inertia of the meter movement would cause the pointer to remain at zero, in

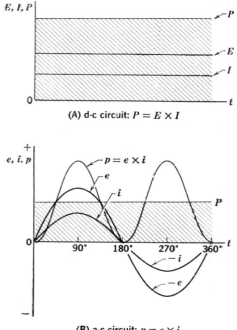

(A) d-c circuit: $P = E \times I$

(B) a-c circuit: $p = e \times i$

Fig. 23-2. A comparison of d-c and a-c power.

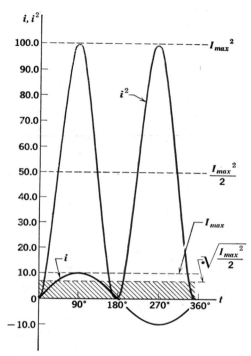

Fig. 23-3. Current and current squared curves showing the effective value of an alternating current.

for the effective value of an alternating current is I, the same as that for steady direct current. Whenever the magnitudes of alternating currents are given in amperes, effective values are understood, unless other values are clearly stated.

From Joule's law, Chapter 20, Section 3, we know that the heating effect of an electric current is proportional to I^2. The average rate of heat production by an alternating current is proportional to the mean (average) of the instantaneous values of current squared. From Fig. 23-3 it is evident that the mean value of i^2 is $\frac{1}{2}I_{max}^2$. This is true because the square of the instantaneous values of the alternating current of frequency f gives a cosine curve of frequency $2f$ which varies between I_{max}^2 and zero. Thus

$$I^2 = \frac{I_{max}^2}{2}$$

and
$$I = \sqrt{\frac{I_{max}^2}{2}} = \frac{I_{max}}{\sqrt{2}}$$
$$I = 0.707\, I_{max}$$

Then $I_{max} = 1.414\, I$

A sine curve of alternating current having a maximum value of 10.0 amperes is plotted in Fig. 23-3. *The effective value is the square root of the mean of the instantaneous values squared* and is frequently called the *root-mean-square* (rms) value. In the example shown, the rms or effective value of current is

$$I = \sqrt{\frac{I_{max}^2}{2}} = \sqrt{\frac{100.\, amp^2}{2}} = \sqrt{50.0\, amp^2}$$
$$I = 7.07\ amp$$

The rms or effective value of an a-c voltage is expressed similarly.

$E = 0.707\, E_{max}$ and $V = 0.707\, V_{max}$

Then

$E_{max} = 1.414\, E$ and $V_{max} = 1.414\, V$

Thus a house-lighting circuit rated at 120-vac varies between $+170$ volts and -170 volts during each cycle. An appliance which draws 10.00 amperes when

effect, averaging out the sine-wave variations. The same would be true in an a-c voltage measurement. *The average value of a sine curve of alternating current or voltage is zero.* This is true regardless of the magnitude of the maximum values attained.

The most useful value of an alternating current is based on its *heating effect* in an electric circuit and is commonly referred to as the *effective value. The **effective value** of an alternating current is the number of amperes which, in a given resistance, produce heat at the same average rate as that number of amperes of steady direct current.*

Let us assume that a resistance element is immersed in a calorimeter and that a steady d-c current of 1 ampere in the circuit raises the temperature of the water 25° in 10 minutes. An alternating current supplied to the same resistance which would raise the temperature the same amount in the same time is said to have an effective value of 1 ampere. The symbol

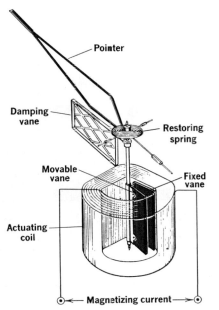

Fig. 23-4. The basic mechanism of a moving iron-vane meter. (Weston Instruments)

connected across this circuit has a current that varies between +14.14 amperes and −14.14 amperes.

If the load is a pure resistance, the current and voltage are in phase, and the average power consumed is 1200 watts. If, however, the current and voltage are not in phase, *the average power of the circuit is not a simple product of the effective values of voltage and current.* This is a basic difference between d-c and a-c circuits and stems from the fact that a phase difference between current and voltage may be produced by capacitance or inductance in an a-c circuit. These effects will be studied in Part 2 of this chapter.

4. a-c meters. The galvanometer, which provides the basic movement for d-c instruments, cannot be used directly in a-c circuits. At ordinary power frequencies inertia prevents the movement from following the alternations. No work is done against the restoring springs and the electric energy is converted to heat.

In some specialized applications, peak reading a-c meters may be used. The cathode-ray oscilloscope can be, in fact, a peak-to-peak reading voltmeter. In general, however, alternating-current instruments are designed to indicate *effective values* of current or voltage. The a-c instruments are of five common types: (*1*) *moving iron-vane meters*, (*2*) *hot-wire meters*, (*3*) *electrodynamometers*, (*4*) *rectifier-type meters*, and (*5*) *induction watt-hour meters*.

1. Moving iron-vane meters. If two similar iron bars are subjected to a common magnetic field, a repelling force is developed between them. This principle is used in iron-vane meters. One iron bar is fixed and the other is pivoted so that it will rotate when a magnetizing current is in the actuating coil. The basic mechanism is shown in Fig. 23-4.

The repulsion principle that actuates the moving vane does not distinguish polarity of the magnetic field, and may be applied in either d-c or a-c meters. Inexpensive a-c instruments are commonly of the moving vane type, the same basic mechanism being used for both voltmeters and ammeters. When a current is in the actuating coil, the moving vane exerts a force against a restoring spring, and the final

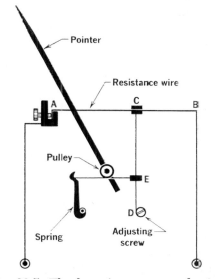

Fig. 23-5. The hot-wire meter mechanism.

pointer position is a measure of the coil current.

2. Hot-wire meters. Electric meters generally depend on some form of electrodynamic action of an electric current for their operation. The hot-wire meter is unique in that it depends on the *heating* action of a current. Consequently it may be used to measure the magnitude of a steady direct current, the average value of a pulsating direct current, or the effective value of an alternating current. A diagram of a hot-wire mechanism is shown in Fig. 23-5.

A fine wire of a platinum alloy is used as the resistance *AB*. When a current passes through the meter circuit, the I^2R loss in wire *AB* causes the temperature to rise and expansion results, reducing the tension on wire *CD*. This allows the spring to pull thread *EF*, which is looped around the pulley, to the left. The pulley rotates, moving the pointer over the meter scale.

Hot-wire meters are sluggish and the pointer moves slowly to the ultimate deflection. In some applications, however, this characteristic is advantageous. These meters are, of course, sensitive to temperature changes. When used as ammeters, they require a shunt for all except very small currents. A high resistance is connected in series with wire *AB* when the mechanism is used as a voltmeter.

3. Electrodynamometers. Better quality instruments for certain a-c measurements at power frequencies are of the electrodynamometer type. The dynamometer mechanism is probably the most versatile device in general use for electric measurements. In principle, the electrodynamometer is similar to the galvanometer movement of d-c meters, but it does not include a permanent magnet. A moving coil rotates in a magnetic field created by a pair of fixed coils carrying a magnetizing current. These coils may be considered to be two parts of a single coil separated in the middle to allow the spindle of the

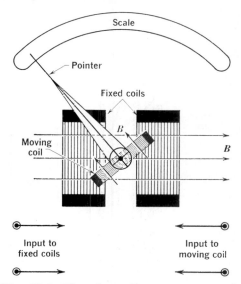

Fig. 23-6. **The electrodynamometer mechanism.**

moving coil to pass through. The basic components of a dynamometer mechanism are shown in Fig. 23-6.

A current in the fixed coils produces a magnetic flux, which at some instant is to the right as in Fig. 23-6. At the same instant the current in the moving coil produces a flux along its axis. The moving coil then tends to turn so as to align the two magnetic fields, the resulting torque producing a pointer deflection indicative of the product of the two coil currents. As an ammeter, the two coils are connected in series and the same current is in both. The instantaneous torque is then proportional to the square of this current, i^2. The average torque is proportional to the *mean squared current* and the scale may be calibrated to read the rms or effective value. Due to some inherent design problems, not easily overcome, portable dynamometer-type ammeters are not common. Iron-vane ammeters are much simpler and less expensive.

When the electrodynamometer is to be used as a voltmeter, the fixed coils are wound of fine wire and connected in series with the moving coil. A high resistance

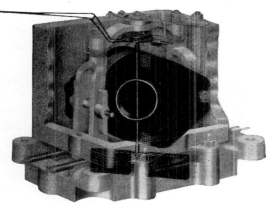

Fig. 23-7. The wattmeter.
(Weston Instruments)

is connected in series with the mechanism to act as a current limiter when the instrument is placed across a circuit. The current in the dynamometer is proportional to the voltage across it and the scale may be calibrated to read the voltage. See Fig. 23-8(*A*).

If the current in the fixed coils is the line current, and the current in the moving coil is derived from the line through a high resistance, the instrument then measures power in watts and is known as a *wattmeter*. In this arrangement the current in the moving coil is proportional to the voltage across the line. The fixed coils are wound with a few turns of coarse wire and the moving coil is wound with fine wire. The position of the pointer indicates the average power, since the torque, at every instant, is proportional to the product of the instantaneous values of current and voltage.

4. Rectifier-type meters. A d-c meter of the galvanometer type may be used for a-c measurements when a rectifier is provided to convert the alternating current to a pulsating direct current. The instrument responds to the average value of the rectified alternating current but is generally calibrated to read effective values. These meters are usually preferred for measurements in the audio-frequency range.

5. Induction watt-hour meters. The electric power company in your community sells *electric energy*, at a cost of a few cents for each kilowatt-hour. An induction type watt-hour meter is commonly used in a-c circuits to measure and record the quantity of electric energy supplied to a customer.

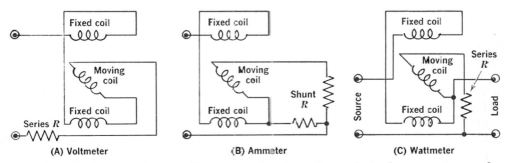

Fig. 23-8. Coil connections for different applications of the electrodynamometer mechanism.

Kilowatt-hours

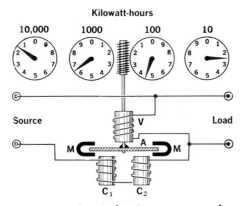

Fig. 23-9. The induction-type watt-hour meter.

The watt-hour meter is essentially a small single-phase induction motor that turns at a rate proportional to the power used. The shaft of the motor armature is geared to a system of dials to indicate, in kilowatt-hours, the energy used in the load on the circuit.

In Fig. 23-9 a simplified diagram of the induction watt-hour meter is shown. A coil V is connected in parallel with the load and acts as a voltage winding. The coils C_1 and C_2 are connected in series with the load and act as current windings. An aluminum disk A turns as an induction-motor armature to follow the sweeping flux set up by the combination of coils. Permanent magnets M induce eddy currents in the rotating disk which oppose the motion of the disk and produce the slippage required for the induction-motor operation.

2 IMPEDANCE

5. Inductance in an a-c circuit. In Chapter 22, Section 22, we stated that inductance is an inertia-like property opposing any *change* in current in a coil and causing a counter emf proportional to the rate of change of current to be induced across the coil. Figure 23-10 shows the wave forms characteristic of a circuit consisting of pure inductance to which an alternating voltage is applied. The instant the current is passing through zero in a positive direction, it is changing at its maximum rate. Thus the counter emf induced across the coil at this instant must be at its negative maximum value. When the current reaches the positive maximum, the rate of change of current is zero, and the induced emf is zero. Again, 90° later, the current is changing in a negative direction at its maximum rate and the counter emf is at its positive maximum.

The counter emf follows behind the current inducing it by 90°, and is opposite in polarity to the applied voltage as shown in Fig. 23-10. The current in the circuit must then *lag behind the applied voltage by*

90°. It is just as appropriate to consider that the voltage leads the current by 90°; the *difference in time phase* is 90°. We may think of alternating currents and voltages as vectors rotating counterclockwise in a polar coordinate system as shown in Fig. 23-11. The phase angle between the voltage and current vectors is commonly re-

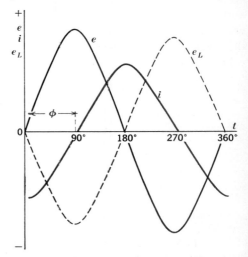

Fig. 23-10. Current and voltages in an a-c circuit containing pure inductance.

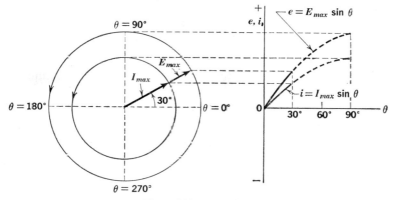

(A) *e* and *i* in pure resistance

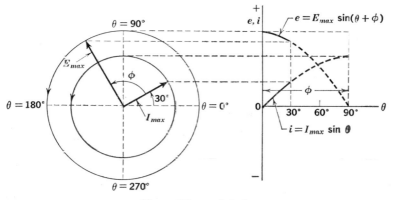

(B) *e* anc *i* in pure inductance

Fig. 23-11. Phase relation of an a-c current and voltage in pure resistance and pure inductance circuits.

ferred to as the angle ϕ (the lower case Greek letter phi). This phase relation in an a-c circuit may be expressed as follows:

$$i = I_{max} \sin \theta$$
$$e = E_{max} \sin (\theta + \phi)$$

The phase angle, ϕ, of a leading voltage is considered to be *positive*, to indicate that the voltage is aheed of the current in phase. Suppose the effective value of voltage represented in Fig. 23-11(B) is 10.0 volts. When the displacement angle θ is 30°, the instantaneous value e will be

$$e = E_{max} \sin (\theta + \phi)$$
$$e = E_{max} \sin (30° + 90°)$$
$$e = E_{max} \sin 120°$$

But

$$E_{max} = 1.414E = 1.414 \times 10.0 \text{ v}$$
$$E_{max} = 14.1 \text{ v}$$

Then

$$e = 14.1 \text{ v} \times \sin 120°$$
$$\sin 120° = \sin 60° = 0.866$$
$$e = 14.1 \text{ v} \times 0.866$$
$$e = 12.2 \text{ v}$$

Plotted as a function of time, the products of the instantaneous values of voltage and current in a pure inductance yield an instantaneous power curve as shown in Fig. 23-12. Observe that the average power is zero. While the current is changing from zero to a maximum, energy is taken from the source and stored in the

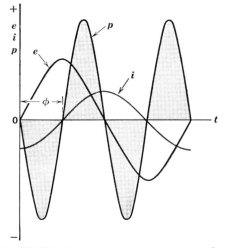

Fig. 23-12. Power curve in a pure inductance.

magnetic field of the inductor. These portions of the power curve are positive.
When the current is changing from a
maximum to zero, all of the energy stored
in the magnetic field is returned to the
source. These portions of the power curve
are negative. Therefore, the net energy
removed from the source during a cycle by
a pure inductance is zero, and the product
of the rms voltage and current can indicate only an *apparent power.*

**6. Inductance and resistance in an
a-c circuit.** An inductor cannot be entirely without resistance. That is, it is not

possible to have a pure inductance in a
circuit; the ordinary resistance of the
conductor is an inherent property of any
coil. We may treat the resistance of an
inductive circuit as a lumped value in
series with a pure inductance. This arrangement is shown in Fig. 23-13(*A*).

The same current must be present in
all parts of a series circuit, so the circuit
current is the logical reference vector to
show the phase relation between current
and voltages in the resistance and inductance. The voltage across the resistance
is in phase with the circuit current; this
in-phase relation is shown in (*B*). The
voltage across the inductance leads the
circuit current by 90°, as shown in (*C*).
The voltage across the series combination
of *R* and *L* then leads the circuit current
by some angle between 90° and zero.

With the circuit current of Fig. 23-13
as a reference, we observe that V_R and V_L
have a phase difference of 90°. Thus the
two voltages in series cannot be added
algebraically, but must be added *vectorially*
to give the circuit voltage, *V.* The *vector
sum* of V_R and V_L is shown in Fig. 23-14;
the phase angle, ϕ, has a positive value
less than 90°.

No power is consumed in the inductance. The average power consumed in
the resistance is equal to the product of

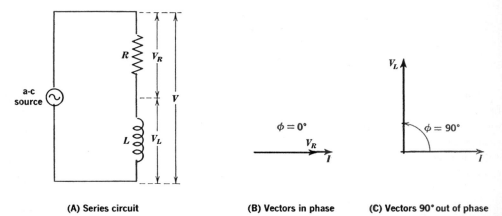

(A) Series circuit   (B) Vectors in phase   (C) Vectors 90° out of phase

Fig. 23-13. An *L–R* circuit showing the phase relations between voltage and current in
the resistance and in the inductance.

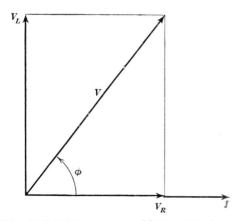

Fig. 23-14. The vector addition of voltages in a series circuit containing inductance and resistance.

the effective values of the circuit current and the voltage across the resistance.

$$P_R = V_R I$$

From the voltage diagram we can see that

$$V_R = V \cos \phi$$

Thus the actual power consumed in the external circuit is

$$P = VI \cos \phi$$

The total power consumed in the internal and external circuits is, of course,

$$P_T = \mathcal{E}I \cos \phi$$

When the phase angle ϕ is *zero* (a pure resistive load), $\cos \phi = 1$, and the product $VI \cos \phi = VI$. When the phase angle ϕ is $+90°$ (a pure inductive load), $\cos \phi = 0$, and the product $VI \cos \phi = 0$. The cosine of ϕ is known as the *power factor* (pf) of an a-c circuit.

$$\text{pf} = \cos \phi = \frac{V_R}{V}$$

Electric power companies strive to maintain a power factor near unity in their distribution lines. Why?

7. Impedance in an a-c circuit. The potential drop across the resistance in the circuit of Fig. 23-13 is represented by the vector V_R in Fig. 23-14. This potential difference is, of course, equal to the Ohm's-law product IR, R being the common re-

sistance to current in the external circuit. The inductance, too, has a potential difference across it as a consequence of its opposition to the current in the circuit. This opposition is, however, *nonresistive* since no power is consumed in the inductance. *The nonresistive opposition to current in an a-c circuit is called* **reactance.** The symbol for reactance is X; the unit is the *ohm*. When reactance in a circuit is due to inductance it is referred to as *inductive reactance*, X_L. Thus the voltage V_L of Fig. 23-14 is equal to the product IX_L, X_L being the reactance of the inductance L in the load.

The inductive reactance of a coil is directly proportional to the frequency of the current in the circuit, since the rate of change of a given current increases with frequency. Inductive reactance is directly proportional to inductance also. The larger the inductance, the greater the opposition to the change in current at a given frequency.

$$X_L = 2\pi f L$$

When f is in cycles per second and L is in henrys, X_L is expressed in ohms of inductive reactance, 2π being a proportionality constant.

The vector sum of IX_L and IR is equal to the voltage applied to the external circuit, V of Fig. 23-14. This potential difference is the product of the circuit current I and the combined effect of the inductive

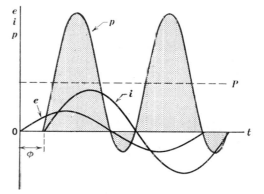

Fig. 23-15. Power in an a-c circuit containing resistance and inductance.

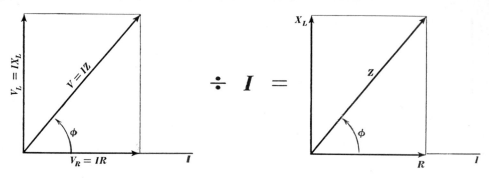

(A) Voltage diagram   **(B) Impedance diagram**

Fig. 23-16. The derivation of an impedance diagram of an *L-R* series circuit.

reactance X_L and the resistance R in the load. *The joint opposition of reactance and resistance to the current in an a-c circuit is called* **impedance.** The symbol for impedance is Z and the unit is the *ohm.* Thus V is equal to the product IZ. See Fig. 23-16(A). By Ohm's law, each of the voltage vectors IX_L, IR, and IZ may be divided by the series current I. This yields respectively X_L, R, and Z, which constitute an *impedance diagram* as shown in Fig. 23-16(B).

From trigonometry, the tangent of the phase angle ϕ is defined by the ratio of the side opposite ϕ to the side adjacent. These sides of the right triangle in the impedance diagram are respectively X and R. Therefore

$$\frac{X}{R} = \tan \phi$$

This equation gives X/R as a *function of* ϕ. It also enables us to determine ϕ as a function of X/R, which is to say that ϕ *is an angle whose tangent is X/R.* This expression gives the *inverse function* of the above equation and is commonly written as

$$\phi = \arctan \frac{X}{R}$$

The impedance Z, a vector quantity, has a magnitude equal to $\sqrt{R^2 + X^2}$ and a direction angle ϕ whose tangent is X/R. It may be written as a *polar vector* of the form $Z \lfloor \phi$ as

$$Z = \sqrt{R^2 + X^2} \lfloor \arctan X/R$$

When the reactance is inductive, $X = X_L$ and ϕ is a positive angle whose tangent is X_L/R.

We may now express Ohm's law in the general forms which apply to a-c circuits. For the entire circuit:

$$E = IZ$$

For the external circuit:

$$V = IZ$$

See the Sample Problem on the opposite page.

8. Capacitance in an a-c circuit. A capacitor in a d-c circuit quickly charges to the applied voltage and effectively opens the circuit. The potential difference across a capacitor can change only as the charge on the capacitor changes. Since $Q = CV$ (Chapter 18, Section 15), for a given capacitor the charge Q, in coulombs, is directly proportional to the potential difference V, in volts. Thus we may refer to the charge in terms of the voltage across the capacitor.

An uncharged capacitor offers no opposition to a charging current from a source of emf. However as a charge builds up on the capacitor plates, a voltage develops across the capacitor which opposes the charging current. When the charge is such

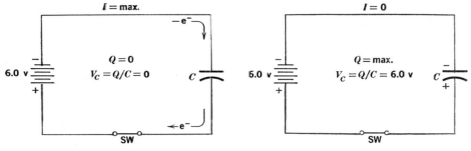

(A) C uncharged　　　　　　　　　　**(B)** C fully charged

Fig. 23-17. As a capacitor is charged, a voltage develops across it which opposes the charging current.

Sample Problem

A coil with a resistance of 30. ohms and an inductance of 0.12 henry is connected across a 120-volt 60.-cycle source. (*a*) What is the magnitude of the circuit current? (*b*) What is the phase angle? (*c*) What power is expended in the external circuit?

Solution

The circuit of Fig. 23-13 and the vector diagram of Fig. 23-14 apply to this problem.

(*a*) By Ohm's law $I = \dfrac{V}{Z}$

We must determine the magnitude of Z.
$$Z = \sqrt{R^2 + X_L^2}$$
where
$$X_L = 2\pi f L = (2\pi \times 60. \times 0.12)\ \Omega = 45\ \Omega$$
$$Z = \sqrt{(30.\ \Omega)^2 + (45\ \Omega)^2}$$
$$Z = 54\ \text{ohms}$$
Then
$$I = \frac{V}{Z} = \frac{120\ \text{v}}{54\ \Omega} = 2.2\ \text{amp, the circuit current}$$

(*b*) $\phi = \arctan \dfrac{X_L}{R} = \arctan \dfrac{45\ \Omega}{30.\ \Omega}$

$\phi = \arctan 1.5$
From Table 3 of the appendix,
$\phi = 56°$, indicating a leading voltage

(*c*) $P = E \times I \times$ power factor
$P = EI \cos \phi$
$P = 120\ \text{v} \times 2.2\ \text{amp} \times \cos 56°$
$P = 120\ \text{v} \times 2.2\ \text{amp} \times 0.56$
$P = 150\ \text{watts}$

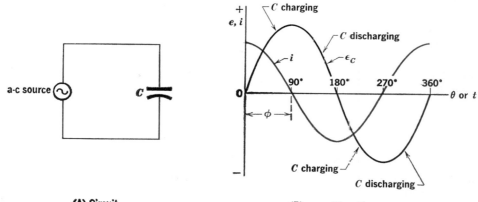

(A) Circuit

(B) e_C and i vs. time

Fig. 23-18. Pure capacitance in an a-c circuit.

that the voltage across the capacitor is equal to the applied voltage, the charging current must be zero. Why? These two conditions are illustrated in Fig. 23-17. We may conclude that *the current in a capacitor circuit is maximum when the voltage across the capacitor is zero, and the current is zero when the capacitor voltage is maximum.*

Let us examine the effect of a pure capacitance in an a-c circuit. When the initial charging current is a positive maximum, the voltage across the capacitor plates is zero. As the capacitor charges, the potential difference builds up and the current decays, the charging current

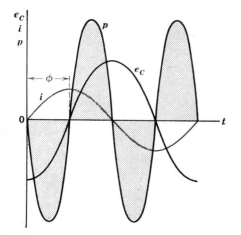

Fig. 23-19. Power curve in a circuit of pure capacitance.

reaching zero when the capacitor voltage is maximum.

As the charging current reverses direction and increases toward a negative maximum, electrons flow from the negative plate of the capacitor through the circuit to the positive plate, removing the charge. The capacitor then charges in the opposite sense and the potential difference reaches a maximum with opposite polarity as the current returns to zero. Thus we see that *the voltage across the capacitor lags the circuit current by 90°.* See Fig. 23-18.

The phase angle ϕ in an a-c circuit of a pure capacitance is $-90°$, and the circuit has a *lagging* voltage, the phase relationship being expressed as

$$i = I_{max} \sin \theta$$
$$e = E_{max} \sin (\theta + \phi)$$

These expressions are similar to those given for i and e in Section 5. However the phase angle of a lagging voltage is considered to be *negative;* hence the sign of ϕ must always be introduced properly.

Suppose the effective value of voltage across a capacitor is 10.0 volts. When the displacement angle θ is 30°, the instantaneous value of e is

$$e = E_{max} \sin (\theta + \phi)$$
$$e = E_{max} \sin [30° + (-90°)]$$
$$e = E_{max} \sin (-60°)$$

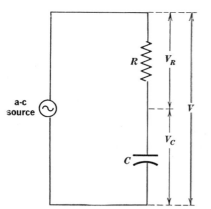

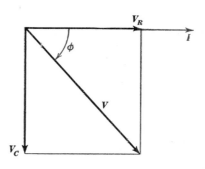

(A) Circuit diagram **(B) Voltage diagram**

Fig. 23-20. An *R-C* series circuit showing the phase relations of the different voltages to the circuit current.

Now

$$E_{max} = 1.414E = 1.414 \times 10.0 \text{ v}$$
$$e = 14.1 \text{ v} \times \sin(-60°)$$

and

$$\sin(-60°) = -0.866$$

Therefore

$$e = 14.1 \text{ v} \times (-0.866)$$
$$e = -12.2 \text{ v}$$

Compare this result with the similar computation in Section 5.

Plotted as a function of time, the product of the instantaneous values of current and voltage in a circuit of pure capacitance results in the instantaneous power curve shown in Fig. 23-19. As in a circuit with pure inductance, the average power is zero. Energy is taken from the source of emf and stored as a charge as the current changes from each maximum to zero. All this energy is returned to the souree as the current rises from zero to either maximum. Thus the product of the effective values of current and voltage indicates an *apparent power*. The phase angle of −90° yields a power factor equal to zero [cos (−90°) = 0] and so the *actual power* consumed must be zero.

9. Capacitance and resistance in an a-c circuit. The opposition to the current in an a-c circuit due to capacitance is *nonresistive* since no power is consumed in the capacitor; it is called *capacitive reactance*. The symbol used for capacitive reactance is X_C and the unit is the *ohm*.

The inherent resistance in any practical circuit containing capacitance may be represented in series with X_C. An *R-C* series circuit is shown in Fig. 23-20. The potential difference across the external circuit, *V*, is the vector sum of V_C and V_R, the series current being used as the reference vector. Of course there is no electron flow through the capacitor; it is alternately charged, first in one sense and then in the other, as the charging current alternates. The phase angle ϕ is negative, characteristic of a lagging voltage.

We may produce the corresponding impedance diagram by dividing each voltage vector by the circuit current. See Fig. 23-21. Just as V_C is negative with respect to V_L of Fig. 23-16(*B*), so is X_C plotted in the opposite direction to X_L.

Since $V_C = Q/C$, the larger the capacitance, the lower the potential difference developed across it for a given charge. *Thus the reactance to a circuit current is inversely proportional to the capacitance in the circuit.* As the frequency of a charging current in a circuit is increased, a shorter time is available during each current cycle for the capacitor to charge and discharge. Smaller changes in voltage occur across the capacitor. *Hence the capacitive reactance to the circuit current is inversely proportional to the current frequency.*

$$X_C = \frac{1}{2\pi fC}$$

When f is in cycles per second and C is in farads, X_C is expressed in ohms of capacitive reactance.

The impedance of a circuit containing capacitance and resistance has a magnitude equal to $\sqrt{R^2 + X_C^2}$ and a phase angle ϕ whose tangent is $-X_C/R$. The impedance vector in its general polar form, $Z \lfloor \phi$, is $\sqrt{R^2 + X^2} \lfloor \arctan \ X/R$ where $X = -X_C$. See the Sample Problem below.

Sample Problem

A capacitance of 20.0 μf and a resistance of 100. Ω are connected in series across a 120.-v 60.0-cycle source. (*a*) Find the impedance of the circuit. (*b*) What is the circuit current? (*c*) What is the potential difference across the capacitor?

Solution

(*a*) The circuit and diagrams of Fig. 23-20 and Fig. 23-21 apply.

$$Z = \sqrt{R^2 + X^2} \ \lfloor \arctan \ X/R$$

But

$$X = X_C = \frac{1}{2\pi fC}$$

$$X = \left(\frac{1}{2\pi \times 60.0 \times 20.0 \times 10^{-6}}\right) \text{ohms}$$

$$X_C = 133 \ \Omega$$

Magnitude of

$$Z = \sqrt{(100 \ \Omega)^2 + (133 \ \Omega)^2}$$
$$Z = 166 \ \Omega$$

$$\phi = \arctan \frac{-X_C}{R} = \arctan \frac{-133 \ \Omega}{100. \ \Omega}$$

$$\phi = \arctan \ -1.33$$

$\phi = -53°$, the phase angle of a lagging voltage

Therefore, the impedance may be expressed as a vector quantity:

$$Z = 166 \ \Omega \ \lfloor -53°$$

(*b*) $I = \dfrac{V}{Z} = \dfrac{120. \text{ v}}{166 \ \Omega}$

$I = 0.723$ amp, the circuit current

(*c*) $V_C = IX_C$

$\qquad V_C = 0.723$ amp $\times \ 133 \ \Omega$

$\qquad V_C = 96.2$ v, the potential difference across C

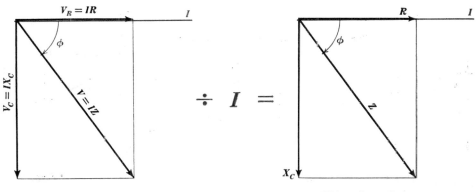

(A) Voltage diagram   (B) Impedance diagram

Fig. 23-21. The derivation of an impedance diagram of an R-C series circuit.

10. R, L, and C in series. Inductance produces a leading voltage and a positive phase angle in an a-c circuit, and capacitance produces a lagging voltage and a negative phase angle. Of course, the voltage across a resistance must be in phase with the current in the resistance. Suppose we connect values of L, R, and C in series across an a-c source of emf as in Fig. 23-22. The *total reactance* of the circuit is

$$X = X_L - X_C$$

since X_L and X_C are 180° apart. The circuit is inductive if X_L exceeds X_C, having a positive phase angle and a leading voltage. If X_C exceeds X_L, the circuit is capacitive, having a negative phase angle and a lagging voltage.

The impedance has the general form, $Z \angle \phi$, as before.

$$Z = \sqrt{R^2 + X^2} \ \angle \ \arctan X/R$$

However X can be either positive or negative (X^2 is always positive) since

$$X = X_L - X_C = 2\pi fL - \frac{1}{2\pi fC}$$

Therefore the magnitude of the impedance may be expressed as

$$Z = \sqrt{R^2 + (X_L - X_C)^2}$$

$$Z = \sqrt{R^2 + \left(2\pi fL - \frac{1}{2\pi fC}\right)^2}$$

When both X_L and X_C are involved in a circuit computation, it is quite important

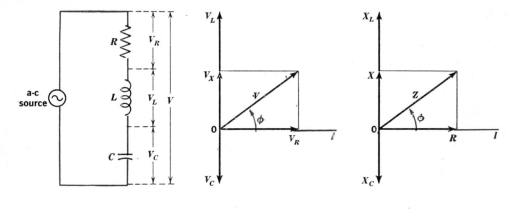

(A) R-L-C series circuit   (B) Voltage diagram   (C) Impedance diagram

Fig. 23-22. An R-L-C series circuit with phase diagrams.

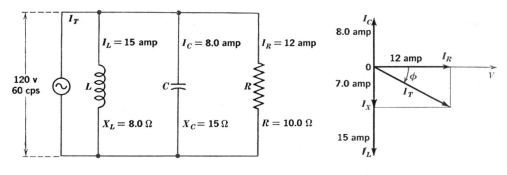

(A) R-L-C parallel circuit

(B) Current diagram

Fig. 23-23. An *L-R-C* parallel circuit and phase diagram.

that the sign of the resulting value of X is introduced properly.

Suppose, for a given frequency, X_L is found to equal 24.0 ohms, X_C to equal 12.0 ohms, and the series resistance to be 16.0 ohms. From these values of R, X_L, and X_C we may determine the impedance of the circuit as a vector quantity.

$$Z = \sqrt{R^2 + X^2} \ \underline{| \ arctan \ X/R}$$

But

$$X = X_L - X_C = 24.0 \ \Omega - 12.0 \ \Omega = 12.0 \ \Omega$$

$$Z = \sqrt{(16.0 \ \Omega)^2 + (12.0 \ \Omega)^2}$$
$$\underline{| \ arctan \ 12.0 \ \Omega/16.0 \ \Omega}$$
$$Z = 20.0 \ \Omega \ \underline{| \ 53°}$$

The direction angle of Z is positive and indicates a leading voltage.

The value found for Z tells us that the magnitude of the impedance is 20. ohms and the voltage across the external circuit must lead the series current by an angle of 53°. Assuming a line voltage across the external circuit of Fig. 23-22 of 100. volts, the magnitude of the circuit current is

$$I = \frac{V}{Z} = \frac{100. \ v}{20.0 \ \Omega} = 5.00 \ amp$$

We may now determine by inspection the magnitudes of the three component voltages across R, L, and C, *which must have a vector sum equal to V.*

$$V_R = IR = 80.0 \ v$$
$$V_C = IX_C = 60.0 \ v$$
$$V_L = IX_L = 120. \ v$$

According to the voltage diagram, Fig. 23-22(*B*), the magnitude of the voltage V across the external circuit is

$$V = \sqrt{V_R^2 + V_X^2}$$

where

$$V_X = (V_L - V_C)$$

Then

$$V = \sqrt{(80.0 \ v)^2 + (60.0 \ v)^2}$$
$$V = 100. \ v$$

Of course, the direction angle of V must be 53° since this is the phase angle ϕ with I as the reference. It is important to recognize that the magnitude of the voltage across a reactance component in an a-c circuit may exceed that of the applied voltage appearing across the entire external circuit.

★ **11. L, R, and C in parallel.** In practical circuits the components are commonly connected in parallel rather than in series. Computations of parallel impedance networks become involved and cumbersome unless the student is familiar with *rectangular* and *polar* forms of complex notations and is adroit in the use of *vector algebra.*

Let us consider the simplest kind of parallel circuit: one consisting of pure inductance, pure capacitance, and pure resistance in parallel. We will assume the resistance of the L and C branches to be negligible. This simple network is shown in Fig. 23-23.

The same value of voltage must exist across each branch of a parallel network. The total current in the network, however, is the sum of the currents in the separate branches. This is a *vector sum* when there are differences in phase between the currents in the branches and the voltage across the network.

In the inductance branch, assumed to have no resistance, the current I_L lags the network voltage V by 90°. With this voltage as the reference vector, I_L is plotted as a lagging current of 15 amperes 90° behind V. See Fig. 23-23(B). The current I_C of 8.0 amperes leads the voltage by 90° and is plotted 90° ahead of V. The current in the resistance branch, I_R, being in phase with V, is plotted along the line of the voltage reference. The total current I_T is the vector sum of the branch currents, and the phase relation is expressed with reference to the network voltage.

$$I_T = \sqrt{I_R^2 + I_x^2} \ \underline{\big|\, \text{arctan}\ I_X/I_R}$$

$$I_T = \sqrt{(12\ \text{amp})^2 + (-7.0\ \text{amp})^2}$$
$$\underline{\big|\, \text{arctan}\ -7.0\ \text{amp}/12\ \text{amp}}$$

$$I_T = 14\ \text{amp}\ \underline{\big|\, -30°}$$

We have determined the circuit current I_T, as a vector quantity, from the current diagram in the same way we determined Z in earlier examples. This current vector has a magnitude of 14 amperes and a phase angle of $-30°$, and is expressed in polar form.

Similarly the circuit voltage, plotted as the reference vector, has a magnitude of 120 volts and a direction angle of 0°. In polar notation, this vector quantity has the form

$$V = 120\ \text{v}\ \underline{\big|\, 0°}$$

Multiplication and division operations with vector quantities may be handled very simply when these quantities are written in polar form. *The product of two polar vectors is found by taking the product of their magnitudes and the sum of their angles.* Thus

$$A \underline{\big|\, a} \times B \underline{\big|\, b} = AB \underline{\big|\, a + b}$$
$$A \underline{\big|\, a} \times C \underline{\big|\, -c} = AC \underline{\big|\, a + (-c)}$$

The quotient of two polar vectors is found by taking the quotient of their magnitudes and the difference of their angles. Thus

$$\frac{A \underline{\big|\, a}}{B \underline{\big|\, b}} = \frac{A}{B} \underline{\big|\, a - b}$$

$$\frac{A \underline{\big|\, a}}{C \underline{\big|\, -c}} = \frac{A}{C} \underline{\big|\, a - (-c)}$$

Unfortunately, polar vectors cannot be added or subtracted so easily. They are first converted to a rectangular form of complex notation.

The total impedance of the parallel branches may be determined by Ohm's law, now that the total current is known.

$$Z = \frac{V}{I_T} = \frac{120\ \text{v}\ \underline{\big|\, 0°}}{14\ \text{amp}\ \underline{\big|\, -30°}}$$

$$Z = \frac{120\ \text{v}}{14\ \text{amp}} \underline{\big|\, 0° - (-30°)}$$

$$Z = 8.6\ \Omega\ \underline{\big|\, 30°}$$

In practical parallel circuits having both resistance and reactance in each branch, we must deal with parallel impedances. In general,

$$\frac{1}{Z_T} = \frac{1}{Z_1} + \frac{1}{Z_2} + \frac{1}{Z_3} + \text{etc.}$$

However, each impedance is a vector quantity, and the computations involving such circuits are somewhat more sophisticated than the example demonstrated.

★ **12. Impedance matching in a-c circuits.** We stated in Chapter 20, Section 6, that maximum power may be transferred to the load in a d-c circuit if the load resistance is equal to the internal resistance of the source of emf. This fact is equally true of a-c circuits in which the loads may be complex impedances.

A device or circuit used as an a-c source

may require a particular load impedance in order to perform satisfactorily. However, it may not be possible to supply a load that even approximates this value. A typical audio-frequency amplifier used to drive a loud-speaker requires a load impedance of 8000 ohms and the loud-speaker may have a nominal impedance of 8 ohms. In order for this combination to function properly, the load must appear as 8000 ohms to the amplifier and the source must appear as 8 ohms to the speaker. The loud-speaker then must be coupled to the amplifier by means of an *impedance matching* device.

A transformer is commonly used to match the impedance of a load to that of a source, in order to obtain the greatest transfer of energy from one circuit to the other. The load impedance connected to the secondary is transformed to the value required by the source.

In a well-designed iron-core transformer practically all of the magnetic flux links both primary and secondary turns. In Chapter 22, Section 25, we expressed the secondary voltage V_S in terms of the turns ratio and the primary voltage V_P.

$$V_S = V_P \frac{N_S}{N_P}$$

Similarly the secondary current is

$$I_S = I_P \frac{N_P}{N_S}$$

According to Ohm's law the secondary im-

pedance, Z_S, and the primary impedance, Z_P, are respectively

$$Z_S = \frac{V_S}{I_S} \quad \text{and} \quad Z_P = \frac{V_P}{I_P}$$

But

$$\frac{V_S}{I_S} = \frac{\dfrac{V_P N_S}{N_P}}{\dfrac{I_P N_P}{N_S}} = \frac{V_P}{I_P}\left(\frac{N_S}{N_P}\right)^2$$

Then

$$\frac{Z_S}{Z_P} = \frac{N_S^2}{N_P^2}$$

or

$$\frac{N_S}{N_P} = \sqrt{\frac{Z_S}{Z_P}}$$

Let us use this expression to determine the turns ratio, primary to secondary, required to couple the amplifier and loud-speaker mentioned earlier.

$$\frac{N_P}{N_S} = \sqrt{\frac{Z_P}{Z_S}} = \sqrt{\frac{8000\ \Omega}{8\ \Omega}}$$

$$\frac{N_P}{N_S} = \sqrt{1000} = 31.6$$

Thus the primary must have 31.6 times the number of turns as the secondary. There are many instances in a-c circuits in which the impedances of the source and the load are fixed by the design requirements of the components, and are unequal in magnitude. By the insertion of a transformer with the proper turns ratio between the source and the load, the impedance of the load may be stepped up or stepped down to match that of the source.

Summary

The power expended in the load of an a-c circuit is determined by the average of the instantaneous values over the period of one cycle. Instantaneous power is the product of the instantaneous current and voltage. In a resistive load the average power is the product of the effective values of current and voltage. In either a pure inductive or pure capacitive load, the average power is zero. In general, power in an a-c circuit is equal to the product of the effective values of current and voltage and the cosine of the phase angle.

Most a-c meters measure effective values of current or voltage. The better quality instruments for use at power frequencies are of the electrodynamometer type. Inexpensive meters may use the repulsion force of the moving iron-vane mechanism. Rectifier-type meters are preferred in the audio-frequency range.

An a-c circuit containing inductance and resistance produces a lagging current. Such a load presents an impedance to the source which is the vector sum of the resistance and the inductive reactance in the circuit. The angle at which the current lags is called the phase angle.

Capacitance and resistance produces an impedance equal to the vector sum of the capacitive reactance and resistance in the circuit. The phase angle in this case is due to a leading current. When both inductance and capacitance are present, the current will lead or lag the voltage depending on the relative magnitudes of the two reactances. Inductive reactance is directly proportional to both frequency and inductance. Capacitive reactance is inversely proportional to both frequency and capacitance.

Both series and parallel circuits containing inductance, reactance, and resistance can be solved by the proper applications of Ohm's law for a-c circuits. These involve the use of voltage, current, and impedance vector diagrams and trigonometry.

Transformers are commonly used in a-c circuits as impedance matching devices when it is important that maximum power be transferred from the source to the load. The power consumed in the secondary is maximum when the turns ratio, $N_S:N_P$, is equal to the square root of the impedance ratio of the load to the source.

TERMS TO DEFINE

capacitive reactance	inductive reactance	phase angle
effective value of current	lagging current	power factor
effective value of voltage	lagging voltage	reactance
electrodynamometer	leading current	rectifier-type meter
hot-wire meter	leading voltage	rms current
impedance	matching transformer	rms voltage
impedance matching	moving iron-vane meter	wattmeter
induction watt-hour meter	Ohm's law for a-c circuits	watt-hour meter

QUESTIONS

A 1. What is the significant relationship between an alternating current and voltage said to be in phase?
2. What type of load in a-c circuits has a current in phase with the voltage across it?
3. What is meant by instantaneous power?
4. (a) Why is it not possible to use a galvanometer-type meter in an a-c circuit? (b) What would happen to the meter if placed in an a-c circuit?
5. Upon what property of an alternating current is its effective value based?

6. Define the effective value of an alternating current.
7. Explain briefly the principle on which the moving iron-vane mechanism functions.
8. In what respect is the mechanism of the hot-wire meter different from other meter mechanisms?
9. What is the phase relation between (a) the current in a pure inductance and the applied voltage; (b) the current and the induced voltage; (c) the applied voltage and the induced voltage?

10. What is the significance of the power factor pertaining to an a-c circuit?

11. Why is reactance described as being non-resistive?

12. (a) Define impedance. (b) What is an impedance diagram?

13. Describe the difference in the performance of a capacitor in a d-c circuit and in an a-c circuit.

14. What is the power factor of an a-c circuit containing (a) pure inductance; (b) pure resistance; (c) pure capacitance?

15. Express Ohm's law (a) for an a-c circuit including a source of emf; (b) for an a-c circuit which does not include a source of emf.

B   16. Explain why the instantaneous power curve for current in a resistive load varies between some positive maximum value and zero.

17. Demonstrate algebraically that the heating effect of an electric current is proportional to the effective value of current squared.

18. Plot the current and current squared curves for an alternating current having a maximum value of 5.7 amperes. Use cross-section paper and a suitable scale for the coordinate axes to produce a graph similar to Fig. 23-3. Show that the rms value of the current is 4.0 amperes.

19. How can the electrodynamometer mechanism be used to measure power?

20. If an a-c circuit has a pure inductance load, the average power delivered to the load is zero. Does this mean that there is no energy transfer between the source and the load? Explain.

21. (a) Considering the expression for X_L in terms of frequency and inductance, draw a rough graph of X_L as a function of frequency for a given inductance. (b) What is the nature of the curve? (c) What is the significance of the fact that X_L is zero when f is zero regardless of the value of L?

22. Considering the expression for X_C in terms of frequency and capacitance, what is the significance of the fact that when the frequency is zero, X_C is infinitely high for any given capacitance?

23. (a) In a series circuit operating at a certain frequency and containing L, R, and C, what determines whether the load is inductive or capacitive? (b) Can you suggest a circumstance in which the load would be resistive?

24. Compare the inductive reactance of a copper wire (a) as a straight conductor; (b) as a solenoid; (c) as a solenoid with an iron core.

25. What is the significance of the negative portions of the power curve shown in Fig. 23-19?

26. Various meters are available, but they do not include a power-factor meter. Suggest a method by which you could determine the power factor of an a-c circuit.

27. Explain why an a-c wattmeter indicates actual power instead of apparent power.

★ 28. Two vector quantities are expressed in polar form and their product is to be determined. Explain how the multiplication is carried out.

★ 29. How is the quotient of two vector quantities found when they are expressed in polar form?

★ 30. (a) Why is it sometimes desirable to match the impedance of a source to that of its load? (b) How may this be done in an a-c circuit?

PROBLEMS

Note: Compute angles to the nearest degree.

A   1. A current in an a-c circuit measures 5.5 amperes. What is the maximum instantaneous magnitude of this current?

2. A capacitor has a voltage rating of 450. v maximum. What is the highest rms voltage that can be impressed across it without danger of dielectric puncture?

3. The emf of an a-c source has an effective value of 122.0 volts. What is the instantaneous value when the displacement angle θ is 50°?

4. An alternating current in a 25.0 ohm resistance produces heat at the rate of 250. watts. (a) What is the effective value of current in the resistance? (b) What is the effective value of voltage across the resistance?

5. What rpm must an eight-pole alternator have to generate an emf at 60 cps?

6. An inductor has an inductance of 2.20 henrys and a resistance of 220. ohms. (a) What is the reactance to an alternating current of 25.0 cps? (b) Draw the impedance diagram and determine graphically the magnitude and phase angle of the impedance.

7. A 2.00 μf capacitor is connected across a 60.0-cycle line and a current of 167 ma is indicated. (a) What is the reactance to the

alternating current? (b) What is the voltage across the line?

8. A capacitance of 2.65 μf is connected across a 120.-volt line and is found to draw 120. milliamperes. What is the frequency of the source?

9. When a resistance of 4.0 ohms and an inductor of negligible resistance are connected in series across a 110 -volt, 60.-cycle line, the current is 20. amperes. What is the inductance of the coil?

★ **10.** A source of emf with an internal impedance of 2500 Ω is to be matched to a load impedance of 4.0 Ω using a matching transformer. What is the turns ratio of the transformer?

B **11.** A 0.5-μf capacitor and a 30.-ohm resistor are connected in series across a source of emf whose frequency is 8.0×10^3 cps. (a) Draw the circuit diagram. (b) Find the capacitive reactance. (c) Draw the vector diagram and determine the magnitude and phase angle of the impedance.

12. The current in the circuit of Problem 11 is found to be 50. milliamperes. (a) What is the magnitude of the voltage across the series circuit? (b) What is the phase relation of this voltage to the circuit current? (c) What is the voltage across the capacitor? (d) What is the voltage across the resistor?

13. A 60.0-cycle circuit has a load consisting of resistance and inductance in series. A voltmeter, ammeter, and wattmeter, properly connected in the circuit, read respectively 117 v, 4.75 amp, and 400. watts. (a) Determine the power factor. (b) What is the phase angle? (c) What is the resistance of the load? (d) What is the reactance of the inductance in the load? (e) Determine the voltage across the resistance. (f) Determine the voltage across the inductance. (g) Draw the voltage diagram with the circuit current as the reference vector. What is the applied voltage found graphically? ★ Express in polar form.

14. A coil has a resistance of 90. ohms and an inductance of 0.019 henry. (a) What is the impedance (complex) at 1.0×10^3 cycles? (b) What is the magnitude of the current when potential difference of 6.0 volts at this frequency is applied across it? (c) How much power is delivered to the coil?

15. A capacitance of 50. μf and a resistance of 50. ohms are connected in series across a 120-volt, 60-cycle line. (a) What is the magnitude of current in the circuit? (b) What power is dissipated? (c) What is the power factor? (d) Determine the voltage across the resistance. (e) Determine the voltage across the capacitance. (f) Draw the voltage diagram with the circuit current as the reference vector. What is the applied voltage found graphically? ★ Express in polar form.

16. An inductance of 4.8 millihenrys, a capacitance of 8.0 μf, and a resistance of 10. ohms are connected in series and a 6.0-volt, 1.0×10^3 cycle signal is applied across the combination. (a) What is the magnitude of the impedance of the series circuit? (b) What is the phase angle? (c) Determine the magnitude of the current in the circuit. (d) Find the potential drop across each component of the load and draw the voltage diagram.

17. An inductor, a resistance, and a capacitor are connected in series across an a-c circuit. A voltmeter reads 90. volts when connected across the inductor, 16 volts across the resistor, and 120 volts across the capacitor. (a) What will the voltmeter read when placed across the series circuit? (b) Draw the voltage diagram and graphically verify your answer to (a). (c) Compute the power factor.

★ **18.** An inductance of 0.14 henry and a resistance of 56 ohms are connected in parallel across a 112-volt, 50-cycle line. (a) Determine the current in the resistance branch. (b) Determine the current in the inductance branch. (c) Draw the current diagram using the applied voltage as the reference vector. (d) Find the magnitude and phase angle of the total current in the circuit. (e) What is the impedance of the circuit?

RESEARCH ON YOUR OWN

1. Make a dynamometer and demonstrate it. Use a spring from a small clock to provide tension, and glass tubing for the bearings.
2. Use a meter movement with a selenium rectifier to make an alternating current voltmeter. Demonstrate it to the class.
3. Demonstrate by means of an oscilloscope the sine wave produced by a transformer.
4. Inquire at your electric power company about the power factor of their lines. Find out whether p-f corrections are made, and how and why they are made.

CHAPTER 24

RESONANCE

1. Inductive reactance vs. frequency.
An inductor in a d-c circuit has no effect on the steady direct current except that due to the ordinary resistance of the wire forming the coil. A steady direct current may be thought of as an alternating current having a frequency of zero cps. Inductive reactance in the d-c circuit must then be zero, since $X_L = 2\pi fL$.

An alternating current changes from its positive maximum to its negative maximum in a time equal to one-half the period T, and if the frequency of this current is increased, the time rate of change of current is increased accordingly. See Fig. 24-1. The inductive reactance presented to the current in an a-c circuit by an inductor increases as the frequency of this current is increased.

Consider the reactance of a certain inductance over a range of frequencies. A plot of the values of inductive reactance as ordinates against frequencies as abscissas produces a linear curve, as shown in Fig. 24-2. Observe that any value of inductance yields a reactance curve which starts at the origin of the coordinate axes; the larger the value of inductance, the greater the slope of the curve.

2. Capacitive reactance vs. frequency.
Capacitance in a d-c circuit, once the capacitor is charged to the applied voltage, acts as an open switch, and the current in the circuit is zero. Thus the capacitive reactance in the circuit is infinitely high regardless of the value of C.

In an a-c circuit containing a fixed value of capacitance, electrons flow in one direction during one half cycle to charge the capacitor in one sense; they flow in the opposite direction during the other half cycle tending to reverse the charge on the capacitor.

If the frequency is very low, the circuit

VOCABULARY

Coupled circuits. Two circuits in which a common impedance permits the transfer of energy from one to the other.

Filter. A frequency-sensitive network which will transmit a continuous band of frequencies and attenuate all other frequencies.

Resonance. The condition in an alternating-current circuit in which the inductive reactance and capacitive reactance are equal and cancel each other.

Selectivity. The property of a tuned circuit which discriminates between signal voltages of different frequencies.

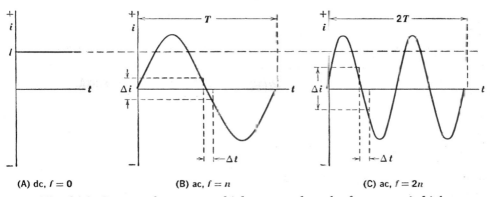

(A) dc, $f = 0$ **(B) ac, $f = n$**   **(C) ac, $f = 2n$**

Fig. 24-1. Current changes at a higher rate when the frequency is higher.

current is small and the capacitive reactance is large since $X_C = \frac{1}{2\pi f C}$. As the frequency is increased, less change occurs in the charge on the capacitor during each half cycle, and there is less reactive opposition to the circuit current. At extremely high frequencies the change in the capacitor charge becomes negligible, and the capacitive reactance in the circuit ceases to be a significant factor in the control of the current. The larger the value of capacitance in the circuit, the more rapidly the capacitive reactance falls away with increasing frequency.

Plotting the values of reactance for a certain capacitance over a range of frequencies produces a curve similar to that shown in Fig. 24-3. Observe that the curve is hyperbolic, typical of the inverse relation between capacitive reactance X_C and frequency. A larger value of capacitance would have a reactance-frequency curve with a greater slope.

3. Series resonance. In Chapter 23, Section 10, we stated that the voltages across an inductance and a capacitance in a series circuit are of opposite polarity. If X_L is larger than X_C, the circuit is inductive, and the voltage across the circuit leads the current; however, if X_C is the larger reactance, the circuit is capacitive and the circuit voltage lags behind the current. In either instance the impedance Z has a magnitude $\sqrt{R^2 + (X_L - X_C)^2}$ and a phase angle ϕ whose tangent is $(X_L - X_C)/R$.

The frequency of an a-c voltage applied to a series circuit with fixed values of L, R, and C determines the reactance of the circuit. Figures 24-2 and 24-3 show that the reactance of the circuit is inductive over a range of high frequencies, and is capacitive over a range of low frequencies. At some intermediate frequency the inductive and capacitive reactances are equal, and the reactance of the circuit

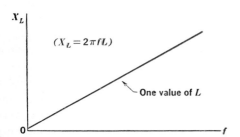

Fig. 24-2. The reactance of a given inductance is plotted as a function of frequency.

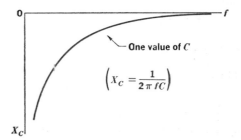

Fig. 24-3. The reactance of a given capacitance is plotted as a function of frequency.

$(X_L - X_C)$ equals zero. This is a special case known as *series resonance;* the frequency at which this occurs is called the *resonant frequency, f_r.* **Series resonance** *is a condition in which the impedance of an L-R-C series circuit is equal to the resistance and the voltage across the circuit is in phase with the circuit current.*

Suppose an inductor of 10. millihenrys inductance and 25 ohms resistance is placed in series with an ammeter and a capacitor of 1.0 microfarad capacitance, and a signal of 10. volts rms from a variable-frequency source such as an audio signal generator is applied. The circuit is shown in Fig. 24-4. As the frequency of the applied signal varies through the audio range, a distinct rise in current occurs as the frequency approaches 1600 cps. The current magnitude quickly falls away as the frequency of the signal increases beyond this value. We may conclude that the series circuit is resonant at 1600 cps.

At resonance, $X_L = X_C$, and the value of each is found as follows:

$$X_L = 2\pi f_r L$$
$$X_L = (2\pi \times 1.6 \times 10^3 \times 1.0 \times 10^{-2})\ \Omega$$
$$X_L = 1.0 \times 10^2\ \Omega$$

$$X_C = \frac{1}{2\pi f_r C}$$
$$X_C = \left(\frac{1}{2\pi \times 1.6 \times 10^2 \times 1.0 \times 10^{-6}}\right)\Omega$$
$$X_C = 1.0 \times 10^2\ \Omega$$

The impedance at resonance is

$$Z = \sqrt{R^2 + X^2}\ \lfloor \arctan X/R$$

But

$$X = X_L - X_C = 0\ \Omega$$

and the phase angle $\phi = \arctan \dfrac{X}{R} = 0°$

Thus

$$Z = R = 25\ \Omega$$

Since the impedance of the series resonant circuit is the minimum value and equal to R, the current is the maximum value and equal to V/R.

$$I_r = \frac{V}{R} = \frac{10.\ \text{v}}{25\ \Omega} = 0.40\ \text{amp}$$
$$V_L = I_r X_L = 0.40\ \text{amp} \times 1.0 \times 10^2\ \Omega$$
$$V_L = 40.\ \text{v}$$
$$V_C = I_r X_C = 0.40\ \text{amp} \times 1.0 \times 10^2\ \Omega$$
$$V_L = 40.\ \text{v}$$
$$I_r X_L - I_r X_C = 40.\ \text{v} - 40.\ \text{v} = 0\ \text{v}$$
$$V_R = I_r \times R = 0.40\ \text{amp} \times 25\ \Omega = 10.\ \text{v}$$

Since the phase angle $\phi = 0°$, the power factor, $\cos \phi, = 1$. Thus the power consumed in the series circuit is maximum at resonance.

$$P = VI_r \cos \phi = VI_r$$

The frequency at which a series circuit resonates is determined by the combination of L and C used. For a particular combination there is one resonant frequency, f_r. At series resonance

$$X_L = X_C$$
$$2\pi f_r L = \frac{1}{2\pi f_r C}$$

Solving for f_r

$$f_r^2 = \frac{1}{4\pi^2 L C}$$

$$f_r = \frac{1}{2\pi \sqrt{LC}}$$

Where L is in henrys and C is in farads, f_r is expressed in cycles per second.

At frequencies below the resonance point, the series circuit is capacitive, behaving as one with an X_C and R in series. At the resonant frequency, of course, the circuit behaves as one containing pure resistance. Above the resonant frequency it is inductive. These characteristics of the L-R-C series circuit are shown clearly in Fig. 24-5 by the reactance curve X.

4. Selectivity in series resonance. A resonant circuit responds to impressed voltages of different frequencies in a very selective manner. The circuit presents a high impedance to a signal voltage far removed from the resonant frequency and the resulting current is correspondingly small. This same circuit presents a low impedance consisting of the circuit re-

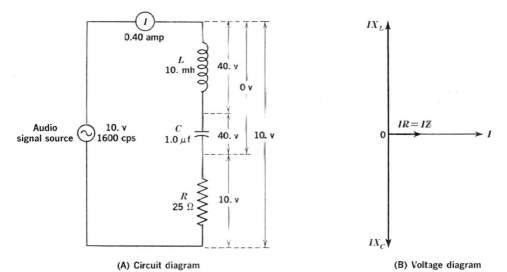

| (A) Circuit diagram | (B) Voltage diagram |

Fig. 24-4. An L-R-C series circuit which has a resonant frequency of 1600 cps.

sistance to a signal voltage at the resonant frequency and the current is correspondingly large.

The property of a tuned circuit which discriminates between signal voltages of different frequencies is known as its **selectivity.** *The* lower the resistance of the series circuit, the higher is the resonant current and the more sharply selective is the circuit. The family of current-resonance curves shown in Fig. 24-6 illustrates the influence of circuit resistance on selectivity. Curves are shown for three different values of circuit resistance.

The usual series-resonant circuit consists of an inductor and a capacitor, the only resistance being that inherent in the circuit, and is almost solely that of the

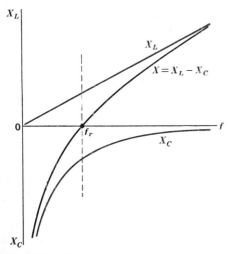

Fig. 24-5. The reactance characteristic of an L-R-C series circuit on either side of the resonant frequency.

Fig. 24-6. The magnitude of current in a series-resonant circuit is plotted as a function of frequency.

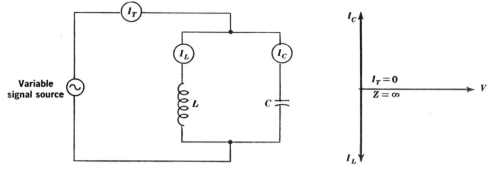

(A) Circuit diagram   (B) Current diagram

Fig. 24-7. An ideal parallel-resonant circuit and its current diagram.

coil. The characteristics of the series-resonant circuit depend primarily on the ratio of the inductive reactance to the circuit resistance, X_L/R. This ratio is commonly called the Q (quality factor) of the circuit. It is essentially a design characteristic of the inductor; the higher the Q, the more sharply selective the series-resonant circuit.

Resonant circuits may be tuned over a range of frequencies by making either the inductance or the capacitance variable. We may vary the position of a powdered-iron core in a coil to change its inductance, but it is more common to tune a circuit to resonance by varying capacitance; mechanical stability is more easily obtained in the case of a variable capacitor. Virtually all manual tuning of radio circuits is done with variable capacitors.

★ **5. Parallel resonance.** Circuit resonance is generally avoided in power circuits, since a high resonant current results in unusually high voltages across the reactance components. However, in radio circuits and in electronics in general, resonance is a most important property.

Figure 24-7 represents an ideal case of parallel resonance, a pure inductance in parallel with a pure capacitance. A constant voltage from a variable frequency source is applied across the parallel circuit. The current in the inductance branch, I_L, lags behind the circuit voltage by 90° since

we assume zero resistance. Similarly, the current in the capacitive branch leads the applied voltage by 90°.

I_L must vary inversely with f since

$$I_L = \frac{V}{X_L} = \frac{V}{2\pi fL}$$

where

$$\frac{V}{2\pi L} = \text{a constant}$$

I_C must vary directly with f since

$$I_C = \frac{V}{X_C} = 2\pi fCV$$

where

$$2\pi CV = \text{a constant}$$

The total current, I_T, is the vector sum of the currents in the two branches, and in our ideal circuit which assumes no resistance in either branch, I_L and I_C are fully 180° out of phase. Thus, signal voltages of low frequencies produce large currents in the inductive branch of the circuit and small currents in the capacitive branch. Signal voltages of high frequencies produce small values of I_L and large values of I_C.

There is some intermediate frequency at which the currents in these two ideal branches are equal. Since I_L and I_C are opposite in phase, their vector sum I_T is equal to zero. See Fig. 24-7(B). The equivalent impedance of the ideal network is infinitely high as $Z_r = V/I_T$. This is a condition of *parallel resonance*. Because

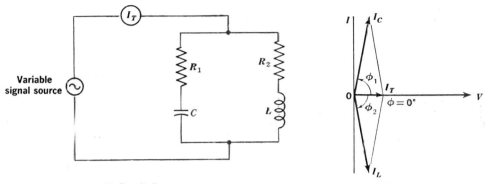

(A) Circuit diagram   **(B) Current diagram**

Fig. 24-8. A practical parallel-resonant circuit and its current diagram.

$X_L = X_C$ at this resonant frequency, f_r, may again be expressed as in the case of series resonance.

$$f_r = \frac{1}{2\pi\sqrt{LC}}$$

In this ideal case of parallel resonance we have the interesting situation in which a large current is in L and C and no current (I_T) is being supplied from the source. At resonance, the parallel network, called a *tank circuit*, is said to *oscillate*. The capacitor alternately charges and discharges through the inductance at the resonant frequency, energy being alternately stored in the capacitor as a charge and in the magnetic field of the inductor. Since we have stipulated that both L and C are pure (having no resistance), no energy is dissipated. The situation is analogous to that of a frictionless pendulum after it has been given an initial kick.

A practical parallel-resonant circuit is shown in Fig. 24-8. We shall assume that the two resistances R_1 and R_2 are equal. At the resonant frequency of the tank circuit, the rms currents in the two branches are equal in magnitude, one leading the applied voltage and the other lagging it by equal phase angles, ϕ_1 and ϕ_2 respectively. If R_1 and R_2 are very small in comparison to X_C and X_L at resonance (a high-Q circuit), these phase angles are

very nearly 90°. Thus the resultant line current I_T in the external circuit is very small and is in phase with the applied voltage. The equivalent impedance of the tank circuit must be very large at resonance, since it is equal to V/I_T. It is interesting to observe that the smaller the resistance of the parallel-resonant circuit the larger the impedance across it.

In L-R-C parallel circuits the resonant rise of impedance can result in very high impedances if the circuit Q is high; this is one of the most important properties of parallel resonance. At resonance there is

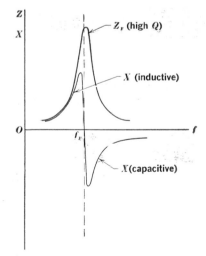

Fig. 24-9. Impedance in a parallel-resonant circuit is plotted as a function of frequency.

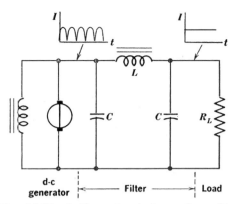

Fig. 24-10. A filter circuit is used to eliminate ripple in the output of a d-c generator.

a very large current oscillating between the inductance and capacitance, and a line current outside the tank circuit which is just large enough to supply the resistance losses in the circuit.

At frequencies below f_r, a tank circuit acts inductively because of the large current in the inductance branch and the small current in the capacitance branch. At frequencies above f_r, the tank circuit acts capacitively since a larger current is in the capacitance branch. Thus the reactance is inductive below f_r and capaci-

tive above f_r. The reactance curve for an L-R-C parallel circuit has the form shown in Fig. 24-9. Observe the similarity between the impedance curve for parallel resonance and the current curve for series resonance in Fig. 24-6.

In Section 4 we expressed the Q of a resonant circuit as being essentially equal to X_L/R. When the Q of a parallel-resonant circuit is high, the impedance *at resonance* may be expressed very conveniently and with negligible error as

$$Z_r = 2\pi f_r L Q = \frac{(2\pi f_r L)^2}{R}$$

See the Sample Problem below.

6. Coupled circuits. The transformer provides us with a common example of *coupled* circuits, energy from the primary circuit being transferred to the secondary circuit by means of the magnetic flux which links both coils. The primary and secondary are magnetically coupled because of their mutual inductance. *Two circuits are said to be **coupled** when a common impedance permits the transfer of energy from one to the other.*

Both series and parallel-resonant circuits may be used as coupling elements where

Sample Problem

A tank circuit consisting of an inductance of 60. microhenrys and 20. ohms resistance in parallel with a capacitor is resonant at a frequency of 1.0 megacycle per second. Find the magnitude of impedance of the circuit at resonance.

Solution

60. μh $= 6.0 \times 10^{-5}$ h

1.0 Mcps $= 1.0 \times 10^6$ cps

$$Z_r = \frac{(2\pi f_r L)^2}{R}$$

$$Z_r = \left[\frac{(2\pi \times 1.0 \times 10^6 \times 6.0 \times 10^{-5})^2}{20.}\right] \Omega$$

$$Z_r = 7200 \ \Omega$$

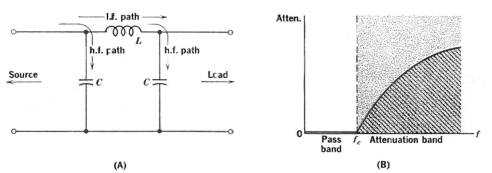

(A)   (B)

Fig. 24-11. A low-pass filter and its performance curve.

it is desired to discriminate between the frequencies of various signals or to transfer energy efficiently at a particular frequency. Resonance is used to increase the magnitude of desired signals and to decrease to a minimum the magnitude of undesired signals in radio and television circuits.

7. Filter circuits. From Fig. 24-2 it is evident that the opposition to alternating currents by an inductance in a circuit increases with frequency. The only opposition to a direct current is due to the resistance of the coil. Figure 24-3 shows us that the opposition to alternating currents by a capacitance in a circuit decreases with frequency.

A series-resonant circuit composed of both inductance and capacitance offers little opposition to alternating currents whose frequencies are in a narrow band centered on the resonant frequency, as shown by the current curves of Fig 24-6.

Currents at all frequencies above and below this *pass* band are severely *attenuated* or reduced in magnitude.

A parallel-resonant circuit opposes and attenuates currents whose frequencies are in the narrow band centered on the resonant frequency. See Fig. 24-9. Currents with frequencies on either side of this *attenuation* band are passed with little opposition.

These frequency-sensitive characteristics of inductors and capacitors can be used to form simple networks which will transmit a continuous band of frequencies and attenuate all other frequencies. Such a network is called a *filter*.

Filter circuits have many useful applications in electric and electronic circuits, perhaps the most common being the smoothing out of a pulsating direct current into a steady d-c value. This is accomplished by filtering out, or attenuating, the high frequency components of the

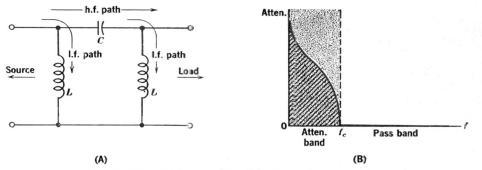

(A)   (B)

Fig. 24-12. A high-pass filter and its performance curve.

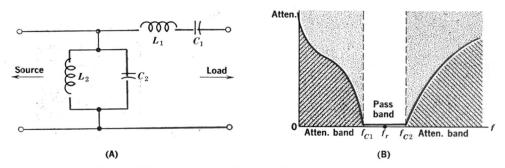

(A)   **(B)**

Fig. 24-13. A band-pass filter and its performance curve.

pulsating current and passing the low frequency and d-c components. Other important applications include the removal of objectionable signals from the antenna circuit of a receiver and the selection of certain harmonics from a mixed signal. In general, filters are used to separate, on a frequency basis, desired signals from undesired signals.

Filters may range from very simple combinations of L and C to very complex networks, depending on the action to be performed. There are three common types of simple filter circuits: (1) *low-pass filters*, (2) *high-pass filters*, and (3) *band-pass filters*.

1. *Low-pass filters.* Low-pass filters are designed to transmit all frequencies from zero to a certain *cut-off frequency f_c*, and to

attenuate all frequencies from f_c to ∞. A typical low-pass filter circuit is shown in Fig. 24-11. The inductance in series with the load offers little opposition to currents of low frequencies, but presents a high-impedance path to currents of high frequencies. The shunt capacitance, on the other hand, offers little opposition to currents of high frequencies (which then bypass the load), but presents a high impedance to low-frequency currents. The cut-off frequency is determined by the values of L and C used in the circuit.

2. *High-pass filters.* If a capacitance is placed in series with a load and inductance is shunted across the load, it is quite evident that the high-frequency components of a signal will be passed and the low-frequency components will be shunted

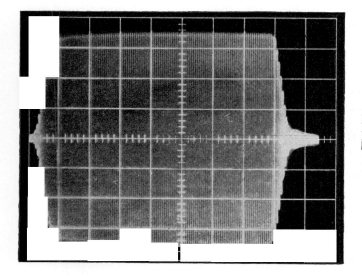

Fig. 24-14. A typical band-pass filter response. (Rixon Electronics, Inc.)

away from the load. A typical high-pass filter circuit is shown in Fig. 24-12, page 549.

3. Band-pass filters. A series-resonant circuit connected in series with a load offers a very low impedance path to currents in a narrow band of frequencies about the resonant frequency. The currents of all other frequencies both above and below this transmission band are seriously attenuated. A parallel-resonant circuit having the same f_r and shunted across the line presents a high impedance to the band passed by the series circuit. It provides a

low impedance path to frequencies above and below this band. A band-pass filter circuit is illustrated in Fig. 24-13.

A *band-elimination filter* could be arranged simply by switching the positions of the series-resonant circuit and the parallel-resonant circuit. The pass band of Fig. 24-13.(*B*) would become an attenuation band and the attenuation bands would become pass bands. While this is not a common form of filter network, it provides a means of eliminating a narrow band of objectionable frequencies from a broad signal.

 # Summary

The reactance of an inductance is zero at zero frequency and increases linearly with frequency; the reactance of a capacitance is infinitely large at zero frequency and decreases nonlinearly with increasing frequency. The frequency at which the inductive reactance and the capacitive reactance of a circuit are equal is known as the resonant frequency of the circuit.

The impedance of a series-resonant circuit is minimum and equal to the circuit resistance at the resonant frequency; the resonant current is the maximum current possible in the series circuit and is in phase with the applied voltage. If the Q of the circuit is high, the resonant current is very large compared to the average circuit current over a range of frequencies, and the current curve is sharply peaked. The selectivity of such a resonant circuit is high.

Parallel-resonance circuits present a very high impedance to a signal at the resonant frequency, a large resonant current being produced within the tank circuit by a very small line current. The tank current is said to oscillate, alternately storing energy in the capacitor and the field of the inductor at the resonant frequency.

The property of resonance is of great importance in electronic circuits. Series or parallel-resonant circuits may be used as one form of coupling to transfer energy from one circuit to another. Resonance plays a part in the performance of certain types of filter circuits where it is desired to select or discriminate against signals of certain frequencies.

TERMS TO DEFINE ─────────────────────────

band-elimination filter	low-pass filter	resonant frequency
band-pass filter	oscillating current	selectivity
coupled circuits	parallel resonance	series resonance
high-pass filter	resonance	tank circuit

QUESTIONS

B **1.** Select three different values of inductance, determine the reactance of each at four different frequencies, and plot a curve of inductive reactance as a function of frequency for each using the same coordinate axes. (*a*) What is the shape of each curve? (*b*) Which has the greatest slope? (*c*) Why should each curve start at the origin of the coordinate axes?

2. How is an oscillating current produced in a resonant circuit?

3. Define series resonance.

4. What is the relation between the voltage across a series *L-R-C* circuit and the current in the circuit at a frequency below the resonant frequency? Explain.

5. What is the relation between the voltage across a series *L-R-C* circuit and the circuit current at a frequency above the resonant frequency? Explain.

6. What factor largely determines the sharpness of the rise of current near the resonance frequency in a series-resonant circuit?

7. What is the advantage of a resonant circuit having a high *Q*?

8. How can the resonant frequency of an *L-R-C* circuit be varied?

9. Suppose an inductor is connected in series with a lamp in an a-c circuit. What is the effect? Explain.

10. A variable capacitor is connected in series in the circuit of Question 9 and, when adjusted, the lamp glows normally. Explain.

11. A series *L-R-C* circuit is connected across an a-c signal source of variable frequency. Draw a curve to show the way in which the circuit current varies with the frequency of the source.

12. How is the *Q* of a resonant circuit affected by an increase in (*a*) resistance; (*b*) inductance; (*c*) frequency?

★ **13.** How do the separate currents in the branches of a parallel-resonant circuit compare (*a*) at frequencies below the resonant frequency; (*b*) at frequencies above the resonant frequency?

★ **14.** Explain why the impedance of a parallel-resonant circuit reaches a maximum at the resonant frequency.

★ **15.** Sketch a curve of impedance of a parallel-resonant circuit as a function of frequency for a range of frequencies above and below f_r. Sketch a second curve on the same graph showing the circuit current as a function of frequency. Why cannot the circuit current fall to zero at f_r in a practical parallel-resonant circuit?

★ **16.** Define parallel resonance.

17. How is energy transferred from the primary circuit to the secondary circuit of a coupling transformer?

18. Suggest a method by which you could eliminate a narrow band of frequencies from a signal composed of a wide range of frequencies.

PROBLEMS

B **1.** A resonant circuit has an inductance of 320 μh and a capacitance of 80. $\mu\mu$f. What is the resonant frequency?

2. Assume that the frequency of the signal voltage applied to the resonant circuit of Problem 1 is varied from a value 25 kc below the resonant frequency to 25 kc above. (*a*) Obtain values of inductive reactance for every 5 kc over this range of frequencies and plot a curve showing inductive reactance as a function of frequency, using the abscissa as the frequency reference. (*b*) Obtain values of capacitive reactance for every 5 kc and plot a curve showing capacitive reactance as a function of frequency, using the same reference abscissa. (*c*) Determine the resonant frequency graphically from your curves by plotting the values for (X_L-X_C).

3. The variable capacitor used to tune a broadcast receiver has a maximum capacitance of 350 $\mu\mu$f. The lowest frequency to which we wish to tune the receiver is 550 kc. What value of inductance should be used in the resonant circuit?

4. The minimum capacitance of the variable capacitor of Problem 3 is 15 $\mu\mu$f. What is the highest resonant frequency that may be obtained from the circuit?

★ **5.** A resonant circuit consists of an inductance of 25 mh and 180 ohms resistance in parallel with a capacitance of 15 $\mu\mu$f. (*a*) What is the magnitude of the impedance of the circuit at resonance? (*b*) How can you explain the difference between the magnitude of the impedance at resonance in this circuit and the circuit resistance?

RESEARCH ON YOUR OWN

1. Connect a $\frac{1}{4}$-watt neon glow lamp in parallel with a .1-ufd capacitor. In series with this connect a 1000-ohm resistor. Connect the combination to a 90-volt B battery. The values of the capacitor and resistor may be varied. What determines the rate of flashing of the bulb? For how many hours do you think this device will operate? Test it and report on your results.

2. Connect an inductive resistance in a direct current circuit and measure its resistance by the voltmeter-ammeter method. Then connect the coil to an alternating current source and measure the current and voltage again. Determine the inductive reactance and the inductance for this particular frequency.

3. Arrange a demonstration of parallel resonance. If a variable-frequency source of emf is available, a variety of inductance and capacitance values may be used. If a 60-cycle source is the only one available, use a choke coil of approximately 20 henrys and several capacitors of from 0.20 μf to 0.50 μf. Connect one a-c milliammeter between the source and the resonant circuit to read the live current. Connect a second a-c milliammeter between the capacitor and the coil to read the tank current. Use different values of capacitance and observe the variations in currents as indicated by the two meters. CAUTION: *Do not allow the current in the coil to exceed its rated value.*

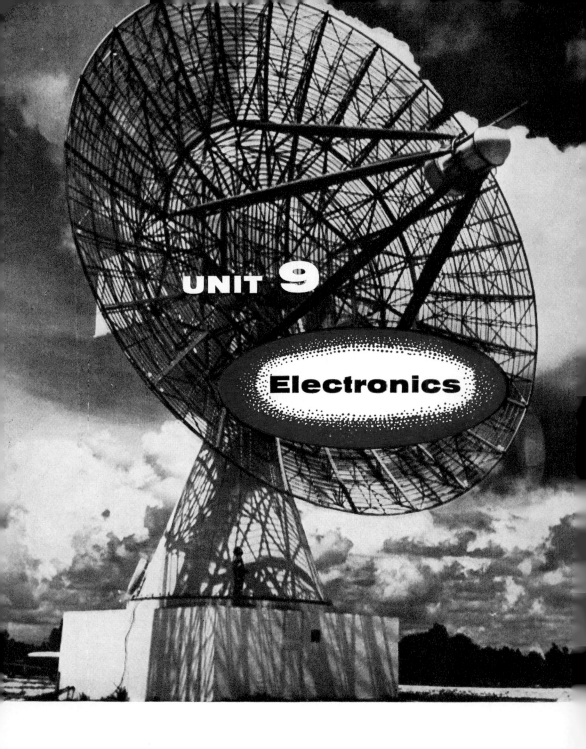

UNIT 9

Electronics

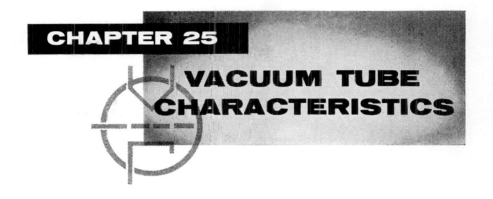

CHAPTER 25
VACUUM TUBE CHARACTERISTICS

1. The importance of vacuum tubes. The vacuum tube has been described as the most important single piece of equipment introduced into electrical engineering during the twentieth century. Its development has produced a new engineering art called *electronics*, which has given us radio, long-distance telephones, sound motion pictures, public-address systems, television, radar, electronic computers, and industrial automation. These, and many other electronic achievements, have had a profound influence on our standard of living. There are tremendous opportunities for rewarding futures in the field of electronics at all levels of endeavor: in technical work, in engineering, and in research and development.

Many improvements have been made in vacuum-tube performance since the

VOCABULARY

Acceptor. An impurity added to a semiconductor to produce a *P*-type crystal.

Amplification factor. A vacuum-tube constant equal to the ratio of a small change in plate voltage to a small change in grid voltage of the opposite sense, which maintains a constant plate current.

Cut-off bias. The smallest negative grid voltage, for a given plate voltage, which causes a vacuum tube to cease to conduct.

Donor. An impurity added to a semiconductor to produce an *N*-type crystal.

Dynamic plate resistance. A vacuum-tube constant; the opposition to the flow of electrons from cathode to plate.

P-N junction. The plane at which a *P*-type semiconductor crystal meets an *N*-type semiconductor crystal.

Secondary emission. Emission of electrons as a result of the bombardment of an electrode by high-velocity electrons.

Space charge. The negative charge in the interelectrode space between the cathode and plate of a vacuum tube.

Thermionic emission. The escaping of electrons from the surface of a hot body.

Transconductance. A vacuum tube constant equal to the ratio of a small change in plate current to the small change in grid voltage producing it, when the plate voltage is held constant.

555

Fig. 25-1. Modern vacuum tubes are designed to perform a variety of highly specialized functions.

invention of the first crude models. Today vacuum tubes are used in electronic circuits to perform many different functions:

1. As *rectifiers*, they convert alternating current to direct current.

2. As *mixers*, they combine separate signals to produce a different signal.

3. As *detectors*, they separate the useful component from a complex signal.

4. As *amplifiers*, they increase the strength of a signal.

5. As *oscillators*, they convert a direct current to an alternating current of a desired frequency.

6. As *wave shapers*, they change a voltage wave form into a desired shape for a special use.

Vacuum-tube operation presents three inherent problems.

1. Vacuum tubes are power-consuming devices. The power output of a vacuum-tube circuit is always considerably less than the total power input.

2. The size of vacuum tubes limits reduction in size of electronic circuits although tubes used today are smaller than early types.

3. The performance of a particular vacuum-tube circuit is limited to a relatively small range of frequencies. A circuit that is capable of amplifying one signal may produce a loss of signal strength at another frequency.

The development of transistors may solve the first two problems associated with vacuum-tube circuits. Transistors require very little power for operation in an electronic circuit, and they occupy a much smaller space than ordinary vacuum tubes. However, vacuum tubes continue to be the major components in electronic circuits.

A vacuum tube usually contains a *cathode* as a source of electrons, an *anode* (commonly called a *plate*) which attracts electrons from the cathode, and one or more *grids* for controlling the flow of electrons between cathode and plate. These electrodes are enclosed in a gas-tight envelope which is highly evacuated. Modified forms of the vacuum tube may contain only a cathode and a plate, or two independent sets of electrodes in a single envelope. In some forms, a small amount of a particular gas is introduced to obtain special operating characteristics.

Common tubes are classified as *diodes*, *triodes*, *tetrodes*, and *pentodes*, according to the number of electrodes present. High vacuum tubes are known as *hard* tubes and those containing a gas under very low pressure are known as *soft* tubes. Special tubes may have special names. For example, the cathode-ray tube is a visual indicating tube used in cathode-ray oscilloscopes, as the picture tube in television sets, and as the indicator in radar equipment.

2. The Edison effect. The operation of the vacuum tube is based on a phenomenon observed by Thomas Edison in 1883. While experimenting with the first electric lamp, he was plagued by the frequent burning out of the carbon filament near the positive end, with an accompanying black deposit inside the bulb in which appeared the shadow of the positive leg of the lamp filament. While searching for a way to correct this difficulty, he sealed a metal plate inside the lamp near the filament and connected it through a galvanometer to the filament battery. He observed a deflection on the galvanometer when the plate was connected to the positive terminal of the battery, but no galvanometer deflection when the plate was connected to the negative terminal. Edison recorded these observations in his notebook and continued his lamp experiments without attempting to explain the phenomenon.

Several years after Edison's experiment, Sir J. J. Thomson discovered the electron and provided the explanation for the *Edison effect*. Electrons escaped from the heated carbon filament and moved unimpeded through the evacuated space to the plate when it was connected to the positive terminal of the filament battery. The negatively charged plate, on the other hand, repelled the escaping electrons and prevented an electron current in the galvanometer circuit.

3. The Fleming valve. Near the end of 1901, "wireless telegraphy," the forerunner of modern radio communications, was successfully used to transmit a radio signal across the Atlantic Ocean. As radio techniques developed, crystals of semiconductors were commonly used as re-

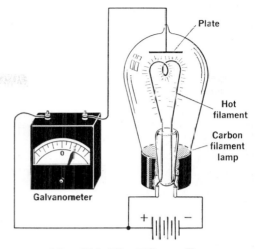

Fig. 25-2. The Edison effect.

ceivers to *detect* the transmitted signals, but these crystals were unsatisfactory in many ways. A better method of detection was clearly needed.

In 1904, Sir J. A. Fleming (1849–1945), an English physicist, patented the first diode, called the *Fleming valve*. He used the Edison effect to develop a crude form of detector for radio signals. Fleming's valve was so insensitive that it found little immediate application, yet it was an important link in the evolution of the vacuum tube.

4. The De Forest triode. Dr. Lee De Forest (1873–   ) is recognized as one of America's pioneers in wireless telegraphy, radio telephony, sound movies, and the development of the vacuum tube. In 1906 he succeeded in amplifying feeble radio signals which neither the Fleming valve nor the crystal detectors were sensitive enough to detect.

De Forest placed a third electrode, consisting of a *grid* of fine wire, between the filament and plate of the diode, as shown in Fig. 25-3. He found that a small variation in voltage applied to the grid produced a larger variation of current in the plate circuit of the tube. Thus the feeble radio signals from an antenna could be amplified by De Forest's *triode* and then

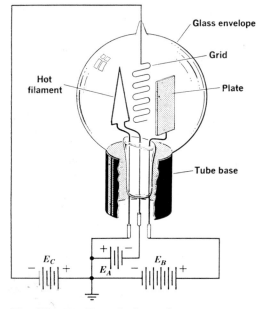

Fig. 25-3. De Forest's three-element vacuum tube, the triode.

successfully detected by the Fleming valve to provide the d-c signal necessary to operate headphones. The success of the De Forest triode led to the development of the modern vacuum tube in its various and complex forms.

5. Thermionic emission. Metallic substances conduct electricity because they have a relatively large number of free electrons. In all instances of conduction of electricity there is a transfer of some kind of charged particle. In a highly evacuated tube the number of gas particles remaining is so small that conduction by ordinary gas ionization is insignificant. Conduction in a high vacuum results from the introduction of charged particles into an evacuated space permeated by an electric field. In high vacuum (hard) tubes, the conducting particles are electrons, supplied by special emitters through a process known as *thermionic emission.*

The free electrons of a metallic conductor are in a state of continuous motion with a velocity that increases with temperature. Their kinetic energies at ordinary

temperatures are not sufficient to enable them to escape through the barrier of attractive forces which exist at the surface of the material. In order to escape from the surface of a conductor, an electron must do work to overcome the surface forces, using the energy it possesses as a result of its motion. The kinetic energy of an electron, therefore, must exceed the work that it must perform, otherwise it cannot escape. At a *high* temperature, where the average kinetic energy of the free electrons is large, a relatively large number will possess sufficient energy to escape through the surface barrier of the material. *Thermionic emission is the escaping of electrons from the surface of a hot body.*

Thermionic emission from a hot solid sealed in an evacuated envelope is analogous to the evaporation of water molecules from the surface of the liquid. The rate at which electrons escape from an emitting surface increases as the temperature of the emitter is raised.

6. Types of emitters. The high temperatures required to produce satisfactory thermionic emission in vacuum tubes limit the number of suitable emitters to such substances as *tungsten, thoriated tungsten,* and certain *oxide-coated metals.* Tungsten and thoriated tungsten operate at very high temperatures and are connected directly to a source of filament current. These *directly heated cathodes,* called *filament cathodes* or simply *filaments,* are used universally as the source of electrons in large transmitting tubes.

Oxide-coated emitters consist of a metal

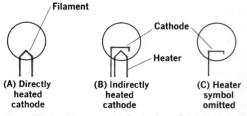

(A) Directly heated cathode   (B) Indirectly heated cathode   (C) Heater symbol omitted

Fig. 25-4. Circuit symbols for directly and indirectly heated cathode.

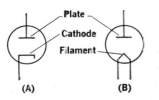

Fig. 25-5. Circuit symbols for diodes with indirectly heated cathode (A) and directly heated cathode (B).

such as nickel, coated with a mixture of barium and strontium oxides over which is formed a surface layer of metallic barium and strontium. The electrons are actually emitted from this metallic surface layer. Such emitters may be heated to their operating temperature either directly as a filament cathode or indirectly by radiation from an incandescent tungsten filament. *Indirectly heated cathodes* are commonly called *heater cathodes* or simply *cathodes*. Since practically all receiving tubes in use today have oxide-coated emitters, we shall concern ourselves principally with vacuum tubes of this type.

7. Diode characteristics. The simplest vacuum tubes are diodes, consisting of two elements, a cathode and a plate. Diode circuit symbols are shown in Fig. 25-5. In the operation of a diode, if the plate is made positive with respect to the cathode, the tube conducts because electrons flow from the region of the cathode to the plate inside the tube, and from the plate through the plate circuit to the cathode outside the tube. If the plate is negative with respect to the cathode, the diode does not conduct and there is no plate current in the external circuit.

As electrons are emitted from the heated cathode of a diode, the space about the cathode becomes negatively charged. This negative charge in the interelectrode space between cathode and plate, called the *space charge*, opposes the escape of additional electrons from the cathode. The number of electrons emitted then is dependent on the temperature of the cathode.

At low positive plate voltages only those electrons near the plate are attracted to it, producing a small plate current. As the plate voltage is increased, greater num-

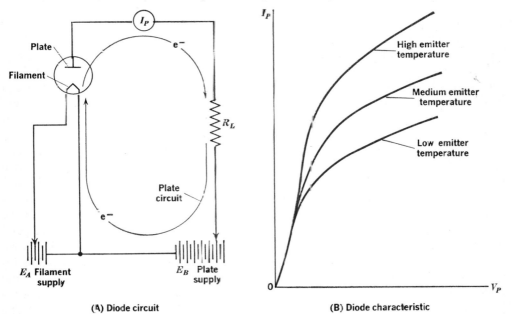

(A) Diode circuit

(B) Diode characteristic

Fig. 25-6. A diode circuit and characteristic curves showing the plate current as a function of plate voltage at different filament temperatures.

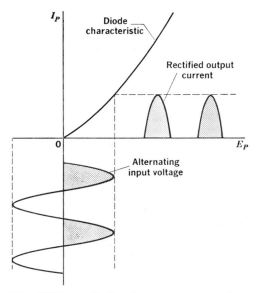

Fig. 25-7. A diode characteristic used to show the rectifying action of a power diode.

bers of electrons are attracted, increasing the plate current and reducing the space charge. The emission of electrons from oxide-coated cathodes is quite abundant and the diode might be damaged before the plate voltage could be raised enough to completely remove the space charge and produce current *saturation*. (That is, the oxide coating might be pulled off the cathode.) The diode plate current varies nonlinearly with the plate voltage throughout the operating range of the tube.

A diode circuit in which we may determine the plate current as a function of plate voltage for different filament temperatures is shown in Fig. 25-6(A). The resulting family of I_P vs. E_P curves is shown in Fig. 25-6(B).

We may classify diode tubes as *power* diodes or *signal* diodes. The difference is primarily one of size and power-handling capabilities. Power diodes are used as rectifiers in power-supply circuits and must be large enough to dissipate the excessive heat generated during their operation. Signal diodes handle signals of negligible power

and are small, being used principally as detectors and wave-shapers. They are frequently enclosed in the same envelope with triodes and pentodes. The receiving tube *type 6AV6* consists of two signal diodes and a triode, all using the same indirectly heated cathode.

8. Triodes can amplify. De Forest perfected the first *triode* amplifier by inserting a third electrode between the cathode and plate of a diode. This electrode consists of an open spiral of fine wire which presents a negligible physical barrier to electrons flowing from cathode to plate. However, a small potential difference between this electrode and the cathode has an important controlling effect on the flow of electrons from cathode to plate, and thus on the current in the plate circuit. For this reason the third electrode is called a *control grid*. The construction detail of a typical triode and the triode circuit symbol are shown in Fig. 25-8.

If the control grid is made sufficiently negative with respect to the cathode, all electrons are repelled toward the cathode. In this condition the plate current is zero, and the triode is said to be *cut off*. The grid-to-cathode voltage is called the grid *bias*. *The smallest negative grid voltage, for a given plate voltage, which causes the tube to cease to conduct is the* **cut-off bias.** This design characteristic of vacuum tubes containing control grids is important in the circuit applications of these tubes.

The effects of different grid-bias voltages on the plate current of a triode are shown in Fig. 25-9. If a negative grid bias less than the cut-off value is used, some electrons pass through the grid and reach the plate to provide some magnitude of plate current. As the negative grid bias is reduced toward zero, the plate current increases accordingly. At zero bias, the plate current is fairly large and is dependent primarily on the plate voltage. The performance of the triode is now essentially the same as a diode of similar construction.

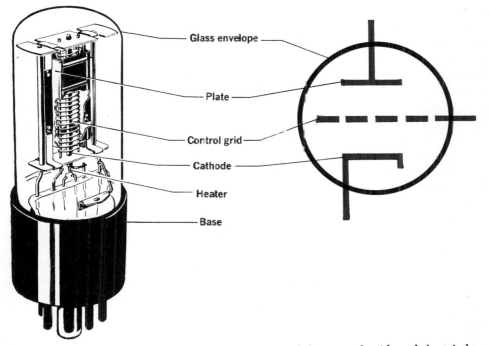

Fig. 25-8. A triode, cut away to show the construction of the control grid, and the triode circuit symbol.

If, on the other hand, the grid is made positive with respect to the cathode, the grid no longer repels the electrons of the space charge but accelerates them in the direction of the plate. The plate current is increased by this action; however, *some electrons are attracted to the grid and produce an appreciable current in the grid circuit.* Grid current causes power dissipation in the grid circuit which, in the usual applica-

tions of vacuum tube circuits, represents a waste of power. Thus the grid is normally maintained at some negative potential with respect to that of the cathode.

★ **9. Triode characteristics.** The characteristics of triode vacuum tubes are based on the relationships between grid voltage, plate current, and plate voltage under normal operating conditions. These relationships provide three important tube

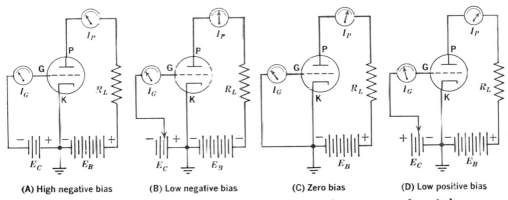

(A) High negative bias   (B) Low negative bias   (C) Zero bias   (D) Low positive bias

Fig. 25-9. The effects of control-grid bias on the plate current of a triode.

constants: (1) *amplification factor,* (2) *dynamic plate resistance,* and (3) *transconductance.* These tube constants depend on the geometry of the electrodes, their spacing and dimensions, and their power-dissipation capabilities.

1. Amplification factor. The measure of the amplifying capability of a triode, that is, the relative effectiveness of grid and plate voltages in controlling plate current, is called the *amplification factor.* The symbol is the Greek letter *mu* (μ). *The **amplification factor** of a tube is the ratio of a small change in plate voltage to a small change in grid voltage of the opposite sense, which maintains a constant plate current.*

$$\mu = -\frac{\Delta e_P}{\Delta e_G} \;(i_P \text{ constant})$$

Where Δe_P is a small change in plate voltage and Δe_G is a small change in grid voltage, μ is the amplification factor (a dimensionless number). The negative sign merely indicates that the changes in plate voltage and grid voltage are not in the same direction.

A family of e_P vs. e_G characteristic curves for a typical triode is shown in Fig. 25-10. Let us select a value of plate voltage on the ordinate axis and adjust the grid voltage to operate the tube at point A on the 4-milliampere curve. If we raise the plate voltage e_P a certain amount, then the grid voltage e_G must be made more negative to hold the plate current i_P to 4 milliamperes. With these adjustments the tube operates at point B. The amplification factor is the ratio of this small change in plate voltage Δe_P to the small change in grid voltage Δe_G necessary to maintain i_P at the constant value of 4 milliamperes.

Triodes designed to have amplification factors of the order of 20 are called *medium-mu* triodes. *High-mu* triodes have amplification factors of from 70 to 100. A *mu* of 20 means literally that a change in grid voltage (an input signal) is twenty times more effective in changing the plate cur-

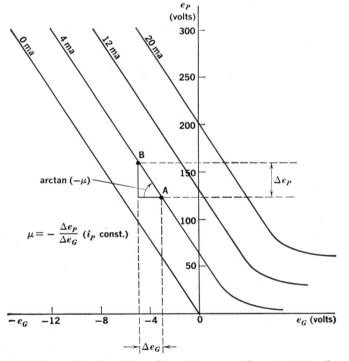

Fig. 25-10. Determination of *mu* from the e_P-e_G characteristic of a triode.

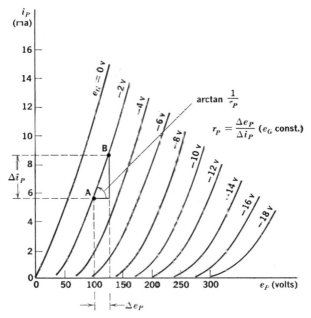

Fig. 25-11. Determination of r_P from the i_P-e_P characteristic of a triode.

rent than a change of plate voltage of the same magnitude.

2. *Dynamic plate resistance*. The **dynamic plate resistance**, r_P, *of a vacuum tube is the opposition to the flow of electrons from cathode to plate*. It is analogous to the *internal* resistance of a battery or generator. The type of emitter, the geometry of the tube, and the space charge largely determine the plate resistance.

The plate resistance is the ratio of a small change in plate voltage Δe_P to the small change in plate current Δi_P which it produces, when the grid voltage e_G is maintained at a constant level.

$$r_P = \frac{\Delta e_P}{\Delta i_P} \text{ (}e_G \text{ constant)}$$

When Δe_P is expressed in volts and Δi_P in amperes, r_P is expressed in ohms.

An i_P vs. e_P family of characteristic curves for a typical triode is shown in Fig. 25-11. Let us assume that a grid bias of −2 volts is maintained and the plate voltage e_P is raised from a value which locates the operation of the tube at point A to a value which changes the operating

point to B. The ratio of the small change in plate voltage Δe_P to the small change in plate current Δi_P which it effects indicates the plate resistance of the tube.

Since the plate resistance is the reciprocal of the slope of the i_P vs. e_P characteristic, it is *lowest* where the slope is *greatest*. The plate resistance of any particular tube depends on the grid and plate voltages *at the operating point* on the i_P vs. e_P characteristic.

3. *Transconductance*. Perhaps the most important single constant of a vacuum tube is the transconductance, g_m. It indicates the effectiveness of the control grid in producing changes in plate current and, consequently, in signal output. *Transconductance is the ratio of the small change in plate current to the small change in grid voltage producing it, when the plate voltage is held constant.*

$$g_m = \frac{\Delta i_P}{\Delta e_G} \text{ (}e_P \text{ constant)}$$

From Ohm's law, resistance in ohms equals the quotient of potential difference in volts divided by the current in

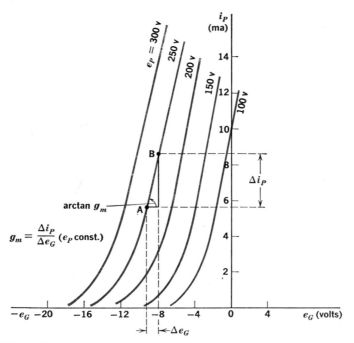

Fig. 25-12. Determination of g_m from the i_P-e_G characteristic of a triode.

amperes. The unit of transconductance is the *reciprocal* of the resistance unit, the ohm, and is called the *mho* (ohm spelled backwards). In a general sense,

$$\text{conductance} = \frac{1}{\text{resistance}}$$

and

$$1 \text{ mho} = \frac{1}{1 \text{ ohm}}$$

Because the mho is too large a unit for practical use in expressing the transconductance of a vacuum tube, the *micromho* (µmho) is commonly used.

$$1 \text{ } \mu\text{mho} = 1 \times 10^{-6} \text{ mho}$$

Where Δi_P is in amperes and Δe_G is in volts, the g_m must be multiplied by 10^2 to be expressed in micromhos.

In Fig. 25-12 we have shown an i_P vs. e_G family of characteristic curves for a typical triode. Let us assume that the plate voltage e_P is held constant at 300 volts and the grid voltage is lowered from the value which locates the tube operation at

point *A* to the value which locates the operating point at *B*. The ratio of the small change in plate current Δi_P to the small change in grid voltage Δe_G indicates the transconductance.

The relationship between the grid voltage e_G, the plate current i_P, and the plate voltage e_P determines the three important tube constants (μ, r_P, and g_m). By combining equations for μ and r_P, we can find

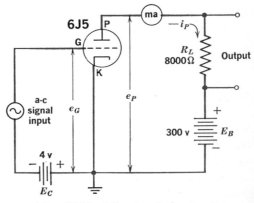

Fig. 25-13. A basic triode circuit.

the relationship between the tube constants:

$$g_m = \frac{\mu}{r_P}$$

In the design of a vacuum tube a low plate resistance and high amplification factor are desired. Thus the transconductance provides an indication of the design merit of a tube. In the common *tube tester*, the g_m of the tube under test is compared with the rated value of a new tube of the same type.

★ **10. A typical triode problem.** We shall use the simplified triode circuit of Fig. 25-13 to illustrate the application of tube characteristics to vacuum-tube circuit problems. The *plate-supply* voltage E_B is a d-c source of 300. volts and the plate-load resistance R_L is a resistance of 8.00×10^3 ohms. The control grid has a d-c biasing voltage E_C of -4 volts.

Let us assume first that the tube is cut off. In this condition the plate circuit is open, the plate current is zero, and there is no potential drop across the load resistance R_L. Thus the plate is at the full supply voltage of 300. volts.

We assume next that the tube is a short circuit, that is, the plate resistance r_P is zero. The plate voltage must be zero and the full supply voltage appears across the load resistance. The plate current is the maximum value for this supply voltage and is determined as follows:

$$I_P = \frac{E_B}{R_L}$$

$$I_P = \frac{300. \text{ v}}{8.00 \times 10^3 \ \Omega}$$

$$I_P = 37.5 \text{ ma}$$

These two limiting conditions define the *load line* which we may construct on the i_P vs. e_P characteristic as shown in Fig. 25-14. The steady state or *quiescent* operation of the tube is determined by the intersection of the load line with the -4-volt curve at point Q. By projection from point Q through the i_P axis, we can

determine that the quiescent plate current I_P is 13.0 milliamperes when no a-c signal is impressed on the grid. By projection from point Q through the e_P axis, we can determine that the quiescent plate voltage E_P is 195 volts. This leaves a potential drop of 104 volts across R_L which is in agreement with the Ohm's-law product $I_P R_L$.

$$13.0 \times 10^{-3} \text{ amp} \times 8.00 \times 10^3 \ \Omega = 104 \text{ volts}$$

Suppose an a-c signal of $E_{max} = 4$ volts is impressed on the control grid. From the quiescent grid bias of -4 volts, the signal swings the grid in a positive sense to 0 volts and in a negative sense to -8 volts. This establishes the *operating region* of the tube along the load line between points A and B. By projections from points A and B through the i_P axis, we can determine the plate-current variation produced by the a-c signal input. Similarly, by projections through the e_P axis, we can determine the plate-voltage variation.

By this graphic application of the i_P vs. e_P characteristic of the 6J5 triode, the operation of the circuit illustrated in Fig. 25-13 becomes apparent. A voltage variation of 8 volts (peak-to-peak) on the grid results in a variation of 85 volts on the plate.

11. Polarity inversion across a vacuum tube. The path of the plate current inside the tube in Fig. 25-13 is from cathode to plate. Outside the tube it is from the plate, through the load resistance, and back to the cathode. Thus the plate side of R_L is *negative with respect to the side connected to the positive terminal of the plate-supply battery* when the tube conducts.

At the instant a signal voltage applied to the grid is at its positive *maximum*, the plate current is maximum also. This maximum current in the load resistance produces a maximum potential drop across R_L and so the plate end of R_L is at its *minimum* instantaneous voltage. The plate, which is at the same potential as this end

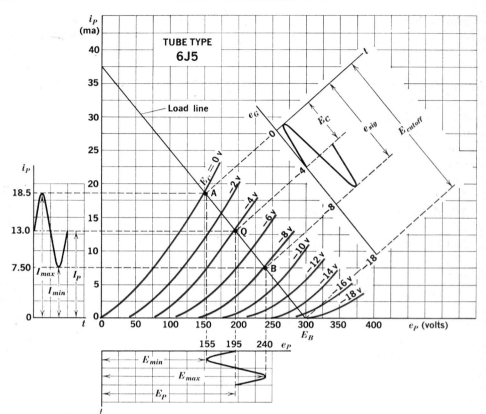

Fig. 25-14. The application of a triode i_P-e_P characteristic to a typical tube problem.

of R_L, must be at its minimum instantaneous value.

When the signal voltage on the grid is at its *minimum* instantaneous value, the plate current and the $i_P R_L$ drop across the plate-load resistance are minimum, and the voltage on the plate must be at its *maximum* instantaneous value. Thus the plate-voltage variations are opposite to those of the control grid. This amounts to a *polarity inversion* between the voltage variations of the plate and grid circuits. The grid voltage, plate current, and plate voltage relationships derived from the i_P vs. e_P characteristic are shown in Fig. 25-15.

12. Methods of supplying bias voltage. The purpose of a bias voltage is to establish the grid at a potential, with respect to the cathode, which will allow the tube to operate suitably. There are three general methods of supplying this voltage: (*1*) *fixed bias method*, (*2*) *cathode-bias method*, and (*3*) *grid-leak bias method*. Triode circuits illustrating these three sources of bias voltage are shown in Fig. 25-16.

1. Fixed bias. Grid bias may be obtained directly from a small *C-battery* or other d-c voltage source provided especially for this purpose. There is no current in the grid circuit as long as the grid is held negative with respect to the cathode. Therefore, C-batteries may be made very small since they function under a no-load condition. This simple fixed-bias method is used in small battery-operated radio receivers and in some special types of circuits.

2. Cathode bias. The most common

method of providing a bias voltage in audio-frequency and radio-frequency circuits uses a cathode resistor and the d-c component of the plate current. See Fig. 25-16(B). A small potential difference $I_P R_K$ is developed across the cathode resistance R_K, making the cathode positive with respect to ground. Since the grid is returned to ground potential, it is, in effect, negative with respect to the cathode by the product $I_P R_K$ volts.

The cathode resistor is shunted by the capacitor C_K, which provides a low-impedance path around R_K for the alternating component of the plate current. Because the plate current of the tube itself is used to develop the biasing voltage in the grid circuit, this arrangement is often called a *self-bias* method.

3. *Grid-leak bias.* In circuits having a relatively large signal input, a capacitor may be charged in the grid circuit to provide a d-c bias voltage. During the portion of the input cycle which drives the grid positive with respect to the cathode, the grid draws current and the capacitor C_G is quickly charged as shown in Fig. 25-16(C). The grid, which is connected to the negative side of the capacitor, is held essentially at ground potential. During the negative swing of the input signal, the cathode-to-grid path inside the tube is open and the discharge path for C_G is through a high resistance R_G. Only a small portion of the charge on C_G is lost during the discharge cycle; thus a substantially constant bias voltage is maintained and the grid is not permitted to follow the positive portions of the input signal.

13. Interelectrode capacitance. The electrodes of a triode form an electrostatic system in which capacitances exist between grid and plate, grid and cathode, and plate and cathode. Collectively these are known as *interelectrode capacitances.*

Interelectrode capacitances are quite small, having magnitudes of the order of

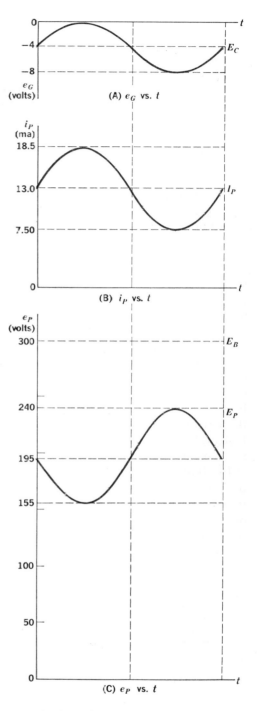

Fig. 25-15. Grid voltage, plate current, and plate voltage variations of a vacuum tube circuit showing voltage inversion between grid and plate circuits.

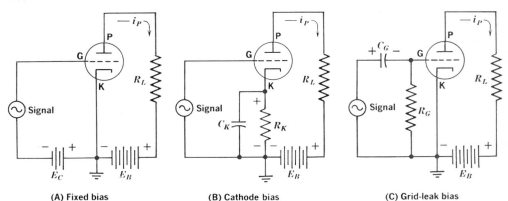

(A) Fixed bias　　　　　　　(B) Cathode bias　　　　　　　(C) Grid-leak bias

Fig. 25-16. Methods of obtaining a biasing voltage to make the grid negative with respect to the cathode.

3 micromicrofarads in triodes. However, the coupling effects they produce between the input and output circuits restrict the use of triodes as amplifiers at radio frequencies. The grid-to-plate capacitance causes the greatest trouble in this respect. As the frequency of a signal increases, the reactance presented by the grid-to-plate capacitance decreases and some of the output signal of the plate circuit is coupled back into the grid circuit. This renders the circuit unstable as an amplifier and limits this use of the triode to the audio-frequency ranges.

14. Tetrodes. The interelectrode capacitance between grid and plate of a triode can be reduced by inserting a second grid, called the *screen grid*, between the control grid and plate. Such four-elec-

trode tubes are known as *tetrodes*. See Fig. 25-18(A). Tetrodes extend the range of frequencies over which an ordinary vacuum tube can be used as an amplifier.

The screen grid is supplied with a positive potential somewhat less than that of the plate. Electrons in transit from the cathode are accelerated by the positive screen grid, increasing the plate current. Some electrons do strike the screen grid and produce a screen current which, as a rule, wastes power and serves no useful purpose.

★ A variation of plate voltage has little effect on the magnitude of plate current, due to the presence of the screen grid. The control grid, on the other hand, retains control over the plate current. Tetrodes have high plate resistance and amplification factors. A typical family of i_P vs. e_P characteristic curves is shown in Fig. 25-18(B).

★ You will observe that the i_P-e_P curves have a negative slope at plate voltages below the fixed screen voltage. When accelerated by the screen grid, some electrons strike the plate with enough force to dislodge other electrons. *Emission as a result of bombardment of an electrode by high-velocity electrons is called* **secondary emission.** When the plate voltage is lower than the screen voltage, secondary-emission electrons are attracted to the screen

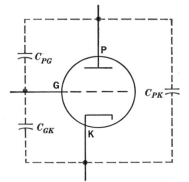

Fig. 25-17. A schematic diagram of the interelectrode capacitances of a triode.

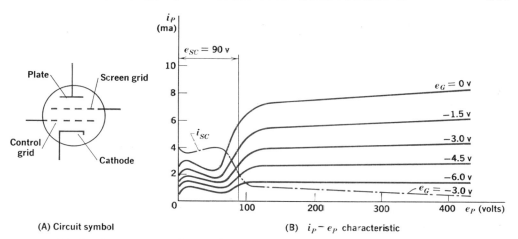

(A) Circuit symbol   (B) $i_p - e_p$ characteristic

Fig. 25-18. The circuit symbol and typical i_p-e_p characteristic curves of a tetrode.

grid. This effect lowers the plate current and necessitates operation of the plate at an abnormally high voltage in order to overcome the effects of secondary emission.

15. Pentodes. The introduction of a third grid, known as the *suppressor grid*, between the screen grid and plate eliminates the effects of secondary emission. This gives the five-electrode tube, or *pentode*, shown schematically in Fig. 25-20(*A*). The suppressor grid is usually connected to the cathode and serves to repel secondary electrons back to the plate.

★ Pentodes have largely replaced tetrodes in receiving tube applications due to the advantage of the lower plate-voltage requirements. At radio frequencies the pentode makes possible a high voltage amplification at moderate values of plate voltage. A typical family of i_P vs. e_P characteristic curves is shown in Fig. 25-20(*B*).

16. Beam-power tubes. A *beam-power* tube is a special kind of tetrode with the performance characteristics of a pentode. It is highly efficient as a power amplifier. The electrodes are arranged so that secondary emission from the plate is suppressed by the negative space charge without the use of a suppressor grid. A beam-confining electrode, connected internally to the cathode, concentrates the transient electrons in the vicinity of the plate. The

structure of a beam-power tube is shown in Fig. 25-21.

17. Crystals are used as diodes. One of the relics of the early days of radio that is found in modern electronic circuits is

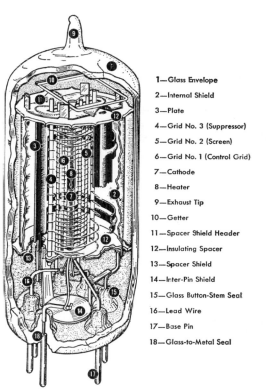

1—Glass Envelope
2—Internal Shield
3—Plate
4—Grid No. 3 (Suppressor)
5—Grid No. 2 (Screen)
6—Grid No. 1 (Control Grid)
7—Cathode
8—Heater
9—Exhaust Tip
10—Getter
11—Spacer Shield Header
12—Insulating Spacer
13—Spacer Shield
14—Inter-Pin Shield
15—Glass Button-Stem Seal
16—Lead Wire
17—Base Pin
18—Glass-to-Metal Seal

Fig. 25-19. A pentode cut away to show the arrangement of electrodes.

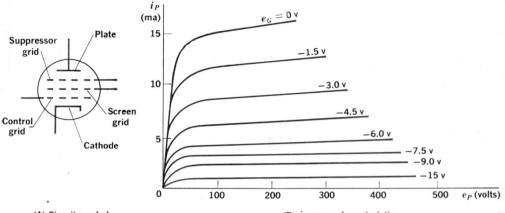

(A) Circuit symbol   (B) $i_p - e_p$ characteristic

Fig. 25-20. The circuit symbol and typical i_p-e_p.

the *crystal diode*. The rectifying property of silicon or galena crystals was used in early receivers before the development of the diode tube. During World War II, improved crystal diodes were developed for use in radar receivers. They are now used extensively in special circuits because of their small size and the fact that they require no heater or filament power.

The modern crystal diode consists of a tiny wafer of silicon or germanium and a platinum *catwhisker*, housed in a sealed capsule. The crystal acts as the cathode of the diode and the catwhisker acts as the anode. The diode characteristic depends on the unique property of a semiconductor which permits a relatively large flow of electrons with a small applied voltage in the *forward* direction, and only a very small flow of electrons in the *reverse* direction, even at a much larger applied voltage.

18. Transistors. The *transistor* was developed by a team of physicists at the Bell Telephone Laboratories in 1948 after nearly ten years of fundamental research in the physics of semiconductors. Transistors are crystals of silicon or germanium containing traces of certain impurities; they can be used to replace vacuum tubes in many types of circuits. They are tiny, rugged structures which require very little power. The development of a family of

transistor triodes, tetrodes, and pentodes has provided a great incentive for the miniaturization of electronic circuits.

The first transistors were known as *point contact* transistors. These have largely been superseded by *junction* transistors. A more recent *surface barrier* transistor promises to extend the upper frequency limit of transistor applications. A miniature portable receiver using junction transistors requires a small 9-volt battery as the source of power. The same receiver using surface barrier transistors operates from a smaller 3-volt battery.

★ **19. P- and N-type semiconductors.** Silicon and germanium are quite similar

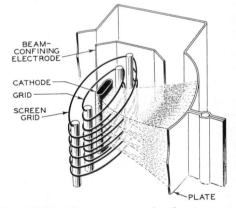

Fig. 25-21. The structure of a beam-power tube employing space-charge suppression of secondary emission.

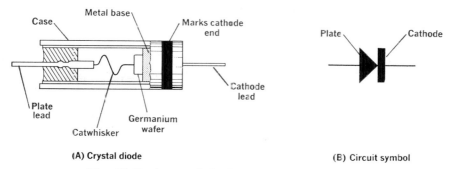

(A) Crystal diode

(B) Circuit symbol

Fig. 25-22. A crystal diode and its circuit symbol.

in their structure and chemical behavior. The atoms of both elements have *four* valence electrons bound in the same way in their respective crystals. In its transistor functions, germanium is perhaps the more versatile semiconductor. It has a diamond cubic crystal lattice in which each atom is bonded to four neighboring atoms through shared electrons, as illustrated in Fig. 25-24. This arrangement ties up the four valence electrons of each atom so that pure germanium would appear to be a nonconductor. *Germanium acquires the*

diode property of rectification and the transistor property of amplification through the presence of certain impurities in the crystal structure. Two types of impurities are important; one is known as a *donor*, the other as an *acceptor.*

Arsenic and antimony are typical donor elements. The atoms of each have *five* valence electrons. When minute traces of antimony are added to germanium, each antimony atom joins the crystal lattice by *donating* one electron to the crystal structure. Four of the five valence electrons are

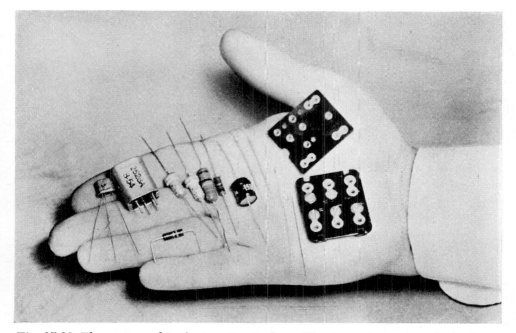

Fig. 25-23. The parts used in the transistorized amplifier in a volume control telephone.

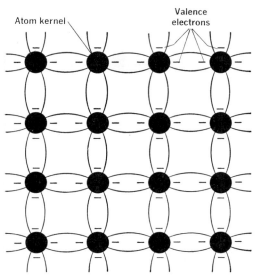

Fig. 25-24. Electron-paired bonds in a pure germanium crystal.

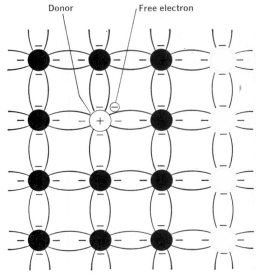

Fig. 25-25. N-type germanium has donor atoms and free electrons in equal numbers.

paired, but the fifth electron is relatively free to wander through the lattice like the free electrons of a metallic conductor. The detached electron leaves behind an antimony atom with a unit positive charge bound into the crystal lattice. Germanium with this type of crystal structure is called *N*-type, or *electron-rich* germanium. ***N-type germanium*** *consists of germanium to which is added equal numbers of free electrons and bound positive charges, so that the net charge is zero.* An *N*-type semiconductor crystal is illustrated in Fig. 25-25.

Atoms with *three* valence electrons, such as those of aluminum and gallium, will act as acceptors. When minute traces of aluminum are added to germanium, each aluminum atom joins the crystal lattice by *accepting* an electron from a neighboring germanium atom. This leaves a *hole* in the electron-pair bond from which the electron is acquired.

We may think of this hole as the equivalent of a *positive charge* since it acts as a trap into which an electron can fall. As an electron fills the hole, it leaves another hole behind, into which another electron can fall. In effect then, the hole (positive

charge) detaches itself and becomes free to move, leaving behind the aluminum atom with a unit negative charge bound into the crystal lattice. Germanium with this crystal structure is called *P*-type, or *hole-rich* germanium. ***P-type germanium***

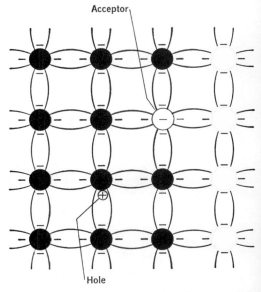

Fig. 25-26. P-type germanium has acceptor atoms and free (positive) holes in equal numbers.

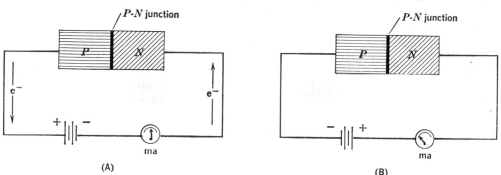

Fig. 25-27. The *P-N* junction is the rectifying element of semiconductor crystals.

consists of germanium to which is added an equal number of free positive holes and bound negative charges, so that the net charge is zero. A P-type semiconductor crystal is illustrated in Fig. 25-26.

★ 20. The P-N junction. Both P-type and N-type crystals are good conductors, and each will conduct equally well in either direction. When the two types are joined together, however, an electric barrier is established where their surfaces meet. *The plane at which the P-type crystal meets the N-type crystal is called the* **P-N junction.** The free holes of the P-crystal cannot pass through the electric barrier at the P-N junction to reach the N-crystal. The free electrons of the N-crystal cannot cross the P-N junction to reach the P-crystal.

A small potential difference impressed across the pair, as in Fig. 25-27(A), will enable the free electrons to cross the junction and pass into the P-crystal. Similarly the holes cross into the N-crystal. You will recall that the apparent movement of holes is in the opposite sense to the actual movement of electrons which fall in the holes of the P-type crystal. Thus an electron current is established across the P-N junction and in the external circuit.

If the battery connections are reversed, as shown in Fig. 25-27(B), the free electrons in the N-crystal and the free holes of the P-crystal are attracted away from the P-N junction. The junction region is left without current carriers; consequently, there is no conduction across the junction and no current in the circuit.

It is the junction which has the distinctive property of permitting electron flow in only one direction with ease, when a small voltage is applied in the proper sense. Thus the P-N junction is the rectifying element of semiconductor crystals.

★ 21. Junction transistors are of two types. The amplifying property of a

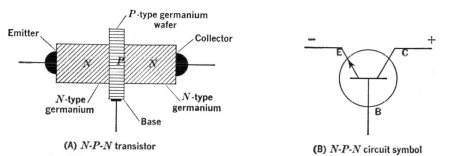

(A) *N-P-N* transistor   (B) *N-P-N* circuit symbol

Fig. 25-28. An *N-P-N* junction transistor and its circuit symbol.

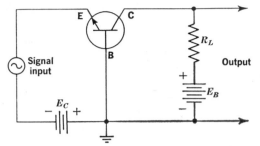

Fig. 25-29. A basic operating circuit of an N-P-N transistor.

transistor is a result of current changes which occur in the different regions of the structure when proper voltages are applied. A transistor is a current amplifier in much the same way its vacuum-tube counterpart is a voltage amplifier.

Junction transistors consist of two P-N junctions back to back. They are made by sandwiching a thin wafer of one type of semiconductor material between two sections of the other type. If the wafer is composed of P-material, the transistor is designated N-P-N. The arrangement of an N-P-N transistor and its circuit symbol are shown in Fig. 25-28.

The N-type material shown on the left of the P-wafer is called the *emitter*. It is normally biased negative with respect to the wafer, which is known as the *base*. The N-material on the right of the wafer is called the *collector* and is biased positive with respect to the base. The basic operating circuit of the N-P-N transistor is shown in Fig. 25-29.

You can compare the operation of the N-P-N junction transistor to that of a triode. The emitter is equivalent to the cathode, the base to the grid, and the collector to the plate.

Transistors in which the wafer is composed of N-type semiconductor material are designated P-N-P. A P-N-P transistor and its circuit symbol are shown in Fig. 25-30.

The basic operating circuit of P-N-P transistors is given in Fig. 25-31. Observe that it is the same as that for N-P-N transistors except that the battery connections are reversed.

The transistor and the vacuum tube each have particular advantages. The technology of transistors is in its infancy, however, and many of the deficiencies which restrict their use in electronic circuits certainly will be overcome. It is interesting to observe that in approximately ten years the transistor reached a state of development which for the vacuum tube took nearly half a century.

22. The cathode-ray tube. The *cathode-ray tube* is a special kind of vacuum tube used in test equipment, radar, and television receivers to present a visual display of information. Electrons are emitted from a cathode, accelerated to a high velocity, and brought to focus on a fluorescent screen. This screen is a translucent backing on the glass face of the tube, composed of certain chemicals which *fluoresce*, or emit

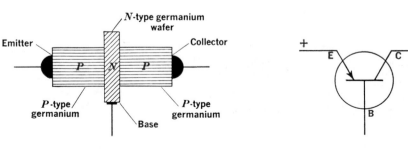

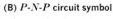

(A) P-N-P transistor   (B) P-N-P circuit symbol

Fig. 25-30. A P-N-P junction transistor and its circuit symbol.